HANDBOOK OF MEDICAL SOCIOLOGY

PRENTICE-HALL INTERNATIONAL, INC., *London*
PRENTICE-HALL OF AUSTRALIA, PTY., LTD., *Sydney*
PRENTICE-HALL OF CANADA, LTD., *Toronto*
PRENTICE-HALL FRANCE, S.A.R.L., *Paris*
PRENTICE-HALL OF JAPAN, INC., *Tokyo*
PRENTICE-HALL DE MEXICO, S.A., *Mexico City*

HANDBOOK OF MEDICAL SOCIOLOGY

Edited by

Howard E. Freeman

Professor of Social Research at the Florence Heller Graduate School for Advanced Studies in Social Welfare, Brandeis University

Sol Levine

Associate Professor of Social Psychology at the School of Public Health, Harvard University

Leo G. Reeder

Associate Professor of Epidemiology in the Schools of Medicine and Public Health of the University of California at Los Angeles

PRENTICE-HALL, INC. *Englewood Cliffs, N. J.*

Printed in
the United States of America
C 37712

Library of Congress Catalog Card No.:
63–15607

Current printing (last digit):
12 11 10 9 8 7 6 5

To

Benjamin D. Paul

ACKNOWLEDGEMENTS

We wish to thank the contributors to this volume for undertaking the difficult task of reviewing, within the confines of a few pages, broad areas in medical sociology. Their advice on the organization of this book, their suggestions on chapters other than their own, and their patience and good will in responding to the many deadlines and requests of the editors are also gratefully appreciated.

Miss Ellen P. Burke typed the several drafts of the manuscript and was responsible for coordinating the flow of materials among contributors, editors, and the publisher. Mrs. Sharon K. Freeman, Miss Helen Gamreki, Miss Helen McNeil, Miss Sharon J. Ringholz, and Mrs. Thelma Shapiro assisted in the editing.

We wish to extend special appreciation to the publisher and to Mr. Al Goodyear and Mr. James Murray of Prentice-Hall, Inc., for their sustained support, counsel, and encouragement in the development of this volume.

INTRODUCTION

Hugh R. Leavell, M.D.

In recent years a phenomenal expansion of interest has developed in the study of the aspects of health problems with which the social sciences have tools to deal. Among the reasons for this new increase of interest are a number of forces which require special mention. Some of these forces are to be found on the health side of the relationship, and some lie on the side of the social sciences. Certain forces in the general environment of the times are also noteworthy.

On the health side, professionals are reviving past interest in the importance of the multiple causation of disease and disorder. The microbiological era introduced by Pasteur brought an enormous change in medical thinking. Searches began for the one specific microbe which was thought to be the prime causative agent for each disease. Research for specific cures became almost frantic, following the dramatic development of the vaccines and immune sera which provided prevention for a number of diseases and cures for others. Knowledge of antibiotics, hormones, and specific nutrients such as vitamins and minerals further fanned the unitary-causation flame. Science all but lost sight of the individual patient living in his social environment. Social medicine, which had been developing even before all this, became sidetracked.

Of course, the early optimism about specific causation of and specific treatment for all man's ills had to be tempered. Accumulating experience showed the fallacy of extrapolating too far from the unquestionably good results found in a limited number of situations. The importance of the environment in all its aspects, of genetic factors, and of the mental and emotional aspects of illness was recognized once more. The concepts of the "whole man," of psychosomatic illness, and of various socioeconomic factors in producing or contributing to disease once again became more widely accepted. However, physicians were not trained in these areas of investigation. So, led by mental health workers, medical people called on social scientists for help.

A parallel situation existed in organized community health work—that is, public health. Much of the productive health research that was going on could be applied on a mass basis to the community's benefit. Various governmental and voluntary organizations—including hospitals—were set up to provide the needed community services and to educate people to use them. At first, there was little realization that health organization and administration was comparable in any significant way with other organizations to be found in the community. Gradually, it became apparent that people in organizations act in somewhat comparable ways, even though the objectives of the organizations differ considerably. Executives and others responsible for health organizations, many of whom were physicians, found that their training in the natural sciences provided little basis upon which to design and conduct studies of organization, of the community itself, and of how the public might be educated to avail itself of the health knowledge pouring out of the rapidly expanding laboratories in hospitals and in medical schools. Once again the social scientists were called upon.

While all these things were going on among health workers, social science was coming of age and proving itself in numerous fields of application. Concepts were being clarified and research tools with greater applicability were becoming available. Looking about for new research areas, a number of social scientists found receptive hosts and collaborators among health workers. Hospitals, with their complex organizational ramifications, were found to be fertile fields for study. Health education of the public obviously involved problems that were interesting to social scientists. Occasional difficulties in collaborative work which developed in some situations only served to prove that sufficient collaboration was being attempted to bring the difficulties to light and to make them of sufficiently broad interest to warrant publication.

The general environment of the times has also had a great influence in bringing the social sciences and health together for their mutual benefit and for the public good. International activities carried on at a greatly increased tempo have made obvious the need to understand the other fellow if international educational exchange and technical cooperation are to be successful, not to mention international military operations. The public's expectation of scientific miracles has led to geometric expansion of funds to support research. Greater public sophistication about things medical, while helping the physician with the health education of his patients, has also impelled the physician himself to carry on this education in a more sophisticated way. Expansion of health insurance and the introduction of other third parties into the patient-physician relationship have introduced factors that make the relationship one which can best be studied by social science techniques. Finally, the rapidly rising costs of health care have aroused people to the point that they insist on having a stake in the matter and demand that the economics and other aspects of the problem be investigated.

It is unnecessary to document here the expansion of interest in health and the social sciences. However, one may point to the establishment in 1955 by the American Sociological Association of a section on medical sociology and note that there are several hundred names of both social scientists and health workers included on a roster of people with special interest in these fields.

Great credit is due the Russell Sage Foundation, The Milbank Fund, The Commonwealth Fund, The Ford Foundation, The Social Science Research Council, and others, for fostering this collaboration. Public health schools, medical schools and schools of nursing were assisted in adding social scientists to their teaching and research staffs; fellowships were provided for social scientists who wished to become more familiar with the health subculture; the publication of pertinent books was encouraged, and so forth. The National Institute of Mental Health also had an early interest in the enterprise, and has done much to strengthen it, as have other elements in the National Institutes of Health.

The field is ripe, then, for the harvest. This book represents a broad cross-section of part of the fund of information and concepts which are already at hand. A good deal of data, too, are included in the various chapters, much of it coming from the work of the authors themselves. Much more data will became available later on as the suggestions made here for further research are followed up. Certainly, one of the major reasons for the existence of the book is the conviction on the part of the editors that much more research is needed, and the hope that this book will help stimulate both health workers and social scientists to get on with the job.

The social science–health field is developing on so many fronts that it is hardly possible for a single person to present its many facets. Hence the device of inviting a number of authors, physicians, and social scientists, who are experts and investigators in their specialties, to write indivdual chapters. This book draws together a wealth of fresh material which will be important to the work of physicians, nurses, social workers, community organizers, and social scientists interested in health.

TABLE OF CONTENTS

Contributors to This Volume

ODIN W. ANDERSON is Associate Professor of Sociology and Research Director of Health Information Foundation, University of Chicago.

HOWARD S. BECKER is Associate Professor of Sociology, Institute for the Study of Human Problems, Stanford University.

JOHN A. CLAUSEN is Professor of Sociology and Director of the Institute of Human Development, University of California at Berkeley.

RONALD G. CORWIN is Assistant Professor of Sociology at Ohio State University.

SYDNEY H. CROOG is Assistant Professor of Sociology at the Harvard School of Public Health.

JACK ELINSON is Administrator of the Research Unit and Associate Professor, Columbia University School of Public Health and Administrative Medicine.

HOWARD E. FREEMAN is Professor of Social Research and Director of the Research Center, Florence Heller Graduate School for Advance Studies in Social Welfare, Brandeis University.

ELIOT FREIDSON is Professor of Sociology at New York University and on the research staff of Montefiore Hospital.

BLANCHE GEER is Associate Professor at Syracuse University.

SAXON GRAHAM is Associate Cancer Research Scientist, Roswell Park Memorial Institute and Assistant Professor of Preventive Medicine and Lecturer in Sociology, University of Buffalo.

STANLEY H. KING is Associate Director of Research of the University Health Service and Lecturer in the Department of Social Relations, Harvard University.

HUGH R. LEAVELL, M.D. is Consultant to the Ford Foundation and Indian Government, New Delhi, India.

SOL LEVINE is Associate Professor in Social Psychology and Director of the Social Science Program at the Harvard School of Public Health.

STEVEN POLGAR is Research Director, The Planned Parenthood Federation of America.

GEORGE G. READER, M.D. is Professor of Medicine at Cornell University Medical College.

LEO G. REEDER is Associate Professor of Epidemiology, University of California, Los Angeles.

GEORGE ROSEN, M.D. is Professor of Health Education, Columbia University School of Public Health and Administrative Medicine.

IRWIN T. SANDERS is Associate Director, International Training and Research, Ford Foundation.

OZZIE G. SIMMONS is Director of the Institute of Behavioral Science and Professor of Sociology at the University of Colorado.

EDWARD A. SUCHMAN is Professor of Sociology at the University of Pittsburgh.

MARVIN J. TAVES is Professor of Sociology at the University of Minnesota.

WALTER I. WARDWELL is Associate Professor of Sociology at the University of Connecticut.

PAUL E. WHITE is Assistant Professor, School of Public Health, Johns Hopkins University.

RICHARD H. WILLIAMS is Chief of the Professional Services Branch, National Institute of Mental Health.

ROBERT N. WILSON is Professor of Sociology, School of Public Health, University of North Carolina.

HANDBOOK OF MEDICAL SOCIOLOGY

1

CONTRIBUTIONS OF SOCIOLOGY TO MEDICINE

George G. Reader, M.D.

Sociology has already contributed much to medicine and gives promise of making an even greater contribution in the future. For a number of years it has had a considerable impact through those social scientists who have "walked the wards" with physicians and nurses, those who have interviewed patients, and those who have taught medical students. This chapter records a physician's recognition of the accomplishments and potential of medical sociology; it attempts to define the nature of a contribution, to examine the role of the sociologist in medicine, and to review the special contributions of social science, both those already made and those pressingly needed.

Criteria for a Contribution

When work in any scientific field is considered for application to practice, the question is asked implicitly: What good is it to the practitioners? Engineering research, for instance, presumably devotes itself to formulation of basic principles; development is concerned with the application of these principles to bridge construction, or automotive propulsion, or generation of electricity. Development itself however also contains the element of design: the application of fundamental principles in new ways. Design in engineering is in many ways akin to the "art" of a practice such as medicine, an individualistic and intuitive approach to solution of some practical and immediate problem. The style of the performer makes it individualistic; his internalized knowledge based on experience makes it intuitive. Occasionally, development—as also may be the case with practice or with applied research in medicine—results in formulation of new basic principles or modification of old ones; often the problems encountered by the practitioner determine the strategy of investigation. Then the dichotomy between research and development becomes less clear. Scientists do more than discover principles and practitioners do more than merely apply them. Scientific investigation is inseparable from good practice; each contributes to the other.

Robert Loeb suggests that medical schools today turn out two general types of physicians: the good-rule-of-thumb doctor and the scientific physician [13]. The good-rule-of-thumb man knows what is in the textbooks and is able to recognize conditions described there when he encounters them in his patients. He then follows the rules for that condition as laid down by others. The scientific physician, on the other hand, understands the basic mechanisms of function and dysfunction and can test appropriate hypotheses in each situation he encounters in patients. As a result, he is continually ready to add to human knowledge, not only by obervation but also by modification of hypotheses and concepts as a result of new findings.

Practitioners themselves may thus make scientific contributions at times as well as apply the findings of other investigators working apart from the practice situation. Either type of finding will hopefully provide all practitioners with new insights or new concepts. The first type might be called a direct contribution, made by practitioners themselves or by investigators working in a clinical field; the second might be designated as indirect, made apart from practice and often by investigators concerned with other problems entirely.

Contributions may be further categorized as descriptive, predictive, or modifying. The descriptive contribution is merely observational or clarifying. As descriptive detail increases, however, predictive power improves.

Contributions of considerable generality may therefore be called predictive. When these are universally accepted by practitioners so that they force changes in practice methods, they may be designated as modifying. It is obvious that these categories overlap, but they are nevertheless helpful in indicating degrees of relevance to practice.

Social science contributions, by their very nature, deal with human relationships: interpersonal or intergroup relationships, individual personality differences, the perceptions and reactions of people to their internal as well as to their external *milieu*. Social science does not deal with pathological lesions, nor with alterations in biological structure, nor with physiological function, nor with the invasive effects of microorganisms; it concerns itself with people who are well or ill, not with the disease process itself. On the other hand, it most specifically has to do with society—with people living in groups and with the structure, function, and change or action of such groups.

Medicine has at times been called a social science, but of course it is not that any more than it is a physical science. Medicine is a synthesis of many disciplines; it is essentially the practice of knowledge and skills and attitudes helpful in the care of the sick. There is a certain body of knowledge unique to this activity which might be termed a science of medicine and which grows by accretion from applications of the physical, natural, and social sciences. Physicians with training in these other disciplines may add to knowledge in the basic science as well as in the applied; by the same token, other scientists may contribute to knowledge in medicine and in their own field as well. Both, as they provide principles on which practice is based and modify techniques of practice, help to build a science of medicine.

In order to understand the nature of a contribution in this field, however, it is important to examine it from the point of view of the practitioner. What is the body of knowledge unique to medical practice? It may perhaps best be considered in terms of the interests of the health professional. He concerns himself with prevention, diagnosis, prognosis, and treatment of illness in individuals if he is a clinician, in communities if he is a public health officer. Prevention implies understanding of causation—both a knowledge of specific etiology and a recognition of circumstances that promote or detract from good health. Diagnosis is the identification and categorization of clinical or epidemiological entities. For generations the clinical entity has been the organizing principle which has directed the clinician's activity. It ranges from the syndrome (a recognizable constellation of signs and symptoms) to a more or less fully understood disease process. Sometimes, as in many dermatological conditions, it is merely a descriptive name; often, as in the infectious diseases, it indicates an understanding of the cause as well as of the course of the illness. Prognosis is the prediction of outcome in an illness. It implies knowledge of the natural history of a disease and the probable response of the particular individual or group to the disease process. Treatment or management includes rehabilitation and requires knowledge of the various factors that may modify the natural course of illness, from specific drugs and physical agents to the salubrious effects of encouragement, support, optimism, rewards, and a beneficial environment. In order to be considered useful contributions by the medical practitioner, social science findings must, therefore, describe more fully and accurately these phases of his dealings with health and illness, or they must increase his ability to predict what he will find as to cause, type of diagnosis, outcome, or success of treatment, or they must modify his methods of practice in some useful way.

Classification of Social Science Contribution

Kendall and Merton have suggested a useful list of substantive areas of sociological research in medicine, namely: social etiology and ecology of disease, social components in therapy and rehabilitation, medicine as a social institution, and sociology of medical education [11]. Most of the direct contributions of sociology can be placed under these headings, especially if medical education is taken to mean the professional socialization of all health personnel.

Indirect contributions

When a social scientist carries out a study in a field other than medicine and his findings are later discovered to be applicable to the medical setting, his contribution may be considered indirect. An example would be the application of Gouldner's findings in industrial bureaucracy [4] to the bureaucracy of the hospital. Another kind of indirect contribution is that made by a sociologist or psychologist who may not be familiar with the actual situation but can fit what he has learned from others or from his own experience as a patient into a larger logical pattern. Parsons' Chapter 10 of *The Social System* [14] is an example of such a contribution.

Anthropology provides a special case in regard to indirect contributions. The anthropologist may, of course, make direct contributions to Western medicine, and some—such as Lyle Saunders [21] or Ben Paul [15] have made them. His observations on primitive peoples, on the other hand, may be applicable to modern medical practice only through analogy, which may nonetheless contribute useful descriptive insights. Unfortunately there has been too little effort as yet to formulate observations on health and illness in other primitive cultures into patterns that permit general predictions of health behavior or that can be useful in modifying practice systematically.

To sum up: sociological contributions in medicine must be descriptive, predictive, or modifying of practice. If they are to be appreciated as immediately useful by the health professions, they must deal with prevention of illness (or causation), diagnosis, prognosis, or treatment. They may be formal—that is, the result of planned research—or they may be informal—that is, the result of advice or speculation. They may be direct as a result of observations made in the medical setting or indirect from research in other areas that is later found applicable to the health field.

A simple paradigm summarizes some of these relationships:

	NATURE OF CONTRIBUTION					
	Descriptive		*Predictive*		*Modifying*	
Focus of Study	*Direct*	*Indirect*	*Direct*	*Indirect*	*Direct*	*Indirect*
Social Etiology and Ecology of Disease						
Social Components in Therapy and Rehabilitation						
Medicine as a Social Institution						
Sociology of Medical Education						

Contributions Made and To Be Made

As has been suggested, sociology has already made many contributions to medicine. By their very presence in hospitals, medical schools, nursing schools, and schools of social work, sociologists have been a considerable addition to the teaching and practice of the health sciences. The table of contents of this volume, as well as the various bibliographies of publications in the field of medical sociology, give some indication of the kinds of contributions that have been made. In terms of the paradigm suggested above, probably the largest proportion of contributions relate to medicine as a social institution and almost as many fall under the rubric, social components in therapy. In the latter case, contributions have been mainly from the field of mental health. Proportionally few have been made thus far that may be classified as studies in social etiology and ecology of disease and even fewer that may be classified as studies in sociology of medical education (even when that is taken to include education in all the health sciences). Also, the large majority of contributions have been direct, with only a relatively small number from general sociology having thus far been applied to medicine. On the other hand, there have also been few studies in medical sociology which have modified the major concepts concerning human behavior. The present distribution merely suggests that medical sociology is still young, even though rapidly growing.

In terms of relevance to medical practice, the contributions to date have dealt more with the setting than with the patient; there have been few on causation (except in epidemiological research), almost none on diagnosis or prognosis, and contributions to treatment have mainly been in terms of the milieu. Sociological contributions to medicine are thus far largely descriptive. As they increase they may be expected to become predictive and there is little doubt that they will eventually modify many aspects of the practice of medicine.

Information about patients

The background characteristics of patients, such as age, sex, socio-economic status, and ethnic group, are usually known to the health personnel caring for them, but there is little systematically recorded about the significance of these variables for health care. A good deal of information is available from standard epidemiological studies about age and sex, so that a chronic cough in a ten-year-old schoolgirl, for instance, is known to have a different implication from one in a 45-year-old male who smokes heavily. Socio-economic status and educational level have been found to correlate with attitudes and information about illness [17] and Zborowski, for instance [23], has shown that ethnic backgrounds and reactions to pain are correlated. But there is a good deal still to be learned about the attitudes and expectations of higher-status groups, particularly private patients. And little is known about the way patients respond to one form or another of patient care.

Identification of functional disability in patients also requires considerably more study than it has received. It is essential to sort out physiological lack of function from behavioral or attitudinal inadequacy if indices of disability are to be determined accurately.

Information about health personnel

Selection of students for the health professions and stimulation of recruitment have proven to be difficult problems. One obstacle is the lack of clearly defined long-term objectives for education of health personnel. The Medical College Aptitude Test, for instance, is a fair predictor of medical school performance—although not as good as college grade scores. But neither index tells much about performance in practice [10]. Peterson's studies [16], in fact, have suggested that only length of service as a medical house officer correlates with performance in practice. Much more needs to be known about the various roles health professionals play, their point of view about these roles, about each other, and about the patients' expectations of the roles, as well as about their opinions as to which role performance is most effective for a particular result.

Hammond and Kern [9] have suggested that a course in comprehensive medicine merely slows down the development of negative attitudes by medical students about patients. Is there some more positive way to orient medical and nursing students constructively toward difficult patients with chronic illnesses? How can students be selected who will exemplify the positive qualities of the kindly nurse and physician? Perhaps a heavier science requirement for admission will help produce better medical scientists, but will it also ensure a supply of physicians interested in their patients as people?

Nature and organization of medical care

Health care is becoming more technological and more highly organized and a few studies have been made that help to explain its special problems. One such study is that by Goss on *Physicians in Bureaucracy* [7]. In this report a crucial question is analyzed—namely: How do the autonomous professional and the teaching hospital accommodate themselves to each other? How, for example, is supervision provided and accepted? Many more such studies are needed which will cover the range of medical organization from group practice to the informal network of solo practitioners that is still the norm in most communities. The consequences of one form of organization as opposed to another are central to the question of quality of care.

Measurement of quality is, of course, a problem in itself. Indices are not readily available and those that have been used are somewhat suspect. Health personnel can be judged in terms of training qualifications, proper licensing, and adherence to educational standards, but these criteria may mean little in terms of performance. Organizational indices may be used, such as continuity and completeness of care and good record-keeping. Or patient satisfaction may be added as a variable in assessing high quality medical care. Many more studies must be made to determine proper scales of measurement, as well as to discover what circumstances are likely to optimize high quality patient care.

In connection with the latter question it is important to know how the various medical care institutions fit together in the community. What is the role of the hospital, the voluntary agency, the health department, the county medical society? Is there some means of communication among these various groups? Is it possible to mobilize them all when necessary in behalf of patients? Are patients moved efficiently from one source of medical service to another to obtain the optimum in care?

Cost of care

There has been a steady increase in hospital costs and a consequent increase in insurance premiums. These cost increases are understandable if one considers the poor wages that have previously been paid to hospital personnel and the steeply rising expense of new medical diagnostic and therapeutic equipment. The allocation of resources is in fact becoming a serious problem. How much can society afford in terms of highly complicated and expensive surgical operations? What is the best way of distributing medical services so that the most people are helped? These questions have previously not commanded the attention of investigators, but technological advance is now forcing the issues upon us. They are not just economic questions but socioeconomic questions that must be approached by physicians, sociologists, and economists working together.

Aside from formal research findings, there may also be informal but direct contributions made by social scientists who are working in the medical setting. As a result of his training, the social scientist brings a particular point of view to bear on day-to-day medical problems. His wisdom, values, and point of view may be valuable to the practitioner in a number of ways.

The Sociologist in Medicine

A number of reviewers have noted that sociologists have only concerned themselves with medicine as a serious field of study in the past decade or so, but by 1962 there were over 700 social scientists who identified themselves with the field as members of the Medical Sociology Section of the American Sociological Association, and many others had made direct or indirect contributions to it. The recent rapid growth is the result of a number of forces, the most important of which is probably the availability of federal government funds for research. Other sources of stimulus have been the opportunities for study provided by hospitals and clinics and the welcome afforded social scientists by their medical colleagues. Patients in teaching hospitals are particularly suitable subjects for study, as are the staff and the setting. An atmosphere of inquiry is already present, and there is great respect for the observation of natural phenomena. Health professionals have usually embraced the opportunity to place themselves and their patients under observation. Some have done so because of a tolerance for all kinds of scientific inquiry; some because there are questions they have hoped would be answered by the social scientist; and some because it has become the thing to do. There has been a fair amount of scepticism and some hostility, too, of course. Methods have been questioned, observation and interview have been looked upon as interfering with patient care, and findings have at times been viewed as too revealing or embarrassing.

Social scientists have entered the medical field with a variety of motivations, and with all kinds of training. There are those who have come as advisors, bringing a sociological perspective to bear on clinical problems. Some of these have gone so far as to designate themselves as "clinical sociologists." They have been eager to assist in the diagnosis and treatment of patients. Whether they have ever been wholly successful is doubtful, since their training does not fit them for diagnosis—that is, identification of disease—nor are they properly socialized to the therapeutic role.[1] A doctor, nurse, or social worker has had long years of attitudinal preparation for fulfilling the role expectations of patients together with a practical knowledge and a store of technical information that the social scientist cannot easily duplicate. This is not to imply that the perceptive social scientist does not contribute greatly as an informal consultant at times, but one of the most useful informal contributions he makes is as an objective social observer. In his essay on "Anti-Minotaur: The Myth of a Value-Free Sociology," [5] Gouldner offers an eloquent statement concerning the impossibility of a social scientist ever being completely value-neutral. Observation, according to him, can never be divorced from values, and social relationships therefore are always seen from one or another frame of value reference. He illustrates his thesis with some of the studies that have been done in medical sociology, and suggests that in the work which culminated in *Experiment Perilous* [3] Fox tended to accept the value system of the physicians she was observing. If a Chicago-trained sociologist, Gouldner points out, were to observe the same set of phenomena, he might well apply a different set of values; Erving Goffman, for example, might consider the activity in Ward F-2 as directed towards "cooling the mark out." Certainly Gouldner is correct in indicating that every observer has a certain bias. One would hope, however, that social scientists have now reached a degree of sophistication in their method whereby their observations are replicable. When properly-trained social scientists differ in their observations of the same social situation, they should still be expected to be able to identify the same salient social phenomena even though their interpretations may emphasize one point rather than another.

Although quite familiar with the professional values by which they live and work, most medical people—like those in other professions—are often unaware of how strongly influenced they are in their opinions by these same values. Probably because of the authoritarian environment in which they develop, young persons—in medicine particularly—have a tendency to see the world about them in terms of black and white value tones. In their eyes there are "good" doctors and "bad" doctors, "good" nurses and "bad" nurses, and "good" patients and "bad" patients. *Crock*, for example, is a term commonly applied to patients who are designated as "bad." When interviewed about the use of this term, young medical students and house officers are found to apply it to any patient who is unsatisfactory for them. A patient who fails to give a clearcut history, a patient who fails to improve under a therapeutic regimen, a patient who offers no clearcut

---

[1] See Chap. 19 for additional discussion of this point and many of the others that follow.

challenge with which the young physician can cope and from which he can obtain satisfaction is so labeled. Social scientists are not free from value prejudices either. They may tend to align themselves with patients or with doctors or with nurses during periods of participant observation, but they are much less partisan than the professional people themselves. The social scientist helps to make the health professional aware of his prejudices and thereby more objective; he sees people as actors, recognizes status differentials without affective coloring, and can point out when value judgments are interfering with the physician's objective appraisal of the facts of the situation.

The optimal conditions for this kind of informal contribution are present when the social scientist is professionally secure and not trying desperately to find a place of his own as a clinician in the medical hierarchy. At the same time the health professionals with whom he is working must have respect for him as a fellow scientist. There must be easy communication between them and ready give and take. Under such circumstances values—including a belief in the worth of objectivity—are shared. The physician or nurse or social worker acquires awareness of the value environment in which he lives and, though he may be no less value-laden, he may become a better observer than would otherwise be possible. The social scientist in this process of interaction may also acquire some of the values of the health professionals: an appreciation of precise measurement in obtaining biological data, an understanding of the importance of visibility and supervision for high quality performance, and an awareness of the importance of practical problems in determining research strategy.

Social scientists have found their way into the medical setting in a number of ways. Some have come as patients or as visitors and have based their views of health care on somewhat isolated subjective experiences. Others have been invited in to do a particular job, such as evaluation of an educational program. Still others have sought opportunities to carry out social research on problems they define themselves. A few have come mainly as teachers, and even fewer as administrators. Like Simmel's stranger [22], these visitors have at first been identified as outsiders and some have remained so; others, however, have become a part of the group. Starting by and large as "cosmopolitans," a few have even become "locals" [6]. There are advantages and disadvantages in both types of adjustment.

The social scientist who comes as a transient visitor may be better able to relate his subjective impressions to the mores of the community at large. He may thus extend his views of society to encompass the medical world and fit it into the larger fabric. On the other hand, the knowledge he acquires is likely to be superficial and may result in advice based on inaccuracies and misperceptions as to effective solutions of medical problems.

Those who remain strangers in the medical environment tend always to formulate problems in terms of their own discipline; their audience is comprised of other social scientists. They may find it difficult to communicate with their medical colleagues and may miss the nuance of the relationships they wish to analyze. The health personnel with whom they interact will learn little about social science from them and will often have doubts about their ability to solve the important problems of patient care. On the other hand, they make substantial contributions to their own field and run little risk of adopting the health professional's perspectives and values.

Those social scientists who come with the aim of sharing knowledge and point of view, however, and who find medical colleagues eager to learn, do not remain strangers long, and if they retain ties with their own reference group, they need not lose their "cosmopolitan" outlook. Together with health professionals, who function as colleagues and collaborators, they will be most likely to derive new hypotheses and create new concepts and develop a new body of knowledge in medical sociology.

From the type of grants presently being made by the National Institutes of Health, it is clear there is great need for social scientists to aid in the research being planned; and the need is for sociologists as collaborators and not as isolates [20]. The epidemiological and community problems now coming to the fore require a combined attack by medically and sociologically trained investigators. In the future, personnel must be trained both in medicine and in sociology if the questions now emerging are to be answered. It is too much to expect that there will be many who will obtain degrees in both fields, but some formal training in sociology for the physician and some exposure to medical courses for the sociologist would seem desirable.

The sociologist as a medical teacher

When physiologists first came into the hospital, clinicians looked upon them askance. What could these people who knew nothing of disease or treatment contribute to the teaching of medical students? Today, of course, they are fully accepted in most American schools, and in fact the clinical teacher who is not something of a physiologist is thought to be poor indeed.

Dana Atchley has traced the convergence of the art of healing and the science of medicine in his semiautobiographical essay "The Healer and the Scientist" [1]. Much of what he calls "art" is now amenable to scientific analysis by the techniques of social science, and as social research into the healing art proceeds, more and more information will become available for transmission to medical students by social scientist teachers. The day is not far distant when the sociologist, like the physiologist, will be considered indispensable to the medical school [8, 18, 19].

Some social scientists are functioning as teachers in American medical schools now, of course, and they have much to teach. Objectivity in observation of social phenomena has already been alluded to; equally important for the medical student is the ability to perceive people as members of social groups and communities. Clinical training in medicine, nursing, social work, and psychology focuses on the individual. Patients tend to be seen as social isolates and the importance of their relationships with others is overshadowed by the concern with their internal function or dysfunction. Group norms are also ignored and the range of normal variations is often forgotten by the clinical student. The sociological teacher can repair these defects and at the same time can place the patient, his illness, and the means of dealing with it in a larger social context.

The place of the sociologist in the medical school

A panel discussion at the meeting of the Medical Sociology Section of the American Sociological Association in 1958 explored the desirability of various locations for a sociologist in the social structure of the medical school [2]. There was some consensus that, whatever his position, the sociologist should be fitted into the regular departmental structure. Since then, as medical sociology has advanced, it is clearer that the formation of a behavioral science department will probably be the best answer. The social scientist will then have more secure and satisfactory status and can compete more effectively for rank, pay, and curriculum hours. The University of Kentucky Medical School has recently instituted such an arrangement, and developments there will be observed with more than passing interest.

The problem of academic freedom

Academic departments of universities have a somewhat more *laissez-faire* view of research activity than do teaching hospitals and medical schools and the transition from one setting to the other may be somewhat troublesome for the social scientist. In his review of social science research institutes, Paul Lazarsfeld points out a similar discrepancy between the institute and the university [12]. The reasons are somewhat similar. When research funds are obtained from foundation or government grants, or when investigations are made for a client, an essentially contractual relationship develops. The contractor is both the individual carrying out the research and the institution. The social science research institute guarantees a certain standard of performance, as does the teaching hospital or medical school. The teaching hospital also has a certain responsibility for patients that requires responsible supervision of clinical research; it must always be able to justify the importance of the research carried out on or with patients. Moreover, most medical institutions tend to be more authoritarian than do strictly academic ones, both by tradition and because of the sense of responsibility engendered by decisions involving patients. Many teaching hospitals have research committees that review all manuscripts before publication. Most departments in medical school have the rule that all grant proposals, reports, and manuscripts submitted for publication must be reviewed by the department chairman before being released. It is also incumbent on the principal investigator in these institutions, of course, to review carefully all the research emanating from a particular project for which he has received a grant.

For the social scientist who has been reared in an academic department where there is little authoritarianism or hierarchical structure, and where the research is done almost entirely as an individual activity without grant obligations, the medical setting may appear quite restrictive. In practice, of course, it is not. Academic freedom is cherished as much in the medical school as elsewhere in the university. Where the aim is to have grant proposals accepted, research successful, and the findings published, help in seeing that these aims are attained is a not unnatural consequence. When the social scientist has demonstrated his ability to obtain and administer grants and has also indicated a sense of responsibility to the reputation of the institution in terms of integrity and reliability, autonomy follows. It is in fact the achievement of this autonomy which is the natural avenue to high status in the medical scientific environment. Most social scientists feel that they should have achieved this with the conferring of the Ph.D. degree, but there are occasional instances where they have been found inadequately socialized to the medical setting and irresponsible in terms of the medical mores. Until the social scientist has proved himself, the medical institution's requirement of supervision is understandable.

Summary and Conclusions

This chapter has reviewed the nature of scientific contributions and specifically those made by social science to the practice of medicine. It has examined the personal contribution of social scientists both as visitors to the medical setting and as colleagues, dissected the role of the social scientist in medicine, and surveyed—all too briefly—the variety of contributions that have been made as well as those needed for the future.

A contribution has been classified as direct or indirect, as descriptive, predictive, or modifying of practice, and as occurring in the areas of social etiology and ecology of disease, social components in therapy and rehabilitation, medicine as a social institution, and sociology of medical education. Contributions have also been noted to deal with prevention of illness, diagnosis, prognosis, or treatment.

The sociologist has been found to participate either actively or passively in the medical environment. As an active participant he appears to contribute most through a colleague relationship with health personnel. He has made a salutary informal contribution through his objectivity towards social phenomena.

Many useful contributions have been made in elucidating the characteristics of patients and their significance for diagnosis and patient care; others have provided new and useful information about recruitment and functions of health personnel; still others have clarified the nature and organization of patient care. Much remains to be done, and it may be hoped that the social scientist and health professional working together will solve the problems still to be posed.

References

1. Atchley, Dana, "The Healer and the Scientist," *Saturday Review*, 37 (January 9, 1954), 7–9.
2. Bloom, Samuel W., Albert F. Wessen, Robert Strauss, George G. Reader, and Jerome K. Myers, "The Sociologist as a Medical Educator: A Discussion," *American Sociological Review*, 25 (February, 1960), 95–101.
3. Fox, Renee C., *Experiment Perilous*. New York: The Free Press of Glencoe, Inc., 1959.
4. Gouldner, Alvin W., *Patterns of Industrial Bureaucracy*. New York: The Free Press of Glencoe, Inc., 1954.
5. ———, "Anti-Minotaur: The Myth of a Value-Free Sociology," *Social Problems*, 9 (Winter, 1962), 199–213.
6. ———, "Cosmopolitans and Locals: Toward an Analysis of Latent Social Roles—I," *Administrative Science Quarterly*, 2 (December, 1957), 281–306.
7. Goss, Mary E. W., *Physicians in Bureaucracy*. Unpublished Ph.D. dissertation, Columbia University.
8. ——— and George G. Reader, "Collaboration between Sociologist and Physician," *Social Problems*, 4 (July, 1956), 82–89.
9. Hammond, Kenneth and Frederick Kern, *Teaching Comprehensive Medical Care*. Cambridge: Harvard University Press, 1959.
10. Hill, Joseph K., "Assessment of Intellectual Promise for Medical School," *Journal of Medical Education*, 34 (October, 1959), 959–64.
11. Kendall, Patricia L. and Robert K. Merton, "Medical Education as a Social Process," *in* E. Gartly Jaco, ed., *Patients, Physicians, and Illness*. New York: The Free Press of Glencoe, Inc., 1958.
12. Lazarsfeld, Paul F. with collaboration of Sidney S. Spivack, "Observations on the Organization of Empirical Social Research in the United States," *Bulletin of the International Social Science Council*, 29 (December, 1961), 1–35.
13. Loeb, Robert, M.D., Professor of Medicine Emeritus, Columbia University, in a personal communication.
14. Parsons, Talcott, *The Social System*. New York: The Free Press of Glencoe, Inc., 1951.

15. Paul, Benjamin D., "Fluoridation and the Social Scientist: A Review," *Journal of Social Issues*, 17 (1961), 1–12.

16. Peterson, Osler L. *et al.*, "An Analytical Study of North Carolina General Practice, 1953–1954," *Journal of Medical Education*, 31 (December, 1956), Part II.

17. Pratt, Lois, "How Do Patients Learn About Disease," *Social Problems*, 4 (July, 1956), 29–40.

18. Reader, George G. and Mary E. W. Goss, "The Sociology of Medicine," *in* Robert K. Merton, Leonard Brown, and L. S. Cottrell, Jr., eds., *Sociology Today*. New York: Basic Books, Inc., 1959, pp. 229–46.

19. ———, "Medical Sociology with Particular Reference to the Study of Hospitals." *Transactions of the Fourth World Congress of Sociology*, 2 (1959), 139–152.

20. *Report on Manpower for Medical Research. Hearings Before a Subcommittee of the Committee on Appropriations.* House of Representatives, 87th Congress, Washington, D.C.: Government Printing Office, 1962.

21. Saunders, Lyle, *Cultural Difference and Medical Care*. New York: Russell Sage Foundation, 1954.

22. Simmel, George, *The Sociology of George Simmel*. New York: The Free Press of Glencoe, Inc., 1950.

23. Zborowski, Mark, "Cultural Components in Responses to Pain," *Journal of Social Issues*, 8 (1952), 16–30.

2

THE EVOLUTION OF SOCIAL MEDICINE

George Rosen, M.D.

Social scientists tend to emphasize the newness of medical sociology. But if viewed as the study of the relationships between health phenomena and social factors and contexts, medical sociology is seen to have deep historical roots.[1] Long before the social scientist identified medical sociology as a specialty, men concerned with affairs of state—economists, physicians, social reformers, historians, and administrators —were preoccupied with sociomedical problems and had made significant contributions to their solution.

---

[1] This chapter is based to a large extent on studies in the history of social medicine carried out over a period of some twenty years. Some of the results of these investigations have appeared in a series of papers [134, 136, 137, 138, 139, 142, 143, 144, 146].

Indeed, in part, the science of sociology owes its origin to this stream of development.

Pre-Mercantilist Thought

Health problems have always been linked with the political, social, and economic conditions of particular groups of people, but in earlier periods these relationships were not the subject of systematic investigation. Nonetheless, observations are available from antiquity: occupation and health are connected in an Egyptian papyrus which comments on the hard life of the people [163]. The influence of certain occupations on health was also noted by physicians and laymen in the Greco-Roman world.[2] Fundamentally, however, the physicians of classical antiquity were not interested in the health of manual laborers. Thus, the Hippocratic treatise—*Airs, Waters, and Places*—endeavored to inform the physician on the relation between environment and health (including such factors as climate, topography, quality of water, and even political organization), but omitted one of the most significant elements: the occupations of men.

This limitation is due in large measure to the social organization of the Greek *polis*, the related attitude toward manual labor, and the differential provision of medical care by social class in the Greco-Roman world. In the fifth century B.C. Plato vividly contrasted the differences in the medical care available to slaves and that available to freemen [119]. Similarly, he compared the medical care of the free manual worker with that of the rich man. In the *Republic*, he has Socrates say to Glaucon: "When a carpenter is ill he asks the physician for a rough-and-ready care. An emetic, a purge, a cautery, or the knife—that is the remedy for him. But if someone prescribes for him a course of dietetics or tells him to wrap his head up and keep himself warm, he replies at once that he has no time to be ill, that he sees no good in a life that is spent in nursing his disease to the neglect of his customary employment. He therefore bids the doctor good-bye, resumes his ordinary way of life, and either gets well, lives, and does his business or, if his constitution fails, he dies and is rid of his troubles."

"I understand," said Glaucon, "and that, of course, is the proper use of medicine for a man in his walk of life" [120].

Clearly the best kind of medical care required time and circumstances favorable to such attention. Very few people, however, could afford to submit to medical care under these conditions. Indeed, the writer of the Hippocratic work, *On Diet*, agreed that the mass of the people "by necessity must lead a haphazard life and . . . neglecting all, cannot take care

---

2 For example, in the Hippocratic writings and in the works of Pliny the Elder, Lucretius, Juvenal, Martial, Lucan, Galen, Silius Italicus, and Statius.

of their health" [70]. Similarly, somewhat over five hundred years later, Plutarch, in an essay on how to keep well, emphasized that he was writing for scholars and for men in public life, not for "men who engaged in the toilsome business of harvesting and caring for their crops . . ." [121].

Although the influence of the structure of society—and particularly of its class divisions—on the provision of medical care was plainly recognized by ancient authors, there was no systematic development of this point. Sporadic observations linking social and cultural factors or situations with the health aspects or the members of a community are recorded in the medieval period. Ibn Khaldûn asserts that "in the later [years] of dynasties, famines, and pestilences become numerous." Plagues occur chiefly because of "the corruption of the air [climate] through [too] large a civilization [population]. . . . This is the reason why pestilences occur much more frequently in densely settled cities than elsewhere, as for instance, in Cairo in the East and Fez in the Maghrib" [80]. In the fourteenth century, Marsiglio of Padua, in his attack on the supremacy of the Pope, commented tangentially on the physician in the body politic as a secular official and professional expert [141]. The so-called *Reformation of the Emperor Sigmund* (about 1439) contains proposals for the reform of medical care in the German cities and insists on the need for a municipal physician in every town. The position, duties, and remuneration of the physician are viewed within the framework of an hierarchical social structure which is reminiscent of Thomistic social philosophy [9, 10]. This work was widely circulated during the fifteenth century and may have influenced German governments to provide care by physicians on a more regular basis than had previously been the case.

The provision of medical care during the Renaissance and later in the seventeenth and eighteenth centuries provided other observations on the relation between social factors and health status. About 1515 a hospital physician was appointed in Strassburg on the ground that medical attention might help some patients and cost less in the long run than if no medical care was provided. It had been noted that patients who received no medical care remained longer in the hospital, and, even though some died, the expenses to the institution were relatively higher [189].

An even more pertinent comment was made by Bernardino Ramazzini in 1713. Concerning medical care for the Italian peasantry, he says:

> The diseases by which the agricultural population—at least in Italy, and especially on either bank of the Po—are wont to be attacked are pleurisy, inflammation of the lungs, asthma, colic, erysipelas, ophthalmia, quinsy, toothache, and dental decay. . . . The mistakes that I observe in the treatment of this class of men are many, and they arise from this fact that the peasantry are supposed on account of their tough constitutions to be able to endure strong remedies better than city folk [4].

Of brickmakers, Ramazzini remarked:

> Workers of this sort are mostly drawn from the peasant class; so, when they are attacked by fever they betake themselves to their huts and leave the affair entirely to nature; or else they are carried off to hospitals and there are treated, like everybody else, with the usual remedies, purging and venesection. For the doctors know nothing of the mode of life of these workers, who are exhausted and prostrated by unceasing toil.

Moreover, he adds:

> For these wretched workers the best remedy would be a fresh-water bath at the earliest stage when they begin to have fever; for their bodies are rough and dry with dirt, and by moistening the skin and opening the pores, the fever would be given an outlet [124].

Clearly, Michels was not unjustified in his claim that Ramazzini had laid the basis for a physiological concept of social class [101]. The humanitarian element in Ramazzini's work is evident, but one must also emphasize his awareness of the significance of economic productivity in relation to health. He was keenly conscious of the value of the mechanical arts for economic development and, more broadly, for the progress of civilization [76]. Nevertheless, he wrote:

> It must be confessed that many arts are the cause of grave injury to those who practise them. Many an artisan has looked to his craft as a means to support life and raise a family, but all he has got from it is some deadly disease. . . . Therefore, medicine, like jurisprudence, should make a contribution to the well-being of workers and see to it that, so far as possible they should exercise their callings without harm [124].

Essentially, Ramazzini stated or implied some of the basic elements of a concept of social medicine. These include the need to study the relations between the health status of a given population group and its living conditions which are determined by its social position; the noxious factors that act in a particular form or with special intensity in the group because of its social position; and the elements that exert a deleterious influence on health and which impede the improvement of the general state of well-being. These ideas, however, were not an isolated phenomenon. On the contrary, Ramazzini's thought is directly in the mainstream of ideas and practices in this period. They were part of a scheme of policy and organization whose supreme aim was to place social and economic life in the service of the power politics of the State. This was the system that came to be known generally as *mercantilism,* or as *cameralism* in its more politically oriented, specifically German form [35, 48, 92, 102, 159, 169].

Mercantilism and the Concept of Medical Police

In England and on the Continent, a central question was: What policy must the government pursue in order to increase the national wealth and the national power? That industry was one of the chief means by which a country could attain wealth was evident. Consequently, labor—one of the most important factors of production—came to be regarded as an essential element in the generation of national wealth. Obviously, any loss of labor productivity due to illness and death was a significant economic problem. Men of affairs grasped that it was not enough simply to recognize natural fertility and population as major conditions of national prosperity. The acceptance of this premise went hand in hand with the responsibility for removing impediments to the full development of these resources. This approach implied the concept of a national health policy, and the implication was accepted and developed in various directions both in England and on the Continent.

Although the idea of a national health policy was not systematically developed in England, bold and penetrating analyses of health problems were made. A most striking contribution was made by William Petty, the versatile father of political arithmetic, who saw that control of communicable diseases and the saving of infant life would contribute most to prevent diminution of population [73, 115]. Consequently, he recommended the creation of isolation hospitals for plague patients and maternity hospitals for unmarried pregnant women. Based on his view that certain occupational groups were of direct concern to the State, Petty proposed studies of occupational morbidity and mortality. He was aware that to achieve these aims an adequate supply of medical personnel would be required. Therefore, he proposed that an analysis—using the methods that John Graunt had employed—be made of health needs, and then that the numbers of physicians, surgeons, and others necessary to meet these needs be calculated.

Petty was not alone in dealing with health problems, nor in endeavoring to analyze them quantitatively. Among his contemporaries and successors these interests were expressed in varying degree. Perhaps closest to Petty was his younger contemporary Nehemiah Grew, also a physician, who is best known today for his work in plant anatomy [76]. Grew's focus of interest was the same as Petty's and his handling of health problems occurs within a similar context. To increase population so as to provide the necessary labor power for economic growth, he recommended in 1707 that the State do all in its power to maintain health and prevent disease. He proposed that the government regulate physicians' fees according to their experience, believing that the cost of medical care could thus be reduced and made accessible to those who needed it.

Even more noteworthy was the plan for a national health service set forth in 1714 by the Quaker cloth merchant and philanthropist, John Bellers [14, 132]. He maintained that illness and untimely death are a waste of human resources, and proposed the erection of a national health institute, the establishment of hospitals and laboratories to be used as teaching and research centers, and the provision of medical care to the sick poor.

Despite their potentialities, the ideas of these thinkers had no immediate tangible or theoretical consequences; they ran counter to major political and administrative trends. Effective implementation would have required a well-developed local administrative mechanism operating under centralized control—which, unfortunately, did not exist. Indeed, the outstanding feature of internal English administration from the middle of the seventeenth century to the Poor Law Amendment Act of 1834 is its intensely parochial character [28].

The mercantilist (cameralist) position in relation to health was also developed on the Continent, particularly in the German states, at about the same time. There, however, it emerged as an integral element in the theory of absolute monarchy. In matters of health, as in all other spheres of activity, the ruler knew what was best for his people, and by means of laws and administrative measures ordered what they should or should not do. The term cameralism has two connotations. On the one hand, it designates the ideas that appeared to explain, justify, and guide the centralizing tendencies and practices in administration and economic policy of an absolute monarchy. On the other hand, it refers to the various attempts of the same period to work out, in terms of emerging contemporary political and social science, a systematic account of the functioning of the various administrative services as a basis for the training of public officials.

Within the cameralist framework, a key concept in relation to problems of health and disease is the idea of *police*, derived from the Greek *politeia*. Characteristically the theory and practice of public administration came to be known as *Polizeiwissenschaft* (the science of police) and the branch of the field dealing with health administration received the designation *Medizinalpolizei* (medical police).

An early but pregnant formulation of the cameralistic approach to the health problems of social life was presented by Veit Ludwig von Seckendorff, a contemporary of William Petty, who throughout most of his life served in various administrative posts at the ducal courts of Gotha and Sachsen-Zeitz [43, 131, 168]. According to Seckendorff, the appropriate aim of government is to establish such ordinances as will assure the welfare of the land and the people. Since prosperity and welfare manifest themselves in growth of population, means must be taken to guard the health of the people so that their number may increase. A governmental program must concern itself with the maintenance and supervision of midwives, care of orphans, appointment of physicians and surgeons, protection against plague and other contagious disease, use of tobacco and spirituous beverages, inspection of food and water, measures for cleaning and draining towns, maintenance of hospitals, and provision of poor relief.

Seckendorff has been called the Adam Smith of cameralism, an illuminating if not entirely apt title [168].

Attention to the political and administrative aspects of health matters expanded during the seventeenth and eighteenth centuries. As in England, a number of administrators, physicians, and philosophers dealt with the theoretical and practical aspects of such problems. Thus, in his many-sided activities, Gottfried Wilhelm von Leibniz, the great German philosopher, scientist, and politician, discussed health problems on numerous occasions. In 1678, he proposed, among other things, the creation of a "political topography or a description of the present condition of the country" [88, 127] which was to include the number of cities, towns, villages, and—where necessary—individual houses, as well as the total population and acreage of the country. There should also be an enumeration of soldiers, merchants, artisans, and journeymen, and information on the state of the crafts. Moreover, there should be a listing of the number of deaths and their causes as there was in England.[3] Von Leibniz knew that such matters fell within the sphere of police. Thus, in 1680, in a series of notes prepared for the Emperor, von Leibniz suggested the creation of a chief administrative office for police affairs which was also to include a health council [88]. During the 1680's, in one of several essays on the need for adequate population and mortality statistics, and related matters, he dealt with the establishment of a registration office, pointing out that in England and France mortality records were available and that information useful for politics and medicine had been derived from these sources. Having given much thought to the questions on which statistical data might supply the answers, he presented fifty-six of them under the heading, "Questions in political arithmetic concerning the life of man and related matters" [87]. He was interested in the total number of people in a country, their distribution according to age and sex, the number of women of childbearing age, the number of men capable of bearing arms, the seasonal prevalence and geographical distribution of disease, the causes of death differentiated according to acute or chronic disease, and the relation of births to deaths.

By the beginning of the eighteenth century, the police concept had been refined to the point where ideas, proposals, and programs began to assume institutional forms. One indication was the establishment by the King of Prussia, in 1727, of two chairs for the teaching of cameralism. The occupants of these positions were to teach the principles of economic management and of police, so that students would be prepared to deal with administrative matters and be eligible as candidates for the Prussian civil service.

As the century advanced, the idea of police was more and more trans-

---

[3] The fifth edition of Graunt's *Observations* appeared in 1676, under Petty's supervision it is said. Leibniz probably refers to this work.

formed into a theory and practice of public administration. This process was intimately related to the needs of the absolute State and its most distinguished representatives were associated with the monarchs of Prussia and Austria. Outstanding in this connection were three men—Darjes, Justi, and Sonnenfels.

According to Roscher, Darjes was the most important of the cameralistic professors patronized by Frederick the Great [131]. Underlying the basic assumptions of Darjes is the political theory developed by Samuel Pufendorf and further elaborated by Christian Thomasius and Christian Wolff. According to this doctrine, the theoretical basis of enlightened absolutism, the State arose out of a social contract entered upon for self-preservation, a situation which impelled men to renounce their freedom. The purpose of the State is to secure for its people the greatest welfare and security, but it was left to the ruler of the State to determine what is the greatest welfare. Thus, the State is entitled to intervene in the affairs of the people in the general interest. Consequently, the officials of the State must be trained to handle the manifold problems arising out of State action and regulation. Hence for Darjes cameralism embraced *Polizeiwissenschaft* as a science of management. He recognized that the welfare of men is related to three factors: economic well-being, health, and the enjoyment of rights.

The leading representative of eighteenth century cameralism was Johannes Heinrich Gottlob von Justi. His development of the concept of police and of its attendant administrative technology represents the most characteristic expression of cameralism during the late eighteenth century, when the concept of medical police was introduced. An advocate of enlightened despotism justifying the policies of Maria Theresia of Austria and Frederick II of Prussia, Justi also based his administrative ideas on the political theory developed by the school of Pufendorf and Wolff. In Justi's view, the internal administration of the State is the center of gravity of its power relationships. Since the paramount aim of the State is to preserve and to extend its means, the monarch has the responsibility for taking such action as will maintain and expand the available resources and make the subjects happy. The science of police is concerned with this objective. Problems of health are considered in connection with the aim of improving and expanding the population. Among the measures proposed toward this end, Justi urged that people who suffer from hereditary diseases or who are unable to procreate should not be permitted to marry; that vice should be treated severely since it diminishes fecundity and discourages marriage; and that dissipation and disease should be prevented when at all possible. Specifically, the government should try to lengthen the life of the people through improved sanitary administration [77].

The third of the leading cameralists, Joseph von Sonnenfels, was appointed professor of cameral science in 1763 [168]. As advisor to Maria

Theresia, Joseph II, and Leopold II, he played an influential role in shaping Austrian political, social, and economic policy. Sonnenfels defined the science of police as a discipline concerned with the establishment and maintenance of the internal security of the State. He detailed a large number of activities and topics that affect public welfare and the health of the subjects. Among these are crimes of violence, relief for the poor, care of the sick, prevention of epidemics, regulation of medical and surgical practice, securing of pure food, cleanliness of cities, methods of procuring abortions, and duelling.

Clearly, by the latter part of the eighteenth century there had come into being in the German states a system of administrative thought and behavior which referred all activities to the welfare of the absolute State as the norm. This political and administrative line of development was paralleled by an equally significant interest among medical men in the relations of health problems to society and—in particular—to the State. While beginnings of this trend were already evident in the early seventeenth century, interest in health as a question of public policy entered upon a new stage of development during the late eighteenth century through the crystallization of the concept of medical police [143]. As far as is known, the term *medical police* was first employed in 1764 by Wolfgang Thomas Rau [43]. According to Rau, the medical profession is obligated not only to treat the sick, but also to supervise the health of the population. In order to have the required competent medical personnel, a medical police ordinance must be enacted which will regulate medical education, supervise apothecary shops and hospitals, prevent epidemics, combat quackery, and enlighten the public.

The influence of Rau's work is evident in the book published in 1771 by Christian Rickmann [43]. Rickmann's book made a strong and demonstrable impression upon his contemporaries. Based on the writings of Sonnenfels and Rau, it advocated the creation of a code of medical police and urged the need for a physician to compile a complete treatise on the subject. A noteworthy point in his division of disease into two major groups based on causation. One he calls *natural;* this emphasizes the contagious and epidemic diseases. The second group Rickmann terms *man-made*; these diseases occur more frequently than those in the first group and are "simply the physical consequences of moral laxity." Among the man-made diseases, he distinguishes between those due to the patient's own dereliction and those caused by the transgressions of others. These distinctions are significant because they present, in a crude and undeveloped manner, an early formulation of the concept of disease as a product of social and cultural maladjustment, a view which was developed more fully and concretely in the nineteenth century.

Other physicians also turned their interest to problems of medical police during the ensuing decade. Indicative of the increasing concentration of interest is the appearance in rapid succession of several relevant publications, each contributing to the subject in its own way [43]. In 1775, Ernst Gottfried Baldinger began to issue his journal, the *Magazin vor Ärzte*, devoted pre-eminently to questions of medical police [43]. In 1782, Baldinger issued one of his official addresses in which he emphasized that medicine was in considerable measure a political science (*Staatswissenschaft*) and that the best medical legislation would remain ineffective unless physicians were well trained and the people enlightened. In 1777, there appeared the *Fundamenta politiae medicae* by J. W. Baumer. More important was a publication by J. P. Brinkmann which appeared in 1778 [171]. In this work, he offered suggestions to improve the health of the rural population, with particular attention to the quality of midwifery and surgery. Like Rickmann (to whom, however, he did not refer), Brinkmann distinguished diseases that are natural and therefore unavoidable from those that are man-made.

These efforts, as well as the contributions of others, culminated in the monumental work on medical police of Johann Peter Frank. Best known today as a pioneer in public health and social medicine, his reputation among his contemporaries was based to an equal if not greater degree on his activities as a clinician, medical educator, and hospital administrator. In 1766, he conceived a plan to write on the measures to be taken by government for the protection of individual and group health—that is, on medical police. The first volume of his *System einer vollständigen medicinischen Polizey* appeared in 1779 and the sixth in 1817. Three more appeared posthumously. This work is today considered a landmark in the history of thought on the social relations of health and disease.

Frank presented a system of public and private hygiene which was based on enormous erudition and rich practical experience. A spirit of enlightenment and humanitarianism is clearly perceptible throughout the entire work, but as might be expected from a public medical official who spent his life in the service of absolute rulers, great and small, the exposition serves not so much for the instruction of the people—or even of physicians—as for the guidance of the officials who are supposed to regulate and supervise for the benefit of society all the spheres of human activity [135]. Frank's *System* appropriately opens with a consideration of population, followed by a detailed consideration of procreation, marriage, and pregnancy. According to Frank, it was the duty of public officials to promote marriage, and he proposed a bachelor tax, a suggestion realized in our time. He was imbued also with the importance of training and education for marriage, insisted that all childbirths be attended by trained persons, and further urged that a midwife be consulted prior to the expected date of confinement. Frank proposed legislation to enforce a reasonable period of bed rest during the puerperium, and to free the mother for several weeks from any work in or outside the house which might prevent her from giving the necessary attention to her child. When necessary, he felt the State should support the mother for the first six weeks after the delivery.

He also considered problems of infant and child health. It is not possible here to deal with the multifarious details of the child welfare program outlined by Frank. Mention must be made, however, of the discussion of the care of school children and the necessary supervision of educational institutions. With his customary thoroughness, Frank covers the welfare of school children, ranging from accident prevention to mental hygiene, and from the lighting, heating, and ventilation of school rooms to the provision of athletic programs.

Frank then turns to food, clothing, recreation, and housing. Food is considered in even greater detail than maternal and child health. Problems of sanitation are examined in relation to housing, sewage disposal, and water supply. Also, of considerable interest, is Frank's discussion of accidents and his position that many accidents are preventable. From this premise, he concluded that the health authorities should initiate a program to deal with factors responsible for such occurrences. It is noteworthy that modern public health has only recently realized the importance of accident prevention. The supplementary volumes that appeared from 1822 to 1827 deal with, among other topics, vital statistics, hospitals, military medicine, epidemic and communicable diseases, and venereal diseases. Difficult as it is to summarize a work as vast as Frank's *System*, it is clear that he achieved his objective of formulating and presenting systematically a coherent, comprehensive health policy.

The publication of Frank's *Medicinische Polizey* exerted an unusually strong influence and helped to spread the idea of medical police beyond the borders of the German states. Evidence of his influence is to be found in countries such as Hungary, Italy, Denmark, and Russia where cultural contact with the Germanies was close. Moreover, during the late eighteenth century and well into the nineteenth century, the idea of medical police appeared not only in the countries mentioned above but also in France, Great Britain, and the United States [144].

Nevertheless, neither his concept of medical police nor the solutions developed on this basis were equally applicable in all countries. The idea of medical police as employed by Frank was rooted in a particular political, economic, and social system. Based on cameralistic promises, medical police as developed by Frank and other German writers was authoritarian and paternalistic. At the end of the eighteenth century, however, social and political conditions obtaining in Great Britain, France, and the United States were markedly different from those in Germany. It was inevitable, therefore, that the concept would be materially altered by impact with fundamentally different political and social institutions. Insofar as the concept of medical police was adopted outside of Germany and brought to bear upon specific problems, it tended to be limited to those areas of community life in which governmental action was most easily accepted, chiefly in the control of communicable disease and in sanitation.

In the Germanies, and also in Italy, economic progress and the social change which it entailed did not keep pace with the example set by England and France. While Britain and Western Europe moved away from the pattern woven out of absolutism and mercantilism, this evolution was retarded in central Europe [19]. Reinforced by the inertia of tradition, the ideal of orderly efficiency remained the goal of public administration, and the concept of medical police continued to be applied within this framework. Measured in terms of the progressive social aspirations connected with the French Revolution and the problems created by the emergent industrial civilization, the idea of medical police faced the past. As part of an ideological and administrative structure whose chief function was to buttress an antiquated edifice, it lost the creative aspects which had characterized it during the eighteenth century. German administrators and authors of the first half of the nineteenth century continued to deal with questions of medical police along the lines drawn by Frank and his contemporaries. By the middle of the nineteenth century, however, the concept of medical police had in large measure become a sterile formula. Such practical significance as it still retained resided largely in administrative and regulatory activities concerned wth communicable disease control, organization and supervision of medical personnel, environmental sanitation, and the provision of medical care to the indigent. But, the broad social approach—the keen awareness of the social relations of health and disease which had characterized the thinking and writing of Johann Peter Frank and his more significant contemporaries—had been drained from the idea of medical police. As a result, when Germany encountered the health problems connected with the new industrial order, a new approach to these problems was necessary.

This does not mean, however, that medical police achieved nothing of importance or permanence. In practice, it meant a program of social action for health and welfare intended primarily to augment the power of the State. Within these limits there was undoubtedly a real concern for social welfare. Frank was fully aware of the impact of poverty among the lower classes—stunting and distorted physical development, lowered resistance to disease, and unfortunate social effects [45]. The most significant attempt to put Frank's ideas into practice was made by Franz Anton Mai, humanitarian and professor of obstetrics at the University of Heidelberg, in a health code submitted to the government of the Palatinate in 1800 [43, 107]. Mai's proposal was not realized, largely because of political conditions. Less ambitious endeavors, however, were more successful, so that though Frank's name is not associated with them he stimulated the enactment of various salutory laws in Europe.

In short, the development and application of the concept of medical police was a pioneer attempt at a systematic analysis of the health problems of community life. In the course of this endeavor a body of knowledge was collected, and these efforts stimulated further study of the social relations of health and disease. To France, however, fell the task of developing theoretically, under the new conditions of the early and middle nineteenth century, the social problems of health defined by Johann Peter Frank and the other workers who created the concept of medical police.

Revolution, Industrialism and Social Medicine in France

Mercantilism, as has been pointed out, played a major role in shaping the seventeenth and eighteenth centuries, and French views on the social relations of health are marked by its influence [146]. Although the French did not during this period arrive at a systematic formulation comparable to the concept of medical police, they were nevertheless aware of the implications of the concept in relation to health matters. (In fact the term *police* is itself of French origin.) As early as 1711, for instance, the Abbé Claude Fleury, tutor to the grandsons of Louis XIV, referred to the subject of health police, indicating its significance for the welfare of the State and the duty of the monarch to concern himself with its problems [155]. However, the term *medical police* was not widely acepted by the French. Although a few, like F. E. Fodéré and C. C. Marc, were in some degree influenced by Frank, the majority of French medical men interested in the social aspects of health and disease pursued an independent course. When French hygienists studied the relation of social and political conditions to health, they did so within a framework very different from that in which the concept of medical police had originated and developed.

By the last decade of the eighteenth century, it was obvious to many Frenchmen that profound changes were needed to deal effectively with problems of health and welfare. This was one of the problems with which the revolutionary governments had to deal in their twofold task of liquidating the old regime and constructing the new France. The acts of the Convention represent the most advanced point attained by the French Revolution in dealing with problems of health and social welfare [142]. In 1793 and 1794, the Convention passed a series of laws establishing a national system of social assistance which included medical care. Application of those laws was incomplete, however, for the available resources were limited, and the need to provide the instruments of war took precedence over all else. After the downfall of the Robespierrists, the Convention and then the Directory retreated from this policy. Nonetheless, certain goals had been set. Ideas on public policy had been developed which were to influence France profoundly (and, through her, other countries) during the first half of the nineteenth century. Ideas of public service, public interest, and social utility provided the seedbed in which germinated new views on the relation between health, medicine, and society [13, 90]. The men of 1789 and 1793 could not foresee the consequences that would stem from their thoughts and acts. The triumph of the machine and the concentration of capital were still in the future, but it was in terms of the situation created by these developments that the men of 1848 endeavored to apply the ideas of their predecessors. In this attempt they carried the ideas to a more advanced level. *Social Medicine*, the idea of 1848, must be seen as the fruit of this historical process, a process which has continued in a variety of circumstances to our own day.

The Revolution and the needs of the Napoleonic regime had gradually begun to industrialize France. But it was only after the Restoration, and particularly during the reign of Louis Philippe (1830–1848), that the French economy created its first railroads and heavy industries. This process of economic development imposed stresses and strains which endured until the 1870's and which were reflected in the evolution of French thought and action on health. During this period, France faced many of the health problems that had already been encountered in England, and which were being met contemporaneously in Belgium, Germany, and the United States. As in England, the introduction of steam power and machinery threw craftsmen out of work and the prospect of work and wages attracted them to urban industrial centers. The French urban population increased from 15 per cent of the total in 1830 to 25 per cent in 1846. Lack of proper housing, overcrowding, and the effects of periodic unemployment combined to make the life of the worker and his family a living death. After the Napoleonic Wars, wages declined steadily. Buret, a contemporary statistician, estimated that from 1816 to 1840 they fell by 25 per cent [22]. It was estimated that only a third of the French people could afford to eat meat. To earn his meager wage the French worker labored from thirteen to sixteen hours a day. Moreover, it was absolutely necessary for women and children to work [160]. As Buchez wrote in 1833:

> In the wage-earning class, children work as soon as they are strong enough to stand on their feet, otherwise they would be too great a burden for their parents to support. . . . Parents have tried to have large families and have considered many children a benefit, for these little unfortunates eat less than they earn, and when they are old enough to insist on keeping their wages, they leave the house and are on their own [20].

These terrible conditions existed throughout the July Monarchy, and it was not until the 1840's that the French government took any remedial action on a national basis. The first piece of labor legislation in French history, a law regulating child labor in factories, was passed in 1841. Meanwhile, the baneful consequences of factory work and of the industrial slums forced themselves upon the attention of physicians, writers, economists, and public officials. Baudelaire asked:

> How can anyone, whatever party one may belong to and whatever prejudices one may have been brought up on, fail to be touched at the sight of this sickly multitude breathing the dust of the factories, swallowing cotton floss, their systems saturated with white lead, mercury and all the poisons necessary to the creation of works of art, sleeping amid vermin in quarters where the greatest and simplest of human virtues nestle by the side of the most hardened vices and the vomit of the penitentiary? [8].

During the same period a vigorous group of physicians and hygienists had been carrying out surveys and statistical studies of actual living conditions among workers in urban communities and the circumstances under which they labored in shops and factories. Practical experience both at home and abroad, acquired during the Revolutionary and Napoleonic Wars, had made many French physicians alert to health problems—especially those of the community.

This orientation was further reinforced by the fact that during the first half of the nineteenth century France was the country most advanced in political and social theory. This was the period of Fourier, Saint-Simon, Comte, Buchez, Leroux, Blanc, Proudhon, Considérant, and Pecqeur; and there was a considerable amount of cross-fertilization between social philosophy and medicine. As a result, French medicine was to a considerable degree permeated with a spirit of social change. An outbreak of cholera at Paris in 1831 (and the desire to propagate their doctrine) led the Saint Simonians to establish a free medical service covering the twelve *arrondissements* of Paris and staffed by physicians belonging to the group. Then, in 1832, the *Globe*, a newspaper of Saint-Simonian persuasion, proposed that the city be provided with an adequate supply of good water, a proper sewerage system, and other facilities calculated to improve sanitary conditions and the health of the people [25, 31]. In turn, physicians participated actively in the various groups dedicated to social change. Most important, perhaps, was Philippe Buchez, who was also a historian, radical politician, and social philosopher [29, 30, 49, 52]. Other physicians were Auguste Boulland, a disciple of Buchez; Ulysse Trélat, with whom Buchez issued a *Journal des progrès des sciences et institutions médicales*; and Ange Guépin, who followed Saint-Simon and in 1835 published a survey of Nantes, his native city [59, 118]. To investigate the problems created by the new social order, numerous statistical analyses were made. The survey as a tool for observation was well-known and had been employed during the eighteenth and early nineteenth centuries, particularly in the form of the regional health survey, or medical topography. This trend was encouraged by the publication of Frank's work and the appearance (between 1792 and 1795) of the first medical geography by L. L. Finke. The third volume of the latter work contains a manual for the preparation of medical topographies [133].

It is not possible to mention all the significant contributions that were made in the ensuing fifty years, but in general these monographs dealt with the physical geography and natural history of the area: nutrition, housing, and customs of the inhabitants; health institutions and personnel; and the relation of these factors to the occurrence of endemic, epidemic, and sporadic diseases. In 1830, for instance, a committee of the New York State Medical Society proposed a plan for a "Medical Topographical Survey of the State" and pointed out that since the chief object of medical topography is "to ascertain the influences of climate, soil, different occupations, and moral and physical causes in the production or modification of diseases," attention must be directed to the age, sex, constitution, occupation, and diet of those most liable to be affected "by endemic or epidemic diseases" [176].

Throughout this period, the methods available for the study of social problems of health were rational empiricism, critical observation, the survey, and, from the late 1820's onward, statistical analysis [140]. Statistical methods were eagerly accepted and applied with considerable vigor, so that increasing numbers of studies of health problems based on numerical data began to appear. Some of the studies were undertaken in the course of official inquiries, others by private citizens whose interest was attracted to a specific social or health problem. Many were concerned with the question of differential mortality and the effect on health of such factors as social class, occupation, race, imprisonment, intemperance, and lack of proper sanitation.

France as a leader in medicine and hygiene during the first half of the nineteenth century produced numerous studies of the kind discussed above [2].[4] The outstanding figure of the period was the physician Louis René Villermé, best known for his study of the health conditions of textile workers. His report, published in 1840, aroused public opinion and led to the child-labor law of 1841. Villermé was interested as well in the relation between social circumstances and differential mortality and morbidity. In 1828, he showed that mortality rates in France were closely linked to the living conditions of the different social classes [178]. Two years later, he published his study of mortality in different sections of Paris, which pointed to a clear relationship between poverty and disease [180]. This

[4] An invaluable source for such studies is the *Annales d'hygiène publique* which began to appear in 1829.

point was reinforced by his study (which appeared in the same year) of infant and child mortality in two districts of Paris [181]. Villermé was likewise concerned with all the factors that enter into the standard of living and with their effect on physical growth and development. In 1829, he reported on the influence of income, nutrition, and housing on growth and physique [156, 179]. He also studied the mean duration of illness at different ages so as to apply this knowledge to the organization of mutual aid societies.

These interests were shared by other investigators. L. F. Benoiston de Chateauneuf studied the differential mortality of rich and poor [26]. He also dealt with the influence of different occupations on pulmonary tuberculosis, a subject also investigated by H. C. Lombard. The other great French hygienist of this period, A. J. B. Parent-Duchâtelet, who is best known today for his treatise on prostitution in Paris, also gave considerable attention to the health problems of various occupations [108, 109]. He dealt with the health problems of sewer workers, and together with D'Arcet studied the effects of tobacco on the health of workers handling it. In 1838, L. Tanquerel des Planches published his classic treatise on lead poisoning, and in 1846, Th. V. J. Roussel published a book on the diseases of workers in match factories, a pioneer study of occupational phosphorus necrosis. Nor were these the only health problems involving social factors and relations that were investigated. Efforts were made to determine why the working class population and the peasants did not readily accept vaccination against smallpox [5, 27]. Medical indices or aspects of social disintegration received attention [17, 34, 175]. In 1828, for example, Étienne de Sainte-Marie surveyed the problems faced by the Health Council of Lyon. In his report, he discussed abortion, alcoholism, prostitution, factory work, and poisoning [153]. Indeed, it is worth noting that the conclusion reached by Durkheim that suicide is indicative of a lack of social integration had already been reached by students of the problem earlier in the nineteenth century.

New conditions led to the emergence of new ideas—products of direct contact with the social reality of industrialism and the lives of the workers. And with them came new or unfamiliar terms to designate these concepts. Socialism became generally current after 1834, having appeared in a historic article by Pierre Leroux [41, 117]. There was a recognition that the good of society, the welfare of the individual, and the interests of the State are not necessarily identical and that it is therefore necessary to study how these may be coordinated for the greatest benefit and to substitute social questions for political questions [42, 155]. It is in this sense that Jules Leroux, in 1833, asserted that the practical purpose of political economy is "the same as that of political science, namely, to found *social* science." It is "the *human factor* . . . which dominates both economic and political factors.

And the science which treats of it, or *social science* properly so called, likewise dominates both political and economic science" [41].

These views were the soil within which the idea of social medicine germinated and out of which the term emerged in 1848. An early use of the term *social hygiene* occurs in a thesis presented by J. A. Rochoux in 1838 [130]. Pointing out that man is a social animal who necessarily exists in society, he asserted that hygiene may be divided into two major branches: private or individual hygiene, which may be left entirely to the initiative of the individual; and public or social hygiene, which requires legal and administrative action. However, Rochoux recognized that such a sharp separation cannot always be maintained in practice; not infrequently the community must take action in the interest of the group which will affect the individual whether or not this is desired.

In 1844, the physician Fourcault used the term *social hygiene* in a work concerned with the prevention of chronic diseases, especially pulmonary phthisis [44]. He was particularly interested in providing for children who had to work and for adult workers who labored under unhealthful conditions. Such action, he claimed, would lead to improved moral conditions among workers, for unemployment and poverty lead to illness, vice, theft, crimes of violence, and suicide. Thus, the use of the adjective *social* in connection with medical problems was by no means new when Jules Guérin introduced the term and the concept *social medicine* in March, 1848. At a time when revolutionary hopes were still running high, Guérin appealed to the French medical profession to act for the public good, to help create the new society for which the February Revolution had opened the way [60, 61, 62]:

> We have already had occasion to indicate the numerous relations which exist between medicine and public affairs. . . . Instead of those half-hearted and uncoordinated approaches which we have tended to include under such rubrics as medical police, public health, and forensic medicine, the time has come to collect these separate parts into an organized whole and to raise them to their highest potential under the designation of *social medicine*, which better expresses their purpose. . . .

Guérin divided social medicine into four parts: social physiology, social pathology, social hygiene, and social therapy. These were to deal respectively with such matters as the relation between the physical and mental condition of a population and its laws or other social institutions; the study of social problems in relation to health and disease; the determination of measures for health promotion and disease prevention; and the provision of medical and other measures to deal with social disintegration and other conditions that societies may experience. In this sense, Guérin saw social medicine as "the key to the most important issues of our period of regeneration . . ." and the medical profession as the most appropriate group to use this tool.

This emphasis on the role of the physician in social matters was the result of several factors. On the one hand, some felt that the doctor was closer than anyone else to the problems of the day; on the other, the situation of the medical profession in most European countries was unsatisfactory both socially and economically, and physicians wished to improve it. Owing to the absence of enough fully qualified physicians, auxiliary and ancillary groups were trained and given permission to practice. Prussia, for example, had not only physicians, but also *Wundärzte* (surgeons), first and second grade; Austria had its *Landärzte*; Britain had physicians, surgeons, and apothecaries; and France had *officiers de santé* for its rural districts. In most European countries at this time there was a demand for a unified medical profession, all of whose members would be qualified by similar training and would receive adequate compensation for their work. It was also felt by some in France and Germany that such an organization of the medical profession might also be used to provide more and better medical care for most of the population. Buchez made such a proposal for a national medical service in 1839, and again in 1848. Raspail, a chemist, advanced a similar idea in 1843, and Küntzli, a physician, offered a plan for such a service in 1846 [83, 86]. Indeed, the problem of medical care for the masses was so urgent that Louis Napoleon in his bid for power endeavored to ingratiate himself with the workers by offering a program of social legislation, including old age pensions, free medical care for the indigent, and a compensation scheme for injured workers.

"Medicine is a social science"—1848 in Germany

The ideas and proposals that were advanced in France before and during the revolutionary movement of 1848 were not limited to that country. From Paris, liberal ideas spread to Germany. Arnold Ruge, a democratic German journalist, wrote in 1844 that "Every attempt to make science serviceable to the world, every association of science with politics is directly linked to France" [150]. Various French investigators studied the influence of poverty, occupation, nutrition, housing, and other factors on health, and these studies influenced German medical men and others concerned with similar matters. During the revolutionary year of 1848 they joined forces to secure overdue health reforms. Prominent among the leaders of this movement were Salomon Neumann, Rudolf Virchow, and Rudolf Leubuscher. These men were keenly aware of the role of social factors in health problems. Basic to their thinking is the view vigorously asserted by Neumann in 1847, that "medical science is intrinsically and essentially a *social* science, and as long as this is not recognized in practice we shall not be able to enjoy its benefits and shall have to be satisfied with an empty shell and a sham" [105]. Or, as Virchow formulated this idea: "Medicine is a social science, and politics nothing but medicine on a grand scale."

The proponents of the idea of medicine as a social science were not dreaming of some vague utopia, but employed it rather as a convenient conceptual formulation under which to sum up definite principles upon which they based a program of action [1]. The first of these principles is that the health of the people is a matter of direct societal concern, and that society has an obligation to protect and assure the health of its members [182].

The second, as noted by Neumann, is that social and economic conditions have an important and—in many instances—crucial impact on health and disease, and that these relations must be subjected to scientific investigation [105, 106]. Virchow's basic standpoint was very similar. His investigation of the Silesian typhus epidemic of 1847 led him to conclude that its causes were as much social, economic, and political as they were biological and physical. He later elaborated this view in a series of articles on public health, in which he discussed the relation of medical problems to social and political developments. Virchow conceived the scope of public health as broadly as possible: "For if medicine is really to accomplish its great task, it must intervene in political and social life. It must point out the hindrances that impede the normal functioning of vital processes, and effect their removal" [183].

The third principle that follows logically is that the steps taken to promote health and to combat disease must be social as well as medical. The broad outlines of the program of action proposed on the basis of these principles are probably best represented by a draft for a Public Health Law submitted to the Berlin Society of Physicians and Surgeons on March 30, 1849 [82]. According to this document, public health has as its objectives: (1) the healthy mental and physical development of the citizen; (2) the prevention of all dangers to health; and (3) the control of disease. Public health must care for society as a whole by considering those conditions that may adversely affect health—such as soil, industry, food, and housing—and it must protect each individual by considering those conditions that prevent him from caring for his health. These may be considered in two major categories: conditions—such as poverty and infirmity—in which the individual has the right to request assistance from the State, and conditions—such as in cases of transmissible disease and mental illness—in which the State has the right and the obligation to interfere with the personal liberty of the individual. Public health can fulfill these duties by supplying well-trained medical personnel in sufficient numbers, and by providing adequate organization and appropriate institutions within which their work can be performed.

It should be clear that during this period the terms *public health, social hygiene,* and *social medicine* were used interchangeably by many. Nor is this surprising, for as long as public health was focused on the improvement of environmental circumstances and permeated with a spirit of social reform, its goals to a considerable extent coincided with and overlapped those advocated by proponents of social medicine [145]. Only as sanitary reform in a narrow sense began to achieve its aims and the developments in medical bacteriology turned attention away from the control of the social and physical environment to the control of specific communicable diseases did public health begin to achieve a distinctive character. In the course of the twentieth century, however, concern with the social aspects of health has again become a prominent feature of public health and has tended to bring it closer to social medicine and to a second, new discipline: medical sociology.

While the Germans did not specifically divide their concept of medicine as a social science into social physiology, pathology, prophylaxis, and therapy, much of what they wrote—and the specific proposals they made for action—imply such a framework. Thus, as an extension of his views on the relations of medicine to society, Virchow developed a theory of epidemic disease as a manifestation of social and cultural maladjustment [184]. He differentiated between natural and artificial epidemics, basing this distinction on the degree to which cultural factors interpose themselves between nature and man. He defined artificial epidemics as "attributes of society, products of a false culture, or of a culture which is not available to all classes. . . . Here belong typhus, scurvy, the sweating sickness, and tuberculosis" [182]. Furthermore, these artificial "epidemics occur not only as a result of social contradictions, but also as significant manifestations of the historical process." Such outbreaks occur at nodal points in history, during periods of political and intellectual revolution. (It is interesting to note that a very similar view was expressed by Sigerist in 1928 [162].)

At the same time, voices were raised for governmental action, and many specific measures were proposed. An important problem was the provision of medical care for the indigent, and proposals were made by Virchow and others for public medical services, including free choice of physician. It was realized, however, that provision of medical care was not enough, that it must go hand in hand with social prophylaxis. In consequence Virchow proclaimed *the right of the citizen to work* as a fundamental principle to be included in the constitution of a democratic State [99]. Here Virchow was no doubt influenced by the action of the French provisional government of 1848 [95].

The problem of the industrial worker also demanded attention. Although industrialization began later in Germany than in England and France, and proceeded at a slower pace during the first half of the nineteenth century, by 1848 the existence of a wage-earning class—an industrial proletariat—could no longer be overlooked. As in England and France, industrialization was ushered in by a slaughter of the innocents. Those that survived the cradle were given over to the tender mercies of the factory and the mine. It was plain, said Virchow, that "the proletariat in ever increasing degree became the victim of disease and epidemics, its children either died prematurely or developed into cripples" [99]. To deal with this problem, his colleague, the psychiatrist Leubuscher, proposed a program of industrial hygiene which emphasized the legislative regulation of working conditions [99]. Particularly important was the question of limiting the working day. Leubuscher advocated the prohibition of labor by children under fourteen, reduction of the working day in dangerous occupations, protection of pregnant women, the establishment of standards for ventilation of workrooms, and the prevention of industrial poisoning through the use of nontoxic materials.

Demands were also made for uniform licensure of medical practitioners, entitling them to practice in every German state; appointment of physicians to official positions on the basis of competitive examinations; and the establishment of a National Ministry of Health [1, 99]. Very important was the recognition of the necessity for reliable statistics in the investigation of the causal relations between social conditions and health problems. Neumann was most active in agitating for the collection of accurate statistics, and for statistical data on all elements of social life that in any way have a bearing on problems of health and illness [105, 106].

The revolution of 1848 was defeated in Germany, as it had been in France, and with this development the medical reform movement came to a quick end. The medical leaders of 1848—Virchow and Neumann—remained active in politics and loyal to their principles. During the decades that followed 1848, the broad program of health reform was transformed into a more limited program of sanitary reform that was practically attainable. Not until the end of the century were the views of Virchow and the other reformers to come to fruition in a new discipline.

From Virchow to Grotjahn

Some awareness of the social problems of health and disease in terms of medical police is evident in Great Britain throughout the earlier nineteenth century. Nevertheless, the idea came to be limited more and more to the control of epidemic disease and the supervision of environmental sanitation [144]. The concept of medical police as developed in Germany could hardly be expected to flourish in Britain where economic liberalism was the prevailing doctrine. This philosophy, with its acceptance of social atomism and the manifestation—through inexorable economic laws—of a predetermined harmony of man and nature, carried with it a stubborn insistence on the absolute necessity of submission to the alleged laws of society. Discrepancy between social fact and social theory was not generally accepted as affecting the hard core of economic liberalism, and it was not until the later nineteenth century that the gradual and peripheral erosion which had been carried on in practice began to receive recognition.

Such an intellectual environment was hardly conducive to analyses of the social aspects of health and disease, and no theoretical formulations comparable to those of the French and the Germans were developed. Nevertheless, stubborn facts intruded themselves into public consciousness as the Industrial Revolution inexorably changed the living conditions of millions of people. Questions of ill health, poor housing, dangerous and injurious occupations, and excessive morbidity and mortality could not be overlooked, and investigations of these social problems were undertaken—often by medical men—to find out how they had arisen and what could be done about them.

The high incidence of communicable disease led to a study by James Philips Kay (which appeared in 1832) of the condition of workers in the cotton mills of Manchester [78]. Vice, physical degradation, poverty, and illness were found to be intimately interlocked. For proof of the relation of ill health to other forms of social pathology, Kay cited the records of the medical charities of Manchester. After reviewing the statistical data, he concluded, for example, that more than half of the inhabitants of Manchester were "either so destitute or so degraded as to require the assistance of public charity, in bringing their offspring into the world" [71]. However, Kay saw no necessary connection between the existing socioeconomic organization and the various social maladjustments that he had observed. Yet his observations remain acute throughout. Discussing Irish immigration and the consequent effect on conditions in Manchester, he indicates an awareness—though as yet unclear and lacking precise formulation—that the dismal scenes in his portrayal are the product of a cultural cataclysm.[5]

Some physicians, however, did recognize that social and economic institutions—especially industrialism—had significant and necessary connections with the problems of the factory workers. Outstanding in this respect was C. Turner Thackrah, whose pioneer treatise on occupational health ap-

[5] Social scientists have recently recognized that the experiences of a large part of European society in the early days of industrial capitalism are comparable to the changes experienced by various African peoples after contact with European civilization and its representatives [173].

peared in 1831. His book became a bible for the factory reformers, and Thackrah actively supported the struggle to restrict child labor [36]. During the 1830's and into the 1840's a gradual but definite shift in thought and attitude on the social aspects of health and disease became evident. The creation of the Poor Law Commission and the studies initiated by its secretary, Edwin Chadwick, provided the basis for this ideological development [65].

Empirical recognition of relations between social problems and medical care went hand in hand with programs for remedial action. Testimony before Lord Ashley's Committee on Medical Poor Relief indicated that, in terms of medical care, pauperism in the legal sense was a relatively smaller matter as compared with medical indigence. On the basis of testimony by the physicians—Southwood Smith, W. P. Alison, and others—the conclusion "that the *preventive* should be combined with the *remedial* provision for the health of the poorer classes" seemed inevitable [18, 65, 91, 123]. One witness, Henry W. Rumsey, recommended that: "Medical care and inspection should be brought as near as possible to the habitations of the poor. In towns it must be forced upon them, both for their own benefit, and for the safety of the community" [65].

Few efforts, however, were made to develop a systematic theoretical basis for such programs. An outstanding exception is Rumsey's endeavor to formulate a theory of public health and medical care within a framework of social organization and action—in short, a social policy for health care. In 1856, he published *Essays on State Medicine*, in which he emphasized that the promotion of health and the prevention of disease were matters of social concern and required governmental action. Rumsey pointed out that various diseases were caused by factors in the social environment; he laid great stress on health education and urged that "district medical officers" be appointed to carry out the proposed programs [151].

At the time when Rumsey expressed these views, the health officer was still a novelty, the first such official having been appointed in 1847 at Liverpool. The appointment of health officers for various towns and districts, as well as increased interest in public health, led the authorities of St. Thomas's Hospital in 1856 to establish a course of lectures on public health, the first of its kind in England. Edward Headlam Greenhow was appointed to this lectureship, and in preparation for his lectures undertook to collect statistical information on the preventable causes of disease. Greenhow concluded that numerous environmental factors cause diseases that can be prevented, and that "some of these causes of preventable sickness and premature death arise necessarily from the circumstances of our social system. . . ." As an example, he discussed the relation of infant mortality to the employment of mothers in factories. During 1862–65, John Simon, Medical Officer to the Privy Council, undertook various medical studies on its behalf, concerning himself particularly with the investigation of food supply, housing and physical environment, and industrial circumstances. The studies showed that these factors were related to the prevalence of ill health among British workers [53, 166, 167].

By the end of the 1860's, a considerable advance had been made in Britain toward a socially oriented view of health and disease. Various administrators, physicians, and philanthropists recognized that the greater or lesser prevalence of disease was intimately related to social and economic factors, and that these relations could be studied precisely, using—for the most part—statistical data and methods. Economic liberalism was still the dominant social philosophy, but in practice and to a lesser degree in theory, it was being challenged as untenable for an industrial society. However, it was not until the 1880's that the interplay of long-term trends and particular events came to a focus in new formulations of social problems and values. Out of this recasting of social goals and ideologies, a theory of social medicine was to emerge in Great Britain in the twentieth century [3, 4, 24, 93, 177, 185].

During the last quarter of the nineteenth century, the basic lines of thought that had been developed earlier in the century and which had been sharply formulated in the concepts of "social medicine" and of "medicine as a social science" were kept alive by far-seeing, socially-minded men [134]. An interesting, well-developed system of social medicine was presented in 1865 by Armand-Joseph Meynne, a Belgian army doctor. Studies of the social, economic, and health status of the Belgian people during the preceding thirty years placed at Meynne's disposal a considerable mass of data [12, 38, 39, 75]. His *Topographie médicale de la Belgique* is divided into four parts: the first deals with the geography, geology, and climatology of Belgium; the second, with the morbidity and mortality of the Belgian population (and includes a discussion of the causes of the most prevalent or most serious diseases); the third, with the relations of the diseases to soil, climate, poverty, nutrition, housing, and alcoholism; the fourth, various measures designed to alleviate or remove the conditions previously described. Special attention must be called to Chapter 6 of Meynne's treatise. Here he takes up the diseases of greater importance, analyzes each in terms of its causation, and indicates the social factors involved. This section is unique; not until Grotjahn's *Soziale Pathologie* does one find anything comparable [100].

A number of other medical men recognized the influence of social conditions on health and discussed this subject from various points of view. In Russia, Friedrich Erismann spoke of the artificial environment imposed upon man by his social condition and of the role of hygiene in preventing or mitigating problems related to this factor [161]. The Swiss physician, Fridolin Schuler, turned his attention to numerous socio-medical problems, but especially to those of factory workers [21]. In France, Alexandre Layet published a socio-medical study of rural populations in 1882. Six years later, Jules Rochard published a treatise on social hygiene, in which he dealt with housing, consumer cooperation, antialcoholism, industrial hygiene, and school health [84, 129].

Among the German representatives of this period, one of the most interesting and least known is Eduard Reich, an eccentric and peripatetic medical scholar. In his *System der Hygiene* which appeared in 1870–71, Reich set up four branches of hygiene: moral, social, dietetic, and police hygiene. Although his categories are not entirely congruent with those in use at present, Reich's social hygiene may be considered as an early combined concept of social medicine and social work. Social hygiene, he asserted, studies phenomena of social life in order to maintain the well-being of the community [43, 128].

The ideas of Eduard Reich remained almost unknown, but similar views were expressed by Max von Pettenkofer, his better known contemporary. Pettenkofer made hygiene an experimental laboratory science, yet he was fully aware that man's health is influenced not only by his physical environment but also by the social world in which he lives. Customs, habits, political and socioeconomic conditions influence the health and mortality of a population [114].

The significant influence that social institutions and conditions exert upon health was also pointed out in 1874 by Nikolaus Alois Geigel, professor of hygiene at Würzburg. He dealt with the effects of the rise of capitalism, the growth of an industrial proletariat, increasing urbanization, and the unhygienic conditions under which workers were compelled to live, and the relations of these changing social and economic conditions to health and illness. Like many of his predecessors and contemporaries, Geigel insisted on the need for accurate statistics that would throw light on social phenomena [47].

Nevertheless, the last decades of the nineteenth century in Germany were not favorable for the development of a clearer conceptual formulation of health and illness in social terms. To most Germans after 1871, the movement of 1848 had little relevance. At the same time, the natural sciences developed rapidly and achieved enormous prestige in medicine. Moreover, the emergence of medical bacteriology seemed to answer the problem of disease causation. Under these conditions it was not difficult to overlook the patient and his environment, and to emphasize the cause and effect relationships between germs and disease. As Emil Behring declared in 1893, the study of infectious diseases could now be pursued unswervingly without being sidetracked by social considerations and reflections on social policy [11].

Yet at the very peak of the bacteriological triumph, interest in the significance of social conditions in the causation of disease led various physicians to react against the exaggerated bacteriological standpoint. Among these were Max Rubner in Germany, Ferdinand Hueppe in Austria, and Émile Duclaux in France. Hueppe summed up this viewpoint in 1899 with the statement: "Hygiene is a social art which has developed in response to social need; consequently it must and will always be social hygiene, or it will not exist at all." Duclaux pointed out that the spread, severity, and duration of communicable diseases involved not only the infectious agents but a number of other factors such as nutrition, working and living conditions, education, and income [37, 72].

Alfred Grotjahn and Social Hygiene

But at the very time that Emil Behring was ardently proclaiming bacteriology as the ultimate medical truth and Koch as its prophet, a young German medical student conceived the idea of systematically investigating medical problems in the light of social science so as "to arrive finally at a theory of social pathology and social hygiene, which with its own methods . . . would be used to investigate and to determine how life and health, particularly of the poorer classes, are dependent on social conditions and the environment" [57, 58, 63]. The student was Alfred Grotjahn, who, in pursuit of this aim, produced a concept of social hygiene (he reserved the term *social medicine* for medical care) which stimulated the theoretical development of social medicine during the first half of the twentieth century.

This was also the period during which the term *medical sociology* made its appearance, a development which was by no means purely coincidental. At the turn of the century many of those engaged in health and social work were not entirely satisfied with what they saw. Booth's investigations in London from 1889 to 1902 and Rowntree's study of York in 1899 showed that a substantial portion of the English laboring population was living at a subsubsistence level. The more the condition of the poorer classes was studied, the more unsatisfactory their health and social situation was found to be. To be sure, the crude death rate had declined, but maternal mortality was still high. Although infant mortality had declined, the condition of children attending school as well as that of preschool children was found to be extremely poor. Malnutrition was rife, and the health and physical fitness of the more poorly paid members of the working class were defective. Similar evils were present in the slum districts of great cities in the United States and in Europe. The inescapable facts of poverty, disease, vice, and suffering as large-scale urban phenomena brought forth groups and programs for reform of social and health conditions in England, America, Germany, and other similarly situated countries. These developments must be seen in the perspective of a worldwide historical evolution that has brought into being the modern State with its concern for individual, family, and community needs for organized social security and health services. By the first decade of the present century, it was no longer possible to consider poverty as the "natural" punishment of the poor for their shortcomings, and poverty came to be diagnosed as a social disease. It was equally clear that the consequences of poverty for health must be dealt with if the community was to be maintained in a healthy state. This was the context out of which both social medicine and medical sociology first emerged.

Grotjahn's theory received its fullest expression in the best-known of his publications, the classic *Soziale Pathologie,* which first appeared in 1911. In it he advanced a number of principles that are fundamental for a systematic study of human disease from a social viewpoint [57]:

1. The significance of a disease from a social point of view is determined in the first place by the *frequency* with which it occurs.
2. It is necessary to know the *form,* as well as the frequency, with which the particular disease occurs most often.
3. The etiological relationship between social conditions and disease may be expressed in four ways: social conditions (a) may create or favor a predisposition for a disease; (b) may themselves cause disease directly; (c) may transmit the causes of disease; and (d) may influence the course of a disease.
4. Not only are the origin and causes of diseases determined by social factors, but these diseases may in turn exert an influence on social conditions, particularly through their outcome.
5. In the case of a disease which is important from a social viewpoint, it must be established whether medical treatment can exert an appreciable influence on its prevalence, and whether such therapeutic success as may be achieved is important from a social point of view.
6. Preventing diseases or influencing their course by social measures requires attention to the social and economic environment of the patient.

Grotjahn realized that many diseases of social importance were chronic in character, and that a large number of these were preventable, or could at least be controlled. He felt that health education could be an extremely important factor in this connection, and was of the opinion that the physician should use his position to promote developments in social hygiene so that the benefits of medical knowledge could be applied to all the people. For the physician to understand these responsibilities, Grotjahn saw that the teaching of social hygiene would have to become a part of the medical curriculum [55]. (He himself taught at the University of Berlin.)

Grotjahn emphasized that investigations in social hygiene would make use of the methods of statistics, demography, anthropology (especially anthropometry), economics, and sociology. His own formal training in social science had been obtained by attending the seminar of Gustav Schmoller. Here he acquired the social science methodology of the period and prepared a paper on the changes in food consumption by workers that had occurred in Germany and other countries as a part of the process of industrialization. In it he warned against judging diets too exclusively on the basis of caloric adequacy [54]. Grotjahn also considered physical and social degeneration as one of the major problems of social hygiene. With this in mind he emphasized the importance of eugenics [56].

Despite Grotjahn's insistence on the need for sociological analysis of health problems, he could not move beyond the scientific level of the period. Sociology in Germany was formal, theoretical, and involved in controversies over value judgments. At a time when Max Weber demanded a sharp separation between basic research and applied science, between social science and social policy, there could hardly be much contact with a social hygiene that Grotjahn regarded as having two aspects: *descriptive* and *normative*. For Grotjahn, social hygiene reached its apogee in its "conscious purpose to spread hygienic measures, which at first always benefit a preferred minority, to the entire population and thus carry on a progressive improvement of existing conditions" [186, 187]. From a sociological point of view, social hygiene remained incomplete.

Grotjahn was the outstanding figure of a group of men who during the first three decades of the twentieth century developed a concept of social medicine that could be used in medical education and medical practice. An important initial impulse toward the development of the field had derived from Bismarck's social insurance program, itself a product of the problems attendant upon industrialism and urbanism. A number of physicians realized, however, that to restrict the field of social medicine to the medical aspects of social insurance was to take too restricted a view of the matter. Consequently, many of those who concerned themselves with social medicine endeavored to define the field so as to broaden it and yet keep it within clear conceptual and practical bounds.

The literature on social medicine that appeared during the period from 1900 to 1930 is extensive, and one can do no more in this survey than to select several authors who in some respect contributed to the development of social medicine. Prominent in this group were Ludwig Teleky, Adolf Gottstein, Alfons Fischer, and J. Kaup. A survey of social medicine as it had developed in Germany prior to World War I is available in a 1913 volume edited by Mosse and Tugendreich. On the whole, the editors follow the ideas and system of Grotjahn. But where the latter believed that social hygiene measures should culminate in eugenic action, the former regarded the equalization of life expectancy for all socioeconomic classes as the goal of social medicine [103].

The level of development attained by social medicine in Germany up to the outbreak of World War I is summed up in the statement made in 1913 by Adolf Gottstein: "Social etiology can now be regarded as accepted" [50, 103, 170]. He and his peers believed that research methods were receiving too little attention and agreed on the pre-eminent significance of statistical materials and methods. Teleky pointed out that the effects of social conditions on health can be determined directly by observation as well as indirectly with the help of statistics. This emphasis may be related to the fact that Teleky's major interest was industrial medicine and hygiene, which require observation. Furthermore, Teleky's emphasis on the pivotal role of social class in relation to health differentials may serve as a clue to an understanding of the lack of emphasis on empirical, firsthand investigations. Social structure manifested itself so prominently in terms of class position and its economic, educational, and other correlates that it seemed to many a fixed variable.

The period following World War I did not add much to the theory of social medicine. Manuals and handbooks for medical administrators, students, and practicing physicians were published, but for the most part these did not concern themselves extensively with theory. A volume by Ickert and Weicksel (1932) is noteworthy because of its division of the field of social medicine into four parts—social physiology and pathology, social diagnosis, social therapy, and social prophylaxis—which are reminiscent of Jules Guérin. Also of interest is their reference to Mary Richmond's concept of social diagnosis, from which stem social therapy and social prophylaxis [74].

Social medicine as it developed in Germany, in particular the ideas of Grotjahn, had a wide influence on the development of this field in other countries, notably in central and eastern Europe. Social medicine has been extensively developed in the Scandinavian countries and in Italy, France, Switzerland, Holland, Belgium, Czechoslovakia, and Yugoslavia. In the Soviet Union, all health problems are considered from a social angle. The developing nations are now beginning to move into this field as they experience increasingly the problems attendant on economic development.

In general, developments in different countries may be regarded as exhibiting different characteristics owing to conditions, traditions, and problems in the particular country. Italians, for example, have tended to emphasize the physiology and pathology of occupation; in France and Belgium attention has been directed to the social hygiene of infancy and childhood, control of tuberculosis and venereal diseases, and occupational health. In Yugoslavia, under Andrija Stampar, the emphasis was on the problems of a rural population; since World War II there has been a shift to problems connected with industrialization and the movement of a rural population to urban centers. A review of social medicine in various countries of the world from the turn of the century to 1950 is to be found in a useful compendium by René Sand, one of the leading representatives of social medicine of the last generation [154, 156, 157].

Social Medicine in Great Britain and the United States

In Great Britain, as in the United States, interest in social medicine is a relatively recent phenomenon. Social factors in health and disease had been recognized by physicians and laymen, but little or no concerted effort had been made to organize and apply such knowledge systematically.[6] Indeed, as we shall see, in the United States such problems tended to emerge as those of medical sociology rather than as problems of social medicine. In Great Britain, influences within medicine itself and in society as a whole led to the appearance, in the 1940's, of both theoretical and practical socio-medical developments. It was recognized that the rise and expansion of medical specialism tended to compartmentalize the thought and action of the physician. The sick person—the patient—had to be seen as a unity involving his environment if the best medical care was to be provided [94, 104]. Moreover, by the 1930's, the ideology of individualism had worn exceedingly thin and a consciousness of social and economic problems was acute. Various studies on the social aspects of health and disease appeared: G. C. M'Gonigle and Kirby's *Poverty and Public Health*; J. B. Orr's *Food, Health, and Income*; and R. M. Titmuss's *Poverty and Population.* Another significant undertaking was the work of the Peckham Health Centre in London, started in 1926 by G. Scott Williamson and Innes H. Pearse [111, 112, 113]. At this institution, the attempt was made to develop health as a positive social value on the basis of a fundamental social unit: the family.

Suggestions and proposals for the teaching of the social aspects of disease under the name *preventive medicine* came from a variety of governmental and private agencies. By 1943 these ideas had advanced so far that an Institute of Social Medicine was set up at Oxford with John A. Ryle as the first Professor of Social Medicine. Some two years later, F. A. E. Crew was appointed to a chair of social medicine at Edinburgh. Since then a num-

---

[6] Contributions to specific social aspects of health or to medical problems having social implications are to be found scattered throughout American medical and public health literature. One need only consult, for example, the early volumes of the reports of the American Public Health Association, or to recall the names of Daniel Drake, John H. Griscom, Stephen Smith, Lemuel Shattuck, Joseph Goldberger, and C. E. A. Winslow. Nevertheless, it is true that these data were never brought together as a basis for a theory of social medicine.

ber of other chairs of social medicine have been created in Great Britain [98]. Ryle defined social medicine as including "the whole of the public and industrial health services, the social services and the remedial services of a community" [152].

Although social medicine is today a recognized subject of instruction in British medical schools, the social element apparently does not involve explicit inclusion of the social sciences (sociology, social anthropology, social psychology). The content of such a course is essentially the same as that offered by a department of preventive medicine in the United States [51, 97, 172]. Meanwhile, research has been carried on very actively. The Medical Research Council's Social Medicine Unit, headed by J. N. Morris, has carried out numerous studies on peptic ulcer, perinatal mortality, coronary heart disease, and hypertension. For the most part the emphases in the socio-medical studies are statistical and epidemiological. Some clinical studies have been undertaken. Investigations from the viewpoint of social administration have largely been the product of Titmuss and his associates at the London School of Economics, while social psychiatry has been advanced by studies at Maudsley Hospital under the leadership of Sir Aubrey Lewis.

The roots of social medicine in the United States are to be found generally in public health and organized social work, which emerged out of organized charity during the 1890's. It was here that health work and the social science of the period found a common ground for action—in the prevention of tuberculosis and the fight for decent working conditions in factories and mines, improved nutrition, and better housing. These efforts emerged as public health and medical sociology; social medicine came later. As early as 1879, John Shaw Billings linked the study of hygiene with sociology [15]. In 1895, Charles McIntire defined medical sociology as

> . . . the science of the social phenomena of the physicians themselves as a class apart and separate; and the science which investigates the laws regulating the relations between the medical profession and human society as a whole; treating of the structure of both, how the present conditions came about, what progress civilization has affected and indeed everything relating to the subject [96].

In some degree McIntire anticipated Straus's distinction between the sociology of medicine and sociology in medicine. Elizabeth Blackwell used the term *medical sociology* in 1902 as the title for a collection of essays ranging in subject from sex hygiene and education to medical education and the religion of health [16]. In 1910, James P. Warbasse published a book entitled *Medical Sociology*, in which he advocated various reform measures, including health education. Warbasse was also an ardent exponent of cooperation between producers and consumers, and endeavored to apply these principles to health problems. The same year also saw the formation of a Section on Sociology in the American Public Health Association which lasted until 1921 when it was disbanded. Its members were physicians and social workers. Among the subjects it considered were such matters as the labor of women and children, housing, and the use of the referendum in obtaining needed health legislation. In essence it reflects the sociology of the period, which was concerned with social problems associated with immigration, race relations, slums, rural life, and related matters. It was closely identified with philanthropy, social work, and that development of liberal Protestantism known as the social gospel [110]. The keynote for the period from the health viewpoint was struck by Hermann Biggs in 1911. He wrote:

> Disease is largely a removable evil, it continues to afflict humanity, not only because of incomplete knowledge of its causes and lack of individual and public hygiene, but also because it is extensively fostered by harsh economic and industrial conditions and by wretched housing in congested communities. These conditions and consequently the diseases which spring from them can be removed by better social organization.

Out of this same context others began to speak of social medicine. Francis Lee Dunham in 1925 tried to develop such a concept. Basic to its origin, according to Dunham, was the need in welfare work "for a field of preventive medicine to which social sciences, psychology, psychiatry, and various other departments shall contribute but upon no one of which shall the entire burden of responsibility fall" [40]. In defining the function of social medicine, Dunham put the emphasis on personal and social adjustment. Social medicine, he said, helps to harmonize human behavior, and to organize conduct. The eugenic approach to social problems is clearly evident in Dunham's thinking. But this venture was stillborn.

One might expect that the advent of the Depression would have turned the minds of some in this direction. Nevertheless, with one outstanding exception, this was not the case. It may be that the almost exclusive concentration on the economic aspects of medical care which occupied many students of health problems militated against the development of a theory of social medicine. The exception was Edgar Sydenstricker, who in 1933 brought out his study on *Health and Environment*—a masterly analysis which broke down the idea of environment into its component aspects, and then showed the relation of each of these to health problems. Sydenstricker thus laid the basis for a theory of social medicine, but unfortunately he never went on to develop such a theory.

Sporadic references to social medicine occur during the 1930's. Michael M. Davis called attention to the possibilities for social research in medicine [32, 33]. The importance of a concept of social medicine was repeatedly emphasized by Henry E. Sigerist [164]. After World War II this idea gained increased interest. In 1947 the New York Academy of Medicine held a three-day Institute on Social Medicine and the papers given on this occasion were published in 1949 under the title *Social Medicine: Its Derivations and Objectives.* In 1947, also, the Milbank Memorial Fund devoted its annual conference to social medicine and published the proceedings in its quarterly.

It was during this period too that the social and health sciences began to converge to produce what has come to be known as medical sociology. Both developments—the interest in social medicine and the emergence of medical sociology—result to a considerable extent from converging trends in the health field and in social science. On the medical side, the acute communicable diseases had come under relatively effective control, and chronic diseases and other noninfectious conditions began to demand attention. Demographic change had led to an increase in the proportion of aged in the population. As the hospital obtained a central role in medical care, the physician became essential for its operation and the institution itself became indispensable for the practice of good medicine. These developments in turn have felt the impact of new patterns of hospital utilization and financing of medical care. As a result, organizational relationships within the hospital have been disturbed and have become unstable. These and many other problems led to a recognition that the social sciences in terms of theory, knowledge, or method might be able to shed light on and help solve some of these problems [148]. On the social science side, interests had developed in the study of the professions and of formal organizations, social factors in perception and attitude formation, and of cultural patterns and value systems of large and small groups. Although many of these areas of interest had been studied earlier, the mobilization of social scientists in World War II and the utilization of their skills hastened the process [79].

Interest in social medicine grew because of the new medical and health problems and the need to deal with them in institutional, family, and community terms. Problems involving chronic illness, the aged, the mentally and emotionally ill, the physically handicapped, the provision of medical care, and the like were the stimuli. As a result, for example, Montefiore Hospital developed a Division of Social Medicine—a pioneer achievement. The development of home care programs, attention to nursing homes, the provision of medical care, and similar activities are all part of the route social medicine has taken in the United States. Along this route, many have had to turn to the social sciences for collaborative action.

Social Medicine and Medical Sociology

To a very large extent the history of social medicine is the history of social policy and social action (welfare). In this sense, social medicine is an applied discipline. Basically, it has been medically oriented even where its proponents have emphasized its basis in social science. Obviously, at any given period those interested in the social problems of health have had to use social science as they found it. To a very large extent, social medicine has been pragmatic, and has used whatever methods were available and seemed to suit its purposes. Thus, the availability of statistical data and survey methods led to their use. Social medicine throughout its history has used methods that did not involve analysis of social structures. Today it is possible to apply such methods to problems of social medicine. Indeed, a great deal of research has already been done along these lines [6, 23, 46, 85, 122, 125, 126, 147, 149, 188].

Clearly, the field of interest designated as medical sociology has expanded greatly. As yet, however, the broad range of the social sciences has not been completely related to the concerns of health workers, although a few authors have attempted general treatises [64, 116, 165]. In the United States, the process of evolution is gradually leading to a meeting and collaboration of the social sciences as represented by medical sociology and the problems represented by social medicine. This is particularly evident in such areas of investigation and action as aging, psychiatry, and medical care [7, 71, 89, 174].

The development of social medicine and medical sociology in the United States reflects both the state of the health and social sciences and the nature of the problems presented by a complex industrial society. In this sense, one can draw an analogy between the role of cameralism and medical police in relation to eighteenth century enlightened absolutism and medical sociology in relation to the rationalization and bureaucratization of health services in twentieth century industrial America. In part at least, this helps to explain why medical sociology appeared in the United States and why its evolution in Europe has been so slow. Since World War II, however, West Germany has begun to develop a medical sociology. There had been some tendencies in this direction earlier in the century, but more recently—under American influence—a definite field of study has appeared [67, 68, 69, 81, 158].

A review of the literature clearly shows that the term *medical sociology* is not satisfactory. Actually, as the field so designated has developed, it is concerned with the sociology of health institutions, health personnel and their problems, and the role of sociology (or, more broadly, the social sciences) in elucidating the social and medical aspects of health and disease. Perhaps, one should endeavor to introduce a new designation: the sociology of health.[7]

---

[7] See Chap. 19 for an appraisal of the present status of the field.

References

1. Ackerknecht, Erwin H., "Beiträge zur Geschichte der Medizinalreform von 1848," *Archiv für Geschichte der Medizin*, 25 (1932), 61–109, 112–83.
2. ———, "Hygiene in France, 1815–1848," *Bull. Hist. Med.*, 22 (March–April, 1948), 117–55.
3. Acland, Henry W., *National Health*. Oxford: James Parker, 1871.
4. ———, *Health* (Address delivered at the Social Science Congress at Plymouth). Oxford: James Parker, 1873.
5. *Annuaire des cinq départements de l'ancienne Normandie*. Caen: 1835. Reviewed in *Annales d'hygiène publique* (1835), p. 233.
6. Apple, Dorrian, "Sociology and Anthropology," *Bibliographies on Nursing* (National League for Nursing), 3 (1957), 69–114.
7. Axelrod, S. J., *Public Assistance Medical Care: Areas of Research and an Annotated Bibliography*. Chicago: American Public Welfare Association, 1959.
8. Baudelaire, Charles, "L'Art romantique," in *Oeuvres* Pléiade, II. Cited by D. O. Evans: *Social Romanticism in France 1830–1848*. Oxford: Clarendon Press, 1951, pp. 7–8.
9. Beer, Karl, ed., *Die Reformation Kaiser Sigmunds. Eine Schrift des 15. Jahrhunderts zur Kirchen-und Reichsreform*, Stuttgart: Beiheft zu den Deutschen Reichstagsakten herausgegeben durch die historiche Kommission bei der Bayerischen Akademie der Wissenschaften, 1933.
10. ———, "Was ein Reformer vor einem halben Jahrtausend von Ärztestand erwartete," *Gesnerus*, 11 (1954), 24–36.
11. Behring, E., *Gesammelte Abhandlungen zur ätiologischen Therapie von ansteckenden Krankheiten*. Stuttgart: Georg Thieme Verlag, 1893, p. xix.
12. de Belgique, Royaume, *Enquête sur la condition des classes ouvrières et sur le travail des enfants*. Bruxelles: 1848.
13. Bélin, J., *La logique d'une idée-force. L'idée d'utilité sociale pendant la Révolution Française, 1789–1792*. Paris: Gallimard, 1939.
14. *John Bellers, 1654–1725: Quaker, Economist and Social Reformer*. (His writings, reprinted, with a memoir by A. Ruth Fry). London: Cassell & Co., Ltd., 1935.
15. Billings, John Shaw, *in* Albert Henry Buck, ed., *Treatise on Hygiene and Public Health*. New York: Wood, 1879, pp. 5–6.
16. Blackwell, Elizabeth, *Essays in Medical Sociology*. 2 vols. London: Ernest Bell, 1902.
17. de Boismont, Brierre, "De l'influence de la civilization sur le suicide," *Annales d'hygiène publique* (1835).
18. Brotherston, J. H. F., "Williams Pulteney Alison, Scottish Pioneer of Social Medicine," *Medical Officer* (June 6, 1958), pp. 331–36.
19. Brunschwig, Henri, *La Crise de l'état prussien à la fin du XVIIIe siècle et la genèse de la mentalité romantique*. Paris: Presses Universitaires de France, 1947.
20. Buchez, P. J. B., *Introduction à la science de l'histoire*. Paris: Paulin, 1833.

21. Buess, Heinrich, "Fridolin Schuler (1832–1903) aus Mollis, ein Vorkämpfer der Sozialmedizin im 19. Jahrhundert," *Die Praxis,* 47 (December, 1958), 1236–39.
22. Buret, E., *La Misère des classes laborieuses en Angleterre et en France.* 2 vols. Paris, 1845–46.
23. Caudill, William, "Applied Anthropology in Medicine," *in* A. L. Kroeber, ed., *Anthropology Today.* Chicago: University of Chicago Press, 1953, pp. 771–806.
24. Chadwick, Edwin, "Results of Different Principles of Legislation and Administration in Europe," *Journal of the Statistical Society of London* (September, 1859), pp. 381–420.
25. Charléty, Sebastien, *Histoire du Saint-Simonisme (1825–64).* Paris: Paul Hartmann, 1931.
26. de Chateauneuf, L. F. Benoiston, "De la durée de la vie chez le riche et chez le pauvre," *Annales d'hygiène publique,* 3 (1830), 5–85.
27. Chevalier, Louis, *Classes laborieuses et classes dangereuses à Paris pendant la première moitié du XIX*e *siècle.* Paris: Plon, 1958, pp. 415–20.
28. Cunningham, W., *The Growth of English Industry and Commerce in Modern Times.* Vol. I. Cambridge: Cambridge University Press, 1912.
29. Cuvillier, Armand, *P.J.B. Buchez et les origines du socialisme chrétien.* Paris: Presses Universitaires de France, 1948.
30. ———, *Hommes et idéologies de 1840.* Paris: Marcel Rivière, 1956.
31. d'Allemagne, H. R., *Les Saint-Simoniens 1827–1837.* Paris: Gründ, 1930.
32. Davis, Michael M., "Wanted: Research in the Economic and Social Aspects of Medicine," *Milbank Memorial Fund Quarterly,* 13 (October, 1935), 339–46.
33. ———, "Social Medicine as a Field for Social Research," *American Journal of Sociology,* 44 (September, 1938), 274–79.
34. Descuret, J. B. F., *La médecine des passions.* Liége, 1844.
35. Dobb, Maurice, *Studies in the Development of Capitalism.* London: Routledge & Kegan Paul, Ltd., 1946, pp. 177–220.
36. Driver, Cecil, *Tory Radical: The Life of Richard Oastler.* New York: Oxford University Press, 1946, pp. 73, 135–36.
37. Duclaux, Emile, *L'hygiène sociale.* Paris: Felix Alcau, 1902.
38. Ducpétiaux, Edouard, *De la condition physique et morale des jeunes ouvriers et des moyens de les améliorer.* 2 vols. 1843.
39. ———, *Budgets économiques des classes ouvrières en Belgique.* 1855.
40. Dunham, Francis Lee, *An Approach to Social Medicine.* Baltimore: The Williams and Wilkins Co., 1925, p. 30.
41. Evans, D. O., *Le Socialisme romantique: Pierre Leroux et ses contemporains.* Paris: M. Rivière, 1941.
42. ———, *Social Romanticism in France 1830–1848.* Oxford: Clarendon Press, 1951.
43. Fischer, Alfons, *Geschichte des deutschen Gesundheitswesens.* 2 vols. Berlin: F. A. Herbig, 1933, I, 327–28; II, 362–65.
44. Fourcault, A., *Hygiène des personnes prédisposées aux maladies chroniques et spécialement à la phthisie pulmonaire, ou moyens de prévenir le développement de ces affections.* Paris: B. Dusillon, 1844, pp. 197–224.

45. Frank, J. P., "The People's Misery: Mother of Disease" (Address delivered in 1790), trans. from the Latin, with an introduction by Henry E. Sigerist, *in Bull. Hist. Med.*, 9 (January, 1941), 81–100.

46. Freeman, H. E. and Leo G. Reeder, "Medical Sociology: A Review of the Literature," *American Sociological Review*, 22 (February, 1957), 74–81.

47. Geigel, N. A., "Öffentliche Gesundheitspflege," in *Handbuch der öffentlichen Gesundheitspflege und der Gewerbekrankheiten*, Bd I of H. von Ziemssen, ed., *Handbuch der speziellen Pathologie und Therapie*. Leipzig, 1874.

48. Gershoy, Leo, *From Despotism to Revolution, 1763–1789*. New York: Harper & Row, Publishers, 1944, pp. 39–43.

49. Godlewski, Henri, "L'étudiant en médecine Philippe Buchez, fondateur du Carbonarisme français," *Bulletin de la Société, française d'histoire de de la médecine* (1937).

50. Gottstein, A., *Die Medizin der Gegenwart in Selbstdarstellungen*, ed. L. R. Grote. Leipzig: Meiners, 1925, pp. 53–91.

51. Grant, John B., "Social Medicine in the Curriculum," *British Medical Journal*, 1 (February 21, 1948), 333–36.

52. Grec, Edouard, *Un médecin novateur, Philippe Buchez (1796–1865)*. Paris: Vignez, 1938.

53. Greenhow, Edward H., *in General Board of Health, Papers Relating to the Sanitary State of the People of England*. London: Eyre and Spottiswoode, 1858, pp. 131–33.

54. Grotjahn, Alfred, *Über Wandlungen in der Volksernährung* (Staats—und socialwissenschaftliche Forschungen Bd. XX, Heft, 2). Leipzig: Duncker & Humblot, 1902.

55. ——— and F. Kriegel, *Jahresbericht über die Fortschritte und Leistungen auf dem Gebiete der socialen Hygiene und Demographie, Dritter Band: Bericht über das Jahr 1903*. Jena: Gustav Fischer, 1904.

56. ———, *Geburten-Rückgang und Geburten-Regelung im Lichte der individuellen und der sozialen Hygiene*. Berlin: Louis Marcus Verlagsbuchhandlung, 1914.

57. ———, *Soziale Pathologie*. 2nd ed., Berlin: August Hirschwald Verlag, 1915, pp. 9–18.

58. ———, *Erlebtes und Erstrebtes. Erinnerungen eines sozialistischen Arztes*. Berlin: F. A. Herberg, 1932, p. 72.

59. Guépin, Ange, *Nantes an XIXe siècle, statistique, topographique, industrielle et morale*. Nantes: P. Sebire, 1835.

60. Guérin, Jules, "Médecine sociale. Au corps médicale de France," *Gazette Médicale de Paris* (March 11, 1848), 203.

61. ———, "Médecine sociale. La Médecine sociale et la médecine socialiste," *Gazette Médicale de Paris* (March 18, 1848), p. 203.

62. ———, "Médecine sociale. De L'association médicale au point de vue de la situation actuelle," *Gazette Médicale de Paris* (March 18, 1848), p. 211.

63. Harms, B., "Alfred Grotjahn und seine Lebensaufgabe," *Zeitschrift fur Sozialhygiene* (1949), pp. 1–4.

64. Hawkins, Norman G., *Medical Sociology: Theory, Scope and Methods.* Springfield, Ill.: Charles C. Thomas, Publisher, 1958.

65. *Health and Sickness of Town Populations, Considered with Reference to Proposed Sanitary Legislation and to the Establishment of a Comprehensive System of Medical Police and District Dispensaries.* London: John W. Parker, 1846, p. 2.

66. Heckscher, E. F., *Mercantilism.* 2 vols. London: George Allen & Unwin, Ltd., 1934.

67. Hellpach, W., "Nervosität und Kultur," *in Kulturprobleme der Gegenwart.* Bd. V. Berlin: Rade, 1902.

68. ———,"Sozialpathologie als Wissenschaft," *Archiv für Sozialwissenschaft* 21 (1905), 275.

69. ———, *Nervenleben und Weltanschauung. Ihre Wechselbeziehungen im deutschen Leben von Heute* (Grenzfragen des Nerven—und Seelenlebens, Bd. 41). Wiesbaden: Bergmann, 1906.

70. Hippocrates, *Diet.* Littré, VI, 594–604.

71. Hoch, Paul H., "Social Psychiatry," *in* Gruhle, Jung, Mayer-Gross and Muller, eds., *Psychiatrie der Gegenwart: Forschung und Praxis.* Berlin: Springer-Verlag, 1961, pp. 9–35.

72. Hueppe, Ferdinand, *Handbuch der Hygiene.* Berlin: Hirschwald, 1899, p. 11.

73. Hull, C. H., ed. *The Economic Writings of Sir William Petty.* Cambridge: Cambridge University Press, 1899, pp. 27, 109–10, 151, 259, 303, 463, 536.

74. Ickert, Franz and Johannes Weicksel, *Grundriss der Sozialen Medizin.* Leipzig: J. A. Barth, 1932.

75. Jacquemyns, G., *Histoire de la crise économique des Flandres.* Bruxelles: Maurice Lamertin, 1929, pp. 295–362.

76. Johnson, E. A., *Predecessors of Adam Smith.* Englewood Cliffs, N. J.: Prentice-Hall, Inc., 1937, pp. 117–38, 259–77.

77. von Justi, J. H. G., *Grundsätze der Policey-Wissenscheft.* Göttingen: 1756, pp. 64–76.

78. Kay, J. P., *The Moral and Physical Condition of the Working Classes Employed in the Cotton Manufacture in Manchester.* London: James Ridgeway, 1832, pp. 40–42.

79. Kendall, Patricia and Robert K. Merton, "Medical Education as a Social Process," *in* E. Gartly Jaco, ed., *Patients, Physicians and Illness.* New York: The Free Press of Glencoe, Inc., 1958, pp. 321–50.

80. Khaldûn, Ibn, *The Muqaddimah: An Introduction to History,* trans. from the Arabic by Franz Rosenthal. Vol. II. New York: Pantheon Books, 1958, pp. 136–37, 245–46, 376–77.

81. König, R. and M. Tönnesmann, *Probleme der Medizin-Soziologie* (Köln Z. Soziol. Sonderheft 3). Köln, Opladen, Westdeutscher Verlag, 1958.

82. Kroeger, Gertrud, *The Concept of Social Medicine as Presented by Physicians and Other Writers in Germany, 1779–1932.* Chicago: Julius Rosenwald Fund, 1937, pp. 14–15.

83. Küntzli, *État de la médecine, position des médecins, garanties sanitaires*

du peuple en France, et plan d'organisation médicale. Paris: Chez l'Auteur, 1847.

84. Layet, A., *Hygiène et maladies des paysans*. Paris: Masson, 1882.
85. Leavell, Hugh R., "Chronic Disease and the Behavioral Sciences," *Journal of Chronic Diseases*, 2 (July, 1955), 113.
86. Le Borgne, G., *Le Médecin*. Paris: J. B. Baillière, 1846, pp. 3–33, 155–221.
87. Leibniz, G. W., *Die Werke von Leibniz*, herausgegeben von Onno Klopp, I. Reihe, Bd. 5. Hannover: 1866, pp. 315*ff*.
88. ———, *Sämtliche Schriften, Dritter Band, 1680–1683*. Leipzig: K. F. Koehler Verlag, 1938, pp. 405.
89. Leighton, A., J. A. Clausen, and R. Wilson, *Explorations in Social Psychiatry*. New York: Basic Books, Inc., 1957.
90. Leroy, Maxim, *Histoire des idées sociales en France*, t. 1 *(de Montesquieu à Robespierre)*. Paris: Gallimard, 1946, pp. 318–24.
91. Liddle, John, "On the Connection between Medical Poor Relief and the Sanitary Condition of the People," *Journal of Public Health*, 1 (1848), 92–95.
92. Lipson, E., "England in the Age of Mercantilism," *Journal of Business History*, 4 (August, 1932), 697–707.
93. Lynd, Helen M., *England in the Eighteen-Eighties*. New York: Oxford University Press, 1945, pp. 3–19, 61–112.
94. Mackenzie, James, *The Future of Medicine*. New York: Oxford University Press, 1919.
95. Marriott, J. A. R., ed., *Louis Blanc's Organisation du Travail, The French Revolution of 1848 in Its Economic Aspect*. Vol. I. Oxford: Clarendon Press, 1913.
96. McIntire, Charles, "The Importance of the Study of Medical Sociology," *Bulletin American Academy Med*. 1 (February, 1894), 425–434.
97. McKeown, Thomas, "The Preparation of a Syllabus in Social Medicine," *Journal of Medical Education*, 32 (February, 1957), 110–114.
98. Mackintosh, James, *Teaching of Hygiene and Public Health in Europe*. Monograph series No. 34, 1957. WHO.
99. *Die Medicinische Reform. Eine Wochenschrift, erschienen vom 10 Juli 1848 bis zum 29 Juni 1849*. Berlin: G. Reimer, 1848–49, pp. 38, 127, 185, 189, 190.
100. Meynne, A. J., *Topographie médicale de la Belgique*. Bruxelles: H. Manceaux, 1865, pp. 123–235.
101. Michels, Roberto, *First Lectures in Political Sociology*, trans. with an introduction by Alfred de Grazia. Minneapolis: University of Minnesota Press, 1949, p. 13.
102. Mitchell, Wesley C., *Lecture Notes on Types of Economic Theory*. 2 vols. New York: Augustus M. Kelley, 1949, I: 15–23, 48–61.
103. Mosse, M. and G. Tugendreich, eds., *Krankheit und soziale Lage*. München: J. F. Lehmanns Verlag, 1913.
104. Newman, George, *Health and Social Evolution*. London: George Allen & Unwin, Ltd., 1931.

105. Neumann, Salomon, *Die öffentliche Gesundheitspflege und das Eigenthum. Kritisches und positives mit Bezug auf die preussische Medizinalverfassungsfrage.* Berlin: Adolf Riess, 1847, pp. 64–65, 84.

106. ———. "Zur medizinischen Statistik des preussischen Staates nach den Acten des statistischen Bureaus für das Jahr 1846, *Archiv für Pathologische Anatomie, und für klinische Medicin,* 3 (1851), 13–141.

107. Oeser, Max, *Geschichte der Stadt Mannheim.* J. Bensheimer, 1908, pp. 359–70.

108. Parent-Duchâtelet, A. J. B., "Les ulcères des extremités inférieures des artisans de Paris," *Annales d'hygiène publique,* 4 (1830), 239.

109. ———, *De la prostitution dans la ville de Paris sous le rapport de l'hygiène publique, de la morale et de l'administration,* Paris: Baillière, 1836.

110. Parsons, Talcott, "Some Problems Confronting Sociology as a Profession," *American Sociological Review,* 24 (August, 1959), 547–59.

111. Pearse, I. H. and G. S. Williamson, *The Case for Action,* London: Faber & Faber, Ltd., 1931.

112. ———, *Biologists in Search of Material. An Interim Report on the Work of the Pioneer Health Centre Peckham.* London: Faber & Faber, Ltd., 1938.

113. Pearse, I. H. and Lucy H. Crocker, *The Peckham Experiment. A Study in the Living Structure of Society.* London: George Allen & Unwin, Ltd., 1943.

114. von Pettenkofer, Max, "The Value of Health to a City, Two Lectures, Delivered in 1873," trans. from the German, with an Introduction by Henry E. Sigerist, *in Bull. Hist. Med.,* 10 (November, 1941), 593–613.

115. Petty, William, *Some Unpublished Writings of Sir William Petty.* Edited from the Bowood Papers by the Marquis of Lansdowne. London: Constable & Company, 1927, I: 33, 35, 36–40, 176, 195, 256–57, 267; II: 55, 170, 176.

116. Pflanz, M., *Sozialer Wandel und Krankheit. Ergebnisse und Probleme der medizinischen Soziologie.* Stuttgart: Ferdinand Enke Verlag, 1962.

117. Picard, Roger, "Sur l'origine des mots socialisme et socialiste," *Revue socialiste,* 51 (1910), 379–80.

118. ———, "Un Saint-Simonien démocrate: le docteur Ange Guépin," *Revue d'histoire economique et sociale,* 13 (1925), 456–94.

119. Plato, *Laws,* 720c, d.

120. ———, *Republic,* 3, 406c.

121. Plutarch, "Advice about Keeping Well," *Moralia.* Trans. Frank Cole Babbitt. London: William Heinemann, Ltd., 1928, II, 291.

122. Polgar, Steven, "Health and Human Behavior: Areas of Interest Common to the Social and Health Sciences." *Current Anthropology,* 3 (December, 1961) 159–205.

123. Poynter, F. N. L., "Thomas Southwood Smith—The Man (1788–1861)," *Proceedings of the Royal Society of Medicine,* 55 (May, 1962), 381–92.

124. Ramazzini, Bernardino, *De morbis artificum diatriba. Diseases of Workers.* The Latin text of 1713 revised, with translation and notes by

Wilmer Cave Wright. Chicago: University of Chicago Press, 1940, pp. 5–11, 347, 449.

125. Reader, George G. and Mary E. W. Goss, "The Sociology of Medicine," *in* R. K. Merton *et al.*, eds., *Sociology Today*. New York: Basic Books, Inc., 1959.

126. ———, "Medical Sociology with Particular Reference to the Study of Hospitals," *Transactions of the Fourth World Congress of Sociology*. Vol. II. Louvain: 1959, pp. 139–152.

127. Reihe, Erste, *Allgemeiner Politischer und Historischer Briefwechsel* (herausgegeben von der Preussischen Akademie der Wissenschaften). Zweiter Band, 1676–79, "G. W. Leibniz: Sämtliche Schriften und Briefe." Darmstadt: Otto Reichl, 1927, pp. 74–77.

128. Reich, Eduard, *System der Hygiene*. Vol. I. Leipzig: Friedrich Fleischer Verlag, 1870–71, pp. xii, xvi, xxii, 267.

129. Rochard, J., *Traité d'hygiène sociale et de prophhylaxie sanitaire*. Paris: Delahaye and Lecrrosiner, 1888.

130. Rochoux, J. A., *Thèse de concours pour la chaire d'hygiène* (presentée et soutenue le janvier 1838), Paris: De Rignoux et Ce, 1838, p. 28.

131. Roscher, Wilhelm, *Geschichte der National-Oekonomik in Deutschland*. 2nd ed. Berlin: R. Oldenbourg, 1924, pp. 238–52.

132. Rosen, George, "An Eighteenth Century Plan for a National Health Service," *Bull. Hist. Med.*, 16 (December, 1944), 429–36.

133. ———, "L. L. Finke on the Different Kinds of Geographies, but Chiefly on Medical Topographies and How to Compose Them," trans. from the German, *Bull. Hist. Med.*, 20 (November, 1946), 527–38.

134. ———, "What is Social Medicine? A Genetic Analysis of the Concept," *Bull. Hist. Med.*, 21 (July–August, 1947), 674–733.

135. ———, "Biography of Dr. Johann Peter Frank . . . Written by Himself, Translated from the German, with an Introduction and Notes," *Journal of the History of Medicine*, 3 (Winter and Spring, 1948), 11–46; 279–314.

136. ———, "The Idea of Social Medicine in America," *Canadian Medical Association Journal*, 61 (September, 1949), 316–23.

137. ———, "Medical Care and Social Policy in Seventeenth Century England," *Bulletin of New York Academy of Medicine*, 2nd series, 29 (April, 1953), 420–37.

138. ———, "Political Order and Human Health in Jeffersonian Thought," *Bull. Hist. Med.*, 26 (January–February, 1952), 32–44.

139. ———, "Economic and Social Policy in the Development of Public Health," *Journal of the History of Medicine*, 8 (October, 1953) 407–30.

140. ———, "Problems in the Application of Statistical Analysis to Questions of Health: 1700–1880," *Bull. Hist. Med.*, 29 (January–February, 1955), 27–45.

141. ———, "The Historical Significance of Some Medical References in the Defensor Pacis of Marsilius of Padua," *Sudhoff's Archiv für Geschichte der Medizin*, 37 (1953), 350–56.

142. ———, "Hospitals, Medical Care and Social Policy in the French Revolution," *Bull. Hist. Med.*, 30 (January–February, 1956), 124–49.

143. ———, "Cameralism and Concept of Medical Police," *Bull. Hist. Med.*, 27 (January–February, 1953), 21–42.
144. ———, "The Fate of the Concept of Medical Police," *Centaurus*, 5 (1957), 97–113.
145. ———, *A History of Public Health*, New York: M.D. Publications, 1958, pp. 201–20, 236–47.
146. ———, "Mercantilism and Health Policy in Eighteenth Century French Thought," *Med. Hist.*, 3 (October, 1959), 259–77.
147. ———, "The Why and the How of Sociology in Medical Training," *Archives of Environmental Health*, 4 (April, 1962), 638–42.
148. ———, "The Hospital—Historical Sociology of a Community Institution," *in* Eliot Freidson, ed., *Sociological Studies on the Hospital*. New York: The Free Press of Glencoe, Inc., in press.
149. ———, and E. Wellin, "A Bookshelf on the Social Sciences and Public Health," *American Journal of Public Health*, 49 (March, 1959), 441–54.
150. Ruge, Arnold, "Plan der Deutsch-Französischen Jahrbücher," *Deutsch-Französische Jahrbücher*. Herausgegeben von Arnold Ruge and Karl Marx. Paris: 1844. Reproduced in facsimile in the series *Neudrucke marxistische Seltenheiten*. Verlag von Rudolf Leibing. Leipzig: L. Franz & Company, 1925, I, 6.
151. Rumsey, Henry W., *Essays on State Medicine*. London: John Churchill, 1856, pp. 248, 280–82.
152. Ryle, John A., "Social Medicine: Its Meaning and Its Scope," *British Medical Journal*, 2 (November 20, 1943), 633–36.
153. de Sainte-Marie, Étienne, *Lecture relative à la police médicale faite au Conseil de salubrité de Lyon et du départment du Rhône en 1826, 1827, 1828*. Paris: Baillière, 1829.
154. Sand, René, *L'Économie humaine par la médecine sociale*. Paris: Les Editions Rieder, 1934, pp. 11–13.
155. ———, *Vers la médecine sociale*. Paris: J. B. Baillière et fils, 1948.
156. ———, *The Advance to Social Medicine*. London: Staples Press, Ltd., 1952, pp. 515–54.
157. *Social Implications of Industrialization and Urbanization in Africa South of the Sahara*. Paris: UNESCO, 1956.
158. Schelsky, H., "Die Soziologie des Krankenhauses im Rahmen einer Soziologie der Medizin," *Krankenhausarzt*, 31 (1958), 169.
159. Schumpeter, Joseph, *History of Economic Analysis*. New York: Oxford University Press, 1954, pp. 335–76.
160. Sée, Henri, *La Vie économique de la France sous la Monarchie censitaire (1815–1848)*. Paris: Alcan, 1927, pp. 91–95.
161. Semashko, N. S., "Friederich Erismann, The Dawn of Russian Hygiene and Public Health," *Bull. Hist. Med.*, 20 (June, 1946), 1–9.
162. Sigerist, H. E., "Kultur und Krankheit," *Kyklos* I: (1928), 60–63.
163. ———, "Historical Background of Industrial and Occupational Diseases," *Bulletin of the New York Academy of Medicine*, Series 2, 12 (November, 1936), 597–609.

164. ———, *The University at the Crossroads.* New York: Henry Schuman, Inc., Publishers, 1946, pp. 106–26, 130.

165. Simmons, Leo W. and Harold G. Wolff, *Social Science in Medicine.* New York: Russell Sage Foundation, 1954.

166. Simon, John, *Public Health Reports.* Vol. IIe. London: J. and A. Churchill, 1887, 97–98.

167. ———, *English Sanitary Institutions.* London: John Murray, 1897, pp. 246–48, 266 (fn), 293.

168. Small, Albion W., *The Cameralists. The Pioneers of German Social Polity.* Chicago: University of Chicago Press, 1909, pp. 60–106.

169. Sommer, Louise, *Die österreichischen Kameralisten in dogmengeschichtlicher Darstellung.* Wien: Carl Konegen, 1920–25. See especially Part I: pp. 43–56.

170. Stürzbecher, M., "Adolf Gottstein als Gesundheitspolitiker," *Medizinische Monatsschrift,* 13 (June, 1959), 374–78.

171. Sudhoff, Karl, *Jeh. Peter Brinkmann, ein Niederrheinischer Arzt im 18. Jahrhundert.* Dusseldorf: 1902.

172. Terris, Milton, "Social Medicine as an Academic Discipline," *Journal of Medical Education,* 33 (August, 1958), 565–73.

173. Thurnwald, R. C., *Black and White in East Africa. The Fabric of a New Civilization.* London: Routledge & Kegan Paul, Ltd., 1935.

174. Tibbitts, Clark, ed., *Handbook of Social Gerontology: Societal Aspects of Aging.* Chicago: University of Chicago Press, 1960.

175. Tissot, Simon, *De la manie du suicide et de l'esprit de révolte.* Paris: 1840.

176. *Transactions of the Medical Society of the State of New York, for the Year 1830.* Albany: Websters and Skinners, 1830, p. 25.

177. Trevelyan, Charles, *Metropolitan Medical Relief.* London: Longmans, Green & Company, Ltd., 1877.

178. Villermé, L. R., "Memoires sur la mortalité en France, dans la classe aisée et dans la class indigente" (with a supplement by Benoiston de Chateauneuf), *Memoires de l'Académie royale de médecine,* 1 (1828), 51–99.

179. ———, "Memoires sur la taille de l'homme en France," *Annales d'hygiène publique,* 1 (1829), 351–99.

180. ———, "De la mortalité dans les divers quartiers de la ville de Paris," *Annales d'hygiène publique,* 3 (1830), 294–341.

181. ———, "Décès à domicile des enfants dans quelques rues du Ier et du XIIe arrondissements," *Annales d'hygiène publique,* 3 (1830).

182. Virchow, Rudolf, "Die öffentliche Gesundheitspflege," *Medicinische Reform,* 5 (August, 1848), 21–22.

183. ———, *Die Einheitsbestrebungen in der wissenschaftlichen Medicin,* Berlin: G. Reimer, 1849, p. 48.

184. ———, "Die Epidemien von 1848, Gelesen in der Jahressitzung der Gesellschaft für wissenschaftliche Medicin am 27 (November, 1848)," *Archiv für pathologische Anatomie und Physiologie und für klinische Medicin,* 3 (1851), 3–12.

185. Webb, Sidney and Beatrice, *The State and the Doctor.* London: Longmans, Green & Company, Ltd., 1910, p. 7.

186. Weber, Max, *Gesammelte Aufsätze zur Wissenschaftslehre.* Tübingen: J. C. B. Mohr, 1922.

187. ———, *Gesammelte Aufsätze zur Soziologie und Sozialpolitik.* Tübingen: J. C. B. Mohr, 1924.

188. Wellin, Edward, *Uses of the Behavioral (Social) Sciences in Public Health.* Unpublished report submitted to the National Institute of Mental Health, U.S.P.H.S., 1961.

189. Winckelmann, O., *Das Fürsorgewesen der Stadt Strassburg vor und nach der Reformation bis zum Ausgang des 16. Jahrhunderts.* Quellen und Forschungen zur Reformationsgeschichte. Vol. 5. Leipzig: 1922, 25.

Part I

THE SOCIOLOGY OF ILLNESS

3

SOCIAL FACTORS IN RELATION TO THE CHRONIC ILLNESSES[1]

Saxon Graham

A *number of forces* operative in the last hundred years have stimulated an interest in and fomented the development of social medicine; similar forces have fostered concern with the chronic diseases. Chronic diseases have always been of interest to physicians. But during the last few-score years solutions have been found to many of the urgent problems of acute disorders, thereby allowing scientists to direct more attention to the chronic diseases.

It will be the purpose of this chapter, first, to outline briefly the recent history of medicine, and

[1] I wish to thank Drs. Edward Marra and Warren Winkelstein for their critical reading of this chapter.

to show the factors which have made the chronic diseases one of the most important preoccupations of medical scientists today. Next, the methodology of social epidemiology as it applies to chronic diseases will be discussed. This will be followed by a discussion of bio-social factors as they relate to the etiology of a variety of chronic diseases, particularly cancer and circulatory diseases. These two classes of diseases will be emphasized in part because cancers and the cardiovascular diseases together account for most of the deaths of mature people, and in part because they present very interesting sociological and biological problems. Following our discussion of the etiology of heart disease and cancer, we will examine briefly the effects of chronic illnesses on the afflicted individual, his family, his physician, and the community.

Trends in the Incidence of Chronic Disease

Had a handbook of medical sociology been produced fifty years ago, it is probable that it would not have contained a chapter on chronic disease. The omission would not necessarily have suggested a lack of interest; it would have been dictated by the necessity of devoting so much space to the infectious diseases that other important concerns would have been excluded. The fact that chronic diseases are included in this discussion is evidence of a new emphasis on an old concern, and this, as we will show, is a product in part of developments in medicine over the last hundred years.

The development of modern medicine

Until the latter half of the nineteenth century, relatively little improvement had been made in techniques for protecting the health of mankind. Prior to this time, of course, important discoveries in basic science had been made, such as the possibilities of the microscope by van Leeuwenhoek, the development of the mercury thermometer by Fahrenheit, the beginnings of an important chemistry by Lavoisier and Davy, and the contributions of Linnaeus and Cuvier in biology [45]. Among the most important were the discoveries of Pasteur and Koch. Their work revealed the pathogenic potential of some of the microorganisms, and provided the impetus for a line of investigation that has been utilized with increasing fruitfulness ever since. Once the principle that specific infectious microorganisms cause particular diseases was established, it was applied successfully to investigations of a host of illnesses.

Knowledge of the origin and cause of infectious diseases had the effect of stimulating a large number of developments of incalculable benefit to mankind. One of the earliest was aseptic surgery. Pasteur's demonstration in 1858 that bacteria were responsible for fermentation gave Joseph Lister a clue to the cause of wound fermentation in his surgical wards at Glasgow Infirmary. Up to that time, infections had been the chief cause of death following surgical operations of any sort, and it was rare that a surgical case did not develop post-operative infection. Newsholme notes that of the thirteen thousand amputations performed by French army surgeons during the Franco-Prussian War, no less than ten thousand proved fatal [37]. Surgery was a risky business. Lister, however, reasoned upon Pasteur's evidence that everything in the surgical environment should be purified of the fermentation-producing bacteria. Using carbolic acid as an antiseptic, Lister found immediately that infection was prevented and healing permitted in a majority of cases. Operations had been performed for at least four thousand years, usually with a disastrous result. The simple measure of asepsis created a revolution.

A second outgrowth of the original bacteriological principle was an effective preventive medicine. Even before bacteriology was developed, there had been understanding that contact with a diseased person or with filth was somehow related to acquisition of the disease. Acting on this idea, public health workers introduced the quarantine and other measures to prevent the spread of disease. But once it was understood why contact with it led to contraction of the disease, once the agent causing a disease was isolated, steps could be taken to develop substances which, when introduced into an individual, would stimulate his system to manufacture antibodies immunizing him from the disease. Jenner's discovery of a smallpox vaccine, developed before the advent of bacteriology simply on the basis of the observation that it worked, plus research which led to an understanding of *why* it was effective, led ultimately to measures for immunization against diphtheria, yellow fever, whooping cough, tetanus, typhoid fever, cholera, poliomyelitis, some of the influenza viruses, and many other diseases. Mass immunization has produced as dramatic results for the scientist in preventive medicine and public health as the aseptic operating room has for the surgeon.

Bacteriological studies contributed to a third important development, also implemented on the public health level. With the understanding that bacteria could cause illness, and that bacteria could be carried from one person, insect, or animal to another, public health workers endeavored to discover means by which to break the chains of contact. This general principle was applied in many ways. Enforced pasteurization of milk killed agents of infection borne in the fluid, breaking the chain of contact of many diseases. Purification of public drinking water had a similar result. Sewage was treated and disposed of in ways such that infection could not be carried by it. Swamps were drained or treated so as to destroy the breeding place of malaria-carrying mosquitoes. All of these procedures and many others were applied on a mass basis with startling results. We have comparative evidence today of the effectiveness of these mass health measures. At the present time, for example, India has only rudimentary measures for the purification of water supplies—two million Indians die annually from water-borne diseases, while the number in the United States is negligible.

In our time, bacteriological developments have produced penicillin, tetracycline, and other similar antibiotic drugs. Stimulated by the success of penicillin, drug manufacturers and others are scouring the world for other molds, some of which, they hope, will have therapeutic effects on diseases for which good remedies have not yet been discovered. It is true that therapeutic advances such as these actually save fewer lives than the routine application of public health measures such as mass immunization and water, milk and sewage treatment. Nevertheless, the importance of antibiotics and their dramatic effect in therapy for such dread killers as tuberculosis, appendicitis, rheumatic fever, spinal meningitis, and other acute infectious diseases cannot be minimized.

Effects of medical advances

We are safe in saying that the effects of the aforementioned innovations in medicine have been great. In some cases, to be sure, the evidence is not clear as to whether or not the advances of medical science have been responsible for a decline in an infectious disease. It is possible that some other factor, such as a decline in the potency of a bacterium strain, has been responsible. Again, the reduction in incidence of some diseases may be a partial response to a gradually improving standard of living for the United States as a whole. Nevertheless, there is no doubt that the great steps taken by medicine, especially in the last fifty years, have had much to do with prolonging the lives and lowering the death and disease rates of the population.

Table 3-1 shows, per 100,000 population, death rates from a number of causes in each decade since 1900; it reveals the dramatic decline in deaths from the infectious diseases which were attacked so successfully by the bacteriological approach. The rates for typhoid fever, dysentery, diphtheria, whooping cough, and measles have all declined substantially—immunization procedures have all but wiped out typhoid, diphtheria, and whooping cough, while pasteurization and water purification have had much to do with reducing infant dysentery. Infectious diseases which formerly attacked adults as well as children have been brought under control. Rates of death from tuberculosis, for example, have dropped consistently; a big decrease occurred in pneumonia about twenty-five years ago; syphilis declined by six-sevenths in the period from 1940–1959. Use of antibiotic drugs was in large part responsible for these successes. In addition, however, effective social organization played an important part in controlling tuberculosis

TABLE 3-1 DEATH RATE, 1900–1959, AND DEATHS, 1959, FROM SELECTED CAUSES

	Death Rate per 100,000 [1]							Number of Deaths
Cause of Death	*1900*	*1910*	*1920*	*1930*	*1940*	*1950*	*1959*	*1959* [2]
All Causes	1,719.1	1,468.0	1,298.9	1,132.1	1,076.4	933.8	941.7	1,659,000
Infectious diseases								
Tuberculosis, all forms	194.4	153.8	113.1	71.1	45.9	22.5	6.7	11,730
Syphilis and its sequelae	12.0	13.5	16.5	15.7	14.4	5.0	1.8	3,190
Typhoid Fever	31.3	22.5	7.6	4.7	1.0	0.1	—	—
Dysentery, all forms	12.0	6.0	4.0	2.8	1.9	0.6	0.2	290
Diphtheria	40.3	21.1	15.3	4.9	1.1	0.3	0.0	60
Whooping cough	12.2	11.6	12.5	4.8	2.2	0.7	0.2	280
Acute poliomyelitis	—	2.9	0.9	1.2	0.8	1.3	0.3	540
Measles	13.3	12.4	8.8	3.2	0.5	0.3	0.2	380
Influenza and pneumonia, except pneumonia of newborn	202.2	155.9	207.3	102.5	70.3	31.3	32.5	57,320
Chronic diseases								
Malignant neoplasms	64.0	76.2	83.4	97.4	120.3	139.8	147.1	259,090
Diabetes mellitus	11.0	15.3	16.1	19.1	26.6	16.2	16.0	28,160
Major cardiovascular renal diseases	345.2	371.9	364.9	414.4	485.7	510.8	519.7	915,610
Ulcer of stomach and duodenum	2.7	4.0	3.6	6.2	6.8	5.5	5.9	10,460
Accidents								
Motor-vehicle accidents	—	1.8	10.3	26.7	26.2	23.1	20.0	35,320
All other accidents	72.3	82.4	59.7	53.1	47.0	37.5	30.7	54,030

[1] Based on population enumerated as of April 1 for 1940 and 1950 and estimated as of July 1 for other years.
[2] Estimates based on a 10 per cent sample of death certificates.

and syphilis. Thus, the efforts of public health organizations in finding and treating tuberculosis cases and their contacts helped reduce incidence of this disease. Again, much of the victory over syphilis was won through the efforts of Surgeon General Thomas Parran. He was able to organize the entire nation for education in methods of syphilis prevention and therapy, and for the provision of medical facilities for control of the disease. The history of syphilis control shows in a graphic way the importance which social organization often has in bringing health to the community.

A look at the other items in the table indicates that although infectious diseases have increasingly come under control, little success has been had in the battle against diseases of adulthood and of the older age groups. The death rate for diabetes and ulcers has not dropped. Cardiovascular-renal diseases and malignant neoplasms (cancer) have actually increased. It is possible that the increases in rates of death from malignant neoplasms and cardiovascular-renal diseases are partly a result of changes in diagnostic procedures in the decades since 1910. Some of the increase also results from people surviving their infancy, because they were protected from the infectious diseases, and in later years becoming victims of chronic diseases. Fifty years ago, fewer persons than today lived long enough to acquire heart disease, cancer, diabetes, and arthritis. But there can be little doubt that the actual rates as well as absolute numbers of deaths from the cancers and circulatory diseases have increased substantially in the last sixty years.

Medical science today and in the future will be increasingly concerned with the diseases of older age groups. These diseases are usually chronic in nature, and therapy for them is often extremely expensive. The problems of chronic disease appear formidable at the moment. It appears that the old epidemiological approaches, which successfully concentrated on finding a bacterial cause of disease, may not be as effective in finding the cause of heart disease, cancer, and mental disease. Medical scientists went a long way with the momentum provided by the findings of early bacteriologists, but now it appears that other basic discoveries must be made to help them in seeking the causes of the newer problems which face them. New approaches to investigating the chronic diseases (including mental illness) must be devised. It may be that a union of sociology with the medical sciences will produce a new and successful epidemiology.

Social Epidemiology of Selected Chronic Diseases

Methods of social epidemiology

A disease may be considered as a tissue change toward a morbid state, brought about by some biochemical or biophysical agent acting directly on the tissue. Usually this action is the last in a series of events that put the host in contact with the disease-producing agent.

Scrotal cancer was peculiarly characteristic to chimney sweeps in eighteenth century England. The train of events leading to contraction of scrotal cancer, as Sir Percival Pott found in studying the disease in 1775, was somewhat as follows: (1) an environmental need for heated dwellings (2) was met with a sociocultural response in the form of widespread installation of home space-heaters (3) the preferred fuel for which produced so much smoke and soot that (4) exhaust passages required frequent cleaning; (5) an occupation, chimney sweep, developed which put the worker into close and frequent contact with soot which caused scrotal cancer.

We have more reliable data about scrotal cancer causation in humans than we have about most other malignant neoplasms. Some as yet unidentified component of soot apparently is a significant cause of scrotal cancer [53], yet we have still to identify the carcinogenic element and its mode of action. Thus, our most reliable knowledge regarding the etiology of scrotal cancer is epidemiological, and in large part involves social facts. Study of the epidemiology of this disease illustrates a number of characteristics of one process of disease causation [15]. First there is an agent producing the tissue change; then there is the vehicle for this agent, for example, soot; some behavior pattern must then expose the host to this vehicle; and finally, the behavior pattern must be peculiar only to certain segments of the population, for example, chimney sweeps. Of course, a

FIGURE 3-1 Etiological Chain of Events Producing Some Disease

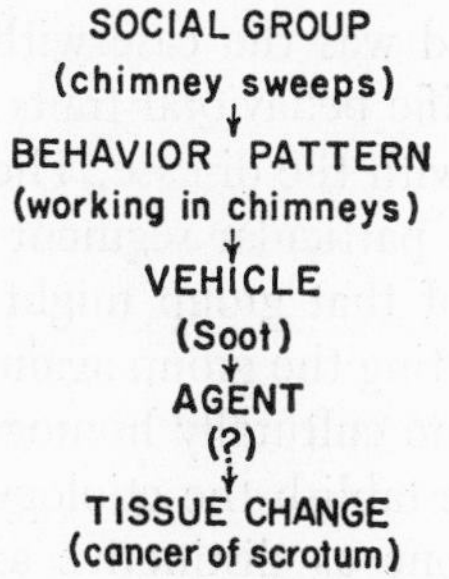

non-behavioral environmental factor may figure importantly in the chain, but few environmental exposures are unencumbered with social overtones. Thus although exposure to the sun is linked with skin cancer, it is obvious that social factors, such as occupation and place of residence, are also related to the disease.

From the point of view of prevention, the chain of events leading to contraction of a disease may be interrupted at any stage, and the disease thereby controlled. Thus, Pott vastly reduced the incidence of scrotal cancer simply by prescribing bathing. It is not necessary, obviously, to recognize the agent that causes the tissue change itself in order to effect prevention. From the point of view of understanding disease etiology, on the other hand, it is apparent that the whole process of disease causation—all of the events leading to disease—must be identified. This involves epidemiological field work as well as laboratory investigation, and the gamut of phenomena from biosocial to biochemical and biophysical must be examined as they relate to the disease. To achieve a coherent and complete theory of causation for a given disease, data of all three sorts must be obtained, and each kind determined to be consistent with the others in relation to the disease. Unless this can be, and is, done the etiology of a disease remains incompletely understood.

The strategy of epidemiological investigations develops from the etiological chain of events that we have described. Where hints of a relation between a behavior pattern and a disease exist—for example, cigarette smoking and lung cancer—the investigation may proceed from a hypothesized behavior trait. Hunches in such instances are derived from knowledge of the function of a given organ related to behavior that conceivably might affect it.

Often, however, no such hypotheses suggest themselves, and the strategy must be modified. Consider that specific behavior traits are frequently peculiar to certain segments of the population—contact with soot, for instance, was peculiar to chimney sweeps. Such a circumstance suggests that investigation of the relative incidences of disease in occupational or other kinds of social groups within a society might be useful. If it is discovered that a singularly high incidence of a disease obtains in a given occupation group, as indeed was the case with scrotal cancer, further investigation may reveal specific behavioral traits peculiar to that group that might account for contact with the disease. The discovery of singularly *low* incidence of a disease in a particular segment of the population suggests that further investigation of that group might uncover the factor that is uniquely shielding or protecting the group against contact with the diseases.

Population groups that are culturally homogeneous are particularly strategic. It is much easier to establish the etiology of a disease in an occupational group, particularly one as distinctive as chimney sweeps, than in groups as heterogeneous, as, say, socio-economic or rural-urban groups. Plots of socio-economic distributions of a disease are useful, but investigation of such fairly heterogeneous categories must be supplemented by other research to determine *why* a given socio-economic class reveals unusually high or low incidence of a disease. Ethnic background, religion, occupation, industry, regional, marital status, age, and other characteristics can be investigated profitably. Nevertheless, gross demographic characteristics are not hard-core variables. They are useful only to suggest possible avenues of future research. For example, the finding that Japanese-Americans have more gastric cancer than others [41] suggests that a comparative investigation of their diets might be useful.

Lung cancer as an example

One of the most graphic illustrations of the role of social factors is the etiology of lung cancer. In 1604 a member of the court of King James I wrote against the use of tobacco on the grounds that it was inimical to health, and tobacco has been designated as harmful ever since. Much more recently, investigators noted a great increase in lung-cancer incidence, and the use of cigarettes, which are a bronchial irritant, was suspected as a cause. As a result, a large number of retrospective studies of hospital populations were undertaken. In every case, these showed a significantly higher incidence of lung cancer among smokers as compared to nonsmokers [49].

FIGURE 3-2 CARCINOMA OF LUNG DEATHS (ALL REPORTED) *

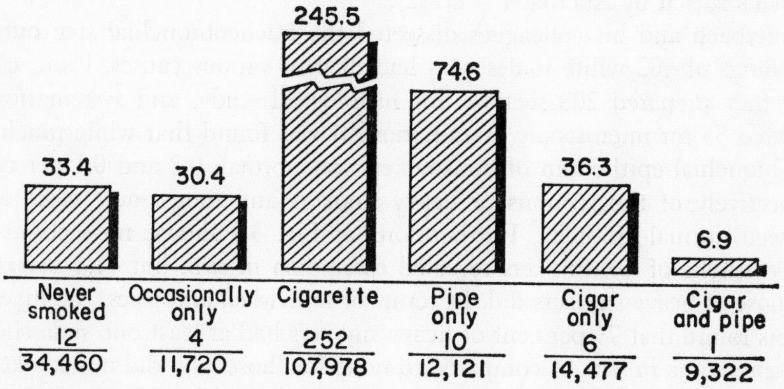

* From E. C. Hammond and D. Horn, "A Study of the Relationship between Smoking and Death Rates: Preliminary report of the 1954 follow-up." Paper presented at the annual meeting of the American Medical Association in Atlantic City, New Jersey, June 6, 1955.

Recently, four prospective studies of large population groups were carried out with the same results [9, 10, 22]. Fig. 3-2 indicates one finding in the study of Hammond and Horn [22]. Briefly, their procedure was to interview approximately 200,000 males regarding their smoking habits, wait an interval of several years, interview them again as to changes in smoking behavior, and measure the mortality from various diseases among smokers and nonsmokers. As is evident from Fig. 3-2, cigarette smokers had much higher rates of mortality from lung cancer than others, 245 per 100,000, as compared to 33 for nonsmokers. Among cigarette smokers, mortality increased directly with increases in number of cigarettes smoked per day. Persons who had stopped smoking during the years investigated had lower rates than those who continued. These findings and those of many other researchers have led the U.S. Surgeon General to warn of the relation of tobacco-smoking to lung cancer.

Critics might argue that possible self-selection of smokers is responsible for the finding, or that an x-factor is really responsible both for lung cancer and smoking, and thereby creates the association between the two. One way to solve this might be to allocate cigarette smoking randomly within a large group of 12-year old human males, control their environment, wait 20 to 30 years for the slow-acting carcinogen to take effect, and then measure the lung-cancer rate. It is unlikely that such an experiment could take place. But the epidemiological evidence based on behavior must be supplemented by laboratory studies. A number have been completed that contribute findings consistent with and supplementary to the epidemiological discoveries. Many studies have found substances in tobacco smoke that are carcinogenic to animals. One of the more interesting laboratory studies on humans is that by Auerbach *et al.* [2].

Auerbach and his colleagues dissected the tracheobronchial tree out of the lungs of 402 white males who had died of various causes. From each tree they prepared 208 sections for histological study, and systematically selected 55 for microscopic examination. It was found that while much of the bronchial epithelium of nonsmokers was normal, 0.2 and 0.1 per cent respectively of the sections of heavy smokers and lung-cancer cases also showed normal epithelia. Furthermore, as Fig. 3-3 shows, no sections of the epithelia of nonsmokers revealed carcinoma *in situ*, but 11.4 per cent of those of heavy smokers did. In terms of individual autopsies, the investigators found that 75 per cent of heavy smokers had at least one slide showing carcinoma *in situ*, as compared to none for those who did not smoke or smoked only occasionally. There is no doubt that risk of lung cancer increases drastically with amount smoked, and that risk can be reduced by stopping smoking. Nevertheless, such evidence, supplemented through replicative studies of autopsy and especially of live material from humans, together with further research on animals and on the mode of action of carcinogenic fractions of tobacco smoke, would further clarify the cigarette-lung cancer relationship. Typically, the social epidemiologic finding must be supplemented by laboratory research, but the opposite is also true—findings from biochemical and biophysical researches must be supplemented by the biosocial. It has been found in studies of mice that crowding of the animals correlates with diminished incidence of mammary

FIGURE 3-3 PERCENTAGE OF SLIDES WITH CARCINOMA *In Situ*

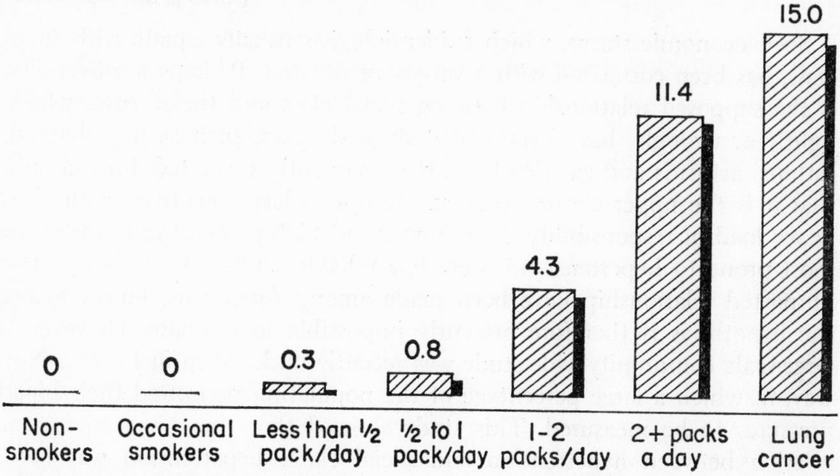

O. Auerbach, A. T. Stout, E. C. Hammond, and L. Garfinkel, "Changes in Bronchial Epithelium in Relation to Cigarette Smoking and in Relation to Lung Cancer," paper presented at the Clinical Meeting of the American Medical Association. Dallas, Texas, December 4, 1959.

cancer [1]. Such a finding is useful as a lead to similar researches on humans.

It is apparent that epidemiology is a multidisciplinary science. The widest possible knowledge regarding etiology can be discovered only by utilizing the approaches and findings of every relevant science to stimulate new discoveries and to corroborate earlier ones.

Social factors in chronic disease

Generally speaking, when scientists become involved in investigations of the epidemiology of a given chronic disease, they look into leads suggested by current knowledge about the disease. Thus it was that a few clinical physicians, having found that almost all of their lung cancer patients were smokers, decided to examine the smoking variable in larger series of cancer patients and controls. The investigator may look into any one of several kinds of human behavior as it might be related to a given disease, depending upon the nature of the disease and what is known about it. It will be my purpose in this section to examine a number of social factors as they have been found to relate to different kinds of diseases. One point I will be making is that the variety of such factors is great. Even gross demographic variables, such as race and social class, can shed light on the etiology of disease. To illustrate this, we will discuss briefly the following social factors: socio-economic status, ethnic background, religion, and variables relating to familial characteristics and behavior.

Socio-economic status

Socio-economic status, which epidemiologists usually equate with social class, has been correlated with a variety of diseases. Perhaps most familiar is the supposed relationship between social class and the diseases which, rightly or wrongly, have been called stress diseases, such as hypertension, asthma, arthritis and gastric ulcers. It is frequently suggested, for example, that it is the upper classes—particularly upper-class executives, with their heavy load of responsibility, long hours, and high-pressure work—who are most prone to hypertension.[2] Very few reliable large-scale studies of this purported relationship have been made among Americans, however, and the hypothesis is therefore presently impossible to evaluate. However, a large-scale community-wide study was recently undertaken in Bergen, Norway, in which a large percentage of the population permitted their blood pressures to be measured. This study showed that there was an *inverse* relation between hypertension and social class: hypertension was more prevalent in the lowest than in the highest social class [3].

The study of social class as related to a variety of other possibly stress-related diseases, such as stomach ulcers, ulcerative colitis, and to hypertension itself is hampered by the difficulty of obtaining complete universes of people having such diseases in communities. Generally speaking, past studies have been conducted on patients in particular hospitals, which meant that study subjects were selected by whatever traits characterized patients in those hospitals. Hospitals are selective of patients particularly on the basis of socio-economic traits, for these diseases especially, making unbiased investigations of this variable difficult.

Social class has been found to be associated with a variety of chronic diseases other than those possibly related to stress. In a study of incidences of cancer at various sites among the entire population of Buffalo conducted from 1948 to 1952, it was found that lung, stomach, and esophageal cancer have increasing incidence with decreasing class rank, and that cancer of the breast increased as social class status did [16] (see Table 3-2). Similar results for these diseases were found in New Haven, Connecticut, and Wales, Denmark, and England. For coronary artery disease, the greatest cause of chronic disease mortality in the United States, other social class relationships have been discovered. The British Registrar General, in his analyses of mortality from coronary artery disease, found a direct relationship between social class (based on occupational groupings) and mortality from this disease [42]. Other investigators using 1949–1951 mortality data for California, have suggested that there is an increase in this disease with

---

[2] See Chap. 4 for a discussion of stress.

TABLE 3-2 Average Annual Age Standardized Incidence Rates in Patients Reported with Cancer at Various Sites by Socio-Economic Quartile (Buffalo, New York, 1948–1952)

	Quartile I (Highest)		*Quartile II*		*Quartile III*		*Quartile IV (Lowest)*	
Site	*Number*	*Rate per 100,000*	*Number*	*Rate per 100,000*	*Number*	*Rate per 100,000*	*Number*	*Rate per 100,000*
Trachea, bronchus and lung (males only)	129	35.8	105	31.1	137	44.8	182	57.9
Stomach (males only)	70	19.6	83	24.9	87	28.0	119	38.0
Esophagus (males only)	24	6.7	35	10.5	28	9.0	58	18.7
Breast (females only)	353	115.8	230	86.9	237	74.2	153	51.6

each increase in class status [4]. The fact that social class-coronary disease relationships have been found in studies replicated in many countries suggests that such relationships are real. But the fact that other investigators, granting they studied small populations, have found no significant correlation suggests that more replication is necessary [33, 48].

Ethnic background

It is probable that this factor is related to the epidemiology of a number of diseases. This is because, first, ethnic background implies homogeneity within the group as to dietary, hygiene, education, religious, and other customs. Inasmuch as these customs may predispose the individual to or protect him from a given disease, we would expect ethnic background to be related to several of the chronic diseases. Despite the fact that this characteristic is potentially so fruitful to epidemiological research, very few studies of it have been undertaken. In the field of cancer, for example, only two large-scale studies of ethnic background have been completed; one by Graham, Levin, and Lilienfeld [17], the other by Haenszel [21]. As Fig. 3-4 shows, Polish-Americans were found to have unusually high relative risks of cancer of the esophagus, lung, and stomach, while Italian-Americans had high risks of cancer of the bladder, large intestine, and pharynx. This finding has stimulated further research into those dietary, drinking, and other habits of Italian- and Polish-Americans that may be related to etiology of the disease, not only in these groups but wherever they occur.

Ethnic background as a factor related to heart disease has been difficult to study. Investigators have usually had to content themselves with studies of prevalence (the number of cases current in a population at a given time) rather than of incidence (the number of new cases occurring at a given time). If the investigator's material is limited to prevalence, and he finds that a given nationality has low prevalence, this may indicate simply that the ethnic group under study gets poor medical care and has a higher mortality rate for this disease than other groups. High prevalence may indicate, not higher incidence, but merely a relatively low mortality rate.

Nevertheless, the few studies made of ethnic background as related to prevalence of coronary disease offer some interesting suggestions. Epstein conducted examinations on about 1600 persons. He concluded that Jews have a higher prevalence of coronary artery disease and also higher serum cholesterol levels than do Italians [14]. Sauer's finding that persons born in the USSR had very high mortality rates from the disease is probably consistent with Epstein's because the largest proportion of Epstein's Jews were Russians [44]. Sauer's finding that the Irish also had high rates is consistent with that of Graham, who studied prevalence in a random sample of Butler County, Pennsylvania [20], and Graham's finding on

FIGURE 3-4 Relative Risk of Developing Cancer

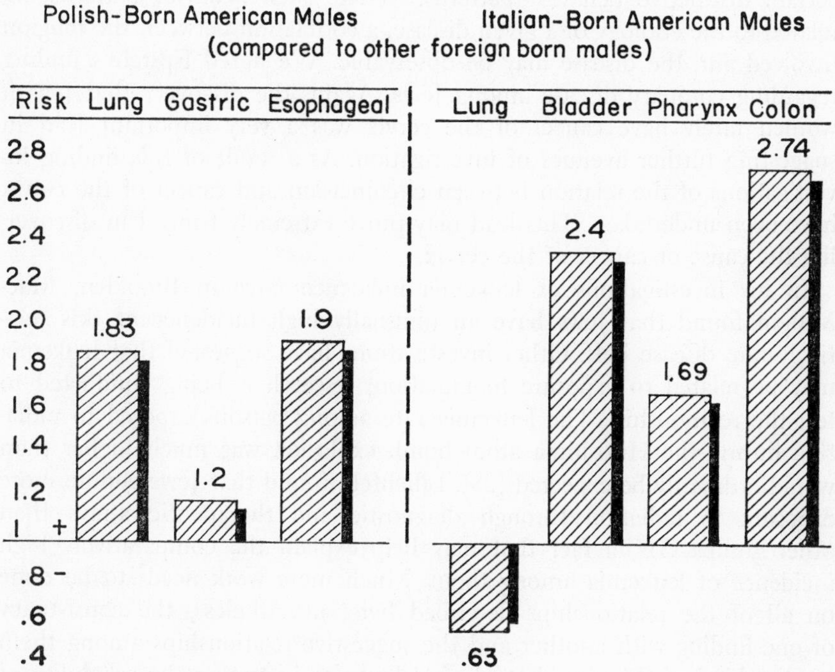

Southern Europeans is also consistent with that of Epstein. Stamler found higher coronary death rates in American males than in Japanese- and Chinese-Americans and American Indians.

In spite of the fact that these studies were solely of prevalence data, the magnitudes of the observed differentials and the consistency of these findings with several others lend credence to them. According to studies done in England and Wales and in California, the upper classes have higher mortality from coronary disease than the lower. Ethnic groups of highest economic status have the highest incidence of this disease. What little is known about the diets of these ethnic groups suggests that they are richer in animal fats than those of others; animal fats have been related to coronary disease in other researches. The findings on diet, social class, and ethnic background appear to be consistent in their relationship to each other. Diet especially seems closely related to the etiology of the disease. More evidence along these lines is offered in the next section on religion.

Religion

The religion of a group may sometimes dictate that it will exhibit certain distinctive behavior patterns. Where such behavior patterns are related to the etiology of a given disease, a correlation between the religion involved and the disease may be observable. We noted Epstein's finding regarding coronary disease among Jews. Again, the discovery that Jewish women rarely have cancer of the cervix was a very important lead in suggesting further avenues of investigation. As a result of this finding investigations of the relation between circumcision and cancer of the cervix have been undertaken. This lead may prove extremely fruitful in discovering the cause of cancer of the cervix.

In his investigations of leukemia incidence rates in Brooklyn, MacMahon found that Jews have an unusually high incidence of this relatively rare disease [34]. Other investigations have suggested that leukemia may be related to exposure to radiation; research is being conducted to test the relationship. The leukemia rate among persons exposed to radiation during the Hiroshima atom bomb explosion was much higher than would ordinarily be expected [28]. Lilienfeld found that Jews endure more exposure to radiation through diagnostic and therapeutic x-rays than other groups [31], a fact that may help explain the comparatively high incidence of leukemia among them. Much more work needs to be done on all of the relationships described here; nevertheless, the consistency of one finding with another and the suggestive relationships among them are the kind of thing epidemiologists look for in testing the reliability of their findings and in extending etiological theories.

Little is known about social correlates of cancer of the testis; only one study on a variety of social factors possibly related to cancer of the testis has been conducted. This research was conducted among 138 testis cancer and 4200 control patients at Roswell Park Memorial Institute in Buffalo. It showed that Protestants have a risk of cancer of the testis 1.5 times that of Catholics (P less than 0.0001), when statistical adjustment techniques removed the confounding effects of ethnic and age differences. Clearly, further research must be done to examine the ways in which behavioral traits associated with these religions conceivably could relate to cancer of the testis.

Toor has found interesting differences in incidence of coronary artery disease, among different groups of Jews in Israel [52]. The Yemenites—Jews deriving from the Near East and usually of low economic status—have a lower incidence of coronary artery disease than the Ashkenazim—European Jews economically much better off. In dietary studies of the two groups, the Ashkenazim were found to ingest significantly larger quantities of animal fats than other Jews. It has not been shown that ingestion of these fats necessarily produces high blood cholesterol levels, although this is possible. Nevertheless, it has been shown that high blood cholesterol is associated with coronary disease, and that the fatty plaques which form on the inside of the blood vessels and cause coronary attacks are composed in part of cholesterol. This evidence regarding the diets and heart disease incidence in two groups of Israeli Jews is consistent with findings presented earlier on social class, ethnic, and dietary characteristics of coronary patients.

Familial characteristics

Just as various culture patterns peculiar to religious groups may be related to a given disease, behavioral traits peculiar to individual families may affect the risk of their members of contracting certain diseases.

Thus, child-rearing practices adopted in certain families may be related to protecting against or fomenting disease. As an example, consider the case of breast cancer. There is apparently some association between breast cancer and *not* nursing offspring [30]. Some commentators have hypothesized that the woman who is much burdened with the cares of raising many children is more likely to have hypertension than the woman without children and without such cares. However, evidence to the contrary is provided by a study undertaken in Norway [3]. In a community-wide study of blood tension, it was found that single women have the highest rates of hypertension of any group of females. Hypertension decreased progressively in married women with no children, married women with one child, married women with two children, and married women with three or more children. In short the incidence of hypertension seems to decline with increase in familial responsibilities.

A second aspect of studies of disease in families investigates relatives of ill persons in an effort to discover whether certain diseases are inherited. Typically, such studies examine the incidence of a given disease among the kin of patients with that disease in comparison with the incidence among relatives of control persons not having the disease. In the past, many geneticists concluded that if a disease appeared more frequently among the relatives of patients with the disease than among the relatives of control persons, the disease did "run in families," and was inherited genetically.

Currently, most geneticists and sociologists realize that aggregation of disease in certain families can be attributed to both social and genetic inheritance, with either one type or the other predominating. Thus, for example, dietary behavior peculiar to individual families may help to account for the fact that gastric cancer has been found to occur approximately twice as often in the families of gastric cancer patients as among the relatives of persons without this disease [18]. It is possible that hypertension may be a disease which "runs in families" because such families have some behavior trait related to hypertension. Winkelstein shows an unusual aggregation of hypertension in certain households (see Fig. 3-5). Some investigators hypothesize that families in which an aggregation of hypertension is found may characteristically ingest diets high in salt. Here are two instances in which familial aggregation of disease may be explained through sociological rather than strictly genetic inheritance mechanisms. We emphasize that as both sociologists and geneticists agree a given manifestation is almost never the exclusive result of either genetic or social inheritance. Most diseases are the result of a pathologic environmental agent brought into contact with a host individual genetically susceptible to this agent.

One convenient way to investigate the extent to which a disease is inherited genetically or sociologically is to study the incidence of the disease among blood relatives of persons with and without the disease as compared to non-blood relatives of these persons, such as spouses. Inasmuch as mates share from marriage onward the same environment as blood relatives (their children, for example), if the aggregation among blood kin is higher than among mates, evidence is provided that inheritance may be more genetic than sociologic. On the other hand, equal incidence among blood and non-blood kin living in the same household is evidence to support a hypothesis of essentially sociologic inheritance [18]. This situation obtains in the example of Winkelstein (Fig. 3-5). Kin of hypertensives have higher blood pressure than kin of controls. This is true of blood relatives as well as "others" in the households, indicating that something in their social environments predisposes certain families to hypertension.

Epidemiology of cancer of the uterine cervix

We have seen that a wide variety of characteristics related to social class, religion, ethnic background, and familial behavior are associated with a number of chronic diseases. Such relationships are useful in suggesting areas for future research. Thus, the finding that Protestants have an unusually high risk of cancer of the testis suggests that examination of the behavior patterns of Protestants might reveal one related to the etiology of this disease. In the case of some chronic disease, many relationships of the kinds discussed above have been discovered. These in turn have suggested the possible existence of additional relationships, and further research to test these newer hypotheses has been undertaken. This is true in the case of the disease which we will discuss in this section, cancer of the cervic uteri; we will attempt here to present a brief but comprehensive picture of the epidemiology of this disease.

FIGURE 3-5 Mean Blood Pressures

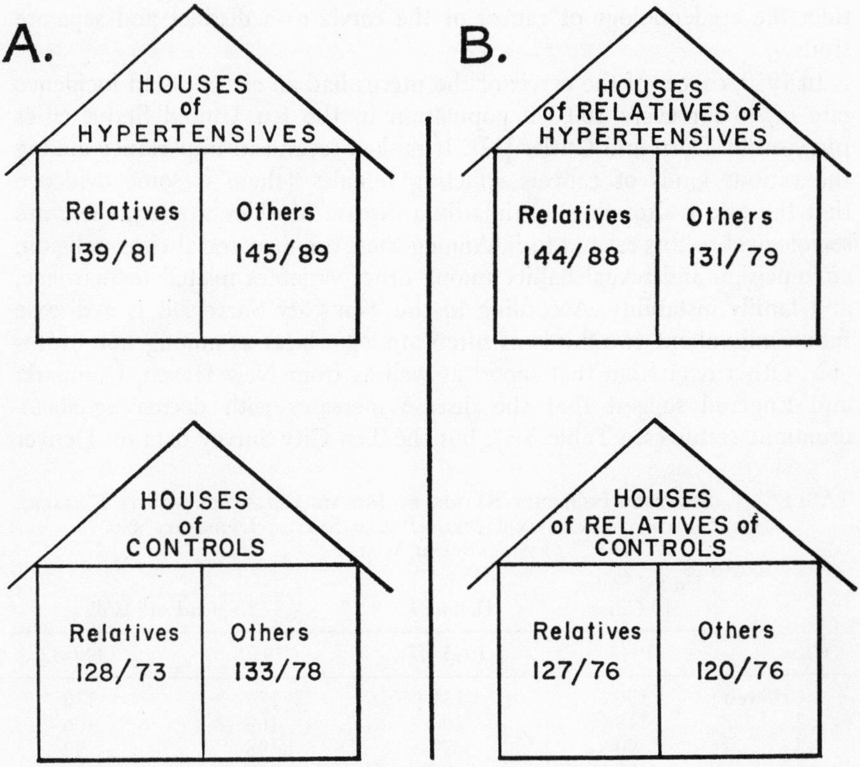

A. Note that the average blood pressure of relatives of hypertensives (139/81) is higher than that of controls (128/73).

B. Similarly, in households of relatives of hypertensives, their blood relations averaged higher (144/88) than did those of controls (127/76). It is interesting, too, that nonblood kin in households of hypertensives have higher means (145/89; 131/79) than those in control households (133/78; 120/76), in both analyses. This suggests that not only is a genetic factor operating to produce higher pressures in relatives of hypertensives, but that their household environments also produce higher averages in nonblood kin than the environments of nonhypertensives.

Adapted from Winkelstein, Warren, Personal Communication, 1961.

Cancer is generally thought to be not one disease but a group of different diseases having at least one characteristic in common: aggregation of abnormal cells at particular sites in the body, such cells having potentialities for invasive growth at the site of origin and for proliferation to other parts of the body. But the various types of cancer differ in many other respects, such as the morphology of the cells involved, the sites which come under attack, and the etiological characteristics which have been found to be related to them. Thus, for most purposes, and even though there may be some etiological factors which all cancers have in common, most epidemiological research must treat the different kinds of cancer as different disease entities. For that reason, it is necessary that we consider the epidemiology of cancer of the cervix as a distinct and separate study.

In 1950, cancer of the cervix of the uterus had an age-adjusted incidence rate of 44 for every 100,000 population in the ten United States cities surveyed by Dorn and Cutler [12]. It ranked second in importance among the various kinds of cancers afflicting females (there is some evidence that the rate is dropping). Primarily a disease of older women, there are sociological factors related to it. Among these are race, social class, religion, circumcision and sexual habits among other variables related to marriage, and family instability. According to the Ten City Survey, it is a disease found only about two-thirds as often among whites as among non-whites [12]. Other data from that report as well as from New Haven, Denmark, and England suggest that the disease increases with decreasing socio-economic status (see Table 3-3), but the Ten City Survey data on Denver

TABLE 3-3 Standard Incidence Ratios, by Income Class, for White Females, Cancer of the Cervix Uteri, United States, Denmark, and England and Wales *

	United States 10 Cities	*Denmark*	*England and Wales*	
Class	*1947*	*1943–47*	*1950*	*1930–32*
1 (lowest)	156	131	150	130
2	113	100	109	106
3	90	79	98	99
4	85	90	69	78
5 (highest)	74	50	61	65

* From Harold F. Dorn, Ph.D., and Sidney J. Cutler, M.A., "Morbidity from Cancer in the United States," Part II, Public Health Monograph No. 56, Washington, D.C., 1959.

and other data on Buffalo do not reveal that correlation [16]. In the Buffalo study, furthermore, when marital status (which is associated with cervix cancer) was statistically controlled the socio-economic pattern was even more obscured. It is obvious that more research needs to be done on the relationship between social class and cancer of the cervix, first to establish whether it exists in other cities, and secondly, to investigate reasons for its existence in those areas where the relationship does appear.

Several decades ago it was discovered that Jewish women have a much lower incidence of cancer of the cervix than non-Jews. Table 3-4, for example, shows differentials between Jews in Israel and a United States population [11]. It is of interest that the rate among Yemenite Jews in Israel is lower than that among Ashkenazim Jews. If such a difference is proven to exist by replicative studies, it might be related to the more orthodox observance of Jewish religious practices among Oriental than among European Jews. Other ethnic relationships have been discovered relative to cancer of the cervix. Thus, as Table 3-5 shows regarding a study in India, Moslems and Parsis had much lower rates than did Protestants and Hindus. There have been intimations, furthermore, that Moslems in the East Indies have less cancer of the cervix than other religious groups. There has been no attempt, however, to replicate this finding.

TABLE 3-4 Incidence of Cancer of the Female Genital Organs: Annual Number of New Cases per 100,000 Female Population, Israel 1952–53, Selected Urban Areas of the United States, 1947–48.

	U.S. (white)	*Israel*		
Primary Site		*Total Israel*	*European Jews*	*Oriental and Mediterranean Jews*
Uterus	56.3	25.9	31.0	18.7
Cervix	32.6	4.9	5.7	4.0
Corpus	10.3	8.1	11.8	2.5
Unspecified	13.2	12.9	13.5	12.2
Ovary	14.7	7.9	11.5	2.3

H. F. Dorn, "Cancer Morbidity Survey: A Tool for Testing Theories of Cancer Etiology," presented before the Epidemiology and Statistics Sections, American Public Health Association, Buffalo, October 14, 1954.

TABLE 3-5 Cervical Cancer as a Percentage of Total Female Cancer Admissions at the Tata Memorial Hospital, Bombay, 1941–1950, and the Premier Radiological Institute and Cancer Hospital, Madras, 1950–1952

	Tata Memorial		*Premier Radiological Institute*	
	Total female cancer admissions	*Per cent cervix cancer*	*Total female cancer admissions*	*Per cent cervix cancer*
Hindus	3,828	45	280	53
Christians	575	29	60	29
Moslems	818	16	67	18
Parsis	396	13	—	—

E. L. Wynder, J. Cornfield, P. D. Schroff, and K. R. Doraiswami, "Study of Environmental Factors and Carcinoma of the Cervix," *American Journal of Obstetrics and Gynecology* (October 1954), pp. 1016–1052.

A number of suggestions have been made to account for the low incidence of cancer of the cervix among Jews and Moslems. One is the female hygiene practices traditional to those groups, as described in an imaginative and valuable anthropological work done by physician E. L. Kennaway [25]; other factors are circumcision of mates and the prescription of abstinence from intercourse during the first week after cessation of menses, noted in Leviticus. Traditional Jewish ritualistic hygiene practices involving sex organs probably are no longer widely observed, at least in the United States, and therefore probably are not a factor in low Jewish cervix cancer rates. Abstinence from intercourse during menses and the first week thereafter would reduce exposure to any possible cancer-causing agent involved in intercourse by almost one-half of the expected period covered by the menstrual cycle. But such abstinence practices do not appear any longer to be followed by large numbers of Jews in the United States. Indeed, Kinsey found a somewhat higher frequency of marital intercourse among Jewish males than among Catholics or Protestants. Because of Jewish endogamy, we are fairly safe in suggesting that the same statement could be made for Jewish females, assuming the accuracy of Kinsey's data [26].

Circumcision, however, is one characteristic which is still common to many of the low-incidence religious and ethnic groups: the Jews, Moslems, and Parsis. Under poor conditions of hygiene, the uncircumcised male may introduce a substance called smegma into contact with the cervix. Inasmuch as human smegma has been found carcinogenic to the mouse cervix, circumcision and smegma as a possible human carcinogen are of epidemiological interest.

Two important studies of the amount of circumcision among mates of cervix cancer patients in hospitals and clinics, as compared to patients with other conditions from the same sources, revealed slightly contradictory findings. The research of Dunn and Buell revealed essentially no differences in exposure of cervix cancer and other patients to circumcised and uncircumcised males [13]. Wynder revealed a somewhat greater excess of exposure to uncircumcised males among women with cancer of the cervix as compared to controls, 80 per cent as opposed to 75 per cent [55]. Because of the conflict in the findings of two researches on this very important question, an answer to why such conflict might exist was sought (see Table 3-6).

In both of the studies, the circumcision status of mates was determined by asking each patient if her husband was circumcised. The validity of such a method of establishing circumcision status was questioned and research accomplished to examine it. Every patient admitted to Roswell Park Institute fills out a detailed questionnaire before he is given his admission examination. The questionnaire inquires into many sociobiologic traits including, for males, circumcision status. In this study, physicians giving the admission examinations were asked to pay special attention to and to record the circumcision status of each male patient. This they did, and with no prior knowledge of the patient's own statement on the subject. Analysis of about 200 male patients' statements revealed disagreement with the physicians' observations in 34.4 per cent [32].

TABLE 3-6 Per Cent Distribution of Cervix and Control Patients with Sexual Experience by Circumcision Status of Partners, White Non-Jewish, and Negro

	White			*Negro*	
	Non-Jewish		*Jewish*		
	Cervix	*Controls*	*Controls*	*Cervix*	*Controls*
Circumcised husbands only: no other partners	3	9	93	0	8
Pre-, extra-, or post-marital partners	3	3	2	8	5
Circumcised and uncircumcised husbands	4	3	1	2	5
Uncircumcised husbands only	80	75	1	65	47
Circumcision status unknown	10	10	3	25	35

E. L. Wynder, J. Cornfield, P. D. Schroff, K. R. Doraiswami, *op. cit.*

This finding suggests that the methodology of previous studies makes their conclusions of dubious validity. It is also an interesting commentary on the kind of errors that can be made in applying interview techniques, even those applied to very concrete questions. Perhaps a better, but certainly more difficult, way to study circumcision as related to cancer of the cervix in the future is to conduct actual examinations of husbands of patients and controls.

We have seen how the finding of a simple relationship between a disease and a religious group has stimulated a large number of studies undertaken in attempts to explain the relationship. There is a possibility that still other differences between Jews and non-Jews could explain the different incidences of the disease. To learn more about the problem, the study of groups which are racially similar but culturally different—such as Moslems and Jews in the Near East—should be undertaken to discover possible differences in incidence of cervical cancer. A genetic hypothesis might be tenable, for the groups which have been found to be low in cervix cancer, the Jews in Israel and the Moslems in India, probably derive from similar racial stock. Sachs, for one has adduced evidence that there is a gene pool held in common by Jews regardless of whether they derive from Eastern or European sources. In frequencies of fingerprint whorls of various types, Jews in one nation show much more similarity to Jews in other nations than to non-Jews in their own country. German Jews, for example, show a greater similarity of frequencies to other Jews than they do to Germans in general [43]. It is possible, therefore, that there is some characteristic protecting Jews against cervix cancer that is inherited genetically within that group.

In addition to factors related to religion and circumcision, a number of other characteristics have been examined as they relate to cervical cancer. With regard specifically to sex behavior, the findings are equivocal. Thus, Jones discovered no significance in the frequency of coitus, but Terris found that cervical cancer patients had considerably more frequent coitus than did patients without disease [24, 50]. The frequencies of coitus among Terris' cancer patients were much higher than those reported by the average woman in Kinsey's research [27]. A number of writers have found evidence that persons with cancer of the cervix married early or had commenced to have intercourse at an earlier age than was the case among control patients [24, 55]. A number of studies have provided the consistent finding that cervical cancer patients had their first and last pregnancies at an earlier age than others. In addition, they are more likely to have been married one or more times than others, and are also less likely to have been childless.

Some investigators, notably Maliphant in Wales and Zeitz at Heidelberg University Clinic, have found that as the number of children borne by a woman increased so did her risk of cervical cancer [36, 56]. But the data of Wynder and those at Roswell Park Memorial Institute contradict this finding [55]. The existence of these among many other contradictions in the conclusions of studies points up a need for replication. Needless to say, in the area of sex and childbirth, reluctance upon the part of cancer and control patients to discuss taboo subjects is a great hindrance to investigation.

The suggestion that frequent intercourse and intercourse commenced early in life may be related etiologically to cancer of the cervix is consistent with findings that among nuns there is almost no cancer of the cervix but that among prostitutes, the rate is high. Levin's finding that cancer of the cervix is related etiologically to the presence of syphilis might explain in part the high incidence among prostitutes [29]. Of equal sociological interest is the finding of a greater frequency of familial instability and poverty among cervical cancer patients than among others [24]. Paloucek, after depth interviews with a series of patients, suggests that such conditions do indeed characterize cervix cancer patients as compared to controls [39]. Of equal but parenthetical interest is Paloucek's finding that persons with a good social prognosis for those variables do have the best physical prognosis for recovery from cervix cancer [38].

A number of other factors have been suggested to be related to this disease, but few large-scale studies have been carried out to test them. For example, many clinicians suspect that the presence of unrepaired lacerations resulting from childbirth may predispose to cancer of the cervix. Others are concerned as to the extent to which carcinoma *in situ* of the cervix, which is found rather more frequently than cervical cancer, actually develops into a malignant, invasive lesion. Other scientists suspect that cervicitis, a common medical complaint, sets the stage for the development of invasive cervical cancer. Because it is very difficult to obtain a universe of patients who have unrepaired birth lacerations, carcinoma *in situ*, or cervicitis, and because it is difficult to study the latter two conditions retrospectively, questions will remain as to their etiologic importance.

The same may be said, perhaps less pessimistically, with regard to most of the relationships discussed in this section. A good deal of contradictory evidence has accrued, and much evidence derives from studies the design of which leaves something to be desired. In those few cases where findings have been replicated several times, such as in the case of low Jewish incidence, further research needs to be undertaken to discover the reasons why the relationships exist. In all of this research, sociological techniques of investigation and sociological knowledge regarding characteristics of various groups in society will be useful in extending the epidemiological understanding of cancer of the cervix.

The Chronic Illnesses as Social Problems

Any force which disturbs the human organism so profoundly and over such a long period as chronic disease, if affecting a large enough proportion of persons in a community, is bound to have far-reaching effects on that population. It should be emphasized that although this discussion has been limited to cancer of the cervix and a relatively few chronic diseases, the number of persons they affect in the Western world is large. The effects of these diseases on the population are reflected in its demographic character, in various social and economic burdens levied upon the society, in peculiar problems affecting therapy and physician-patient relationships, and in the special rehabilitation and prevention problems which they present. Physician-patient relationships, therapeutic organization and other problems will be fully discussed in Chapters 11, 12, and 15. These subjects will be dealt with in the following section only as they refer to the chronic diseases.

Demographic effects

For some years the age distribution of the United States has been changing, a result in part of advances of medical science against infectious disease. More and more people are living beyond the childhood years into middle- and old-age. In 1900, the death rate per 1000 population was 17.2; by 1959 the rate had dropped to 9.6. The annual mortality rate for white males under one year of age decreased from 123.3 per thousand in the years 1909 to 1911 to 28.8 per thousand in 1952. Thus, in that age group most profoundly affected by successes in prevention and treatment of communicable disease, death rates plummeted.

What happened in the older age groups, on the other hand, was quite different. The mortality rate for white males 65 years of age was 43.8 per thousand in 1909–11; by 1951 it had dropped to 34.5 [5]. Thus, the decline in death rate in the older age group has been only a fraction of that of the under-one-year-old group. Mortality in the youngest age group declined approximately 77 per cent, while the 65 year olds have experienced a decline of only about 20 per cent.

One thing which we may infer from these figures is that the advances in medical science, fairly limited as they are to communicable diseases, have greatly increased life expectancy at birth but have not been as great a benefit to persons in the older age groups as those in the younger. One must conclude on the basis of this evidence if no other, that the diseases affecting older age groups have not come under the same strict control as the diseases affecting young age groups.

Social and economic costs

The social and economic burdens which must be borne by societies large numbers of whose people succumb to chronic disease—while of a different nature than burdens formerly imposed by such diseases as plague, cholera, smallpox, and other scourges—are nevertheless severe. First of all, chronic diseases strike middle-aged and older persons, in large numbers. These are the people who have mastered their occupations; they are the ones who have experience. Death and disablement of them means great losses to society. The peak period of incidence of some chronic diseases, such as cancer of the prostate, affects post-retirement age-groups. Other diseases, however, have highest incidence in the fifth and sixth decades of life, normally the time when the individual has reached the height of his powers and is able to make his greatest contribution to society. Lung cancer, for example, is a disease of extremely high and increasing incidence among males. Inasmuch as only two or three per cent of male lung cancer patients survive more than five years, the social cost is obvious. Coronary disease is a disease of even higher incidence, and it, too, strikes many adults in their most productive years.

Even when chronic diseases do not result in the obvious social loss, death of experienced individuals, the social burden they impose in disabling such individuals is just as great. A person who has had a heart attack or cerebral vascular accident is often very limited in his activity. Not only is he frequently not able to function at peak efficiency in the most productive years of his life, but in varying degrees he can become a burden on his family and community. If he is completely incapacitated and requires continual care, the cost of the disability is very high. Disabling diseases, such as the various forms of arthritis, are not severe enough to kill the patient yet render him in various degrees helpless and dependent upon others for care. A 1954 survey of Butler County, Pennsylvania, made to discover the extent of disability in the population of this mixed urban and rural area, showed that 16 per 1000 population were currently disabled; a total of 141.4 man-years per 1000 population was lost because of disability. As shown in Fig. 3-6, three diseases—arthritis, diabetes, and circulatory disorders—were cited as causes of almost 40 per cent of the disabilities found [19]. A study carried out on a sample of the national population again showed the extent of disability and the fact that many are disabled by chronic disease [8]. The considerable costs of disability derive not only from the loss of the services of a productive individual in the prime of his life, but also from the fact that the services of others must be used to support and sustain him.

Special problems are posed to communities and families which must support persons with chronic illnesses. On the community level, solutions in the form of special hospitals for chronic disease have been tried. Indeed, many hospitals once devoted to treatment of tuberculosis have been altered to care for persons with other chronic diseases. It is probable that in the near future a large number of hospitals specializing not in emergency care but in the treatment of chronic diseases and in long-term care of disabled persons will be developed as well. In addition it is quite possible that nursing homes will increase in numbers, as will special satellite institutions organized and run by general hospitals to provide non-emergency long-term care.

In some instances home-care programs have been developed by hospitals to enable chronically ill patients to be cared for by their families. This is feasible, of course, where the care needed does not require too much time or skill, and where the facilities of the home are adequate. Because of the great cost of hospital care as it is organized today to meet emergency medical and surgical demands, it is probable that ordinary hospital facilities in the future will be used only for acute flare-ups of chronic disease.

Because the therapeutic period for chronic diseases often is so long and because lengthy disability is often entailed, the costs of care are very high in relation to what the average family can pay. It is not unusual for an average case of cancer to cost a family many thousands of dollars.[3] The family is indeed fortunate that has sufficient savings to take care of such an emergency. For the most part, however, such savings have been put aside to pay for education of children or other family necessities. Frequently, there are no savings and the possessions of the family must be liquidated in order to meet hospital and physicians' bills. In cases where no

---

[3] See Chap. 14 on costs of medical care.

FIGURE 3-6 MEDICAL CONDITIONS CONTRIBUTING TO MOTOR DISABILITIES, BUTLER COUNTY, PENNSYLVANIA

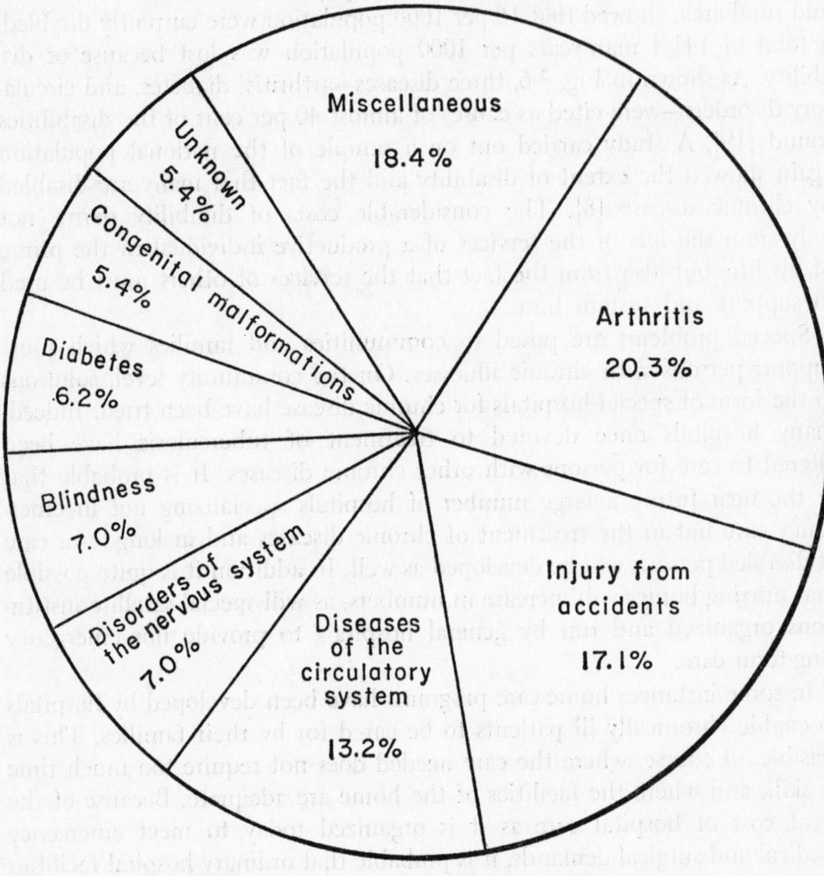

S. Graham, "Disability in Butler County," *Public Health Reports,* 71 (November, 1956), pp. 115–18.

family resources remain to be liquidated, care frequently is unobtainable. Some patients are able to obtain adequate care with help from charitable organizations, but most are not. At best, charity care cannot include the most expensive treatments simply because neither charity, physician, hospital, nor patient can afford to pay the bill. Furthermore, many patients unable to meet the costs of care themselves forgo charity care, even when it is available. When the catastrophic costs of therapy occur after the breadwinner in the family has retired and his income is reduced, as is often the case, it is obvious that the economic problem to the patient, his community, and the therapeutic organization is great. It is equally obvious that solutions to the problem of paying for chronic disease therapy must be found.

Physician-patient relationships in chronic disease

In situations where the onset of a previously undiagnosed chronic disease is rapid and quickly fatal, such as in the fatal coronary attack, the blow of sudden death to the family of the patient is profound. On the other hand, the effect on the family of long-term illness is also profound, particularly when it is well recognized that the illness is bound to terminate in death. When the terminal nature of an illness is well understood, the family and the patient himself are able to plan for the financial future.[4] In addition, a number of decisions can be made in regard to changes in living quarters and style of living, as well as in economic practices of the family. Because such planning is necessary for the well-being of the family, it is important that the family and the patient know his health situation. The physician is the only person who can inform the family of the patient's condition and, for the most part, physicians feel that when a terminal illness is encountered, the family and patient should be made aware of it so that plans for the future can be made. It is likely, however, that the physician who knows his patient well does not deliberately withhold or impart information from that patient. Without saying so in so many words, the physician makes the patient aware of his life expectancy, but does not destroy all hope of recovery. In certain cases, on the other hand, the sensitive physician who has gotten to know a patient and his family intimately may feel that, for the patient's peace of mind, he should not be told. In such cases, he gives the information only to other family members.

In cases where the patient is aware of the nature of his terminal illness, the patient may justifiably demand that the physician employ all reasonable methods of therapy at his command, even unproven ones. The patient who knows that experiments to determine new methods of therapy for the disease he suffers are in progress, may justifiably feel that he should be given the opportunity to try the new therapeutic agent in the hopes that it will have some effect in arresting his disease. In situations where such a drug has been thoroughly tested on animals and seen to have very small toxic side-effects, the physician may try new drugs on the patient in tentative fashion to see whether the illness cannot be brought under control. Such experimentation on patients is often supported by grants of the Public Health Service, under the conditions described above. Where the drug has been closely screened in trials on animals, where the unpleasant

---

[4] See Chap. 11 for a general discussion of physician-patient relations.

side-effects are known to be unimportant in comparison with the possible therapeutic results, large-scale screening to find better drugs is always underway. From the patient's point of view, his participation in such research programs does not involve merely experimentation in the scientific sense, but the possibility of finding a cure for a disease which is ordinarily terminal or greatly disabling and which affects him personally.

One who suffers a disease not terminal but disabling can, of course, return to his home disabled to remain unproductive and a burden on his family and community for the rest of his life. But with sympathetic help from qualified people, whatever sociological and physical potential remains to him can be augmented in such a way that he will be able, if not to support himself, at least to be less of a burden on others. In the United States, a few physicians have been working many years on the problems of rehabilitation, but in comparison with the need for rehabilitation which chronic disease imposes, the number of people engaged in the field is small.

Rehabilitation requires the services of a wide variety of specialists. Medical practitioners of various sorts are needed to deal with various aspects of rehabilitation in any given case. Most useful are those trained and experienced specifically in rehabilitation, in educating unused muscles to do new things, in helping patients to use limited mental or sensory faculties, and in training them to make adjustments to unusual physical handicaps which have evolved in the course of the disease. In addition, social workers are needed to investigate the family and community situation of the patient to see how best he may fit himself in to the social fabric again. In all of this enterprise, sociologists could conduct valuable research into the best methods of bringing about physical and social rehabilitation, particularly to discover those milieus most amenable to successful rehabilitation. The work of Simmons and Freeman, who inquired into how the different milieus of released psychiatric patients related to their recovery, is an illustration of the kind of research which sociologists could do in the field of rehabilitation [46].

Prevention of chronic diseases

An overriding interest in therapy often implies reduced concern with *prevention* of disease, a failing of both the public and medical scientists alike. For the patient afflicted with a chronic disease, therapy today too often can do little but give him some relief or an added few months of life. It is probable, of course, that within a few years therapy for even the most highly fatal diseases will be much more successful. Nonetheless, with the costs of therapy high as they are, the advantages in attacking the problem of preventing the disease in the first place seem to be obvious.

The difficulty in attempting prevention of diseases of chronic nature is that at this time our knowledge of prevention is even less extensive and useful than that of therapy. Nevertheless, even now enough is known about factors associated with causes of a variety of chronic diseases that the physician who is concerned about prevention of illness in his patients often will discuss with them research findings such as those outlined earlier in this chapter. Because epidemiologists have found a very close relationship between smoking and lung cancer, and between stopping smoking and reduction in lung cancer, the physician concerned with prevention will frequently urge his patients to stop smoking. In similar fashion, because cholesterol is an important constituent of the fatty plaques which clog the coronary arteries, and because of the evidence that diets high in cholesterol seem to be characteristic of coronary disease patients, some physicians tell their middle-aged patients to avoid whole milk, butter, fatty meats, and other sources of dietary cholesterol. For the same reasons, some physicians will tell their patients to obtain regular exercise and avoid obesity. All of these suggestions involve important changes in very intimate aspects of the patient's behavior patterns. Changes in dietery habits are most elemental, and anyone who has tried to stop smoking knows the difficulty involved. It is quite possible, however, that new knowledge of the ways people can change their behavior patterns can be furnished by the application of sociological research techniques to testing hypotheses suggested by sociological theory. Research is just beginning in this area. Daniel Horn, a social psychologist, has studied the circumstances under which teenagers begin smoking in an attempt to discover more about this problem [22]. Presumably, knowledge of why people start smoking would be useful in helping them stop. Certainly it might be useful in helping them not to acquire the habit in the first place. Other research currently is taking place directly on the problem of giving up smoking once the habit has been adopted, utilizing sociological theories and findings regarding the innovation process. It is clear that this particular kind of problem can serve as an interesting area in which to develop and test new sociological hypotheses in the field of innovation. It is also clear that as sociologists work more and more on the innovation process and as such knowledge is used in research on disease prevention, the benefits accruing to society through reduction of death and disability from chronic disease might be profound.

References

1. Andervont, H. B., "Influence of Environment on Mammary Cancer in Mice," *Journal of the National Cancer Institute*, 4 (1954), 579*ff*.
2. Auerbach, Oscar, A. T. Stout, E. C. Hammond, and L. Garfinkel, "Changes in Bronchial Epithelium in Relation to Cigarette Smoking and in Relation to Lung Cancer." Paper presented at the Clinical Meeting of the American Medical Association, Dallas, Texas, December 4, 1959.
3. Boe, Johs, Sigurd Humerfelt, and Froystein Wedervang, *The Blood Pressure in a Population*. Bergen: A. S. John Griegs Boktrykkeri, 1956.

4. Breslow, Lester and Philip Buell, "Mortality from Coronary Heart Disease and Physical Activity of Working, California," *Journal of Chronic Disease*, 11 (1960), 421–44.
5. Bureau of Census, *Statistical Abstract of the United States*, 1956, Washington, D.C.: Government Printing Office, 1957.
6. Chen, W. Y., L. B. Crittenden, Nathan Mantel, and W. R. Cameron, "Site Distribution of Cancer Deaths in Husband-Wife and Sibling Pairs," *Journal of the National Cancer Institute*, 27 (1961), 875–92.
7. Clemmesen, Johannes and Jens Sorsen, "Malignant Neoplasias of Haemopoietic and Connective Tissues in Various Countries," *Danish Medical Bulletin*, 5 (March, 1958), 73–123.
8. Department of Health, Education, and Welfare, *Health Statistics: Disability Days, United States, July 1957–June, 1958*. Washington, D.C.: Government Printing Office, 1959.
9. Doll, Richard and A. B. Hill, "Lung Cancer and Other Causes of Death in Relation to Smoking: Second Report on Mortality of British Doctors," *British Medical Journal*, 2 (1956), 1071*ff*.
10. Dorn, Harold F., "Smoking and Cancer." Social Statistics Section Proceedings of the American Statistical Association, 1958.
11. ———, "Cancer Morbidity Survey: A Tool for Testing Theories of Cancer Etiology." Paper presented before the Epidemiology and Statistics Sections, American Public Health Association, Buffalo, October 14, 1954.
12. ——— and S. J. Cutler, "Morbidity from Cancer in the United States," Public Health Monograph 46, Washington, D.C.: Government Printing Office, 1959.
13. Dunn, John E. and Philip Buell, "Association of Cervical Cancer with Circumcision of Sexual Partner," *Journal of the National Cancer Institute*, 22 (1959), 749–64.
14. Epstein, Frederick H., E. P. Boas, and Rita Simpson, "The Epidemiology of Atherosclerosis among a Random Sample of Clothing Workers of Different Ethnic Origins in New York City, I," *Journal of Chronic Disease*, 5 (1957), 300–28.
15. Graham, Saxon, "Social Factors in the Epidemiology of Cancer at Various Sites," *Annals of the New York Academy of Science*, 84 (December, 1960), 807–15.
16. ———, Morton Levin, and Abraham M. Lilienfeld, "The Socio-Economic Distribution of Cancer at Various Sites in Buffalo, New York, 1948–1952," *Cancer*, 13 (1960), 180*ff*.
17. ———, "Ethnic Background as Related to Cancer at Various Sites, Roswell Park Memorial Institute, 1946–1957." Paper presented at the meeting of the American Sociological Society, St. Louis, Missouri, September 1, 1961. To be published in *Cancer*.
18. Graham, Saxon and Abraham M. Lilienfeld, "Genetic Studies of Gastric Cancer in Humans: An Appraisal," *Cancer*, 11 (September, 1958), 945–58.
19. Graham, Saxon, "Disability in Butler County," *Public Health Reports*, 71 (November, 1956), 115–18.

20. ———, "Ethnic Background and Illness in a Pennsylvania County," *Social Problems*, 4 (July, 1956), 76–82.
21. Haenszel, William, "Cancer Mortality among the Foreign Born in the United States," *Journal of the National Cancer Institute*, 26 (January, 1961), 37–132.
22. Hammond, E. Cuyler and D. Horn, "Smoking and Death Rates—Report on Forty-four Months of Follow-up, 187,783 Men," *Journal of the American Medical Association*, 166 (1958), 1159–1308.
23. Horn, Daniel, Frederick A. Courts, Robert M. Taylor, and Erwin Solomon, "Cigarette Smoking among High School Students," *American Journal of Public Health*, 49 (November, 1959), 1497–1511.
24. Jones, Edward G., Ian MacDonald, and Lester Breslow, "A Study of Epidemiologic Factors in Carcinoma of the Uterine Cervix," *American Journal of Obstetrics and Gynecology*, 76 (July, 1958), 1–10.
25. Kennaway, E. L., "Racial and Social Incidence of Cancer of the Uterus," *British Journal of Cancer*, 2 (September, 1948), 177*ff*.
26. Kinsey, Alfred C., Wardell B. Pomeroy, and Clyde E. Martin, *Sexual Behavior in the Human Male*. Philadelphia: W.B. Saunders Company, 1948.
27. ———, and Paul H. Gebhard, *Sexual Behavior in the Human Female*. Philadelphia: W.B. Saunders Company, 1953.
28. Lange, R. D., W. C. Maloney, and T. Yamawaki, "Leukemia in Atomic Bomb Survivors," *Blood*, 9, 66*ff*, 574*ff*.
29. Levin, Morton L., L. C. Kress, and H. Goldstein, "Syphilis and Cancer: Reported Syphilis Prevalence among 7,760 Cancer Patients," *New York State Journal of Medicine*, 42 (1942), 1737*ff*.
30. Levin, Morton L., Saxon Graham, A. M. Lilienfeld, and Paul Sheehe, "Nursing, Fertility, and Other Factors in the Epidemiology of Cancer of the Breast." Paper presented at the meetings of the American Public Health Association, Miami, October, 1962.
31. Lilienfeld, Abraham, "Diagnostic and Therapeutic X-Radiation in an Urban Population," *Public Health Reports*, 74 (January 4, 1959), 29–36.
32. ——— and Saxon Graham, "Validity of Determining Circumcision Status by Questionnaire as Related to Epidemiological Studies of Cancer of the Cervix," *Journal of the National Cancer Institute*, 21 (1958), 713–20.
33. Lilienfeld, Abraham, "Variation in Mortality from Heart Disease," *Public Health Reports*, 71 (1956), 545–53.
34. MacMahon, Brian and Ernest K. Koller, "Ethnic Differences in the Incidence of Leukemia," *Blood*, 12 (January, 1957), 1–10.
35. MacMahon, Brian, Thomas F. Pugh, and Johannes Ipsen, *Epidemiologic Method*. Boston: Little, Brown, & Company, 1960.
36. Maliphant, R. G., "The Incidence of Cancer of the Uterine-cervix," *British Medical Journal*, 1 (June 4, 1949), 978*ff*.
37. Newsholme, Arthur, *Story of Modern Preventive Medicine*. New York: The Williams & Wilkins Co., 1929.
38. Paloucek, Frank P., and J. B. Graham, "Precipitating Factors in Cancer of the Cervix," *Surgical Forum of the American College of Surgeons*, 10 (1959).

39. Paloucek, Frank P., in a personal communication, 1962.
40. Pollack, Herbert and Dean E. Krueger, eds., *Epidemiology of Cardiovascular Diseases: Methodology*. Supplement to *American Journal of Public Health*, 50 (October, 1960).
41. Quisenberry, W. B., I. L. Tilden, and J. L. Rosengard, "Racial Incidence of Cancer in Hawaii: A Study of 3,257 Cases of Malignant Neoplastic Diseases," *Hawaiian Medical Journal*, 13 (1954), 449*ff*.
42. Registrar General for England and Wales, *Decennial Supplement, England and Wales, 1951, Occupational Mortality, Part I*, London: Her Majesty's Stationery Office, 1954.
43. Sachs, Leo and Mariassa Bat-Miriam, "The Genetics of Jewish Populations: I. Finger Print Patterns of Jewish Populations in Israel," *American Journal of Human Genetics*, 9 (June, 1957), 117–26.
44. Sauer, Herbert I., "Epidemiology of a Cardiovascular Mortality—Geographic and Ethnic," *American Journal of Public Health*, 52 (January, 1962), 94–105.
45. Shryock, Richard H., *The Development of Modern Medicine*. New York: Alfred A. Knopf, Inc., 1947.
46. Simmons, Ozzie G. and Howard E. Freeman, "Familial Expectations and Posthospital Performance of Mental Patients," *Human Relations*, 7 (1959), 233*ff*.
47. Stamler, J., M. Kjelsberg, Y. Hall, and N. Scotch, "Epidemiologic Studies of Cardiovascular—Renal Diseases: III. Analysis of Mortality by Age—Sex—Nationality," *Journal of Chronic Disease*, 12 (1960), 464–75.
48. Stamler, J., M. Kjelsberg, and Y. Hall, "Epidemiologic Study on Cardiovascular and Renal Diseases: I. Analysis of Mortality by Age—Race—Sex—Ocupation," *Journal of Chronic Disease*, 12 (1960), 440–55.
49. Study Group on Smoking and Health, "Smoking and Health," *Science*, 125 (June 7, 1957), 1129–33.
50. Terris, Milton and Margaret C. Oalmann. "Carcinoma of the Cervix," *Journal of the American Medical Association*, 174 (December 3, 1960), 1847–51.
51. Thomas, W. I. and F. Znaniecki, *Polish Peasant in Europe and America*, New York: R. C. Badger, 1918–1920.
52. Toor, Mordecai, A. Katchalsky, J. Agmon, and D. Allalouf, "Atherosclerosis and Related Factors in Immigrants to Israel," *Circulation*, 12 (August, 1960), pp. 265–279.
53. Whitmore, W. F., "Tumors of the Male Generative Tract," *in* J. B. Field (ed.), *Cancer Diagnosis and Treatment*. Boston: Little, Brown & Company, 1959.
54. Winkelstein, Warren, in a personal communication, 1961.
55. Wynder, Ernest L., Jerome Cornfield, P. D. Schroff, and K. R. Doraiswami, "Study of Environmental Factors and Carcinoma of the Cervix," *American Journal of Obstetrics and Gynecology* (October, 1954), 1016–52.
56. von Zeitz, H., "Gestation und Carcinoma Coll I Uteri 1," *Deutsche Medizinische Wochenschrift*, 83 (1955), 64–68.

4

SOCIAL PSYCHOLOGICAL FACTORS IN ILLNESS

Stanley H. King

Evidence of a state of illness in the human organism is weighted heavily with biological factors, such as elevation of temperature, change in pulse beat and respiration, swelling of tissues, alteration in the composition of blood and urine, and proliferation of abnormal cells. Biological and physical factors are also important in the background and onset of illness. Bacteria and viruses, vitamins, minerals, fats and other substances in nutrition, constitutional heritage through the genes, the onslaughts of physical forces, and the ingestion of various chemical substances—these are examples of important biological and physical agents in disease and illness.

Illness, however, is not solely a biological and physical phenomenon but an event that occurs in a social context and reflects the intimate association of the person with other human beings. Both the intrapersonal and interpersonal environments are sources of important events that affect the human organism relative to illness.

The relationships between physical, biological, and psychosocial factors in illness are intricate and subtle. Although astute diagnosticians and therapists always have utilized an intuitive understanding of the interaction of these determinants, a detailed theory has yet to be developed and substantiated. The research done to date, however, does suggest certain patterns of interaction between the three factors. These patterns constitute the subject of this chapter.

Two different perspectives are necessary, one in which etiological or causal factors are the focus of interest, and one in which patient reactions to illness become central. The first deals with the effects of psychological and social variables on physiological processes leading to a state of illness, the second with the effects of biological variables—as evident in illness—on psychodynamic balance and interpersonal relations.

Etiology and the Social Environment

Central to the concept of etiology is the demonstration of causes. Beginning with the experiments of the great bacteriologists of the last century, the idea of specific cause has come to be a valuable tool in diagnosing and treating diseases, especially those of infectious origin. In much of medical education and practice, the concept of specific cause is still a dominant trend. But many of the health problems which face the modern physician do not yield to a simple explanation in terms of specific or single cause. Multiple causation has become a more familiar concept in the theoretical framework of the diagnostician. The idea of cause has thus lost some of its clarity and directness. The impact of a whole series of forces may culminate in illness, but the contribution of each variable to that process, and at times even the mere identification of the variables themselves, can be complicated and bewildering. Medicine faces an increasing array of illness conditions in which unraveling of etiology is complicated, especially in the chronic and psychosomatic diseases.

When the impact of the social environment in the etiology of illness is considered, the assignment of a *direct* cause is often difficult if not impossible. Causal pathways often must be inferred rather than demonstrated, so that psychosocial factors in etiology must at the moment remain a topic characterized more by conjecture than by certainty. With that caution in mind, different ways in which psychosocial variables may be associated with the onset of disease can now be delineated.

Of first importance are stress situations in which the interaction of the individual with his interpersonal environment produces emotional reaction and conflict with an accompanying alteration of physiological balance, often beyond the range of normal fluctuations. The end result of long continued conflict may be irreversible tissue changes or chronic disease. Here we are in the realm of illness which can be identified broadly as *psychosomatic*. A second class of events concerns those situations in which psychological and social variables may aggravate or facilitate the action of biological or physical disease agents. These agents combine with the psychosocial situation in some manner, perhaps through an additive or a disruptive process, to bring on illness. The third category covers the results of style of life—where living arrangements, customs, and other social features may bring the individual into a situation where he is rendered vulnerable to disease.

In the first of these categories the primary interest of the research scientist is in individual psychological factors, but with the aim also of making generalizations that can apply to groups of individuals. More often than not, the research technique is the clinical method. In the second category, interest lies in both individual and group factors, and emphasis must be placed on adequate numbers of research subjects in various social designations. The research approach most typically used is that of the cross-sectional survey. The third category is concerned mainly with group factors but with the aim of seeking implications for the individual. This research approach, like the second, utilizes a large number of subjects but also follows them over time.

Stress and disease

In everyday conversation, as well as in accounts of human behavior in fiction and other kinds of literature, there are frequent observations about the relationship between strong emotions and certain types of physiologic reactivity. The flushed face and clenched fist of anger, a "sputtering" rage, eyes wide with fear, butterflies in the stomach at times of anxious anticipation, loss of energy and desire in sadness—these descriptions, and many more—are part of the common parlance. Emotional involvement, especially when it takes the form of anger or fear, gives rise to bodily reactions that differ to a considerable degree from the normal state.

In the last few decades the relationship between emotions and physiologic changes has become an issue for experimental research. Much of the early work was done by Cannon [8], whose primary interest lay in the visceral aspects of emotional expression and the excitement of the sympathetic division of the autonomic nervous system. His experiments led to a description of the "fight-flight reaction," a physiologic state in which the body was mobilized through the action of the sympathetic nervous system either to run away from danger or to stand and fight. The emotions involved were either fear or rage, and Cannon viewed the action as mediated primarily through the secretion of adrenalin by the adrenal medulla. He concluded that both fear and rage were associated with the action of adrenalin, but recognized that the action of adrenalin could not account for all the phenomena that he observed. Subsequent to the publication of Cannon's main work, there has been a growing volume of research on the relationship between emotional states and specific bodily changes, of which some of the representative studies should be cited.

In one project, fear and anger were found to be associated with different physiologic reactivity, a result at variance with that reported by Cannon but explicable in large part by advances in chemical knowledge after Cannon's time. Funkenstein, King, and Drolette [16] studied healthy college students under specified stress conditions, obtaining data about their emotional reactions by observation and interview, and about their cardiovascular reactions by the use of a ballistocardiograph. Subjects who were angry at the experimenter or the experimental situation produced ballistocardiograph tracings that were similar to those produced by an infusion of noradrenalin. On the other hand, subjects who became angry with themselves, or who said they were anxious, produced ballistocardiograph tracings that were similar to those produced by an infusion of adrenalin. Thus anger directed outward was associated with a noradrenalin-like physiologic response, while inwardly-directed anger or fear was associated with an adrenalin-like response. These findings were similar to conclusions reached by Ax [6] in specific fear-inducing and anger-inducing experiments.

Later investigations have tended to confirm these results. Working with a human centrifuge and using injections of mecholyl and urinary secretion of adrenalin and noradrenalin, Cohen and Silverman [10] found anxiety to be associated with release of adrenalin and outwardly directed aggression to be associated with release of noradrenalin. They suggest that these relationships may be due to the activation of specific hypothalamic areas but point out that emotional reaction and cardiovascular response is more complicated than a simple affect-hypothalamic-hormonal model. However, specific emotional states do seem to be associated with specific vascular responses in some manner.

Other kinds of data come from the now classic studies by Wolf and Wolff [44, 45] of Tom, the man with a gastric fistula. As a child Tom had drunk some scalding hot clam chowder, an act which resulted in the occlusion of his esophagus and the necessity of opening an artificial fistula in his stomach and abdominal wall through which he could be fed. He was observed for extended periods of time in the laboratory, allowing a comparison of changes in gastric activity with variations in emotional state. When Tom was fearful or sad there was a pallor of the gastric mucosa and an inhibition of gastric secretions and muscular contractions. On the other hand, when Tom exhibited a state of emotional conflict involving anxiety, hostility, and resentment, there was engorgement of the gastric mucosa, with accompanying hypermotility, hyperemia, and an accelerated acid secretion. If the emotional conflict was prolonged, the physiological reaction led to hemorrhages, lesions, and eventually to the formation of ulcers.

Studies of other areas of the body, including the nasal mucosa, skin, and colon, have come from the group of researchers in Wolff's laboratory [46]. Strong emotional reactions, often to symbolic threats from the environment, were clearly associated with tissue changes in these areas, even to the point of gross changes and pain, changes like ulceration or pronounced swelling.

Laboratory studies seem to have established a relationship between emotion and physiologic reactivity but as investigations continue it is evident that the relationship is complex and the step to irreversible tissue changes and disease in patients cannot be demonstrated easily. Reiser [38] notes that laboratory studies have the problem of explaining why some subjects show little or no demonstrable change in response to experimental procedures that evoke vigorous changes in other subjects, or why some subjects will react vigorously at one time and minimally at other times to the same stimulus. Also, how can the researcher explain the exaggerated or prolonged physiologic response that occurs unexpectedly? The activation of the neuroendocrine apparatus in the face of psychological conflict, and the direction and intensity that neuroendocrine response will take, continues to pose questions for the investigator.

When we consider the kind of tissue change that indicates disease, clinical evidence points to the fact that emotional conflict appears to play an important etiologic role, but the mechanisms involved are still the object of much theoretical controversy. By reviewing the major positions, we can come to the important issues which face those who are interested in the problems of psychosomatic disease [17 ,25, 31].

Of great initial impact on the field of psychosomatic medicine was the *specificity theory*, especially as advanced by Alexander [3]. A specific, typical unconscious conflict results in a specific disease; in the case of peptic ulcer, for example, the conflict being over dependency strivings. With the unconscious conflict comes anxiety, a danger signal to the ego, which leads to the ultilization of certain unconscious defense mechanisms, including regression. These emotional reactions are associated with specific sympathetic or parasympathetic innervation which affects specific organs. Chronic tension from repressed conflicts can lead to chronic overreaction in the organ;—as, for example, a constant oversecretion of hydrochloric acid in the stomach, which in turn may produce pathological tissue changes in susceptible individuals. Alexander saw the ulcer patient as a person with a passive-dependent character structure who was blocked in some way from expressing his dependency needs and regressed unconsciously to an infantile oral state with increased gastric secretion.

Further contribution to the specificity theory in relation to peptic ulcer has come from the work of Mirsky [33, 43]. He maintains that gastric activity is paralleled by the level of serum pepsinogen, which in turn is related to genetic factors. Ulcer occurs only in those individuals who are born as high secretors of pepsinogen. However, the early relationship with parents is also important in terms of providing or not providing the basis for a conflict about dependency. Only those individuals among the high secretors who develop such conflicts are susceptible to ulcer. Finally, there must be a stressful situation in later life which activates the dependency conflict if the susceptible individual is to develop a case of peptic ulcer. Thus the specificity theory has been extended to take into account not only a specific kind of conflict but also genetic biological factors and life stress situations.

The specificity theory has been challenged on several counts, especially with regard to the difficulty of demonstrating an identical conflict in all cases of the same disease. Also, there is a question as to whether or not the same kind of conflict situation may be associated with several different diseases. Prediction of disease from conflict has not been too successful, although Mirsky's work points to the possibility that such prediction might be made if variables other than the specific conflict are taken into account.

Another kind of theoretical approach might be characterized as the *regression theory*. Michaels [32] has taken the position that the somatic expression of a psychological conflict results in physiological reaction similar to that which would be found on the infantile level, especially in terms of a relatively greater reactivity to stimuli and a more marked disturbance of homeostasis. Margolin [30] adds that the infantile physiological responses were appropriate at one time in the person's life but not so at the adult level, so that psychosomatic disease is the expression of inappropriate response. Szasz [41] speaks of "regressive innervation," involving the parasympathetic nervous system as important in psychosomatic disorder. The parasympathetic system develops earlier than the sympathetic; hence extensive innervation of the parasympathetic system represents a regressive phenomenon. He argues that the majority of diseases usually classified as psychosomatic are the result of localized, chronic parasympathetic innervation.

The regression theory thus focuses on the defense mechanism which is brought into play by psychological conflict, emphasizing that regression has crucial physiological as well as psychological consequences. Again, however, serious questions have been raised about the validity of this theoretical approach. That excessive fluctuations in physiological response are tolerated better in infancy is open to doubt, as in the case of hypertension. At the same time certain reactions may have little or no counterpart in infancy, as in ulcerative colitis. Finally Mirsky's data suggest that certain people may have genetic sensitivities which do not diminish as they grow older, precluding a regressive phenomenon of a physiological nature in their cases.

A third theoretical approach, espoused by Wolff [46, 47] and his co-workers, involves a nonspecificity theory of *protective adaptive response.* Disease is the end result of protective reactions by the organism in the face of stress resulting from symbolic threats to the total organism. Physiological reactions in an organ or tissue that originally were protective in nature may become conditioned responses to noxious psychological stimuli. Furthermore, the physiological response may in and of itself take on symbolic meanings, such as shutting out or ejecting painful situations. An individual responds to different stresses in a way that is consistent for him and is based on his genetic equipment and the results of his prior conditionings. Wolff emphasizes the importance of the way that the individual perceives situations in which he participates rather than the way that an objective observer might perceive them.

Data from a number of different ethnic groups are cited by Hinkle [19, 20] to show that over time a small proportion of subjects have the majority of illness conditions, even though they may not have had a greater number of objectively determined stress experiences. They have, however, perceived their lives as more demanding, depriving, threatening, and conflict-producing than have their contemporaries. The reasons for these variations in perception, however, still are not clear.

The various theoretical approaches leave unresolved a number of issues and problems. The issue is specific emotional conflict leading to specific disease *v.* idiosyncratic response to stress according to previous conditionings. The latter view holds that overreactivity of tissues rests more on the individual's continuing experience, while the former emphasizes relationships between emotional conflicts and biological patterns which are more or less true for all individuals. Selectivity of causal pathways to disease is therefore more open in the nonspecificity theories. Hinkle's position is that the perception of the environment as "threatening" leads to a greater amount of disease of *all kinds.* The specificity *v.* nonspecificity issue thus has implications for prediction; that is, who will become ill and with what disease. At the present time the nonspecificity approach seems to be more relevant to the question of who will become ill, while the specificity scheme has more significance for the type of illness that will ensue.

The specificity and nonspecificity theories differ in emphasis on conscious and unconscious processes. The relevance of either theory to disease may, therefore, rest in part on the mediation of conscious and unconscious emotional processes in the central nervous system. How much this may be a matter of early conditioning experiences, how much the use of relatively specific or diffuse neural pathways, how much a matter of developmental or genetical determination, are all critical questions that await further research. The "level" of consciousness, however, is an important variable for both empirical research and the construction of theory.

There are a number of other questions to be answered, especially in reference to the specificity theory. For example, among all individuals who have a certain repressed emotional conflict, what other factors operate to produce the disease? If physiological predisposition is important, as Mirsky suggests, might the same conflict lead to a different disease in individuals with a different physiological predisposition? Also, what are the effects of changes in society on the development of repressed emotional conflicts? Are these effects associated with changes in the incidence of disease, as in the shift of peptic ulcer rates for men and women? In the last century the rates for women in the United States and Great Britain were higher than for men. Now the reverse is true.

A second important issue pertains to the relationship between emotional factors and other variables, especially those of a physical or biological nature. Of special interest are the cardiovascular diseases, and coronary artery disease in particular. How is heart disease related to genetic factors, to diet, to exercise, and to emotional stress? The weight of the argument thus far has been on diet as the chief agent in producing high levels of cholesterol, and consequently on diet control as one way to reduce the danger of certain kinds of heart attacks. At the same time some investigators point to the fact that cholesterol levels change with variations in emotional tension. In their study of tax accountants, Friedman, Rosenman, and Carroll [14, 15] demonstrated that severe occupational stress was associated with increases in both serum cholesterol and blood-clotting time, and that these changes could not be ascribed to variation in weight, exercise, or diet. They argue that the data on diet, cholesterol, and coronary artery disease need to be examined in the light of institutionalized occupational or other emotional stress, and that future epidemiological investigations on coronary artery disease should seek control data on emotional stress.

In another study, Russek [39] presents data to show that young coronary patients as compared with controls more often showed evidence of overwork, a strong need for recognition, a sense of obligation to others, compulsiveness, unstinting effort, and an inability to recognize their own stress end-point. He recognizes that both diet and heredity are crucial variables in coronary disease in young adults but feels that emotional stress is also of great significance.

Unfortunately, the role of emotional factors in the etiology of disease has often been regarded as an "all or none" proposition. The research scientist either tends to ignore or discount the relevance of emotional stress or else he ascribes to it a power that overrules relevant biological and physical data. Some interpretations of disease as symbolic manifestations of emotional conflict, for example, strain the credulity of the outside observer. Research in psychosomatic illness has been moving steadily to the point of positing an admixture of variables, and the issue becomes one of a technique for handling the interaction of these variables—as in the interaction of diet, stress, exercise, and heredity in coronary artery disease. Most or all of the psychosomatic diseases probably can only be understood in terms of a compounded etiology, and relationships among the factors leading to onset of disease will be an issue for some time to come.

Two final points should be made about the relationship between emotional factors and other variables. First, data are needed which can best be supplied by the sociologist, especially in epidemiological studies. Although there is a uniqueness to each individual's perception of his environment, there are perceptions of interpersonal events which all members of the group share. Thus the sociologist can point up stress points structured by the social order or role conflict situations which can become strategic places for research. A case in point would be the analysis of an organization and the impingement of the organization on individuals within it, as Argyris [4, 5] has done. Also, the study of cholesterol by Friedman, *et al.*, shows how important social events can affect individuals who fill crucial social roles in relation to those events. In sum, sociological data can add basic data to the issue of defining the relevant variables in psychosomatic illness.

The second point concerns a serious difficulty in research design. Most of the data which have been gathered about psychosomatic illness have come "after the fact," and background variables—especially in terms of early experiences—must be filtered through the screen of subsequent experience. In some disease situations the charge can be made that the psychological data can be explained in large measure as part of the reaction to the disease itself. The problem is complicated by the relatively low incidence or slow onset of certain diseases. Rheumatoid arthritis is perhaps a good example of these difficulties. Large-scale longitudinal studies of random groups from the population are prohibitively expensive, yet only through such studies can definitive data be gathered that will have prospective value.

Psychosocial factors as facilitators of illness

Basic to an understanding of the secondary effects of psychological or social data in precipitating illness is the distinction between *necessary* and *sufficient* cause. Some factor, which can be labeled the "necessary cause," must be present for disease or illness to occur, but its presence alone is not sufficient to produce disease. Other factors, one or more, must coincide with the necessary cause and provide the sufficient conditions for the disease. These other factors are called "sufficient causes." In certain situations the necessary cause may be a bacterium or virus without which the disease could not develop. However, body resistance may be such that until some alteration occurs in homeostasis the bacterium or virus will not be able to multiply and produce the clinical manifestations of illness. Sufficient causes, often psychological or social as well as physical, can provide the impetus for that alteration in homeostasis. Dubos [12] cites herpes simplex, more commonly known as fever blisters or cold sores, as an example. The herpetic blisters are due to the effects of a virus, usually acquired early in life and thereafter constantly present in the body of the infected individual. Disease is produced, however, only when certain conditions upset the chemical balance of the body, as in the case of overexposure to ultraviolet light in the form of sunshine, or as in menstruation, emotional stress, or infection with the common cold. The herpes virus in this situation would be the necessary cause (since the blisters would not occur without its presence), while the other factors, physical, biological, or emotional, provide the sufficient conditions under which the disease will occur.

There is some evidence to suggest that tuberculosis can occur in response to social environmental conditions and psychological stress factors. Based on a study of patients in Seattle, Holmes and his associates [21] found a number of factors in the backgrounds or life situations of the patients which appeared to be relevant to the onset of the disease. For example, data that related to the life experiences of each patient were plotted for a twelve-year period preceding hospitalization. In the majority of patients there was a gradual increase of experiences which were perceived by the individual as significant and stressful, and these culminated in a crisis situation during the two-year period prior to hospitalization. From psychiatric studies of patients in the same sanitarium, the authors noted that in general the patients were poorly equipped to deal effectively with the realities of social relationships, especially when these were full of tension.

In a related study Hawkins [18] considered all the newly detected cases of tuberculosis in Seattle within a given year in relation to census tract data. The city was divided into four rather distinct socioeconomic residential areas from the city center with its "skid road," through working class, middle class, out to the area of the well-to-do. Tuberculosis rates per 100,000 population were then computed for each of the four areas, keeping separate the variables of age, sex, and race. As ecologists would predict, the highest rates occurred in the area at the center of the city. However, when rates in the four areas were considered by race, the white rate was highest in the center city area, the non-white rate was highest in the outer well-to-do area. In other words, rates for whites and non-whites were inversely proportional to the degree to which their ethnic members were dominant in the area.

These data are mainly suggestive, but they do indicate the possibility that psychological and social factors may play some part in the onset of tuberculosis. Dubos has noted that the tubercle bacillus can be found in a great many people who do not show clinical manifestations of the disease, hence the bacillus itself, though necessary, may not be sufficient to cause the disease. The stresses arising from interpersonal relationships and social demand may, in some people who carry the tubercle bacillus, be sufficient for the disease to occur.

Again the matter of pathway or mechanism becomes important. Holmes and his co-workers suggest that endogenous adrenocortical hormones influence resistance to tuberculosis and that the secretion of these hormones can be altered by chronic psychological stress in response to threats from the environment. Demonstration of this mechanism, however, still awaits solid verification.

These two examples of herpes simplex and tuberculosis are only illustrative of the proposition that psychosocial variables can act as facilitators in illness. Some of the degenerative diseases of the older years also may be facilitated by the emotional upheavals of retirement or rapidly changing social conditions. At the moment clinical hunches in these areas are more numerous than controlled studies. However, the interaction between psychosocial variables as sufficient causes and biological or physical variables as necessary causes is receiving a steadily increasing amount of research attention.

Social milieu factors in illness

The culture in which an individual lives includes customs and traditions, values, patterns of interaction between classes of people, methods of trade and subsistence, and techniques for bringing both positive and negative sanctions on the members of the culture. If we think of culture as both the direct and indirect social milieu surrounding the individual, then we can posit a number of cultural factors in illness. For example, in some of the underdeveloped countries with warm climates, an agricultural, low-subsistence economy keeps many individuals in close contact with farm animals, especially cows, and perpetuates the ecological relationships between flies, animals, humus material, and people. Under these conditions fly-borne diseases can flourish. The relationship becomes difficult to change if tradition and a sense of psychological security are bound up with a close physical association to animals. The relationship of psychosocial variables to illness in this instance is one where the social milieu places the individual in a position where he is vulnerable to disease or injury from any number of other factors.

Of special interest is the effect of the social milieu on nutritional factors, seen in terms of the limitation on available foods by the nature of the climate or soil, by the economy of the society, or by the customs of the social group. Jelliffe [22] cites the effects of limitation on food by both economy and customs in rural West Bengal in producing diseases of protein malnutrition, especially kwashiorkor. In a culture where the availability of protein foods was restricted, some of those which theoretically could be utilized were proscribed by custom, either completely or at important stages in the early development of the child. Under these circumstances children were especially vulnerable to nutritional deficiency diseases.

Excessive amounts of certain kinds of foods in the diet may also be implicated in illness. If high fat intake is important in the onset of atherosclerosis, then in cultures that produce large amounts of certain kinds of foods, especially animal fats, and in which the nutritional value of these foods is emphasized, a set of conditions results that may render people in the culture more vulnerable to heart disease. Although heart disease was discussed earlier in this chapter, the matter of culture and diet as influential variables belongs in this section. Keys [26] and his co-workers have placed great emphasis on the diet patterns of various cultural groups throughout the world and related these patterns to high fat intake and coronary artery disease.

Cultural taboos can also be important indirect factors in illness. An individual may be blocked by these taboos from getting the proper information about avoiding illness. Control of syphilis and gonorrhea, for example, depends in part on adequate knowledge by the public about the transmission of the disease, the use of contraceptives to prevent transmission, prompt treatment of infected persons to prevent infection of others, as well as the adequate case finding of infected individuals. Thus the cultural taboos against public discussion of sexual matters, including venereal disease, can prevent adequate public health campaigns. As Graham points out (see Chap. 3), an intensive education campaign during World War II broke through the cultural taboos and control of venereal disease was facilitated.

Social change and the disruption of established cultural patterns may bring about many conditions that are conducive to illness. Change in economic position often means change in nutritional patterns but not necessarily for the better. New occupational hazards may be introduced. Shifts in behavioral patterns among family members may take away the sources of advice for prevention or treatment of illness or may throw intolerable strain on the physical and emotional capacities of parents and children. With drastic social changes occurring in many parts of the world today, their effect on health and illness becomes a significant factor. (This point is considered again in Chap. 15.)

Social milieu factors, including the pressures of social change, do not fit easily into the conception of cause, especially if one is inclined to think of cause in terms of direct relationships. Medical thinking is still influenced by the idea of single cause which represents a direct relationship. Some physicians, therefore, may find it meaningless or unimportant to work out the relationships among life style variables and illness conditions. In terms of immediate preventive or curative procedures, they are justified. But in terms of long-term preventive measures, man's relation to his cultural surroundings and their effect on his bodily functioning is an area worth continued study.

Illness as a Psychosocial Phenomenon

Illness is a universal phenomenon. Occurring in all societies, it forces temporary disruption of regular patterns of social relationships. Fulfillment of normal role responsibilities by the sick person is often impossible and often the role responsibilities of the patient's family cannot be carried out. Job, home, and community, the major sectors of social roles, are all affected to varying degrees by illness. At the same time psychological balance is threatened by illness. Anxiety can be aroused, often deep and abiding anxiety, depression may occur, and patterns of emotional response may be expressed that are not characteristic of mature adult behavior. Illness provides an opportunity for many "childish" responses. At the same time, because it is an experience of strong emotional significance, illness can be the framework for the expression of great courage, of love, and of faith. As a social and psychological event illness is rarely uneventful, usually stressful, and occasionally most disruptive.

The sick role

Considering the ubiquitous nature of illness in human societies, it is not surprising that a special social role should develop for the sick person, including rather clearly defined expectations for behavior on the part of the patient and reciprocal responsibilities between the one who is sick and those who interact with him. Behavior of the sick person, therefore, is constrained or limited by the role expectations of the society in which he lives.

Parsons [34, 35] has defined the demands and expectations of the sick role in Western societies, particularly the United States as follows: There is a disturbance of the capacity of the individual to perform ordinary tasks or roles in his social group, an incapacity which is "not his fault," not an act of conscious decision. Furthermore, the incapacity must be reversed by some kind of therapeutic process, natural or man made. The ill person is exempted from his normal role and task obligations, varying in accordance with the nature and degree of his illness. Even a common cold carries with it some legitimate exemptions from social obligations. Although being ill and being exempted from role responsibilities is a "legitimate" state in a social sense, this legitimacy is only partial and conditional. Illness is basically undesirable, socially speaking, and the person who is in the sick role has an obligation to try to get well and to cooperate with other people in that effort. Both the ill person and those responsible for his welfare have an obligation to seek technically competent help for the therapeutic process. In our society the principal source of such help lies in organized medicine.

The sick role, therefore, has two rights and two duties. The rights are exemptions from normal social responsibilities and the recognition that the ill person is not to blame for his state. The obligations are a desire to get well and to seek technically competent help to achieve that end. As we shall see in a moment, these rights and obligations can conflict with deep-seated personality mechanisms and cause strain in certain kinds of social groups, especially the family and the hospital.

The undesirable aspect of illness, in the social sense, is that illness is a form of deviance. Parsons differentiates between deviance that has a normative focus and that which has a situational focus, the former including immorality and crime. Within a situational focus, deviance involves an inability to meet commitments or to utilize capacities for task and role performance. One might say that illness is, therefore, a kind of alienation in American society, alienation from a set of expectations that puts particular stress upon independent achievement. The passivity and dependence involved in illness are also characteristics of behavior which are counter to the activism of American society. Not only is the individual unable to fulfill everyday tasks and roles, but he also cannot meet some of the value orientations of the society.

As a socially disruptive or deviant factor in social functioning, illness cannot be allowed to spread, bacteriologically or motivationally. Thus the sick role is legitimate only in a conditional sense, meaning that the deviancy of the role must be recognized by the patient and his family, and that steps be taken to get well, to move back into the healthy role. When the sick person is a patient in a hospital or in bed at home, he is permitted to indulge his dependency needs under strictly regulated conditions, with the proviso that sickness should only be a temporary state and that he should do everything he can to get well.

Conflict between social expectations and personality dynamics centers on the "secondary gain" which can accrue from the rights of the sick role. The enforced state of dependency in illness can gratify strong needs to be taken care of, as the individual was cared for as a child. Freedom from ordinary social responsibility can be a great joy to some people, a state not to be surrendered easily. Hospital staff members are familiar with the patient who has a resurgence of symptoms just prior to a planned discharge date, symptoms sometimes of sufficient severity as to require continued hospitalization. Staff are also familiar with the malingerer who may feign illness or magnify his symptoms beyond demonstrable severity in order to be placed in the sick role, or who may wish to stay in the hospital beyond the time when medical decision seeks his discharge. Public institutions, with their provision of free medical care, provide a situation where dependency needs can be gratified beyond legitimate expectations, but private institutions are not without the conflict. It is interesting to note that in these situations the "moral indignation" aroused in staff members is so strong that they may have real difficulty in trying to understand the psychodynamic basis for dependency needs on the part of a particular patient, or even in wanting to know about the psychodynamics.

The dependency of the sick role can also provide a basis for the gratification of aggressive needs in terms of control over other people. The sick person may use his position to force other people to accede to his wishes, not only in terms of immediate gratification like special foods, but also in long-term plans like job changes or living arrangements. In a functional sense, the person occupying the sick role abuses his rights to be taken care of by extending them into areas which are not immediate to the illness, and in a sense abrogates his responsibilities to try to get well. Family members and others close to the sick person are the ones most likely to feel the effect of aggressive control rather than medical personnel. Principally, this is due to the fact that the relationship between the sick person and family members is largely on an emotional basis, while that between the sick person and medical personnel is much more on an objective, emotionally neutral basis. Emotional relationships can often be manipulated more easily than those which are more neutral in nature, at least in the sense that they are more subtle and often involve unconscious processes. Medical personnel are not entirely exempt from aggressive control by the patient, however, especially if he is wealthy or has a position that is socially important to the hospital, especially if he is a "VIP." Demands for special attention involving time and resources can be made and must be met under these circumstances, but not without considerable strain in the social system of the hospital.

Conflict of a rather different kind arises when the sick person has strong needs for autonomy and independence and gets anxious and upset when he is in a dependent position. In fulfilling the expectations of the sick role, the individual must place himself in the hands of those who have the technical competence to help him get well. Thus the right of dependency and exemption from normal responsibilities combines with the obligation to defer decisions about treatment to professional persons. The combination can pose a serious threat to the psychic balance of a person who is afraid of dependency. The conflict thus engendered can show itself in a variety of ways, not the least of which is sarcasm, complaining, and a generally disagreeable disposition. In this way the patient fights the system which threatens him. From a more serious point of view, the conflict can result in disregard for medical advice or control: not taking medicines which are prescribed, getting out of bed too soon, or leaving the hospital against medical advice. Many coronary patients continue to lead a strenuous life against the advice of their physicians—often with fatal consequences. In this case perhaps the threat of dependency is more salient than the threat of death.

Illness and the concept of self

Illness poses a series of threats to the organism, not the least of which may be death. Although the illness may be one that will improve without help or a condition that can be treated successfully by modern medicine, thoughts of death may be introduced, even though fleetingly. The more serious or ambiguous the illness, the more likely that death will be on the patient's mind at some point. Reduced function can also be viewed as a threat, temporary in many cases but more lasting in others, as in the coronary patient for example. Reduced function represents a sense of loss, of incompleteness, and if long continued will necessitate a shift in the conception an individual has of himself and his body. Of a different nature is the threat induced by the change in customary routines and relationships seen in a decrease of function within the family or job. Social homeostasis is disturbed in illness as well as biological homeostasis.

Under the condition of threat, anxiety is aroused and ego mechanisms are brought into play in order to control and minimize the anxiety. Chief among these seems to be emotional regression, a slipping back to the kinds of reactions that are more indicative of childhood than of mature adulthood [11, 29]. Under this regression the ill person may manifest a number of different kinds of behavior. One among them is egocentricity, a concern about himself and his problem that pushes other interests to the periphery of attention. He wants to talk about *his* illness and *his* pain, not illness or pain in the abstract. A visitor's recital of former operations holds little interest for him; in fact he may impatiently shift the conversation back to his own case. His illness is the center of his world.

There may be an exaggerated concern with trifling matters that relate to the self, such as expecting others to attend to his wants, to provide services, often to do errands that would ordinarily be of little concern to the patient. In extreme, one finds the sickroom despot: dominant, intolerant, infuriating to doctor, nurse, and family. In caricature, there is the husband who is home in bed with a cold, running his wife in circles with demands for service and whims of every sort. In most cases we have a person who is more subjective than usual as he perceives the situation around him.

Egocentricity and constriction of interests may be due in part to the physiological effects of illness, to a narrowing of the perceptual range which is associated with fever, altered blood composition, or other factors. In part, the exemption from normal role responsibilities contributes to the constriction: the amount of sensory input—especially of symbolic material—is reduced and therefore a variety of interests is no longer stimulated. In part, the constriction may result from the organism's mechanisms for fighting disease and injury; by excluding thoughts of other matters, energy can be concentrated on the process of getting well. Whatever the cause, among those who are ill an avid baseball fan may be quite unconcerned that his team is languishing in the cellar, a manufacturer undismayed by a threatened strike in his plant, a professor oblivious to the fact that there is no one to take his classes. Clearly this is a time when it is unwise to ask the sick person to make decisions or expect help from him on matters outside the sick room.

As part of the regression, there may be an exaggerated emotional reactivity. Many patients cry more easily than usual, or lose their tempers, but of especial significance is the increased strength of needs for help, for attention, and for affection [23]. The prescription of TLC—tender, loving care—so often heard in nursing circles, is a prime need of many patients. Its absence can be a source of bitter complaints directed at members of the patient's family or hospital personnel [1, 2, 7, 13, 27]. On the other hand, most patients are grateful for expressions of attention from friends and family, for personal considerations by nurses or doctors, for actions small or large that symbolically indicate affection. Many of these patients would not feel so strong a need for affection-indicating actions were they well and leading a normal life.

Still another kind of behavior can be found that is related to the regression process, behavior which involves some subtle shifts in the perception of people in the environment. In particular, physicians and nurses are subject to this shift, but if the ill person is hospitalized, other kinds of people may also be involved. Putting the shift in terms of role, medical care personnel may be invested on an unconscious level with role characteristics of family members, particularly of mother and father [11]. Because the physician holds important and perhaps ultimate responsibility for the patient, because he seems all-wise and all-powerful, his relationship to the patient may be perceived by the latter much like that of father to child. Patterns of behavior which characterized the father-child relationship may, therefore, be projected into dealings with the doctor, whether these be patterns of submission, rebellion, or a dogged stubbornness. The nurse may be invested with characteristics of the mother role, what one anthropologist,

LaBarre, has called the "id mother" [28]. Thus the patient may perceive the nurse as comforting, protecting, supporting, as meeting his needs for help, and as giving him security in his state of dependence. As with perceptions of the doctor, both conscious and unconscious manifestations of the perception may be present. The intensity and instability of emotional reaction can lead the patient to expressions of sincere appreciation at one point, while at other times rage and frustration may be forthcoming. Accepting the emotional reactivity of the patient for what it is and not allowing herself to become disturbed can be a powerful force on the part of the nurse in speeding physical and psychological recovery by the patient.

Stages of illness

The emotional reactions just described occur most frequently in the stage of ongoing illness. There are two other stages of illness which also must be considered inasmuch as they have consequences both for interpersonal interaction and self-concept. A pre-illness or prodromal stage often precedes that of actual illness, especially in cases where the onset is not sudden. Resistance to thoughts of the sick role or a "flight into health" may be characteristic of this first stage. Symptoms may be ignored or even denied. Pace of activity may be stepped up, as if to prove a healthy state, or measures may be taken to ward off the oncoming illness. Patent medicines, aspirin, alcohol, orange juice are only some of the things that may be consumed as preventive measures. Some people say to themselves that if they keep busy the illness won't be able to catch up with them, or if they put it out of their minds it will go away. The psychological mechanisms at this stage seem to be of two sorts, a preventive ritual that is based in part on realistic appraisal of the situation and/or a denial that is based more on a kind of magical thinking that says in effect, out of mind, out of reality.

In many cases either mechanism may be short-lived or of no major consequence. In some cases, however, resistance to the thoughts of illness may take extreme forms, extreme in the sense that medical attention is not sought when symptoms clearly warrant it. Early detection of disease, as in cancer, may be the most important step in preventing death, hence delay in seeing the doctor may be a serious matter. Studies of cancer patients, as well as of surgical patients in general, show that fear and denial occur frequently among the many reasons elicited for delay [9, 37, 40, 42]. If more data from these patients were available about their fantasies and unconscious processes, the importance of denial and flight from illness would probably be even greater. Denial may be the only defense which some personalities can effectively utilize, even to the point of fatal consequences.

During the stage of convalescence, the sick role must be put aside and the role of the well or healthy individual adopted once again. The process is often a gradual one, because the physical effects of most illnesses do not cease suddenly. In terms of role expectations, a person returning to home or job may be given a period of grace when full demands for role performance are not made, or excuses are freely accepted for inadequate performance. The period prior to the resumption of normal life, however, is that of our present concern. Again one can find parallels in stages of psychological development, particularly that of adolescence. One of the major tasks of the adolescent in Western society lies in shifting from dependence to autonomy, a task which some accomplish in fits and starts and with many longing glances backward, and others by a headlong rush into adulthood. In the same way the patient may be reluctant to part with the attention and care he has received while sick, may venture only hesitantly or slowly into full resumption of activity. Medical personnel may expect the patient to do more for himself, to be less egocentric, to increase his horizon of interests once again. They may withdraw some of their attention and support, partly because other patients may need it more, partly because the patient must again pick up his own life without emotional entanglements from the illness situation. For some patients this has an exhilaration like that which accompanies newly-won independence by adolescents. For others the reaction may be ambivalent. And for a few patients convalescence may pose a threat that drives them into illness again.

The sick person and his family

With the nuclear family as the crucial social unit in our present society, there are potential stresses inherent in the relationship between the ill person and his family, stresses which are not likely to be as severe in an extended family. Parsons and Fox [36] argue that the great increase of hospital facilities in our society is attributable not only to technological advances but also to the vulnerabilities of the nuclear family in sickness. They cite the emotional intensity of relationships in the small family as one which allows little room for absorbing shock. They also suggest that most American families find it difficult to maintain an optimum balance between the supportive and dependent aspects of sickness on the one hand and the disciplinary aspects of treatment on the other. In serious illness these stresses can be minimized if the ill person is treated outside the family, particularly in the hospital. The reluctance of physicians to treat serious illness other than in the hospital, even when technical aspects of care could be carried out at home, may rest in part on an intuition that the ensuing strain would be a further factor to contend with in treatment. Parsons and Fox's interpretation is made from strictly a functional point of view, in the sociological sense. Although difficult to test, it does have marked heuristic value.

A useful framework for analyzing the problem of the relationship between the ill person and his family is that of role allocation and meaning within the family. Particularly relevant is the way in which allocation and meaning may vary in families from different social class and ethnic groups. Work, authority or decision making, and emotional support or affection are the areas where allocation and meaning of roles will have the greatest impact on illness. Some examples in each area will make the point clear.

Work or "the job" affects family life differently throughout the class structure [24]. In the upper middle class a career is likely to be a dominant feature, especially in the business world, and family life must be built around the exigencies of the career. Interference with work for an extended period of time or at certain crucial choice points in organizational functioning may disrupt the career. Frequent illnesses, a long-term illness, or one at a specific point in time may, therefore, jeopardize chances of advancement. Sickness by either the husband or wife may affect this process, by taking the husband out of the career line temporarily, or by reducing the support he can get for career activities from his wife. In the working class a job does not play such a central place in the family, since it is viewed largely as a mechanism by which the material things of life can be obtained rather than as an end in itself. Illness is not likely to affect seniority and with insurance plans the financial burden of an illness may not be overwhelming. This is not to say that illness in a working class family is not disruptive, but its effect in terms of work roles has subtle differences from families in other social classes.

Families also vary in the division of authority and responsibility for decisions, a factor often affected by ethnic background and traditional family structure. Where the decision-making process is shared between husband and wife, an illness on the part of one or the other will not seriously affect that process. Urban American families of second or third generation frequently represent this kind of division of responsibility. If, however, decisions are usually made by the husband and his authority is not questioned, difficulties can arise when he becomes ill. The wife may not have the training to make decisions or may feel an emotional reluctance to do so. When other male members of the extended family are not present to take over the authority, the wife may be very anxious and find it difficult not to communicate the anxiety to her ill partner. In some rural families, in Spanish-American families, or in first generation families with a patriarchical organization, illness of the husband can pose a serious threat to the effective functioning of the family unit.

Finally, the question of emotional support can be viewed in terms of allocation among family members. Frequently the wife-mother is called upon to assume the greatest share of support-giving activities, especially if the husband's energies are directed toward a career. When she becomes ill the affection fabric of the family may be strained. Perhaps this is not a serious problem in most families, because her illness may be short or adjustments of function can be made by other family members, but it does remain as a potential threat.

Reaction to illness is in part an individual psychological phenomenon based on adjustment to the anxiety induced by fear of death, of mutilation or of reduced function. In the last analysis each person must face these anxieties on his own, for although others can help him, the core of his psychological world is himself. Reaction to illness at the same time is a social phenomenon, affecting the pattern of interrelationships between the ill person and others close to him, particularly his family. The demands and expectations that go with social roles are disrupted by illness, not only for the ill person, but also for those with whom he has reciprocal relationships. Individual and social reactions to illness do not exist apart from each other, even though they have been separated here for analytical purposes, and a full understanding of the implications of illness must consider both the idiosyncrasies of the individual and the social milieu in which he lives.

References

1. Abdellah, F. G. and E. Levine, "Developing a Measure of Patient and Personnel Satisfaction with Nursing Care," *Nursing Research*, 5 (February, 1957).
2. ———, "Polling Patients and Personnel," *Hospitals* (November 1, 16; December 1, 16; 1957).
3. Alexander, Franz, *Psychosomatic Medicine*. New York: W. W. Norton & Company, Inc., 1950.
4. Argyris, Chris, *Diagnosing Human Relations in Organizations: A Case Study of a Hospital*. New Haven: Labor and Management Center, Yale University, 1956.
5. ———, *Personality and Organization: The Conflict between System and the Individual*. New York: Harper & Son, Publishers, 1957.
6. Ax, A. F., "The Physiological Differentiation between Fear and Anger in Humans," *Psychosomatic Medicine*, 15 (1953), 433–42.
7. Berg, R. H., "A Report on Hospitals," *Look*, 23 (February 3, 1959), 15–19.
8. Cannon, Walter B., *The Wisdom of the Body*. New York: W. W. Norton & Company, Inc., 1932.
9. Cobb, B., *et al.*, "Patient-Responsible Delay of Treatment in Cancer: Social Psychological Study," *Cancer*, 7 (September, 1954), 920–26.
10. Cohen, S. I. and A. J. Silverman, "Psychophysiological Investigations of Vascular Response Variability," *Journal of Psychosomatic Research*, 3 (1959), 185–210.
11. Dichter, E., "The Hospital-Patient Relationship," *Modern Hospital*, 53, 54 (September, October, November, December, 1954; January, February, 1955).

12. Dubos, Rene, "The Gold Headed Cane in the Laboratory," *in* National Institutes of Health, *Annual Lectures,* Washington, D.C.: U.S. Department of Health, Education, and Welfare, 1953, pp. 89–102.
13. Freidson, Eliot and Jacob J. Feldman, *The Public Looks at Hospitals.* New York: Health Information Foundation, Research Series 4, 1958.
14. Friedman, M., R. H. Rosenman, and V. Carroll, "Changes in the Serum Cholesterol and Blood Clotting Time in Men Subjected to Cyclic Variation of Occupational Stress," *Circulation,* 17 (May, 1958), 852–61.
15. Friedman, M. and R. H. Rosenman, "Association of Specific Overt Behavior Pattern with Blood and Cardiovascular Findings," *Journal of the American Medical Association,* 169 (March 21, 1959), 1286–96.
16. Funkenstein, Daniel H., Stanley H. King, and Margaret Drolette, *Mastery of Stress.* Cambridge: Harvard University Press, 1957.
17. Gitelson, M., "A Critique of Current Concepts in Psychosomatic Medicine," *Bulletin of the Menninger Clinic,* 23 (1959), pp. 165–78.
18. Hawkins, N. G. and T. H. Holmes, "Environmental Considerations in Tuberculosis: Ecologic Factors in Tuberculosis Morbidity," *Transactions of the Fiftieth Anniversary Meeting of the National Tuberculosis Association,* 1954, pp. 233–38.
19. Hinkle, L. E. *et al.,* "An Investigation of the Relation between Life Experience, Personality Characteristics, and General Susceptibility to Illness," *Psychosomatic Medicine,* 20 (July-August, 1958), 278–95.
20. Hinkle, L. E., "Ecological Observations on the Relation of Physical Illness, Mental Illness, and the Social Environment," *Psychosomatic Medicine,* 23 (July-August, 1961), 289–97.
21. Holmes, T. H. *et al.,* "Psychosocial and Psychophysiologic Studies of Tuberculosis," *Psychosomatic Medicine,* 19 (March-April, 1957), 134–43.
22. Jelliffe, D. B., "Social Culture and Nutrition," *Pediatrics,* 20 (July, 1957), 128–38.
23. Joseph, A., "Physician and Patient," *Applied Anthropology,* 1 (1942), 1–6.
24. Kahl, Joseph A., *The American Class Structure.* New York: Holt, Rinehart & Winston, Inc., 1953.
25. Kaplan, H. I. and H. S. Kaplan, "Current Theoretical Concepts in Psychosomatic Medicine," *American Journal of Psychiatry,* 115 (June, 1959), 1091–96.
26. Keys, Ancel, "The Diet and the Development of Coronary Heart Disease," *Journal of Chronic Diseases,* 4 (October, 1956), 364–80.
27. Koos, E. L., " 'Metropolis'—What City People Think of Their Medical Services," *American Journal of Public Health,* 45 (December, 1955), 1551–57.
28. LaBarre, W., "The Patient and His Families, *Casework Papers* 1958. New York: Family Service Association of America, 1958, pp. 61–71.
29. Lederer, H. D., "How the Sick View Their World," *Journal of Social Issues,* 8 (1952), 4–16.
30. Margolin, S. G., "Genetic and Dynamic Psychophysiological Determinants of Pathophysiological Processes," *in* F. Deutsch, ed., *The Psychosomatic Concept in Psychoanalysis.* New York: International Universities Press, 1953.

31. Mendelson, M., S. Hirsch, and C. S. Webber, "A Critical Examination of Some Recent Theoretical Models in Psychosomatic Medicine," *Psychosomatic Medicine*, 18 (October, 1956), 363–73.

32. Michaels, J. J., "A Psychiatric Adventure in Comparative Pathophysiology of the Infant and Adult with some Theoretical Suggestions in Regard to Regression in Somatic Visceral Functions," *Journal of Nervous and Mental Diseases*, 100 (1944), 49–63.

33. Mirsky, I. A., "Psychoanalysis and the Biological Sciences," *in* F. Alexander and H. Ross, eds., *Twenty Years of Psychoanalysis*. New York: W. W. Norton & Company, Inc., 1953.

34. Parsons, Talcott, *The Social System*. New York: The Free Press of Glencoe, Inc., 1951.

35. ———, "Definitions of Health and Illness in the Light of American Values and Social Structure," *in* E. Gartly Jaco, ed., *Patients, Physicians, and Illness*. New York: The Free Press of Glencoe, Inc., 1958, 165–87.

36. ——— and R. Fox, "Illness, Therapy, and the Modern Urban American Family," *Journal of Social Issues*, 8 (1952), 31–44.

37. Paterson, R., "Why Do Cancer Patients Delay?" *The Canadian Medical Association Journal*, 73 (December 15, 1955), 931–40.

38. Reiser, Morton F., "Reflections on Interpretation of Psychophysiologic Experiments," *Psychosomatic Medicine*, 23 (September-October, 1961), 430–39.

39. Russek, H. I., "Role of Heredity, Diet, and Emotional Stress in Coronary Heart Disease," *Journal of the American Medical Association*, 171 (October 3, 1959), 503–508.

40. Swan, Aitken and R. Paterson, "The Cancer Patient: Delay in Seeking Advice," *British Medical Journal*, 1 (March 12, 1955), 623*ff*.

41. Szasz, T. S., "Psychoanalysis and the Autonomic Nervous System," *Psychoanalytic Review*, 39 (1952), 115–51.

42. Titchener, J. L. *et al.*, "Problems of Delay in Seeking Surgical Care," *Journal of the American Medical Association*, 160 (April 7, 1956), 1187–93.

43. Weiner, H., M. Thaler, M. F. Reiser, and I. A. Mirsky, "Etiology of Duodenal Ulcer: I. Relation of Specific Psychological Characteristics to Rate of Gastric Secretion (Serum Pepsinogen)," *Psychosomatic Medicine*, 19 (January-February, 1957), 1–10.

44. Wolf, S. and H. G. Wolff, "Evidence on the Genesis of Peptic Ulcer in Man," *Journal of the American Medical Association*, 120 (October 31, 1942), 670–75.

45. Wolff, H. G., "Protective Reaction Patterns and Disease," *Annals of Internal Medicine*, 27 (1947), 944–69.

46. Many of these studies are summarized in an article by H. G. Wolff, "Changes in the Vulnerability of Tissue: An Aspect of Man's Response to Threat," *in* National Institutes of Health, *Annual Lectures*, Washington, D.C.: U.S. Department of Health, Education, and Welfare, 1953, 38–71.

47. Wolff, H. G., *Stress and Disease*. Springfield, Ill.: C. C. Thomas, Publisher, 1953.

5

THE ADDICTIVE DISEASES AS SOCIO-ENVIRONMENTAL HEALTH PROBLEMS

Edward A. Suchman

The health of man is rooted in his environment. Environmental conditions affect the growth and development of infectious agents and the resistance of susceptible hosts. In recent years, since man's relatively successful conquest of the communicable diseases and the rapid growth in importance of the chronic degenerative diseases, increased attention has been focused on the social as well as the physical aspects of man's environment. *How* man lives has become as important as *where* he lives.

Socio-Environmental Factors in Health

Socio-environmental factors determine how man lives; thus these factors are intimately related to an individual's exposure and susceptibility to disease. His group memberships, his family structure, his work and his recreation all influence where he lives, what he eats, and how he sleeps and exercises, and these in turn determine his physical and mental state of health. Socio-environmental factors, furthermore, help or impede the progress of an illness after its onset: they are largely responsible for an individual's awareness of and interpretation of symptoms, his arrangements for medical care, and his behavior as a patient.

On a much broader level, changes in the physical environment, brought about by modified social conditions, may affect subsequent changes in a community's state of health. The development of cities and suburbs, the shifts in demographic composition of the population, and the changes in customs and morals, have had a marked impact on the levels of health of community members and on the quality and quantity of medical care which they receive.

If one's model of causality is limited to the traditional mechanistic model of single causes, then socio-environmental factors probably cannot be viewed as directly causing disease; they can only influence, positively or negatively, the potential of the "real" causal agent. If one accepts the concept of multiple causation, however, socio-environmental factors can be viewed as one of the direct causes of disease.

There is a complex interplay between socio-environmental factors, social problems, health conditions, and public health programs. Each one may lead to the other in a myriad of different ways. On the one hand, socio-environmental factors may result in physical conditions conducive to ill health. These unhealthy physical conditions may in turn be defined as social problems if the community becomes concerned and seeks to remove them. For example, poor housing (a physical condition) may lead to the growth of slums (a social problem), which in turn increases exposure to tuberculosis (a health condition), which then requires the development of a preventive and therapeutic measure (a public health program). On the other hand, certain public health problems, such as venereal disease, become social problems as they impinge upon the value structure of the community. In such cases, moralistic attitudes may interfere with scientific analysis, and both the diagnosis and treatment of the health problem often become an area of conflict between medical and lay forces.

The interaction between health problems and social values underlies much of the current controversy in the field of additive disorders. Socio-environmental forces have created a class of socio-medical pathological conditions, such as alcoholism and narcotics addiction, which must be viewed as both social and medical problems. To a large extent this interrelationship is a reciprocal one. On the one hand, a social problem such as juvenile delinquency may lead to a medical problem, *e.g.*, narcotics addiction. On the other hand, narcotics addiction may also lead to juvenile delinquency.

In actuality, the social and health aspects of the problems considered in this chapter cannot be clearly isolated from each other. Our premise is that certain social and health problems are closely related and that the value system of a society will do much to determine their definition and the types of corrective actions that can be taken. As we shall see, this premise underlies much of the current controversy in the field of addictive disorders.

The Addictive Disorders

Perhaps the prime example of this intricate relationship between socio-environmental conditions and health problems is afforded by the so-called addictive disorders of alcoholism and drug addiction. An addiction is primarily a man-made illness which has its roots in socio-environmental conditions. There is no infectious agent, as in the case of the communicable diseases. The addiction represents a behavioral disorder which may lead to an organic condition harmful to the individual's health and society's welfare. The motivating factors frequently are embedded in the psychological needs of the individual, while exposure to and use of the addictive substances is largely determined by his social environment. Clausen views drug use as only one possible manifestation of the social disorganization of environmental slum conditions [16].

The judicious use of most addictive substances is beneficial to man; abused they create serious medical and public health problems. Their capacity to make man forget his physical and mental aches and pains is the source of both their strength and danger. Inhibiting as they do the individual's control over his own action, their use—or at least their overuse—has become subject to moral judgment. Their uncontrolled use is apt to evoke condemnation rather than sympathy from the rest of society and to result in legal punishment rather than medical care.

Currently, the most important of these addictive substances is alcohol; next in importance are the narcotizing drugs such as morphine, cocaine, and opium. In recent years, barbiturates, amphetamine, and a whole new array of tranquilizers have taken their place alongside the natural drugs as relievers of physical pain and mental distress—and enslavers of all those who cannot regulate their dependency upon them.

Historically, man has always sought respite from the trials and tribulations of daily life in certain drugs, herbs, and potions which have the capacity of relieving tensions and anxieties and transforming reality. In many societies these chemical tranquilizers have attained acceptance and even approval. Their use is often associated with ceremonial occasions and various rituals have developed to govern when and how they are to be taken. Why, then, do they constitute an important public health problem today?

To understand the answer to this question, one must be aware of the tremendous influence which public opinion exerts over defining the legitimate concerns of medicine and public health. A health condition typically becomes a public health problem when a society or an important segment of its members develops the necessary concern to demand remedial medical action. It is only in recent years that alcoholism and drug addiction have gained prominence as public health problems—but the basis for concern is still to be found not so much in the medical as in the social consequences of these disorders. Although alcohol and narcotics can have detrimental effects upon the physical health of the individual, it is their effect upon his social behavior which alarms society and elicits a demand for public health action.

There is no universally accepted definition of an addiction. Medically, the term is largely restricted to those substances which produce a physiological dependence—the body develops a physical need for the drug in order to maintain normal functioning. Withholding the drug produces withdrawal sickness, an abstinence syndrome of definite physical and mental symptoms. Thus, there is a distinction between habit-forming substances such as tobacco and coffee, which create a psychological dependency, and addictive drugs, such as the opiate derivatives, which result in a true physical dependency.

While this distinction has pharmacological significance, it is not of major importance for understanding the type of socio-medical problem created by the development of a dependency, either psychological or physical, upon such substances as alcohol or narcotics. We will therefore accept as our definition of addiction "any behavioral disorder resulting from the repetitive use of and subsequent craving for some particular substance." Thus, alcohol may not create a true physical dependence, but it does produce a behavioral disorder based upon an uncontrollable need which results in a socio-medical problem of major proportions.

The general view is that the process of addiction involves a combination of psychological need which makes the host susceptible to the promise of relief through use of the addictive substance, of social pressure and support from a subgroup of addicted individuals, and of environmental conditions which make the addictive substance and the means for its use available. The process itself, once initiated, becomes self-reinforcing. The temporary relief from stress may make the act itself rewarding, and a psychological dependence is built up in which the individual forsakes other means of alleviating his tensions and anxieties. In the case of some narcotics, an actual physiological dependence may be created—the body needs the addictive substance. Unsuccessful experiences with abstinence accompanied by painful withdrawal symptoms create the self-image of one hopelessly hooked, and the self-definition as an addict. Rejection by the larger society and segregation with others like himself may lead to the development of sub-group values and customs which further reinforce the addictive pattern and the development of deviant, antisocial behavior. The addictive process indeed does represent a vicious chain of events which requires a concentrated attack at many different points and from many different approaches. The currently high rate of recidivism for both alcoholism and narcotics addiction bears witness to the inadequacy of traditional forms of medical treatment.

Alcoholism

It is necessary to distinguish between the social use of alcohol and chronic alcoholism. As a form of social behavior, drinking is deeply rooted in the folkways and mores of Western society. As a means of escape from tension and anxiety, drinking may satisfy some of the psychological needs of the individual and many people consume alcoholic beverages without developing a dependency upon them. The temporary effects of alcohol create many social problems—social drinking is a major cause of automobile and pedestrian accidents [43]. But as a habit-forming substance with deleterious effects upon organic structure and function, alcohol also creates a major medical problem.

Definition and description of alcoholism

As defined by the World Health Organization, alcoholism is "a chronic illness that manifests itself as a disorder of behavior. It is characterized by the repeated usage of alcoholic beverages to an extent that exceeds customary dietary use or compliance with social customs of the community and that interferes with the drinker's health or his economic or social functioning" [20]. According to the American Medical Association, alcoholism refers to "those excessive drinkers whose dependence on alcohol has attained such a degree that it shows a noticeable disturbance or interference with their bodily or mental health, their interpersonal relations, and their satisfactory social and economic functioning."

From these definitions it is apparent that alcoholism as an individual and public health problem is largely determined by personal circumstances and public reaction rather than by an objective medical symptomatology and diagnosis. The World Health Organization makes a distinction between two types of drinkers—the "habitual symptomatic excessive drinkers" and the "addictive drinkers." The habitual symptomatic excessive drinker places greatest emphasis on the duration of drinking bouts rather than on their intensity. His drinking is planned to enable him to maintain a limited level of effect from alcohol for as long a time as possible. The addictive drinker, on the other hand, seeks to attain a maximum degree of intoxication in as short a time as possible. He seems to have an impulsive drive to raise the level of blood concentration of alcohol as quickly as possible.

These are only two of the many different patterns that alcoholism may assume. Jellinek has recently hypothesized five different patterns representing different stages of alcoholism [26]. This individual variation makes it extremely difficult to diagnose alcoholism, except in the most advanced stages and furthermore necessitates an individualistic therapeutic approach to each patient.

Extent and distribution

Statistics concerning the extent and distribution of alcoholism are fairly indefinite. The prevalence and incidence of a disease is measured in terms of morbidity and mortality statistics, but because of the social stigma attached to alcoholism, an unknown number of cases remain hidden. Many physicians are reluctant to report alcoholism as a cause of death; chronic alcoholics are frequently institutionalized without being reported; and in many other cases private physicians, clinics, and hospitals refuse to accept alcoholics for treatment [45]. Most existing statistics come from arrests for drunkenness or various admissions to mental hospitals, which are inherently selective and biased. A true count of alcoholism would require specially designed field studies of total populations, an extremely difficult task [24].

Granted these shortcomings, it has been estimated that there are more than 4.5 million alcoholics in the United States. The rate of alcoholism varies—Washington, D.C., and California are in first and second place respectively and Idaho is in last place [28]. Rates in urban areas exceed rural ones. Among the larger cities, San Francisco ranks first, followed by Boston and Los Angeles, in that order. Of the 4.5 million problem drinkers, one million are considered chronic alcoholics. This represents a prevalence rate of 2.4 per cent for the total population. Cases are largely concentrated among males 20 years of age and older (7.5 per cent).

According to Keller and Efron, the rate of alcoholism in the United States showed an increase of 44 per cent between 1940 and 1953. This increase was larger among women than men, greatest in New England and smallest in the Pacific region. The authors suggest, however, that these "increases" may be an artifact of improved diagnosis and more complete reporting [28].

Using a formula based on the relationship of cirrhosis of the liver and the occurrence of identifiable mental or physical sequelae to excessive consumption, the World Health Organization places the United States first, with an alcoholism rate—with and without complications—of 4,390 per 100 thousand adults. The United States is followed by France with a rate of 2,850 per 100 thousand. Italy is lowest with a rate of only 500 per 100 thousand. In general, the rates of alcoholism are estimated to be lowest in the Mediterranean countries and in China and highest in Northeast Europe. These estimates, of course, are subject to tests of reliability and validity [19].

Bales discusses the influence of drinking customs on the rate of alcoholism [5]. In general, the Jews appear to have an exceptionally low rate of alcoholism; the Irish, a high rate. The low alcoholism rate among the Jews and Italians may stem from their use of alcohol as a mealtime beverage or as part of solemn ceremonial occasions.

The frequency of chronic alcoholism is also found to vary with sex and age. It is more prevalent among males between 35 and 55 years of age. The ratio of male alcoholics to female alcoholics in the United States is about 6 to 1; in Great Britain, 2 to 1; and in Scandinavia, 23 to 1. These differences underscore the socio-environmental basis of this disease, since they probably arise from the different roles and statuses occupied by women in these countries. Little is known about the female drinker, although in general she arouses more concern and social disapproval than the man. Gelber offers several interesting suggestions for research on women drinkers [23].

Social factors in etiology

Alcoholism has often been referred to as a symptom rather than a disease in itself. Excessive drinking may be regarded as only the outward manifestation of some underlying social or psychological condition which creates the need for alcohol—*e.g.*, the need to escape from feelings of inadequacy, insecurity, anxiety, or depression. A combination of psychological need and social custom underlies the development of this form of addictive behavior.

According to Fox, alcoholics may be grouped into three categories:

1. Situational drinkers who . . . . turn to drink to see them through difficult situations. These situational drinkers may or may not be able to return to controlled drinking.
2. Secondary addicts who find that after years of steady drinking they can no longer resume controlled drinking.
3. Primary addicts who are basically maladjusted and use alcohol to help them meet their daily social and psychological problems [22].

Several investigators have proposed a single type of alcoholic personality —an individual whose psychological makeup predisposes him to alcohol. As described by Monique:

> The alcoholic temperament remains more or less constant in all alcoholics. . . . Sooner or later they realize they have no control over their drinking and go to great lengths to hide this fact from others. . . . The bouts increase in severity and frequency. The compulsion to drink transcends family, social position, professional and all else. Alcohol is essential and must be had at all costs [35].

But although many alcoholics do exhibit such traits, there are many others who do not. At the present time there does not seem to be sufficient evidence to warrant the identification of any single personality type as especially prone to alcoholism. There are also many cases of individuals who possess these same traits as alcoholics but who do not become addicted.

The consequences of alcoholism

The personal, social, and economic costs of excessive use of alcohol run high. The personal disintegration that accompanies chronic alcoholism destroys not only the drinker but also entangles almost all other individuals close to him. It has been estimated that there are some 10 million wives, husbands, parents, or children in the United States who must live with the alcoholic and who suffer from his disordered behavior. Alcoholism is a major concomitant of divorce. The social costs of alcoholism include the expense of maintaining a large number of community facilities—police, courts, prisons, welfare agencies, hospital and medical care facilities, family and domestic relations organizations—which expend a large share of their resources in dealing with alcoholics or the people affected by them.

An industrial survey by the Western Electric Corporation indicated that the average company can expect about 3 per cent of its employees to be alcoholics [36]. The National Council on Alcoholism points out that 70 per cent of the compulsive alcoholics are employed. Economically, the costs of alcohol to industry in terms of absenteeism, decreased productivity, hospitalization and medical expenses, accidents, and personnel turnover have been estimated in the billions of dollars. These costs do not include the indirect effects due to inefficiency from hangovers and the negative effects on the morale of other workers.

Social factors in the control of alcoholism

The prevention, treatment, and control of alcoholism may be approached from three points of view—medical, psychological, and social. Medically, the problem involves the care of the chronic alcoholic, especially during periods of acute alcoholism. Many private physicians are still reluctant to take alcoholics as patients while some public hospitals continue to refuse to admit patients classified as alcoholics [45]. The reluctance of many hospitals and physicians to treat alcoholics is understandable in view of the extremely low rate of successful medical cure. Nevertheless most alcoholics require physical rehabilitation before they can start the long hard road back and medical care is an essential part of the therapeutic process [8].

One form of emotional support and guidance comes from an organization known as Alcoholics Anonymous. Composed of alcoholics who attempt to help each other, this organization apparently has one of the best records for successful cures. Organized in 1935, it now has more than 5000 groups throughout the world and is credited with helping more than 250,000 men and women.

In addition to medical, psychiatric, and social approaches to the treatment of alcoholism, there is a broader public health approach which stresses community responsibility [33]. More and more voluntary and public social agencies are establishing community programs for care and rehabilitation of alcoholics and less reliance is being placed upon prisons and mental hospitals. Communities are beginning to provide shelters where alcoholics can stay while receiving care, out-patient clinics for treatment, counseling and guidance centers, rehabilitation services, and follow-up care by public health nurses. In addition to these increased community services, which no longer condemn the alcoholic to a "Skid Row" existence, public health educational programs are being introduced into schools and throughout the community.

Public health education concerning alcoholism is particularly sensitive to the underlying conflict between the medical condition and public morality. There are many opponents who believe that open discussion, especially in the public schools, only increases curiosity and undermines the resistance of the listeners. A major characteristic of these so-called "social" diseases is the conflict they produce between objective medical care and the subjective value system of a society. Rather than discuss these conditions openly, large segments of society would choose to suffer the disease. And even when education and discussion are permitted, the emphasis is usually upon abstinence rather than upon recognition of the discrepancy between public behavior and public morality. Thus health education concerning alcoholism in public schools advocates total abstinence—despite the fact that 65 per cent of all adults drink [4].

Impinging as these diseases do upon public morality, legislative and judicial measures are apt to be invoked in an attempt to deal with them. A large number of all arrests are for drunkenness (Kruse estimates 40 per cent) [30]. A major attempt to legislate control of alcoholism can be seen in the ill-fated Eighteenth Amendment prohibiting the manufacture, sale, or use of alcoholic beverages.

Drug Addiction

The second major addictive disorder today is the use of drugs, especially narcotics. Like alcoholism, drug addiction may be viewed as a symptom of an underlying behavioral disorder rather than as a disease in its own right. The personality problem of the alcoholic, however, may be quite different from that of the narcotic addict. Alcohol tends to make a person aggressive, while most narcotics usually produce a desire to get away from it all. The user of drugs, perhaps because of their more dramatic physiological effects, suffers from even more seething social condemnation than does the user of alcohol. Hanlon characterizes the current medical attitude as follows: "Alcoholism is to tuberculosis as narcotic addiction is to leprosy" [25].

Definition and description of drug addiction

Drug addiction, like alcoholism, represents a compulsive need on the part of the addicted individual. The addiction proceeds more rapidly than in the case of alcohol and the signs of addiction are more clear-cut. Contrary to popular opinion, however, not all users of drugs are addicts. The World Health Organization distinguishes between drug addiction and drug habituation—a condition marked by a desire but not a compulsion to use drugs and the absence of any physical dependence upon the drug. As defined by the World Health Organization, drug addiction is "a state of periodic or chronic intoxication produced by the repeated consumption of a drug (natural or synthetic)" [15]. The characteristics of drug addiction include: an overpowering desire or need to continue taking the drug and to obtain it by any means, a tendency to increase the dose, a psychological and eventually a physical dependence upon the drug, withdrawal sickness or syndrome upon abstinence, and a detrimental effect upon the individual and society.

It is this last characteristic which is currently making drug addiction a serious public health problem. The unregulated sale of addictive drugs is illegal. It has been estimated that a narcotic addict requires a minimum of five to fifteen dollars per day to secure the drugs he needs. To obtain the money to buy these drugs, the addict often turns to crime. A study by Zimmering found that almost all of the young male drug addicts at Bellevue Hospital engaged in crime when they needed the money to purchase drugs [49].

As in the case of most forms of addictive behavior, one may hypothesize stages of addiction rather than an all-or-none diagnosis. Chein has developed a nine-point scale of severity of narcotics involvement based upon a combination of tolerance, dependency, and craving. At one end of the scale are those individuals with occasional sporadic use, while at the other end are those individuals with a craving for the drug, a history of dependence and a conviction of being permanently "hooked" [12]. This self-image of addiction, together with the expectation and fear of withdrawal symptoms, are basic forces in the reinforcement of addictive behavior [32].

The various narcotics produce certain characteristic effects—cocaine, for instance, acts as a stimulant and produces a feeling of elation; morphine, on the other hand, acts as a depressant, producing feelings of ease and contentment. The use of heroin results in tolerance (the need for increased dosage) and physical dependence; marijuana and cocaine do not.

The kind of drug used by an addict will depend upon such factors as geographical location, socio-economic status, sex and personality structure, as well as price and availability of drugs. In general, morphine is the most commonly used drug, but studies of addicts in New York City show an overwhelming number of drug users to be using heroin [34]. A study of arrests for drug addiction or use in California in 1960 found that one out of every four arrests was for using marijuana.

Extent and distribution of drug addiction

Valid data on the incidence and prevalence of drug addiction are even more difficult to obtain than those for alcoholism and are drawn largely from criminal records. A recent estimate placed the number of narcotic addicts in the United States at approximately 45,000 as of December 31, 1959, although some experts insist that the figure should be closer to 500,000. New York City alone is believed to account for more than half of the known cases of addicts, with an estimated 25,000 cases. These addicts are reported as accounting for half the crime in New York County with an estimated annual loss of $250 million in stolen property. A report for 1960 by the California State Bureau of Criminal Statistics lists 19,243 arrests for narcotic offenses with more than two-thirds occurring in Los Angeles County. These arrests accounted for more than one-third of all adult arrests in 1960 [10].

There is some evidence that there has been a considerable decrease in prevalence of drug addiction in the last fifty years. For example, the world-wide legal production of heroin has dropped from 839 kilograms in 1948 to 132 kilograms in 1954, while seizure of illicit morphine by the U.S. Federal Bureau of Narcotics in 1956 was only 4000 ounces in contrast to 75,000 ounces in 1922. However, there is some evidence that narcotics addiction in such metropolitan centers as New York City, Chicago, and Los Angeles is on the increase. It is concentrated in the socially disorganized sections of the cities and especially among Negroes and Puerto Ricans. As Clausen points out:

> The areas of highest rates of drug use tend to be inhabited by the most disadvantaged minority groups and by the least successful or most deviant

> members of other population groups. These are the areas with the highest rates of adult crime, the highest rates of prostitution and illegitimacy, the highest prevalence of infant mortality and of tuberculosis, the highest proportion of broken families and of non-family living arrangements [16].

Ausubel also suggests that "the disproportionate number of addicts who originate in the lower class can undoubtedly be attributed to the greater availability of drugs in slum areas" [3].

The characteristic pattern of drug addiction appears to have undergone a change since World War II. Before 1940, drug addicts were older, a higher proportion were women, and they were less concentrated among non-white groups. The explanation for this shift may lie in a change from the use of drugs as physical pain-killers to their use for "kicks." Unlike alcohol, narcotics addiction is a behavioral disorder of youth. There is now a large concentration of cases in the 15–25-year-old group, 30 per cent of whom become addicted before their 20th year. Addiction among boys is almost ten times as great as it is among girls [9]. In certain deviant groups, such as juvenile gangs in New York City, the taking of narcotics appears to have achieved a certain amount of acceptability and even approval [21].

Social factors in etiology

The causes of narcotics addiction are probably similar to those of alcoholism. There is a need to escape from reality, from oneself, and from one's group. Like alcoholics, narcotic addicts tend to be immature, anxious, maladjusted, and dominated by feelings of inadequacy and insecurity [48]. Pescor's analysis of personality data for 1,036 addict patients at Lexington Hospital found 1 out of 5 to have inebriate tendencies [40].

Of particular interest are the factors underlying the choice of narcotics as the form of addiction. Studies have shown that drug use is largely a socially acquired pattern of behavior. Almost all addicts first learn about the use of drugs through association with someone who is already using them [18]. A study of marijuana use in Chicago places greatest importance upon the social experience as opposed to psychological predisposition as the initiating force in drug addiction [7].

Alksne reports that social pressure was the major reason given by a majority of addicts for trying a drug [1]. A California study of 19,243 arrests for narcotic offenses in 1960 concluded that "most youths are probably enticed, or at least given their first opportunity for using narcotics, by someone on a more personal level. . . . [a] girl friend or buddy, for example. . . ." [10]. In many cases an addict will become a "pusher" in order to secure the necessary funds to assure his own supply of narcotics.

The importance of personal association among drug addicts has led some sociologists to posit the presence of an addict subculture. As summarized by Ray:

> The social world of addiction contains a loose system of organizational and cultural elements, including a special language or argot, certain artifacts, a commodity market and pricing system, a system of stratification, and ethical codes. The addict's commitment to these values gives him a status and an identity [41].

These addict sub-groups develop strong interpersonal bonds, similar images of appropriate and acceptable narcotic behavior, a language and rituals of their own and share feelings of rejecting and being rejected by society [11]. They are usually found in high delinquency areas, belong to delinquent groups, and their history is marked by deviant and antisocial behavior. The members of these groups often hold strong allegiances to each other and to the norms of the sub-group at the same time that they reject the values of the larger society.

This point of view is developed in great detail by Cloward and Ohlin as a theory of delinquent behavior. In a discussion on pressures leading to "retreatist" subcultures, they place great stress upon the patterns of association that are built up in socially deviant sub-groups. In relation to drug addiction, they claim:

> The drug user, in other words, must be understood not only in terms of his personality and the social structure, which creates a readiness to engage in drug use, but also in terms of the new patterns of association and values to which he is exposed as he seeks access to drugs. The more the individual is caught in this web of association, the more likely that he will persist in drug use, for he has become incorporated in a subculture that exerts control over his behavior [17].

But the psychological factor in drug addiction is interlocked in mutually dependent ways with social and medical factors. Prevention and control of the addictive disorders require a comprehensive attack which makes use of each of all these approaches.

Social factors in control

The confusion as to whether drug addiction is a legal or a medical problem underlies much of the current effort at control. In fact, the addict who wishes to break the habit must sometimes turn himself over to the courts in order to secure treatment. A recent report by the Joint Committee of the American Bar Association and the American Medical Association on Drug Addiction strongly recommends that drug addiction be viewed as a disease and not a crime and that the current laws be revised to abolish prison terms for addicts, to allow qualified doctors to dispense narcotics, and to establish experimental out-patient clinics for the care of addicts. This Committee points to the success of these measures in other countries, such as Britain, where narcotics addiction is claimed to be practically non-existent [27]. Lindesmith found that very few drug addicts in Britain were imprisoned for any kind of offense. He also points out that under the

British system, "there is little or no economic incentive to spread the habit to others" [31]. Schur's analysis of drug addiction under British policy also offers much support for a medically-oriented rather than a legal approach to the control of drug addiction [44]. Kolb believes that addicts who return to use of drugs after treatment should be allowed to have maintenance doses under medical supervision. Treated in this way, he feels that chronic addicts "would work, support themselves, and create no public problem" [29]. This point of view is opposed by the World Health Organization which argues that "the maintenance of drug addiction is not treatment" [14].

The controversy of legal versus medical responsibility for the drug addict is complicated by the fact that the currently prescribed medical treatment is ineffective. It calls for detoxification and rehabilitation. The United States Public Heath Service maintains hospitals at Lexington, Kentucky, and Fort Worth, Texas, where addicts may undergo six months of treatment and rehabilitation, but the number of hospital beds available for detoxification in local hospitals is sadly deficient. Furthermore, like the alcoholic, the drug addict makes a poor patient. He is apt to be uncooperative, deceitful and troublesome. The addict in addition constitutes a potential source of difficulty for the doctor with Federal and State law enforcement officers.

Detoxification can be achieved quite easily, but the recidivism rate is extremely high. In a study of addicts who had been discharged at least six months from Lexington Hospital, Pescor found only 13.5 per cent still abstinent [39]. In 1955, at Lexington Hospital, out of 3,724 admissions, two-thirds were readmissions. Alksne, in his study of former patients of Riverside Hospital in New York, found a similarly low proportion of abstainers [1]. A study of the cycle of abstinence and relapse among heroin addicts placed particular emphasis upon the addict's self-image during periods of abstinence and relapse.

> . . . the abstainer's social expectations during a period when he is off drugs are frequently not gratified. Here again, socially disjunctive experiences bring about a questioning of the value of an abstainer identity and promote reflections in which addict and non-addict identities and relationships are compared. The abstainer's realignment of his values with those of the world of addiction results in the redefinition of self as an addict and has as a consequence the actions necessary to relapse [41].

The high rate of relapse is attributed largely to the continued association of the patient with addicts after detoxification. The "cured" addict returns to the same addict subculture from whence he came and he quickly reverts to his former pattern of drug use. The hospitalization experience itself may even serve to reinforce addict beliefs and values through close association with other addicts and provide knowledge concerning new contacts. Lindesmith found that addicts are more likely to relapse unintentionally by "playing around" with drugs again than to resume their addiction deliberately. He found that attitudes developed during addiction, such as the belief that drugs are good for every ailment and the rejection of moral taboos, predispose the former addict to revert to the use of drugs [32].

Wikler raises a crucial question concerning the evaluation of a "cure" in narcotics addiction. He notes that the abstinence rate of Lexington patients (about 20 per cent) compares quite favorably with the recovery rate from certain chronic diseases, like diabetes mellitus or pulmonary tuberculosis [46]. However, the diabetic's return to hospital care is not viewed with the disapproval and condemnation that is focused on the narcotic addict's return.

Winick proposes that the term "cure" be used with caution in cases of drug addiction. Instead he suggests terms like "successful treatment" and "total abstinence" [47]. Chein offers an interesting interpretation of recidivism as in itself a necessary, perhaps even constructive part of the therapeutic process:

> However, there is reason to believe that relapse and repeated institutionalization need not be a mere repetition of the original cycle but rather may be an ascending spiral, leading, often after several such cycles—*i.e.*, of treatment, release, relapse and reinstitutionalization—to a final achievement of an equilibrium which makes life without recourse to drugs possible for the young man. Consequently, the return to the community after treatment must be seen as a stage in a long-range process of rehabilitation in which temporary relapse should be perceived both by user and social worker or law officer as a possibly constructive and certainly as an expected development [13].

The high rate of recidivism underscores the need to couple detoxification with physical and psychological rehabilitation and to attempt to change the environment to which the "cured" addict returns. Most important is a change in the community's attitude toward the former addict. As it is now, the addict returning to the community is likely to find himself treated as an ex-convict, for whom there are few employment possibilities. This negative public attitude may only drive him back all the more quickly into the addict sub-group, with an even more confirmed antisocial attitude. From a social point of view, the narcotic addict, like the delinquent, is largely the product of his environment, and until environmental conditions conducive to the development of such forms of deviant behavior are changed, little progress will be made in meeting the narcotics problem [38].

Two other problems related to the prevention and control of drug addiction are of general significance for social factors in the control of the addictive type of disease. The first concerns the degree of voluntary control to be permitted the addict in seeking a cure; the second relates to the efficacy of public education to the dangers of addiction. Both of these approaches contain inherent dilemmas. By definition, the addict cannot control his need for alcohol or drugs. How, then, can he be expected voluntarily to enforce the rigorous routine involved in breaking a habit which has such deep psychological roots? Yet everything we know about psychotherapy and personality change indicates the essential importance of having the patient's voluntary cooperation.

The dilemma in regard to education about alcohol and drugs involves the classical problem of dispensing information about a vice which contains certain attractive elements, without creating even more sinners. Given an underlying need in many individuals for the kind of relief from anxiety and tension offered by alcohol and drugs, perhaps it is best not to tell such people about the existence of these forms of escape [2]. But how, then, are such susceptible individuals to be warned against a potential danger which they well may stumble upon by themselves? These two dilemmas underlie much of the heated controversy that exists today concerning the prevention and control of the addictive disorders, as well as certain other so-called social diseases, such as venereal disease. In the United States at the present time, treatment for alcoholism is generally voluntary, but narcotics addiction is considered a crime and the addict is often subjected to compulsory detoxification. The success of Alcoholics Anonymous compared to the failure of compulsory hospitalization for narcotics addiction argues in favor of the voluntary approach. As Chein maintains:

> Every experience we've had shows that the addict would not be cured under any compulsion. Part of an optimum therapeutic program is to give the addict a chance to fail. He will begin to realize that he is truly ill and not simply caught by unfortunate circumstances. You cannot give psychotherapy to a person who does not think there is anything wrong with him [37].

The problem is that most drug addicts are not interested in treatment and will not volunteer. The World Health Organization recommends some form of legal compulsion because "Most addicts require some degree of coercion, preferably civil commitment for medical treatment, to force them to desist from what is to them often a pleasurable experience" [14]. Pescor's comparison of voluntary with involuntary cures among addicts at Lexington Hospital showed that the average for the longest period of abstinence for ex-patients was 2.2 years after voluntary cure and 1.8 years after involuntary cure. He concludes that voluntary cures are generally more effective than enforced cures [40]. But Lexington records indicate that many voluntary patients sign themselves out long before completion of treatment. Perhaps one answer to this dilemma might involve a voluntary decision by the addict to subject himself to an enforced course of treatment.

Future Prospects for the Addictive Disorders

The punitive treatment of addicts is slowly giving way to a more therapeutic approach. The medical profession is beginning to accept responsibility for the care of addicts and the field of public health is seeking methods of prevention and rehabilitation. Local hospitals are setting aside beds for the treatment of alcoholics and drug addicts. Public health agencies are expanding their efforts to increase public understanding of the problem, to secure the cooperation of the addicted individual, and to provide community facilities for detoxification and rehabilitation.

But the ultimate success of any efforts to meet the problem of the addictive disorders must rest with society itself. Public attitudes towards the addict must change. He must be seen for what he is—a physically and mentally sick individual. The stigma of weakness and depravity must be removed. A therapeutic approach must be substituted for punishment. The community must continue to fight to remove or ameliorate the socio-environmental conditions which expose the individual to addictive influences and to provide the needed rehabilitative measures to help the cured addict make a fresh start.

Treatment and rehabilitation program

A major need in the field of addictive disorders today is for action programs which help to keep the cured alcoholic or narcotics addict from returning to the use of the addictive substance. The basis of his addiction rests largely upon his inability to find some other less harmful substitute to satisfy his craving for the kind of reaction afforded by the addictive substance. Thus, the basic ingredient of any effective addiction control program must be the provision of a continuing source of substitute support which enables the the ex-addict to meet his craving without returning to the use of drugs. There is probably no real cure for the addictive disorders, just as no cure exists for many chronic diseases—there is only a slow rehabilitative process which involves continuous support and a changed way of life. Perhaps this is the major reason why single shot approaches to the control of addiction show such discouragingly high rates of recidivism. The former addict will relapse after any single "cure," unless he is provided with some kind of ongoing support.

There are a number of forms such "after-cure" programs can take: the local neighborhood "club" for ex-addicts; the halfway house which serves as a supervised residence; the sheltered workshop which offers employment in a supportive environment; and the work and training camp which moves the ex-addict from his old environment into a therapeutic community. These programs combine a supportive therapeutic environment with realistic help in vocational guidance, housing, family counseling, and recreation.

Needed research on addictive disorders

Much remains to be learned about the addictive disorders. Relatively little research has been done on their etiology, prevention, treatment, and control. The physiological process whereby these substances induce addiction, and the system of effecting detoxification and withdrawal from addiction are fairly well known. What is not yet known is how to keep cured addicts from relapsing, how to free them of the underlying psychological and social forces which compel them to seek an escape into the make-believe world of drug-induced dreams and fantasies.

Very little is known at present about the epidemiology of these disorders. Current data on the incidence, prevalence, and distribution of addiction in the total population are woefully inadequate. Which groups are particularly susceptible? What personal characteristics distinguish high-risk from low-risk groups? Why do some geographical areas show such high addiction rates while in others the problem is practically nonexistent?

New methods of dealing with the addiction problem must be developed and evaluated. Physicians and hospitals must replace police and prisons. Such methods as out-patient clinics, short-term hospitalization, training and work camps, and rehabilitation centers must be utilized. Such problems as the use of voluntary or compulsory treatment methods, group psychotherapy, social work with the families of addicts, and the use of public health nurses in after-care must be explored. Better public health education programs are required both to increase knowledge concerning the temptations and the dangers of addiction and to change the public's attitude toward the addict.

Rooted as they are in the social and psychological forces in the individual's environment, the addictive disorders create a new type of health problem which cannot be understood or managed in terms of the traditional infectious agents or degenerative processes of the communicable and chronic diseases. They represent a new class of behavioral disorders which require a redefinition of etiological and therapeutic concepts and a reformulation of prevention and treatment programs. The task of building an effective approach to this increasingly important public health problem is a real challenge to the newly developed field of social medicine.

References

1. Alksne, Harold, S. Patrick, R. Trussell, and J. Elinson, "A Follow-up Study of Treated Adolescent Narcotic User." Mimeographed report, 1960.
2. Anslinger, Harry J., "Drug Addicts," *Journal of the American Medical Association*, 144 (1950), 333.
3. Ausubel, David P., *Drug Addiction: Physiological, Psychological and Sociological Aspects*. New York: Random House, 1958, p. 64.
4. Bacon, Seldon D., "Alcoholism: Its Extent, Therapy and Prevention." *Federal Probation II*, No. 2, 1947.
5. Bales, Robert F., "Cultural Differences in Rates of Alcoholism," *Quarterly Journal of Studies on Alcohol*, 6 (March, 1946), 480–99.
6. ———, "The Therapeutic Role of Alcoholics Anonymous as Seen by a Sociologist," *Quarterly Journal of Studies on Alcohol*, 5 (September, 1944), 267–78.
7. Becker, Howard S., "Becoming a Marijuana User," *American Journal of Sociology*, 59 (November, 1953), 235–42.
8. Block, Marvin A., "Medical Treatment of Alcoholism," *Journal of the American Medical Association*, 162 (1956), 1610–19.
9. Bureau of Narcotics, U.S. Treasury Department, *Traffic in Opium and Other Dangerous Drugs*. Washington, D.C.: Government Printing Office, issued annually.
10. *California State Bureau of Criminal Statistics*, Annual Report, 1961.
11. Chein, Isador and Eva Rosenfeld, "Juvenile Narcotics Use," *Law and Contemporary Problems*, 22 (Winter, 1957).
12. ———, D. Gerard, R. Lee, and E. Rosenfeld, *The Road to H: Some Aspects of Juvenile Delinquency and Drug Use*. New York: Research Center for Human Relations, New York University, 1961. Dittoed.
13. *Ibid*., p. 119.
14. *Chronicle of the World Health Organization*, "Treatment and Care of Drug Addicts," 11 (October, 1957), 323.
15. *Chronicle of the World Health Organization*, "Drug Addiction or Drug Habituation," 11 (May, 1957), 165.
16. Clausen, John A., "Drug Addiction," in Robert K. Merton and Robert A. Nisbet, eds., *Contemporary Social Problems*. New York: Harcourt, Brace & World, Inc., 1961, pp. 194–95. For a sociological analysis of drug use, see also John A. Clausen, "Social Patterns, Personality and Adolescent Drug Use," in Alexander Leighton, J. Clausen and R. Wilson, eds., *Explorations in Social Psychiatry*. New York: Basic Books, Inc., 1957, pp. 230–77.
17. Cloward, Richard A. and Lloyd E. Ohlin, *Delinquency and Opportunity: A Theory of Delinquent Gangs*. New York: The Free Press of Glencoe, Inc., 1960.
18. Dia, Bingham, *Opium Addiction in Chicago*. Shanghai: The Commercial Press, 1937.

19. *Expert Committee on Mental Health. Alcoholism Subcommittee, World Health Organization*, Geneva: Medical Report Series, No. 42, 1951.)

20. *Expert Committee on Mental Health. Alcoholism Subcommittee, World Health Organization*, Geneva: Medical Report Series, No. 48, August, 1952.

21. Finestone, Harold, "Cats, Kicks and Color," *Social Problems* 5 (July, 1957), 3–13.

22. Fox, R., "Treatment of Alcoholism" *in* H. M. Heimwitch, ed., *Alcoholism: Basic Aspects and Treatment*. Washington, D.C.: American Association for the Advancement of Science, 1957, pp. 164–65.

23. Gelber, Ida, *Alcoholism in New York City*. New York: New York City Department of Health, 1960.

24. Gordon, John, "Treatment of Alcoholism," *New York State Journal of Medicine*, 58 (June, 1958), 1011–18.

25. Hanlon, John J., *Principles of Public Health Administration*. St. Louis: The C. V. Mosby Co., 1960, p. 581.

26. Jellinek, E. M., *The Disease Concept of Alcoholism*. New Haven: Hillhouse Press, 1960.

27. *Joint Committee of the American Bar Association and the American Medical Association. Drug Addiction: Crime or Disease?* Bloomington: Indiana University Press, 1961.

28. Keller, Mark and Vera Efron, "The Prevalence of Alcoholism," *Quarterly Journal of Studies on Alcohol*, 16 (December, 1955), 619–644.

29. Kolb, Lawrence, "Narcotic Addiction—An Interview," *Spectrum* 5 (March, 1957), 136.

30. Kruse, Harry D., *Problem Drinking and Alcoholism*. New York: The New York State Interdepartmental Health Resources Board, 1957.

31. Lindesmith, Alfred, "The British System of Narcotics Control," *Law and Contemporary Problems*, 22 (Winter, 1957), 138–54.

32. ———, *Opiate Addiction*. Bloomington, Ind.: Principia Press, 1947.

33. McCarthy, R. G., "Public Health Approach to the Control of Alcoholism," *American Journal of Public Health*, 40 (November, 1950), 1412.

34. Meyer, Alan S., *Social and Psychological Factors in Opiate Addiction*. New York: Bureau of Applied Social Research, Columbia University, 1952.

35. Monique, S. J., "The Alcoholic," *Alcohol Hygiene*, 3 (March, 1957), 5–10.

36. Moore, P. A., *Western Electric Programs in Alcoholism*. Chicago: Western Electric Company, Industrial Relations Department.

37. *New York Herald Tribune*, March 12, 1960.

38. Patrick, Sherman W., *The "Score": A Survey of New York City's Narcotics Program*. Unpublished thesis, New York University, 1962.

39. Pescor, Michael J., "Follow-up Study of Treated Narcotic Drug Addicts," *Public Health Reports*, Supplement No. 170 (1943), pp. 1–18.

40. ———, "A Statistical Analysis of the Clinical Records of Hospitalized Drug Addicts," *Public Health Reports*, Supplement No. 143, (1943).

41. Ray, Marsh B., "The Cycle of Abstinence and Relapse among Heroin Addicts," *Social Problems*, 9 (Fall, 1961), 132–40.

42. Riley, John W. and C. S. Marden, "The Social Patterns of Alcohol Drinking," *Quarterly Journal of Studies on Alcohol*, 8 (September, 1947), 265–73.

43. Schmidt, W. S. and R. G. Smart, "Alcoholics, Drinking and Traffic Accidents," *Quarterly Journal of Studies on Alcohol*, 20 (September, 1959), 631–44.

44. Schur, Edwin M., "Drug Addiction under British Policy," *Social Problems*, 9 (Fall, 1961), 156–66.

45. Straus, Robert, "Medical Practice and the Alcoholic," *Annals of the American Academy of Political and Social Science*, 315 (June, 1958), 117–24. The entire issue of this journal is devoted to the topic, "Alcoholism in the United States."

46. Wikler, Abraham, "Clinical Aspects of Diagnosis and Treatment of Addictions," *Bulletin of the Menninger Clinic*, 15 (1951).

47. Winick, Charles, "Narcotics Addiction and Its Treatment," *Law and Contemporary Problems*, 22 (Winter, 1957), 31. This entire issue is devoted to a symposium on narcotics.

48. Yost, O. R., *The Bane of Drug Addiction*. New York: The Macmillan Company, 1954.

49. Zimmering, Paul, J. Toolan, R. Safrin, and S. Wortis, "Heroin Addiction in Adolescent Boys," *Journal of Nervous and Mental Diseases*, 114 (1951), 19–34.

6

SOCIOLOGY OF MENTAL DISEASE

John A. Clausen

It has been suggested that the concepts of health and disease may be extended beyond the province of somatic processes and into the realm of social behaviors.[1] The biological organism is also a behaving person, and behaviors may be viewed in terms of whether they are normal or deviant or, in some sense, pathological. Because standards for assessing deviance or behavioral pathology are formulated by the particular society in which one lives, the problem of specifying the nature and content of mental disease is greatly complicated.

[1] See Chap. 4.

The Nature and Extent of Mental Disease

Mental illness is primarily manifest in behavior. It may be associated with a variety of physical symptoms or with no physical symptoms whatsoever. The terms "mental illness" or "mental disease" refer to a large number of disorders, some quite distinct from others and some merging almost imperceptibly into others in the behaviors and feelings exhibited by the patient. Thus, the term "mental disease" has somewhat the same range of connotations as does the term "physical disease." There is, indeed, a tendency to set one off against the other and to maintain a dualism of body and mind. But mind is not to be conceptualized as "non-body." It is an aspect of the behaving organism, an incorporation and integration of experience which serves to direct and regulate the organism's reactions to its environment.

Like any other regulatory system within the organism, mental processes will at times be subject to unusual stresses or will, for one reason or another, be inadequate to the demands placed upon them. Everyone finds that there are times when it is difficult to think clearly; most of us at some time or other feel a bit depressed, or jumpy, or short-tempered. But it is only when thinking becomes so confused that one can no longer perceive and interpret accurately what is going on around him, or when depressed feelings, or anxiety, or irritation with others become so dominant that he cannot carry out normal activities, that mental disease can actually be said to be present.

The major types of mental disease

There are a number of ways of classifying mental diseases and, despite the efforts of international committees under the aegis of the World Health Organization, present classification systems differ from country to country. Even in the United States, diagnostic practices vary greatly from state to state, and from psychiatric school to school. Ideally a system of classification would be based on adequate formulations of the nature of the disease entities. It is precisely because no such formulations exist that classification of mental disorders must still be based upon combinations of symptoms, physiological states, prior history, and situational responsiveness.

There is, however, general agreement as to certain gross aspects and categories of mental disease.[2] The most severe disorders include those

---

[2] The standard nomenclature used in the United States is contained in *Diagnostic and Statistical Manual, Mental Disorders* (Washington, D.C.: American Psychiatric Association, 1952).

illnesses classified in the United States as the psychoses and the acute and chronic brain syndromes with psychotic reaction. These are the diseases that most often lead to the label "insanity"—a legal term, not a medical concept. A psychotic reaction entails a gross derangement of mental processes and an inability to evaluate external reality correctly. Often the psychotic person may function in non-demanding roles with reasonable success for years, despite some "quirks," but in modern industrial society he tends sooner or later to be confronted by situations which precipitate agitated and bizarre behavior leading to hospitalization.

Schizophrenia: The most serious of all mental disorders, from the standpoint of frequency, duration, and degree of impairment of function, is schizophrenia. This disease or class of diseases (there is much disagreement on the point) is most frequent among young adults, though it may occur at any age level. Originally called *dementia praecox* ("psychosis of adolescence") because so many cases occur in late adolescence, schizophrenia usually entails a profound degree of psychological withdrawal from others, coupled with a variety of distortions and derangements of thought processes, such as delusions and bizarre thoughts. The "split personality" of the schizophrenic refers to the divorcing of emotional and cognitive processes. Thus the emotional state of the schizophrenic will very often seem inappropriate to his thought processes and the situations in which he finds himself.

Manic-Depressive and Involutional Psychoses: Occurring most often in middle age are the acute depressive states which tend to characterize both manic-depressive and involutional psychoses. The classic manic-depressive type alternates between periods of manic excitement and extreme euphoria and periods of utter despair and depression. The manic phases seem to be much more rare than the depressive. This type of psychosis tends to be recurrent, with periods of remission in which the patient is free of symptoms for months or years at a time. Involutional melancholia is often difficult to distinguish from manic-depressive reaction but tends more often to be found in somewhat older patients, since, as the name implies, the symptoms are thought to be related to the involution or decline of sexual functions.

Chronic Brain Syndromes: Most important in this category are the mental diseases of old age, *senile dementia* and psychosis with cerebral arteriosclerosis. Such disorders produce a variety of symptoms—confusion, suspiciousness, lack of concern for amenities, loss of control of bodily functions—which make the older person difficult to care for in the small urban household. Although such disorders often result from some organic damage to the brain, mental disease in the later years is also related to personality attributes and to psychological stresses. About a fourth of all mental hospital admissions are of patients with the diseases of old age.

Other chronic brain syndromes are psychotic reactions stemming from syphilis (paresis), those resulting from chronic alcoholism, and those which are a product of continued trauma to the brain—such as may be received by professional boxers. All these types of mental illness tend to occur much more frequently among males than among females, simply because of the more frequent exposure of males to the etiologically relevant agents or situations.

The Psychoneuroses: Psychoneurotic reactions are disturbances in the functioning of personalities. They do involve *dys-ease,* for the chief characteristic of such disorders is intense anxiety. The anxiety may be consciously felt and directly expressed, or unconsciously felt and expressed by the utilization of various indirect defense mechanisms. The symptoms of the neurosis depend on the way that the person has learned to handle his anxiety. Common forms are the diffuse and uncontrolled anxiety reaction, the symbolically focused phobic reaction (specific fears), the organically expressed conversion reaction (paralysis, tics, and the like), obsessive-compulsive reactions in which there is a persistence of unwanted ideas or repetitive impulses to perform nonrational acts, and depressive reactions, in which feelings of guilt are usually involved.

Psychoneuroses were a major reason for rejection of men for Selective Service during World War II and are a major reason for absenteeism and ineffective performance in industry and the occupational sphere generally. They impair the functioning of a very high proportion of the population to some degree at one time or another. But most psychoneurosis goes untreated, perhaps because it less often involves the acute disruption of life patterns that is found in psychosis.

Psychosomatic Disorders: Somewhat akin to the psychoneuroses are those disorders that manifest themselves in physiological malfunction without apparent organic cause.[3] Almost everyone reacts to emotional stress—at least occasionally—with transitory physical discomfort. This may take the form of a headache, an attack of diarrhea, a skin rash or some other relatively mild symptom. But for some persons the symptoms may be so intense as to threaten life itself, as in ulcerative colitis, severe asthma, or *anorexia nervosa* (loss of appetite, often coupled with vomiting). Although psychiatrists are deeply involved in research and treatment relating to such disorders, the fact that symptomatology is somatic removes these illnesses from the realm generally regarded as mental illness.

Incidence, prevalence, and the problems of their measurement

On any given day, there are over 600 thousand patients in mental hospitals in the United States, about the same number of patients as are

[3] The relationships between emotional states and physiological function have been discussed in Chapter 4.

found in all other kinds of hospitals for all other kinds of illness [41]. Since the prevalence of an illness is measured by the number of cases in a given population at a given time, the prevalence of hospitalization for mental illness is just about the same as that for all other illnesses combined.

The incidence of an illness is the number of new cases of the illness occurring in a given period—usually a week, a month or a year. The incidence of mental illness requiring hospitalization is much lower than that of physical illness requiring hospitalization. The relatively higher prevalence rate of mental illness results from the fact that even acute episodes of mental illness tend to respond only slowly to treatment and care and that many mental illnesses are chronic.

Perhaps the best indication of the general frequency of severe mental illness in the United States is the probability that about 1 person in 12 will be hospitalized for a mental illness sometime during his life [23]. That is, if present age-specific rates of illness, use of hospitalization, and average life span remain constant about 8 per cent of the population now living will eventually be hospitalized for a mental illness. Although this expectancy of hospitalization is higher than in the past, it does not appear that the likelihood of becoming mentally ill prior to or during the prime of life has increased. For example, statistics relating to the number of mentally ill persons confined in jails, almshouses, and other institutions in Massachusetts prior to 1850 suggest that for all but the aged, rates of psychosis were at least as high then as at present [21].

The increase in hospitalization of older persons appears primarily to reflect increased longevity and changed living arrangements. Many more people now live beyond 70, and the incidence of evidences of mental deterioration increases sharply beyond this age [23]. Moreover, many families living in relatively small dwelling units in urban environments are unable to accommodate adequately the physical and psychological needs of older members who may be confused and lacking in ability to care for themselves.

Of course, not all mentally ill persons—not even all psychotic persons—are hospitalized. Unlike the physically ill, the mentally ill may be unaware of the nature of their difficulties and therefore quite unwilling to seek treatment or help. Neurotic patients and most psychotics are frequently aware of being unhappy or upset, but this awareness does not impel them toward medical care. Therefore, the number of patients who are hospitalized or otherwise under treatment (psychotherapy or other out-patient care) does not give an accurate estimate of the over-all amount of mental illness in the United States or in any other nation or society.

An accurate assessment of the mental health status of the total population would require periodic examinations of cross-sections of the population. Even if it were feasible to carry out such examinations, it is doubtful that accurate classifications could be made without very intensive observation of individuals over time and in a variety of situations. Although certain psychological tests and measures of personality are useful for rough screening of the population, they do not permit accurate classification of individual ability to function in diverse situations and roles, nor do they permit accurate diagnostic classification for the wide range of psychiatric disorders. Most of the available information about the frequency of mental illness and the characteristics of the mentally ill therefore is necessarily based on data relating to *treated* mental illness. In a country such as the United States, where treatment facilities for the mentally ill are relatively good, it seems likely that most persons who develop severe mental illness ultimately come under professional care.

The Social Epidemiology of Mental Disorder

Epidemiological research—the study of the distribution and correlates of diseases in time and space—serves two important functions: it frequently provides clues to the complex, multifactorial causation of diseases whose etiology has not been definitely established and provides basic information on the needs for disease control and treatment programs for a given population. To be of value, such research requires that experts be able to classify instances of the disease with a fair degree of certainty and that most persons suffering from the disease come to the attention of these experts. This means that persons from various sub-groups of the population must be equally likely to come to professional attention.

Stages of becoming a patient

Psychosis seldom develops overnight. Studies of the antecedents of hospitalization have found that in most instances there has been a period of months or even years during which the patient has been nervous, upset, moody, or beset by a variety of somatic complaints. Even when more extreme signs of emotional disorder such as delusions, hallucinations or bizarre behaviors are present, however, the families of the patient frequently interpret these simply as signs of "upsetness" or strain [9]. For many, the realization that mental illness is entailed comes only when some crisis requires that the ill member be restrained or attended to in a manner outside the family's usual repertoire of responses. For long periods, the family may try to protect the ill member or placate him, never realizing that he is ill and needs treatment. Very often, the stresses entailed in trying to live with a mentally ill person will engender mutual hostility and recriminations.

The psychotic person tends to see the problem not in himself but in those around him or in circumstances over which he has no control.[4] He may deny any implication that he is ill or needs help. This denial may be massive and unremitting or it may alternate with periods of willingness to consider the need for help. Whether the psychotic comes into treatment voluntarily or is committed to a mental hospital by legal action will depend in large part on the extent to which persuasive communication can be established at some point in the process.

If professional resources for dealing with mental illness are not available, it appears that there is frequently a mobilization of family and friends to deal with the crisis in whatever way the culture defines as appropriate. Reports of psychotic episodes witnessed by anthropologists suggest that there are frequently ritualized ways of redefining the nature of the dilemmas confronting the disturbed person, and that hostility and tension may be sufficiently dissolved by these modes of response to permit a reintegration of the individual into stable relationships [10].

In Western society, however, severe mental illness generally results in hospitalization. The image of the mental hospital contributes to the resistance of the patient to accepting the nature of his problem. At some point, however, the mentally disturbed person either behaves so disruptively as to force a resolution (commitment by family, associates, or legal action) or is persuaded of the need for care. He then becomes, officially, a mental patient, subject to diagnosis (and therefore to inclusion in statistics on the distribution of mental illness), and, hopefully, to treatment and return to the community.

Social and cultural factors in mental illness

Some mental disorders, like paresis and alcoholic psychoses, are clearly of organic etiology. The organic causes are themselves linked with social, cultural, and psychological factors, but the psychotic behavior is a result of definite damage to the central nervous system.[5] Other mental illnesses, like those of old age, appear to derive from the interaction between biological effects of aging and the social situations and experiences of older persons. Still other disorders, such as schizophrenia, and manic-depressive and involutional psychoses, appear to be linked both to heredity and to personality development and life experience.

No study of the social correlates of mental illness has been more influential than Faris and Dunham's analysis of the distribution of rates of hospitalization by ecological areas within the cities of Chicago and Providence [17]. They demonstrated that the annual rates of first admissions to

---

[4] The problem is most acute in instances of paranoid symptomatology. A good analysis of the nature of the paranoid's "self-fulfilling prophecy" is given by Lemert [32].

[5] See Chap. 5.

public and private mental hospitals varied substantially, being highest in and around the central business district and lowest at the periphery of the city. This was true not only for patients hospitalized for psychoses resulting from alcoholism and syphilis—who tend to congregate in the deteriorated flop house and rooming house areas near the central business districts —but also for patients hospitalized for schizophrenia.

The distribution of manic-depressive psychoses, on the other hand, was unrelated to the ecological pattern of the cities. The areas with highest rates of schizophrenia were characterized by high population heterogeneity and mobility and by low socio-economic status. Hollingshead and Redlich found that rates of treated schizophrenia in New Haven were roughly 8 times as high in the lowest of five social strata as in the upper two strata [25]. They based their study, however, on prevalence of schizophrenia (the number of persons under treatment on a given date) rather than on incidence (new cases in a given period of time). There was a pronounced tendency for lower-status persons to be retained in the mental hospital longer than upper-status persons, thus greatly increasing the prevalence of illness in the lower-status strata at any given time. Although their limited data on the incidence of schizophrenia by class were inconclusive, Hollingshead and Redlich have conclusively documented certain other effects of social class. For example, upper-status schizophrenic patients were referred for treatment far more often by family or friends, while lower-status schizophrenics were referred by police and courts or by social agencies. Again, upper-status patients more often received psychotherapy; lower-status patients, organic therapy or custodial care. Further, lower-status patients were retained in hospital for substantially longer periods than were those of higher status.

There are many relevant studies on the distribution of mental illness among class and sub-cultural groups in the population of the United States and abroad. Several recent volumes present critical evaluations of knowledge and methodological problems in this area of research [7, 16, 53]. In summary, it can be reported that rural-urban differences in rates of hospitalization are slight and, indeed, variable; high geographical mobility is associated with high rates of hospitalized mental illness, though the direction of causal influence is not clear; and differences between racial and nationality groups appear to be highly related to social status, mobility, and cultural emphases.

Differences between the sexes seem largely to reflect cultural definitions of sex roles. Hospitalization of males ocurs somewhat more often at the younger ages but may simply reflect more frequent manifestations of aggression, leading to hospitalization by virtue of police action, or social response to failure to sustain the normal male role of regular employment. A number of studies have documented that symptomatology is markedly patterned by cultural norms [39] but there is no conclusive evidence that cultures differ greatly in rates of psychosis [4, 15].

The interpretations of such differentials as having been observed in rates of hospitalization for mental illness will remain difficult and equivocal until more precise information is available on social responses to various manifestations of mental illness in different segments of the population. There is evidence that the better educated members of the population are more aware of emotional problems and more receptive to the idea of seeking help for them [24]. It also appears that lower-status families may more often tolerate extreme deviance in a family member for months or years without seeking professional help. At the same time, lower-status persons in trouble are more likely to come to the attention of the police and are less able to afford alternative means of dealing with mental illness.

As a result of the problems of interpreting hospital statistics, the most significant knowledge of the role of social and cultural factors in the etiology of mental illness is likely to come from systematic studies of personality development, family functioning, and adaptation to stressful situations. In recent years an excellent beginning has been made through intensive clinical studies and through studies employing careful statistical designs and adequate controls to establish the nature of the differences in life experience between mentally ill persons and normal persons from the same social backgrounds [26, 48, 49]. In addition, major efforts to study the relationship of social and cultural factors to all forms of mental disorder in the community have been carried out by Leighton, Srole and others [30, 50]. Each study contributes only a few small places to the puzzle, but the outline of the picture is beginning to emerge.

Professional Resources for Dealing with Mental Disorder

Because severe mental disorder constitutes a threat to stable social relationships and often entails long periods of incapacitation, mental illness has been a matter of more governmental concern than have other forms of illness. Each state in the United States has enacted laws which specify the circumstances and the procedure by which a person may be declared insane and therefore deprived of his liberty [45], and all states provide hospitals for the long-term care of the insane. But the primary resource for the care and treatment of the mentally ill is not the institutional apparatus.

The mental health professions

The primary responsibility for the diagnosis and care of the mentally ill rests, of course, with the medical profession, or, more specifically, with the psychiatrist. As of 1960, the American Psychiatric Association had approximately 10 thousand members. To qualify for membership (in associate status), a physician must have completed one year of psychiatric residency training or one year of practice in a mental hospital. A substantially smaller number of psychiatrists qualify for certification by the American Board of Examiners in Psychiatry and Neurology, which requires that the candidate complete three years of residency training in an approved institution, secure an additional two years of relevant experience, and pass comprehensive written and oral examinations. Psychoanalytic training normally requires an additional three to five years. There were less than one thousand qualified psychoanalysts in the United States in 1960.

Prior to World War II, membership in the American Psychiatric Association was less than 4000. The demand for trained psychiatrists was greatly increased during World War II, as a consequence of the high rate both of initial rejections and of discharges of military personnel for psychiatric disability. The Federal government contributed greatly to the training of additional psychiatrists through the programs of the Veterans Administration and the National Institute of Mental Health. Although great progress has been achieved both in the number of psychiatrists trained and in the quality of psychiatric training programs, the demand for trained psychiatrists has continued to increase at an even more rapid rate. Only a small proportion of psychiatrists are involved in the treatment of institutionalized patients; many more are engaged in private practice.

The largest single professional group serving the mentally ill in the community consists of social workers. There are over 80 thousand persons serving as social workers, but only about 22,500 are members of the National Association of Social Workers and only about 2500 are fully qualified psychiatric social workers. In addition to the psychiatric social workers, however, many other social workers are employed in agencies providing services to meet mental health needs of individuals and families. They serve as interviewers and counselors in a wide variety of community programs and often serve as the chief liaison between the family and the hospitalized mental patient.

In recent years psychologists and public health nurses have been increasingly involved in mental health activities in the community. Psychologists, psychiatric nurses, and occupational therapists also play important roles in the mental hospital.

Institutional organization

The mental hospitals constitute the most costly and most heavily staffed facility for dealing with mental illness. To serve the needs of over 600 thousand patients, the mental hospitals employ over 150 thousand full-time staff members; more than one-half are nursing assistants or attendants and another one-fourth are maintenance personnel. Psychiatrists constitute only approximately 2 per cent of the full-time personnel of mental hospitals [41].

A substantial number of psychiatrists are involved in community mental health clinics, of which there were about 700 operating full-time and about 600 operating part-time in the United States in 1960.[6] The mental health clinic is most often a team operation, involving a psychiatrist who serves as director and chief therapist, one or more social workers who conduct intake interviews and provide therapy to less disturbed patients and to family members, and a clinical psychologist or psychometrician who does diagnostic testing and occasionally conducts research. The major emphases of mental health clinics have been the emotional problems of children and the anxieties of their parents, and the extreme interpersonal or neurotic difficulties of married couples or single adults. These clinics are used to capacity almost as soon as they are opened. By virtue of their long waiting-lists, few clinics have managed to offer help to the acutely disturbed person who needs immediate attention.

In addition to the hospitals and the clinics there are the many community agencies which provide services to individuals and to families. These may offer specific mental health services—as in the case of many private physicians, school guidance personnel, marriage counselors in social agencies, or clergymen trained in pastoral counseling—or they may serve to direct persons with emotional difficulties to appropriate diagnostic or treatment services [44, 52].

Problems in the use of resources

Given the breadth of our professional resources and community organization for dealing with mental illness, it is dismaying that they do not more adequately meet the needs of the acutely ill. It sometimes appears that our most highly trained personnel deal with the least pressing problems. The private practice of medicine is vastly more rewarding financially than is service in a mental hospital. The operation of clinics to serve the mildly distressed neurotic is much less demanding than efforts to assess and deal with incipient psychotic breakdown. It is possible to justify many present policies on the ground that they serve "preventive" functions, and to some degree this is probably true. Meanwhile, however, acutely disturbed persons in many communities are unable to get any help short of hospitalization. A study of hospitalized patients in Washington, D.C., for example, revealed that patient and families met rebuff after rebuff in their efforts to secure help before hospitalization and experienced many difficulties in arranging hospitalization [9].

---

[6] Statistics on the number and types of mental health clinics, and on the patients served, are compiled and published periodically by the Biometrics Branch, National Institute of Mental Health.

The Patient in the Mental Hospital

The meaning of hospitalization to the patient

Once the patient is in the hospital, the nature of his problem has been at least temporarily defined for family and associates. For the patient himself, however, the meaning of hospitalization is much more complex. He is not merely a sick person who can look forward to a brief period of treatment and care. As Enid Mills has observed, for mental patients:

> . . . admission to hospital is a public acknowledgement of an illness which profoundly affects their relationships with their family and the society in which they live. Their judgment, their competence to handle their responsibilities, even their feelings and wishes, become suspect, and they are liable to find everything they may say or do discounted as mere aberrations. Because of this, few people will readily accept the implication of becoming a hospital patient, and their experience in hospital will in turn affect the way in which they regard their illness [37].

The large, relatively isolated, prison-like mental hospitals are a product of late nineteenth century thinking—an effort to deal efficiently with mental patients by establishing large institutions which could be run by bureaucratic regimentation rather than by personalized attention. These enormous state institutions may have had some advantages as a substitute for jailing of mental patients, but in comparison with the best asylums and rest homes of the early nineteenth century, they represent a substantial setback [27].

Goffman has described some of the essential characteristics of the large, regimented mental hospital, a "total institution" which processes inmates in its impersonal way [22]. The newly admitted patient seldom receives any introduction to staff or to other patients or any orientation to the regimes and expectations to which he will be subject. His personal belongings and those trappings which serve to symbolize his identity are often taken from him. He is an inmate, subject to the rules of the institution and often to the whims of its least-trained personnel. Under these circumstances, the dominant motivation of the patient is to get out, which entails learning to control or at least conceal certain impulses and to present the kind of demeanor which will lead to release.

Social structure and interaction in the mental hospital

Roughly 85 per cent of all mental hospital patients are in state mental hospitals. The large majority of these patients have been legally committed to the hospital, which thus has a custodial as well as a therapeutic responsibility for the patient. Physicians comprise only about 2 per cent of the staffs of public mental hospitals; graduate nurses, less than 5 per cent;

while other nurses and nursing assistants (frequently known as attendants) comprise over half of the total employee staffs.

The public mental hospital usually operates on a minimal budget. Salaries are not competitive with those in the larger community, and the attendants or nursing aides therefore tend to come from the ranks of the unskilled and poorly educated. There is a tremendous gap in cultural level and in social status between the medical staff and the attendant staff. The "mobility blocked" nature of roles in the mental hospital, coupled with the impossible span of control designated by the formal organizational structure and with the difference between the goals and conceptions about mental illness held by the medical staff and those held by the attendant staff give rise to an informal organizational system which often sets the atmosphere of the hospital [3, 14].

Although supervision of the wards and all decisions relating to patient care and release from the hospital are the responsibilities of the medical personnel, the limited number of physicians available in most public hospitals precludes any substantial amount of contact between doctor and patients. The doctors and even the graduate nurses must spend much of their time in maintaining records and handling problems of patient disposition. As a consequence, in many hospitals it is the attendants who control the operations of the wards, largely by their control over access of patients to physicians and of physicians to information about patients. One of the most significant influences for more adequate mental hospital care has been the increased attention in recent years to recruitment, training and supervision of the attendant staffs [21].

Even the most influential private and teaching hospitals have problems. In their study of a psychoanalytically-oriented prestigious private hospital, Stanton and Schwartz described the problems of communication between staff members in various roles and the impact of staff disagreements on the emotional state of the patients [51]. Episodes of excited or upset behavior frequently occurred when the patient's therapist and the ward administrator or another staff member were in disagreement about the treatment of the patient. Often the patient's upset behavior subsided rapidly following a resolution of staff differences.

Caudill has studied role perceptions, communication patterns, patient concerns, and the occurrence of collective disturbance in a university hospital [6]. The perceptions of various categories of staff and of patients as to their mutual relationships were seldom congruent, and gave rise to frequent misunderstandings. Where such misunderstandings involved major concerns of staff groups or of patients, there was a tendency toward mutual avoidance and withdrawal, leading to a rise of tensions which then resulted in a collective disturbance. The re-establishment of communication appeared to lead to a decline in tension and excitement. A somewhat similar pattern, characterized as cyclical oscillations, was noted by Rapoport in his study of ideology and patient care in a therapeutic community [42]. The unit studied by Rapoport was expressly designed to avoid the hierarchical and coercive character of the more typical mental hospital [28]. This and other studies of small, well-staffed mental hospitals make clear that the task of providing a therapeutic milieu, coping with the diverse needs of patients (many of which have nothing to do with their being ill or disturbed), coping with the staff's inevitable anxieties that do derive from work with disturbed persons, and, finally, preparing the patient for return as an effective participant in the community poses a number of problems not yet mastered.

Apart from increased knowledge of institutional dynamics and therapeutic processes, studies of mental hospital wards have made clear that even severely ill patients retain a good bit of their capacity for collective social life. Friendship patterns and clique formation tend to occur on much the same basis as in the outside world, though the complexity of ward social organization declines with increasing severity of illness. Dunham and Weinberg note that the inmate culture serves at least four functions for patients:

> First, it provides the patient with ways by which he can defend himself against the impact of the attendant culture. Second, it enables the new patients introduced into a milieu of mentally abnormal persons to make some sort of adjustment to the other patients. Third, it facilitates the new patient in coming to terms with the requirements of hospital life. Finally, it develops and transmits techniques which will expedite release [14].

Community Aspects of Rehabilitation

The return of the patient from the mental hospital to the community is a tremendously important symbolic transition for patient and family, but it does not usually represent a return of the patient to full role functioning. Depending on the nature of the illness and the length of hospitalization, the patient may still manifest various symptoms of illness or at least display uncertainty and anxiety. In most state hospital systems, the patient will be returned home for trial visits or for indefinite periods for up to one year before being formally discharged from the hospital. If there are periods of regression into more acute stages, the patient can be returned to the hospital without going through additional legal action for commitment.

Unfortunately, there is usually a sharp discontinuity between the care provided by the hospital and the services available to ex-patient and family in the community. In many states, mental hospitals are under state jurisdiction while community mental health programs are under local jurisdiction, and communication between the two systems is poor and unpredictable [20].

The patient in the family

A number of studies have investigated the relationship between the patient's ability to function in the community and the characteristics of the setting to which he returns. Release from the hospital depends in part on the pressure exerted by family members to have the patient back, or, conversely, on their reluctance or even refusal to accept him. Once the patient is returned, the expectations of those with whom he lives become a major factor in influencing his remaining in the community. Tolerance of deviance and of a low level of instrumental performance may permit patients who manifest large residuals of symptomatic behavior to remain, while high demands for conventional and instrumentally effective behavior may result in sending back to the hospital even patients with relatively slight deficits in performance.

In a study of a cross-section of male psychotics released from mental hospitals in the Boston area, Freeman and Simons found a marked difference between the level of work performance and social participation of adult patients living in parental homes and those in conjugal settings [19]. More than three-fifths of the former patients in conjugal settings were rated high in both work performance and social participation, as against less than one-fifth of those in parental families. More than half of the former patients living in parental homes were rated low in work performance and social participation, as against only 7 per cent of the former patients living with their wives. As would be expected, many more patients living in conjugal homes were returned to the hospital when their performance was low. Similar findings have been noted in a study by Brown of chronic schizophrenic patients discharged from mental hospitals near London [5]. Patients returned from the hospital to parental homes or to live with siblings were more likely to remain in the community than those who returned to live with their wives. Most successful of all among these chronic patients were those who arranged to live in lodgings where they could avoid intimate contact with others; least successful were those who lived in hostels or shelters for the "down and out."

In general, there are substantial differences in the performance of a patient who has experienced many years of hospitalization and that of the person who was hospitalized for a brief period of acute distress. Quite apart from the psychologically devastating effects which many years in the chronic ward of a mental hospital have on him, the former patient is in need of resocialization and acceptance if he is to build up an image of himself as an adequate member of society. After a long interval, the patient's family roles are likely to have been redistributed: he cannot easily fit into the old patterns of expectations, for they have disappeared [9]. Wives who have had to take over the role of breadwinner for the family and who have become accustomed to other responsibilities and freedoms are often reluctant to yield them to the returned husband. Husbands who have worked out new regimes after the hospitalization of their wives may be unwilling to go back to former arrangements. Parents, who have in the past carried full responsibility for the dependent child, are more often willing to accept a reversion to this role and are more tightly bound by prevailing mores to make a home for the child, whatever his age or condition [37].

The actual dynamics of family relationships after hospitalization for mental illness have been little studied. There is evidence that the social participation of former patients is substantially lower than that of matched controls [26] and it may be hypothesized that those patients who do return to and remain in the conjugal family will tend to show a high degree of emotional interdependence. There is also a good deal of fragmentary evidence that the closer (physically and psychologically) the patient remains to the family and the community during his hospitalization, the better the chances for his resumption of stable role relationships afterwards.

Public attitudes toward mental illness

The terms "mental health" and "mental illness" are not widely used in the vernacular. "Insanity" and "insane asylum" have been terms with strong negative connotations, tinged with dread. By and large, the public image of insanity has been the stereotype of the raving maniac, dangerous and bizarre in his behavior. Despite a good deal of effort by voluntary and professional organizations in the field of mental health, the mass media have perpetuated this stereotype. Yet, as Nunnally has demonstrated, the lay public actually has more sophistication about mental illness than is shown in most of the radio and television representations, current fiction and magazine and press accounts depicting the mentally ill almost entirely in stereotyped terms [38].

The stigmatization of mental illness has been widely recognized and deplored by humanitarian leaders for several centuries. The mental hygiene movement in the United States had its inception in the desire both to improve patient care in the mental hospitals and to combat the stigma attaching to severe mental illness.[7] Yet no systematic attempts were made

[7] The prime mover in the establishment, in 1909, of the National Committee for Mental Hygiene was Clifford Beers, a former mental patient who was determined to change public conceptions of mental illness. His book, *A Mind That Found Itself*, became the rallying cry for the movement.

to assess public attitudes toward mental illness until after World War II. Since 1948 there have been a number of studies which have sought to assess the public's knowledge about mental illness and mental health services.[8] Although these studies have differed somewhat in their aims and emphases, they generally attest to the negative image that the public has of mental illness and to widespread ignorance about treatment and mental health services. The deviance represented by mental illness gives rise to apprehension and avoidance. While most people deny that they themselves experience such feelings, they readily attribute them to others.

The Cummings have characterized public response to mental illness as a pattern of "isolation and denial" [11]. That is, the public tends to wall off the mentally ill, both figuratively and literally, and would prefer to deny that they exist. There are some indications that publicity attending recent developments in patient care—especially those associated with the wide-spread use of tranquillizers and with open-door policies in a number of hospitals—have brought about an increase in the level of public awareness and information, but definitive data are not yet available.

The community approach to treatment and rehabilitation

One of the most promising developments in the care of seriously ill patients has taken place in England and in several countries in northwestern Europe. This has been the integration of local community resources with those of the mental hospital. In some programs, as in that developed by Querido and his associates in Amsterdam, the primary emphasis has been upon first aid in the community. Mental health personnel are available at all times to deal with psychiatric emergencies at the scene, and to provide continuing care in the community. In other communities the primary emphasis has been on the flexible use of the mental hospital, outpatient clinics, day hospitals, and "halfway houses" to provide comprehensive care which will minimize long-term hospitalization [34]. In keeping with the recommendations of the Royal Commission on the Law Relating to Mental Illness and Mental Deficiency, British mental hospitals have moved far toward the goal of treating mental patients non-coercively [43]. Open wards, minimal periods of involuntary confinement for markedly disturbed patients, and a willingness to experiment with various forms of social therapy and hospital organizations have permitted more adequate care without requiring new hospital construction. The interaction between such programs, community attitudes and patient care is described by Duncan MacMillan, Superintendent of the Mapperlay Hospital at Nottingham:

> An improved attitude to the hospital gradually leads to a more enlightened attitude to mental illness in general, and this influences the

[8] See references [8] and [24] for additional references.

> attitude of the patient to his illness. He seeks treatment earlier, and is more cooperative because he is less apprehensive, and is willing to accept the help of the mental hospital as if it were a general hospital. The patient is also influenced by the atmosphere of the hospital, and the staff of the admission wards believe that the most important factor in gaining the cooperation of the short-term compulsory patient is the attitude of the other patients [34].

The Possibilities of a Preventive Approach

Impressive as have been advances in treatment and cure of disease, the major contributions of science to health and longevity have come primarily through discovering methods of prevention. Through environmental sanitation, prophylactic innoculation, the assessment of health hazards and their elimination by legislative or educational action, the public health approach has made it possible for large numbers of humans to live longer. Mental illness has only recently become of concern to the field of public health. The National Mental Health Act of 1946, which established the National Institute of Mental Health within the United States Public Health Service, provided—for the first time—a substantial measure of federal support for research on the diagnosis, etiology, and treatment of mental illness. In 1955, Congress appropriated a large sum for "an objective, thorough, and nationwide analysis and re-evaluation of the human and economic problems of mental illness" [1]. The resultant series of reports [1, 24, and 44] has put heaviest emphasis on the training of personnel for research and treatment, the elaboration of nonmedical community services and resources, new approaches to patient care, and—above all—increased support of long-range basic research.

Outright prevention of illness is rarely possible without an adequate knowledge of etiology. Psychoses associated with nutritional deficiencies have been virtually eliminated in the United States, and a marked decrease in new cases of general paresis has been achieved. The illnesses which contribute most to our mental hospital population—the functional psychoses and the disorders of old age—appear to be of multifactorial etiology which is not subject to sufficiently precise specification and control to permit comparable preventive efforts. Even in the instance of functional psychoses, however, a measure of prevention may be secured through partial control of factors associated with high disease incidence. Thus, increased use of genetic counseling, more adequate prenatal care, prevention of maternal deprivation, and the provision of support and reassurance to persons undergoing extreme stress might be expected to lead to some decrease in the incidence of psychotic breakdown both through reducing the number of vulnerable persons and through diminishing the effects of stress.

Mental health education, particularly with reference to child-rearing, has received much attention in recent years and has strong advocates as an instrument of prevention. Research on personality development suggests, however, that available knowledge of the determinants of a healthy personality is less adequate than many psychiatrists had assumed. Moreover, the most significant factors influencing personality development in the family do not appear to relate to parental ignorance or sophistication but to parental needs and pressures. As a result of uncertainties and disagreements on these topics, many of the delegates at a recent national conference expressed the view that mental health education should for the present aim primarily at changing public conceptions of mental illness and of the means of treatment [36].

Perhaps the greatest promise for the future is in the further development of social psychiatry, combining long-term systematic study of the distribution and correlates of mental illness with the design of more flexible treatment programs aimed at meeting the needs of specific population groups. Regardless of the cause of psychotic symptomatology, it is conceivable that overt psychotic behavior may be prevented by the use of drugs or other biological interventions. Even in this case, however, there is likely to be a need for more adequate knowledge of the ways in which the distressed person can best be recognized, given assistance and reincorporated into full social participation.

References

1. *Action for Mental Health, Final Report of the Joint Commission on Mental Health.* New York: Basic Books, Inc., 1961.
2. Albee, George W., *Mental Health Manpower Trends.* New York: Basic Books, Inc., 1959.
3. Belknap, Ivan, *Human Problems of a State Mental Hospital.* New York: McGraw-Hill Book Company, Inc., 1956.
4. Benedict, Paul R. and Irving Jacks, "Mental Illness in Primitive Societies," *Psychiatry,* 17 (November, 1954), 377–90.
5. Brown, George W., "Experiences of Discharged Chronic Schizophrenic Patients in Various Types of Living Group," *The Milbank Memorial Fund Quarterly,* 37 (April, 1959), 105–31.
6. Caudill, William, *The Mental Hospital as a Small Society.* Cambridge: Harvard University Press, 1958.
7. *Causes of Mental Disorders: A Review of Epidemiological Knowledge.* New York: Milbank Memorial Fund, 1961.
8. Clausen, John A., *Sociology and the Field of Mental Health.* New York: Russell Sage Foundation, 1956.
9. ——— and Marian R. Yarrow, eds., "The Impact of Mental Illness on the Family," *Journal of Social Issues,* 11 (1955), 3–67.
10. Cohen, Yehudi A., *Social Structure and Personality.* New York: Holt, Rinehart & Winston, Inc., 1961, Chap. 15.

11. Cumming, Elaine and John Cumming, *Closed Ranks*. Cambridge: Harvard University Press, 1957.
12. Davis, Kingsley, "Mental Hygiene and the Class Structure," *Psychiatry*, 1 (February, 1938), 55–65.
13. Dinitz, S., M. Lefton, S. Angrist, and B. Pasamanick, "Psychiatric and Social Attributes as Predictors of Case Outcome in Mental Hospitalization," *Social Problems*, 8 (Spring, 1961), 322–28.
14. Dunham, H. Warren and S. Kirson Weinberg, *The Culture of the State Mental Hospital*. Detroit: Wayne State University Press, 1960.
15. Eaton, Joseph W. and Robert J. Weil, *Culture and Mental Disorders*. New York: The Free Press of Glencoe, Inc., 1955.
16. *Encyclopedia of Mental Health*. New York: Franklin Watts, 1963.
17. Faris, Robert E. L. and H. Warren Dunham, *Mental Disorders in Urban Areas*. Chicago: University of Chicago Press, 1939.
18. Freeman, Howard E. and Ozzie G. Simmons, "Feeling of Stigma Among Relatives of Former Mental Patients," *Social Problems*, 8 (Spring, 1961), 312–21.
19. ———, "Mental Patients in the Community: Family Settings and Performance Levels," *American Sociological Review*, 23 (April, 1958), 147–54.
20. ———, "Treatment Experiences of Mental Patients and Their Families," *American Journal of Public Health*, 51 (September, 1961), 1266–73.
21. Greenblatt, Milton, Daniel J. Levinson, and Richard H. Williams, eds., *The Patient and the Mental Hospital*. New York: The Free Press of Glencoe, Inc., 1957.
22. Goffman, Erving, *Asylums*. Garden City, New York: Doubleday & Company, Inc., 1961.
23. Goldhamer, Herbert and Andrew Marshall, *Psychosis and Civilization*. New York: The Free Press of Glencoe, Inc., 1953.
24. Gurin, Gerald, Joseph Veroff, and Sheila Feld, *Americans View Their Mental Health*. New York: Basic Books, Inc., 1960.
25. Hollingshead, August B. and Frederick C. Redlich, *Social Class and Mental Illness*. New York: John Wiley & Sons, Inc., 1958.
26. Jackson, Don D., ed., *The Etiology of Schizophrenia*. New York: Basic Books, Inc., 1960.
27. Jones, Kathleen, *Lunacy, Law and Conscience, 1744–1845*. New York: Humanities Press, 1955.
28. Jones, Maxwell, *The Therapeutic Community*. New York: Basic Books, Inc., 1953.
29. Kohn, Melvin L. and John T. Clausen, "Social Isolation and Schizophrenia," *American Sociological Review*, 20 (June, 1955), 265–73.
30. Leighton, Alexander H., *My Name is Legion*. New York: Basic Books, Inc., 1959.
31. ———, John A. Clausen, and Robert N. Wilson, eds., *Explorations in Social Psychiatry*. New York: Basic Books, Inc., 1957.
32. Lemert, Edwin M., "Paranoia and the Dynamics of Exclusion," *Sociometry*, 25 (March, 1962), 3–20.

33. Lennard, Henry L. and Arnold Bernstein, *The Anatomy of Psychotherapy*. New York: Columbia University Press, 1960.
34. Macmillan, Duncan, "Community Treatment of Mental Illness," *Lancet* (July 26, 1958), 201–204.
35. Malzberg, Benjamin and Everett S. Lee, *Migration and Mental Disease*. New York: Social Science Research Council, 1956.
36. *Mental Health Education: A Critique*. Philadelphia: Pennsylvania Mental Health, Inc., 1960.
37. Mills, Enid, *Living with Mental Illness*. London: Routledge & Kegan Paul, Ltd., 1962.
38. Nunnally, Jum C., *Popular Conceptions of Mental Health*. New York: Holt, Rinehart & Winston, Inc., 1961.
39. Opler, Mervin K., ed., *Culture and Mental Health*. New York: The Macmillan Company, 1959.
40. Pasamanick, Benjamin, ed., *Epidemiology of Mental Disorder*. Washington, D.C.: American Association for the Advancement of Science, 1959.
41. *Patients in Mental Institutions, 1957*. Washington, D.C.: Government Printing Office, 1960.
42. Rapoport, Robert N., *Community as Doctor*. London: Tavistock Publications, 1960.
43. *Report of the Royal Commission on the Law Relating to Mental Illness and Mental Deficiency*. London: Her Majesty's Stationery Office, 1957.
44. Robinson, Reginald, David F. DeMarche, and Mildred K. Wagle, *Community Resources in Mental Health*. New York: Basic Books, Inc., 1960.
45. Roemer, Ruth, "Mental Health Legislation Affecting Patient Care," *American Journal of Public Health*, 52 (April, 1962), 592–99.
46. Rose, Arnold M., ed., *Mental Health and Mental Disorder*. New York: W. W. Norton & Company, Inc., 1957.
47. Sampson, Harold, *et al.*, "The Mental Hospital and Marital Family Ties," *Social Problems*, 9 (Fall, 1961), 141–55.
48. Sarbin, Theodore R., *Studies in Behavior Pathology*. New York: Holt, Rinehart & Winston, Inc., 1961.
49. Spiegel, John P. and Norman W. Bell, "The Family of the Psychiatric Patient," *in American Handbook of Psychiatry*. New York: Basic Books, Inc., 1959, pp. 114–49.
50. Srole, Leo, *et al.*, *Mental Health in the Metropolis*. New York: McGraw-Hill Book Company, Inc., 1962.
51. Stanton, Alfred H. and Morris S. Schwartz, *The Mental Hospital*. New York: Basic Books, Inc., 1954.
52. Stevenson, George S., *Mental Health Planning for Social Action*. New York: McGraw-Hill Book Company, Inc., 1956.
53. Zubin, Joseph, ed., *Field Studies in the Mental Disorders*. New York: Grune & Stratton, Inc., 1961.

Part II

PRACTITIONERS, PATIENTS, AND MEDICAL SETTINGS

7

MEDICAL EDUCATION

Howard S. Becker
Blanche Geer

Each year, some 8500 students begin a four-year undergraduate medical training in the United States. The medical schools in which such training is given are ideal laboratories for the study of such sociological problems as the development of the self, processes of group formation, and institutional structure. The research that has been done has produced a body of findings, hypotheses, and insights in which social scientists as well as medical educators may find interest.

Medical educators are concerned—perhaps more now than in the past—with the kind of training they give their students: they are worried about the kinds of physicians being turned out; they have begun to experiment with new methods of selection; they are interested in trying new teaching methods; and they wish to redesign their curricula. The perspectives and findings of sociological research may help them to deal with the problems of medical education and to implement changes in the educational process.

Recruitment

Medical students tend to be recruited from the higher socio-economic groups in our society. More than half of those graduating in 1960 had fathers who were professionals, proprietors, or managers [28]. On the other hand, a substantial minority had fathers in white-collar, manual, or farm work. It has been shown, too, that in the period 1900–1950 there has been an increasing democratization of recruitment, with progressively increasing proportions of physicians tending to come from lower ranks in the social structure [1].

The process of recruitment into medicine—the choice by persons of a medical career and progressive commitment to it—appears to vary greatly. Many come from families where the father or a close relative is a practicing physician. In these cases, the process described by Oswald Hall probably is crucial:

> . . . one can see why doctors tend to be recruited from the families of professional workers. The latter possess the mechanisms for generating and nurturing the medical ambition. Only the members of a profession can translate the public protestations of the profession into the vernacular of useful advice. . . . In most cases family or friends played a significant role by envisaging the career line and reinforcing the efforts of the recruit. They accomplished the latter by giving encouragement, helping establish the appropriate routines, arranging the necessary privacy, discouraging anomalous behavior, and defining the day-to-day rewards [15].

Other students have no such advantages. They tend to make their decision to enter medicine somewhat later. Little is known about the processes involved, about the way ambitions are generated and nurtured without parental help [27].[1]

The Effects of Medical Education

Much of the research done by sociologists on medical education has concerned itself with the consequences of medical education for the student. How does he change over the four years? In what ways does his ex-

---

1 See Chap. 8 for a comparison with recruitment processes into nursing.

perience in school affect him? In what ways has it left him untouched? How will his experience in school affect his practice as a doctor?

A medical education, first of all and most obviously, gives the student the rudiments of medical knowledge and technique. He learns the signs and symptoms of many diseases. He learns how to take a medical history from a patient and how to perform a physical examination. He learns to order laboratory tests and to interpret their results. He acquires the skill of arriving at a diagnosis by deductive reasoning. He learns the various methods of treatment that are available for the conditions he diagnoses.

The efficiency of the modern medical school in inculcating information is attested by the student's success in passing national board examinations and state licensing examinations. Yet the acquisition of knowledge, the most obvious effect of medical education, may not be lasting. Peterson, *et al.*, in a study of general practitioners in North Carolina, found only a very slight relationship between the rank the doctor held in his medical school graduating class and the quality of his practice [26]. The doctors who had ranked high in their graduating classes were only a little more likely to perform a complete physical examination than those who had ranked poorly. Those who ranked in the top 30 per cent of their graduating classes were likely to practice in a more knowledgeable way but "the difference is not striking, and the range of performance even among the top group of students was wide" [26].

Furthermore, even this slight difference tends to disappear among those doctors who have been out of school more than a few years. The relationship between rank in graduating class and quality of practice appears only for the men between 28 and 35, who have just begun practice, and disappears completely for those over 35 [26].

What one learns in school may not be as important as the conditions under which he practices afterward: if patients and colleagues do not expect a doctor to maintain a high level of medical knowledge, he may quickly lose it.

Sociologists, in fact, have concerned themselves less with the learning of specific medical facts and techniques than with the more generalized effects of medical education. In particular, they have studied the medical student's acquisition of the values of the medical profession. They assume that the institutional system of medicine, if it is to perform effectively the necessary function of maintaining the level of health in the society, must operate on the basis of such values, for example, as affective neutrality and universalism. If this is the case, physicians (who occupy the key positions in the institutional system) must internalize the values. The medical school prepares doctors for their institutional roles by inculcating them.

Fox has argued that medical students acquire important values characteristic of the medical profession through the influence of their day-today experience in the medical school [13]. For instance, she suggests that students develop a tolerance for uncertainty, a characteristic point of view the practicing physician must have if he is to perform successfully. Similarly, she finds that students develop the ability to live up to the norm of detached concern: they learn how to be interested in a patient without becoming emotionally involved.

A study at the University of Kansas medical school concluded that students acquired at least the knowledge of certain basic medical values—two of which were likely to be important parts of the culture of medicine: the values of clinical experience and medical responsibility. Clinical experience is experience gained from actual medical practice as opposed to that acquired from laboratory research or reading in books and articles. Medical responsibility is the responsibility of the doctor for the welfare of his patient; it is the responsibility he has for the damage he may do to a patient if he performs badly and, conversely, for the good he can do if he performs properly [4]. It may not be as correct to say that students acquired the values of experience and responsibility as to say that they learned to think in the terms suggested by these phrases, that they acquired the perspectives associated with these phrases. While we do not know how long they continue to think in these terms, the evidence showed that they tended to organize their own views of their medical future in these terms. They tended to make choices among kinds of internships on the basis, for instance, of how much responsibility each kind allowed them to exercise [4]. Similarly, they use the notion of medical responsibility in assessing the desirability of possible specialties and organizational settings for practice [4].

Further research is needed to discover the extent to which practicing physicians base their actions on the values of experience and responsibility, and the situations of medical practice in which such values are maintained and those in which they are not.

Lay people, physicians, and sociologists alike have taken the view that one major effect of a medical education is to make the medical student more cynical and less idealistic. This view is based for the most part on the common observation that medical students lose interest in patients as people and come to regard them as mere embodiments of disease entities. Students appear to become callous in the face of death and human suffering. Eron, for instance, found that medical students tended to score higher on a "Cynicism" scale and lower on a "Humanitarian" scale as they moved through the four years of school [12]. Similarly, Christie and Merton report that seniors from several medical schools score higher on a scale which measures "Machiavellianism" than do college students, business executives, or Washington lobbyists [8]. Nathanson, comparing interviews of freshmen with those of senior medical students, concludes that freshmen are oriented to the interests of the patient and think of the colleague relationship as potentially subversive, while seniors stress the need for preserving the solidarity and protecting the interests of the professional group [25].

Nathanson, however, puts the matter of idealism and cynicism in a different perspective. She concludes, on the basis of her interview data, that students' conceptions of the doctor's role become more specific and less stereotyped as they go through school [25]. The findings of the Kansas study suggest that the apparent cynicism of the medical student is actually a consequence of the greater specificity of his perspectives [4]. On the one hand, the student's attitudes are specific to his role as student. He tends to ignore death and human suffering because, being a student and not a practicing physician, he is not in a position to do anything about either. Thus, he tends to regard patients as objects from which he can learn. In the second place, the students' ideas become much more specifically medical. When they enter school, they have only the ordinary lay notions about medicine. Many of these are unrealistic and would not serve as a practical guide to activity in the role of a physician. For instance, as both the Nathanson and the Kansas studies show, medical students enter school desiring to "help" people but with no technical understanding of how to do it. As they go through medical school they discover specific things that ought to be done. For instance, graduating students often said that they would see no more than twenty patients a day when they were in practice, so that they would have time to examine each one fully, realizing that this would limit their income. The desire to limit one's practice is idealistic, given the settings in which medicine is now practiced.

In short, while students may (from the layman's point of view) acquire a cynical veneer during the four years of medical school, they also acquire specific notions of how to implement the underlying idealism with which they entered medical school and propose to do this when they do become practicing physicians [3, 5].

Another effect of medical education is a growing tendency of the student as he moves through school to develop a professional self-image—to take on the identity of a doctor. Huntington showed that the proportion of students who thought of themselves primarily as doctors rather than students increased regularly from 31 per cent in the first year to 83 per cent at the end of the fourth year. She also showed that the student's tendency to think of himself primarily as a doctor is related to the kind of person he is dealing with. Students do not think the faculty define them as doctors and in dealing with the faculty do not think of themselves as doctors. On the other hand, they think patients do define them as doctors and 31 per cent of them view themselves accordingly [18]. (We should note that these students are from Western Reserve, a school in which students have close and continuing contact with patients from the beginning of the first year.)

Similarly, Nathanson found that freshmen do not think of themselves as doctors but that seniors do finally become satisfied that their image of themselves as doctors is accepted by others. However, students complained about not being recognized as doctors by their teachers during the third year, complaining particularly that they were not given sufficient responsibility for patients, something they regarded as an essential component of the doctor's role [25].

A final question which has provoked much research concerns the effect medical school has on the career choices made by the graduating student. Does it affect his decision to go into general practice or to specialize? Does it affect his choice of specialty?

Several studies indicate that medical school tends to cause students to shift their preference from general practice to a specialized practice. However, this simple statement masks a complex process. It appears that a certain number of students enter medical school definitely intending to specialize and in the main do not change their minds. Another group definitely intends to go into general practice. A few of them are likely to change their minds and decide that they would prefer to specialize. A sizable number of students enter medical school not knowing for sure what they want to do and it is this undecided group that accounts for the rise in the number of students who intend to specialize. In short, the educational experience affects mainly those who have made no firm career plans, pushing them in the direction of specialization [4, 10, 14, 16, 20, 22].

If medical education affects the career plans of those who are undecided, what accounts for the choices of those who have already made their minds up when they enter school? This appears to be related to the student's social background. Students who come from low income families, who come from rural areas, who have had greater financial difficulty in getting through school, tend to prefer general practice. The more well-to-do students prefer to specialize [10]. This is undoubtedly accounted for by the fact that specialization requires a considerably longer period of training during which the student makes very little money. Only those whose family background permits them to feel they can afford this extra period with low income are likely to choose specialization.

Why do the undecided (and a few of those who have decided early on general practice) eventually choose to specialize? Evidence from several studies indicates that students come to believe the body of knowledge necessary to perform adequately in general practice is too extensive to acquire in the relatively short time they spend in medical school and internship [4, 13, 22]. In fact, many doubt that anyone can properly master all the knowledge necessary. Therefore, they may decide to practice in a limited field. The effect of the medical school experience on a student's choice of specialty seems to be indirect.

Most students change their choice of specialty while they are in school. In one study only one-fifth of the students consistently chose the same field through all four years of school [20]. (However, many of them shifted back and forth and ended up choosing the one they had started with.) We do not know, from the data available, how many graduating students actually go into the specialties they say they are going into. We believe, however, that there is a good deal of changing even after graduation.

In short, it appears that medical school does not operate to produce a firm choice of a specialty. But it does have an effect. The Kansas study found that while students did not make firm choices of specialties, they acquired relatively stable criteria for choosing among specialties. Students varied—both among themselves and over time—in the importance they attached to different criteria. They also varied a great deal in how they assessed various specialties in relation to these criteria. They might disagree among themselves as to whether a particular specialty was interesting, provided an adequate income, and so on [4].

The Kansas study found that idealistic criteria such as the intrinsic medical interest of the field and the ability to help patients ranked very high, while wages and hours were seldom considered [4]. This finding is supported by the results of a survey of a national sample of American medical students. Cahalan, Collette, and Hilmer [5] report that the reasons most often given by medical students for preferring a specialty were: intellectual challenge and learning opportunity provided by the specialty (33 per cent); attractiveness of the subject matter or aims of the specialty (24 per cent); the certainty of benefits to patients (18 per cent); comprehensiveness of the specialty (16 per cent); a preference for dealing with the type of patients to be treated (14 per cent); and the nature of the practitioner's relationship to the patient (14 per cent). Beale and Kriesberg, analyzing other data from the same survey, report that while the number of students who think income and hours of work important tends to rise during the years in medical school, sizable majorities of the students in each school year say that having the opportunity to know their patients well and meeting particularly challenging diagnostic problems will be most important in their choices of a specialty [3].

To sum up, the effects of medical school are not clearcut or easy to discern. Students learn medical facts and acquire knowledge of medical technique. They acquire a working understanding of certain basic medical values, such as clinical experience and medical responsibility. They become less generally idealistic in a lay sense and more specifically idealistic in medical terms. They begin to think about possible modes of practice and choose among these, developing criteria on which to base their choices from their experience in the medical school.

One thing is certain: they never develop exactly as the faculty would wish them to. Medical educators are always uneasy, wishing they could do something to give their students more knowledge, better values, and more worthwhile perspectives on medical practice. To understand why students learn some things and do not learn others, we must understand the nature of the student's experience in medical school: the situation he faces, the resources he has to deal with them, and the solutions he eventually finds for the problems his situation poses.

Environment and Student Culture in Medical School

The environment freshmen encounter when they enter medical school is more academic than medical.[2] The student takes courses in the preclinical sciences (anatomy, biochemistry, physiology, and the like) taught by Ph.D.s whose career interests lie in the research of their disciplines rather than in medical practice. The student is further separated from the faculty by the fact that the large class is taught as a unit in which all students do the same work at the same time. It is a familiar environment—the same round of lectures, laboratories, reading, and examinations the student has known throughout his years in school and college. He seldom, if ever, sees clinical personnel or patients.

The emphasis upon the academic, and particularly upon examinations, catches the typical freshman unprepared. While he does not expect to begin treating patients right away and knows there will be courses and tests, he expects medical school to be different from college where much of his work seemed to have little direct bearing on his personal goals. In medical school, he thinks, everything will have practical application. He is that most idealistic of students—one who wants to learn for himself. He enters medical school convinced that medicine is the best of all professions, strongly committed to serving humanity, and highly motivated to learn everything the school can teach about what one must know in order to practice medicine [4].

The freshmen's values lead them to work 70 to 80 hours a week in the early months of medical school. But they find that no matter how hard they work, they cannot learn everything. Faced with an apparently insoluble problem, freshmen enter a period of doubt and confusion, marked by increasing interaction with fellow students in discussions of the best

[2] This discussion is largely based on a report of the Kansas study [4]. We think the school typical of most medical schools at present. There are, however, certain variations in curriculum and emphasis. In a few schools even freshmen see patients; in others, students get little clinical experience. Several schools involve students heavily in research, and in others the standard four-year program has recently been combined with undergraduate studies. These variations in curriculum may well produce different patterns of experience for students from that given here. Extensive research on the effects of curricular variation is needed.

way to study. The difficulties of the first examinations upset many students accustomed to good grades in college. Eventually, the freshmen agree that the best thing to do is to stop trying to learn everything, to decide instead which things are most important and concentrate on them [4].

At first students are divided on what criterion to use in selecting what is important. Some choose the things they think will be important when they get out into practice. Others decide the most important thing to do is to pass examinations. They try to find out what the faculty wants them to know and study only the things that are likely to appear on examinations. Their level of effort remains high, but they direct their efforts toward finding the most economical ways of learning. They prefer textbooks and lectures to experiments and demonstrations, and established facts to research and theory [4].

Initial barriers to interaction between members of student groups of different social backgrounds are broken down as the freshmen get to know each other as working associates in lab sections, and nearly all members of the class cooperate in sharing information derived from faculty "tips" and files of old examinations [4]. Thus, students find a collective solution to their common pressing problem—the fact that there is more to learn than they have time for in the time available.

In the clinical years, the student faces additional problems which arise in his new situation as part of the hospital environment. Academic studies now share importance with his new role as an apprentice who learns by doing many of the things his teacher does. Under the supervision of staff physicians and residents, the student takes histories from patients, performs physical examinations, undertakes therapeutic procedures, and makes his own differential diagnoses [4]. He must still deal with the faculty as teachers and examiners, but now has the additional problem of working closely with fellow students in the small groups in which they are assigned to ward duties on the various hospital services, and of carrying forward his learning in the hierarchical organization of the hospital where many others precede him in access to his chief source of learning, the patient [4].

Clinical faculty members are practicing physicians with many duties besides that of teaching medical students. They teach and supervise the work of resident physicians and interns and they have medical responsibility for patients and administrative responsibilities on their services. This means that the medical student is now at the bottom of the ladder, outranked in experience, responsibility, and access to the faculty by a hierarchy of other learners. The student has the further handicap that, of all these categories of learners, he is the only one without legal authority to practice medicine.

The very high status of his physician-teachers, his own lowly place in the hospital hierarchy, and the introduction of patients as a chief source of learning provide the student with many new problems. Most of his examinations are now oral; he also has frequent examination-like encounters at a patient's bedside or in the hall during rounds when the faculty quizzes him on the diagnosis and progress of a patient he has been assigned.

This is a very personal style of teaching, without the privacy of the examination paper. A student may be humiliated before fellow students and make a bad impression on the faculty if he gives a wrong answer. Since a staff physician may ask whatever he wishes—unconstrained, as he would be in the formal teaching situation, by the subject matter already covered in the course—students regard the faculty as unpredictable and capricious. The textbook is no longer good authority; it is outweighed by the staff physician's many years of clinical experience. Since students feel it necessary to make a good impression, they are careful to give high priority to learning and doing the things they think will please the faculty [4].

The fact that students are now assigned to a given hospital service in small groups of only 8 to 15 makes it necessary for them to develop ways of dealing with each other. Students expect one another to do a fair share of ward or clinic work assigned them as a group. They reach collective agreements on the amount of this work that members of the group will do. They discourage a student who wishes to do more than the others because his efforts might put the group in a bad light. Students set work norms only in situations where the faculty does not set a quantitatively defined goal, and where limitation of work will not reduce the amount of learning of facts and procedures the students think necessary for practice. Students cooperate to help their fellows avoid making a bad impression on the faculty by doing their work for them on the ward in emergencies and help each other acquire clinical experience by trading off patients or opportunities to perform therapeutic procedures. A student who has several patients with a given disease, for example, may trade one with a fellow student who has not had any [4].

Students value clinical experience with patients highly and strive to get it in every way they can. They want most to see patients with the diseases they expect to treat frequently when they get into practice. They want to have first-hand experience with what is described in their texts, and value patients who provide this. During their time on wards and in clinics they pursue their superiors (particularly the residents) to get information from them—practical tips on diagnosis and treatment which they call "pearls" and detailed descriptions of what to do for patients in particular circumstances. They are eager to examine patients who provide opportunities to practice the skills of hearing, seeing, and feeling, and to increase their ability to recognize diagnostic signs by repeated experience with such things as the distinctive rash of measles or the heart murmurs characteristic of the several varieties of heart disease.

As bottom men in the hospital hierarchy, students further try to prepare themselves for practice by getting as much medical responsibility as their situation allows. They seek out opportunities to perform therapeutic or diagnostic procedures or carry out treatment based on their own findings. Things students do themselves which involve (or are believed to involve) some degree of danger to the patient and skill on the student's part are particularly valued. Students see these procedures (lumbar taps, or delivering babies, for instance) being performed by the licensed physicians of the hospital—interns, residents or staff members—and base their self-esteem on being allowed to take similar responsibility for patients and handle it well. They dislike work (the admissions laboratory tests, for example) which is not, in their eyes, the work of practicing physicians, even though it has been assigned them by the faculty [4].

In many ways the students' collective perspectives and the student culture these comprise run counter to faculty wishes. The freshmen work very hard, and the faculty appreciates this, but they solve the problem of having too much to learn by directing their efforts toward finding out "what the faculty wants" and studying the things that will be on examinations—a solution far from satisfactory to the teacher who wants students to think for themselves and work up to their own capacities. Freshmen often reject faculty efforts to get them to adopt critical attitudes toward textbooks; they seldom (from the faculty point of view) take enough interest in theory and research. While there is disagreement among first-year faculty members on the proper direction of student effort, most of them find the freshmen too pragmatic and fact-bound [4].

The clinical faculty, itself more varied, is even more varied in its demands upon students. The staff does not approve of student efforts to please with the "right" answer. It worries when students shirk certain duties and restrict production on group assignments. It does not see why students spend so much effort and time in pursuit of clinical experience and medical responsibility. On the contrary, staff members wish students would learn material for its own sake, not theirs. They want students to carry out all assignments responsibly. They want them to realize that medical school is only the first step in a life-long medical education, that there will be more than enough opportunities to get experience and exercise responsibility after school. They cannot understand students' exclusive interest in common diseases and their failure to take advantage of the opportunities afforded by the medical center to see rare cases seldom encountered in practice [4].

The direction of students' effort therefore often diverges from faculty wishes. In view of the student's subordinate position, his high motivation to learn which continues throughout four years of school, his respect—even awe—of the faculty and his earnest efforts to please, how can we account for this divergence? For in spite of their desire to do what the faculty wants, in pursuing their notion of learning what they think they will need to practice medicine, students exercise a great deal of autonomy.

The Faculty and Student Autonomy

Across the country, medical faculties complain about the results of their work and search for ways to do better. It may be true that teaching has not yet reached the status of an exact science; yet it seems clear that some of the faculty complaints of the difficulties in teaching are more related to the development of student culture than to the state of the teaching arts. Several aspects of the organization of medical school faculties and their beliefs prevent them from using their power to make the students do what they want—that is, a medical faculty could have a much more powerful impact on student culture than it ordinarily does.

One very important fact that limits the action a medical faculty can take is the real lack of consensus among its members. Medical educators will agree on very general propositions, such as that students need to be trained at least to the extent that they will not endanger human life when they enter practice. But beyond these very general and somewhat vague propositions, there is little consensus on what should be done in the day-to-day operation of a medical school. Teachers do not agree on the best methods of teaching; some are in favor of "spoon-feeding," others prefer a method that maximizes the amount of independent thinking a student must do [4]. Nor do teachers agree on medical matters; they are apt, for instance, to disagree on the kind of treatment appropriate for a given disease (the differences between internal medicine and surgery in this respect are striking). They differ also on the importance of the social and psychological aspects of illness and medical care [6]. It would not be unfair to say that the working consensus of the faculty is minimal, best represented by the schedule of the curriculum, which allocates a specific number of hours to each discipline or specialty. We do not mean, however, that everybody is happy with this allocation; rather, they are resigned or adjusted to it. A study of a national sample of clinical faculty members provides interesting data on this point [21]. Most of the clinicians asked their opinion of the basic science curriculum of the first two years did not recommend any change at all—though there has been a great deal of talk about changing the basic science curriculum. The changes that were recommended were directly tied to the specific interests of different departments. For instance, internists and psychiatrists wanted to allot less time to anatomy, which is of relatively little interest to them, but surgeons who use anatomy every day wanted no change in this. Similarly, psychiatrists wanted to allot more time to behavioral sciences but surgeons did not.

A second fact which allows students freedom to develop their own perspectives on their work in medical school is the autonomy of the several departments within the school. If departments were relatively weak, a determined administration could make extensive changes in the way school is carried on and students' behavior might be quite different. But it is common knowledge that medical school departments have a great deal of autonomy. Their independence may stem from the fact that the teaching of the departments (in the clinical years) is so closely interwoven with the care of patients. Few departments will allow any change to be made in the way they handle patients simply for reasons deemed pedagogically important by the administration. They say that the welfare of the patient comes first and that they will not change and they do not.

In practice, this means that each department is likely to go its own way. Together, they present students with a variety of viewpoints on many major problems, both of medicine and of medical education. There is much talk now of the integration of medical knowledge and of teaching integrated courses. It is very likely that the autonomy of disciplines and departments will continue to be such that what integration is done will have to be done by the student himself, because the faculty are not able to agree. (There has been almost no study of the political arrangements *within* medical institutions, such as hospitals and medical schools. This is a very important area for future research in medical education.)

Another reason faculty members do not take the actions that might produce better results than they now feel they achieve is that there are various external constraints on their behavior. One, for example, is the fact that the members of a clinical faculty typically practice medicine themselves. This means that a certain amount of their time must be devoted to matters that have nothing to do with students and have instead to do with their own practices and the care of their patients. It may be that the degree to which teaching is affected by this factor is related to the financial arrangements of the school with its faculty. Research is needed to determine whether, for instance, a staff that is on full-time salary pays more attention to its teaching duties and gives more time and attention to students than one that makes a considerable proportion of its income from patients' fees.

Other constraints are imposed by the various organizations within medicine and medical education that set standards for schools to live up to. For instance, an organization may base its judgment on the performance of a school's students on the national board examinations given at the end of the sophomore and senior years. The school need not require its students to take the exams but most do. The faculty, though they may realize that such instruments as the national board examinations are not perfect, also recognize that the job they are doing in their own field may be judged by the scores their students make. Thus they may feel that they cannot make changes in curriculum and teaching methods because the changes might jeopardize their students' chance to make a good score on the national board examination. A basic science department might wish to institute a radically new method of teaching but be inhibited by the knowledge that the examination will be written by people who hold different views on this point. The pressure for standardization of educational practice which comes from national organizations of one kind or another can effectively keep a faculty from instituting changes that might come nearer to achieving their goals and preventing the autonomy of students from interfering with those goals.

Another fact that interferes with any attempt by the faculty to redirect the level and direction of student effort is their unfamiliarity with the conditions of private practice. Most students in American medical schools intend to go into private practice. On the other hand, it is increasingly true of medical school teachers that they have never been in the private practice of medicine. (Of course, there are some schools in which the majority of teachers do spend most of their time in private practice.) Also, many students intend to be general practitioners. Those of their teachers who are physicians are very likely never to have been in general practice. Students may discount much of what a faculty member says because they feel that he has not had the experience of general practice [17]. For instance, a surgeon may tell students that they should never attempt, as general practitioners, to remove an appendix. But the students may often feel, rightly or wrongly, that as general practitioners they may sometimes find themselves in circumstances where they have no choice but to perform an appendectomy. They feel that the faculty member probably does not understand the circumstances (as, for instance, of small town practice) which might make this a necessity.

Many medical teachers probably recognize that they do not exactly know what a private general practitioner might need to know and this may account for some of their uncertainty about curriculum. They may recognize that no student can learn everything that all the faculty, taken together, know. But they do not, lacking knowledge of the conditions under which students will practice, have any way of selecting which things the student will find it most necessary to know. In fact, the conditions of general practice vary greatly, so that there would be great difficulty in organizing a curriculum providing the optimum training for a potential G.P. Some students will end up practicing alone in small isolated towns. Others will be partners of older and more experienced men. Still others will be members of a community clinic staff, with well-trained specialists as colleagues. Some students will be able to send difficult cases to medical centers that are conveniently located nearby; others will have to handle them themselves. Finally, the situation of the general practitioner is changing rapidly and it is difficult to foresee what new variations will arise in years to come.

Another major obstacle to faculty action directed toward changing the way students work in medical school is the existence of what we may call "inhibiting ideologies." These are sets of beliefs the faculty holds which make it seem to them unlikely that their schemes will work or unlikely that they know enough to devise good schemes for change. One of these ideologies we have already touched on, namely the belief that the conditions under which students will practice are such that the faculty probably cannot know what most needs to be taught.

Another ideology that inhibits faculty action is the belief that students are not as good as they used to be or that a particular school does not recruit students that are among the best available. This belief is widespread among medical educators now. It is a fact that the number of students graduating from college who apply to medical school has dropped in the very recent past [19]. Medical educators tend to think that the larger the number of students from among whom they can select their freshman class, the more likely they are to get very good students. Consequently, when the number of students applying to medical school drops, faculties around the country believe that they are not getting as good students as they used to get when they had more applicants. They may then draw the conclusion that it is really impossible to expect any more academic work of the students because they are not capable of delivering any more. They may decide that the students, being less "selected," are therefore incapable of doing any better and that any scheme for change is doomed before it starts by the students' limitations.

Another inhibiting ideology takes cognizance of the fact that most medical students are now married. Faculty members believe that the obligations the student assumes with marriage drain from him time and interest he might otherwise apply to his medical studies. If he were not married he might stay in the hospital longer, read in the library, work in the laboratory, or see and examine his patients. Generally, they are probably inclined to think student marriage a bad thing. But they recognize that the trend toward early marriage is a national one. They realize that if they restricted the student body to unmarried people they would have an even smaller number of applicants to choose from. Accepting the fact of student marriage, they do not feel free to force the students to spend too much time away from their families. They are thus inhibited by their own humane instincts from doing things that might get the students to spend more time at the hospital.

In short, members of medical faculties are prevented in a number of ways from attempting to make major changes in the way the schools operate. Many of these factors inhibiting change are deeply rooted in the structure of the medical profession and of medical education. They cannot be changed without prolonged political effort, for in many cases there are quite divergent interests involved. It is our impression that much of the talk about change in medical education consists of a search for panaceas: schemes which will cause great changes in all the places that change is desired without in any way hurting anyone's interests or causing any basic change in the operating structure that now exists. It is false hope to think that such panaceas exist. Many studies of college teaching have shown that a change in the style of grading, or the integration of two courses that formerly were separate, does not change the way students work [24]. In any institution, one can make big changes only by making big changes. This is a truism about social organization, but one that is often overlooked.

On the other hand, panaceas do work in some ways. The effect of a panacea probably is to provide a ritualized way of dealing with dissatisfaction (for instance, the dissatisfaction an idealistic medical faculty feels with its work) without at the same time disturbing a somewhat fragile consensus (such as the consensus faculty have achieved on how to run a medical school). The panacea seems to be something that could be done, something "practical," and therefore gives the faculty the feeling that they are at least trying to do something about their problems; but it does not affect anything enough to hurt anyone and cause trouble.

Much research is needed on the forces promoting and obstructing change. We need to know about the political structure of medical schools. Who has power? Who influences the working consensus on which the school operates? We also need to know more about the external constraints on faculty members as they try to deal with their problem. Finally, we need to know a great deal about the beliefs with which a faculty approaches its job. What things do they think possible? What things impossible? Why do they think some things possible and others not?

References

1. Adams, Stuart, "Trends in Occupational Origins of Physicians," *American Sociological Review*, 18 (August, 1953), 404–409.
2. Back, Kurt W., Robert E. Coker, Jr., Thomas G. Donnelly, and Bernard S. Phillips, "Public Health as a Career in Medicine: Secondary Choice within a Profession," *American Sociological Review*, 23 (October, 1958), 533–41.
3. Beale, Lathrop V. and Louis Kriesberg, "Career-Relevant Values of Medical Students—A Research Note," *Journal of the American Medical Association*, 171 (November 14, 1959), 1447–48.
4. Becker, Howard S., Blanche Geer, Everett C. Hughes, and Anselm L. Strauss, *Boys in White: Student Culture in Medical School*. Chicago: University of Chicago Press, 1961.

5. Cahalan, Don, Patricia Collette, and Norman A. Hilmar, "Career Interests and Expectations of U. S. Medical Students," *Journal of Medical Education*, 32 (August, 1957), 557–63.

6. Caplovitz, David, "Value-Orientations of Medical Students and Faculty Members." Paper read at the meeting of the American Sociological Society. Washington, D.C., August, 1957.

7. ———, *Student-Faculty Relations in Medical School: A Study of Professional Socialization*. Unpublished Ph.D. thesis, Columbia University, 1960.

8. Christie, Richard and Robert K. Merton, "Procedures for the Sociological Study of the Values Climate of Medical Schools," *Journal of Medical Education*, Part II, 33 (October, 1958), 125–53.

9. Coker, Robert E., Jr., Kurt W. Back, Thomas G. Donnelly, Norman Miller, and Bernard S. Phillips, "Public Health as Viewed by the Medical Student," *American Journal of Public Health*, 49 (May, 1959), 601–609.

10. Coker, Robert E., Jr., Norman Miller, Kurt W. Back, and Thomas Donnelly, "The Medical Student, Specialization and General Practice." Paper read at the 105th annual session of the Medical Society of the State of North Carolina, 1959.

11. Coker, Robert E., Jr., Norman Miller, Kurt W. Back, Lloyd H. Strickland, and Thomas G. Donnelly, "Patterns of Influence: Medical School Faculty Members and the Values and Specialty Interests of Medical Students." Paper read at the annual meeting of the Association of American Medical Colleges, 1959.

12. Eron, Leonard D., "Effect of Medical Education on Medical Students," *Journal of Medical Education*, 10 (October, 1955), 559–66.

13. Fox, Renée C., "Training for Uncertainty," *in* Robert K. Merton, George G. Reader, M.D., and Patricia L. Kendall, eds., *The Student-Physician*. Cambridge: Harvard University Press, 1957, pp. 207–41.

14. Glaser, William A., "Internship Appointments of Medical Students," *Administrative Science Quarterly*, 4 (December, 1959), 337–56.

15. Hall, Oswald, "The Stages of a Medical Career," *American Journal of Sociology*, 53 (March, 1948), 327–36.

16. Hammond, Kenneth R., Fred Kern, *et al.*, *Teaching Comprehensive Medical Care: A Psychological Study of a Change in Medical Education*. Cambridge: Harvard University Press, 1959.

17. Hughes, Everett C., "Stress and Strain in Professional Education," *Harvard Educational Review*, 29 (Fall, 1959), 319–29.

18. Huntington, Mary Jean, "The Development of a Professional Self-Image," *in* Robert K. Merton, George G. Reader, M.D., and Patricia L. Kendall, eds., *The Student-Physician*. Cambridge: Harvard University Press, 1957, pp. 179–87.

19. Hutchins, Edwin D. and Helen Hofer Gee, "The Study of Applicants, 1959–60," *Journal of Medical Education*, 36 (April, 1961), 289–304.

20. Kandel, Denise Bystryn, William A. Glaser, and Jane Emery, "Changes in Career: Expectations of Medical Students." Paper read at the annual meeting of the American Sociological Society, 1958.

21. Kendall, Patricia L., "Clinical Teachers' Use of the Basic Science Curriculum," *Journal of Medical Education*, 35 (February, 1960), 148–57.

22. ——— and Hanan C. Selvin, "Tendencies toward Specialization in Medical Training," *in* Robert K. Merton, George G. Reader, M.D., and Patricia L. Kendall, eds., *The Student-Physician*. Cambridge: Harvard University Press, 1957, pp. 153–74.

23. Levine, Gene N. and Natalie Rogoff, with the assistance of David Caplovitz, "Diversities and Role Conceptions: Some Opinions of Clinical Faculty Members at Cornell Medical College." Unpublished document from the Bureau of Applied Social Research, Columbia University, November, 1955.

24. McKeachie, W. J., "Procedures and Techniques of Teaching: A Survey of Experimental Studies," *in* Nevitt Sanford, *The American College*. New York: John Wiley & Sons, Inc., 1962, pp. 312–64.

25. Nathanson, Constance A., *Learning the Doctor's Role: A Study of First and Fourth Year Medical Students*. Unpublished M.A. thesis, University of Chicago, 1958.

26. Peterson, Osler L. *et al.*, "An Analytical Study of North Carolina General Practice, 1953–54," *Journal of Medical Education*, 31 (December, 1956, Part 2).

27. Rogoff, Natalie, "The Decision to Study Medicine," *in* Robert K. Merton, George G. Reader, M.D., and Patricia L. Kendall, eds., *The Student-Physician*. Cambridge: Harvard University Press, 1957, pp. 109–29.

28. Schumacher, Charles F., "The 1960 Medical School Graduate: His Biographical History," *Journal of Medical Education*, 36 (May, 1961), 398–406.

8

NURSING AND OTHER HEALTH PROFESSIONS[1]

Ronald G. Corwin
Marvin J. Taves

Nursing is seeking a place for itself in an increasingly specialized world. Behind this search for identity are (1) a drive for prestige, (2) disparities between ideology and the actual job experience of nurses, and (3) competing expectations of role performance. The confusion is reflected in a series of contrasting career themes: ambiguous roles amidst an abundance of job descriptions and regulations; high morale and a favorable view of the status of nursing within the profession but dissatisfaction with conditions of em-

[1] Acknowledgements are due to Mr. Ramon Oldenburg, Mrs. Jean Moonan, and Mrs. Sheryl Hahn for their editorial and clerical assistance.

ployment; and commitment to the field of nursing together with transitory investment in the career.

Nursing, although different from medicine and perhaps also from the other health professions, has no more adjustments to make to contemporary society than other occupational groups in the health field. But long established ideologies make those adjustments more painful than those required of such newer professions as medical social work. That the profession is of feminine composition further exaggerates the minority character it shares with all ancillary health professions. However, precisely because it is somewhat atypical, nursing serves to highlight some of the problems common to many subordinate medical personnel.

The task of analyzing any profession is complex and difficult. Nurses work under a great variety of situations in hospitals and community settings. The heterogeneous character of nursing roles compounds the difficulties of generalizing. Questionnaires are often utilized to obtain information about nursing situations. But, although they have allowed quantitative descriptions of nurses' views, the more difficult recesses of nursing—the sensitive vocational secrets which the profession is reluctant to speak about—are virtually untapped. Although the keen self-awareness of nurses makes them receptive to research, they manage to maintain an almost impregnable front about the more delicate problems of their profession, such as nurse-patient conflicts, disagreements between teachers and students, and conflicts between schools of nursing and hospitals. Because of these and other problems there is a great deal of knowledge about the opinions of nurses, but much less information about their actual conduct. There is, therefore, ample reason to be cautious about the generalization potential of most of the observations in this chapter.

The Status of Nursing

The status of nursing is best understood in terms of its humanitarian, bureaucratic, and professional role conceptions. The feminine composition of nursing leaves an inescapable stamp on it. Haines observes that throughout its history, the status of nursing has reflected the status of women in general—nurses' subordinate role among medical personnel corresponds with that of women in American society [27]. But similar to many other socially underprivileged groups, women in general and nurses in particular are self-consciously engaged in a struggle to achieve recognition.

From its origin early in the eleventh century, nursing inherited the drudgery connected with sick care, first performed by women in monasteries as a religious duty and later in tax-supported institutions for meager pay [16]. Yet even then, the nurse had a claim to social prestige. An altruistic motive was attributed to her—she worked "in a sacred aura" which gave her a kind of moral superiority, for to be in a position to help others is a mark of superiority. This service ideology, the traditional basis of nurses' respectability, remains central to the nursing image; it has elevated nursing from a servile occupation to a position of prestige by reinforcing an altruistic image of the vocation.

The nurse's present identity has been fashioned by still another feature of a former era: nurses early achieved relatively autonomous status as private practitioners. By the turn of the century the majority of graduate nurses were in private practice. The nurse's hours were long and she was at the convenience of the family which employed her, but in the absence of the physician, she was held responsible for the patient's well-being [51]. Over a period of time this authority has been altered by the conditions which increased the demand for nurses in the early part of the century—specialization and increased admissions to hospitals brought about a variety of social changes. Currently, only about 15 per cent of registered nurses are in private practice. Hospitals and related institutions are the prime users of nursing services, employing nearly two-thirds of the 460,000 professional nurses in this country [19]. The nurse has become an institutional employee.

Like other ancillary professionals working in hospitals, the nurse's autonomy has receded before the organization of large modern hospitals. It has been charged that the nurse is in fact neither a professional nor a ministering angel, but rather an administrator and a technician, a member of an organized bureaucracy whose work—which includes all things not done by other people—is directed by persons outside the profession, namely doctors and hospital administrators [52, 53]. She has been described as a worker trained for a role of blind obedience to orders rather than for one of autonomy [7], one who takes and carries out orders, an employee who is rewarded more for loyalty to a hospital than loyalty to the profession [16]. Indeed, she is described as more docile and subordinated than any other American worker [58].

Despite such observations, the hospital nurse today should not be epitomized as servile. In fact it is her very role within the administrative structure of the hospital which is becoming the new basis of her authority, which is derived in part from the trend toward the practice of "team" nursing. The ratio of nonprofessional nursing personnel to patients has increased at a rate double that of the professional nurse-patient ratio [44]. Since most of these nonprofessional team workers are subordinate to the nurse, her importance in the hospital has increased. The nurse in the modern hospital organizes and supervises a growing staff of technicians, aides, orderlies, students, and practical nurses. As a result, on a national average, nurses spend 62 per cent of their time away from patients, much of it in administrative duties [44]. Nurses report that they spend nearly one-fourth of their time on paperwork. Many feel that the forms and records they spend time filling out are seldom consulted [44, 53]. Despite their complaints, nurses tend to accept the bureaucratic role. They acknowledge the necessity of maintaining a smooth-running hospital, and are strongly conscious of and oriented to hospital rules [50].

The consequence of the present administrative role has been stated succinctly: "The present function of the graduate nurse is not to nurse the patient, but to see that he is nursed" [52]. This work pattern is not quite what the student nurse expects, nor what the public imagines. In contrast to the service image, the image of the nurse as an administrator supervising others—even males—does not correspond with the traditionally subordinate role of women. Nor does it correspond with the traditional basis of her integrity—her close, personal relationship with patients. Her intimacy with patients is jeopardized by the depersonalized and standardized routine characteristic of the new era of mass medical care.[2] One observer laments that because of the energy devoted to mechanical procedures in the hospital the patient is no longer the center of attention [1]. Despite such complaints, the bureaucratized work pattern does provide the nurse with an unprecedented amount of authority.

Because she is an employee, the nurse's avenue of career advancement has shifted from an individual to an organizational context. While many nurses do not fully accept this avenue, the employee role is nevertheless part of the nurse's identity, for her very success is dependent on her loyalty to the hospital. In a pilot study, friendships of staff nurses with their superiors affected the nurses' job competency evaluations, but consensus with superiors about duties did not [12]. Where formal means of controlling personal values are absent or prohibited by official norms, the endorsement of their friends by superiors seems to be a way of guaranteeing that the basic ends of the organization are complied with. Whether consensus with superiors or friendship with them is more important depends on other conditions such as the degree of existing consensus among hospital officials, assessability of formal evaluation criteria, and ethical standards which regulate the evaluation process. In any case, loyalty to the organization is an important consideration.

The criteria which her superiors use to evaluate the nurse undoubtedly affect her behavior. Most of the official rewards are for skills which do not involve patient contact—record keeping, operation of technical apparatus, reading, committee work, or teaching. No matter how well-ingrained in her is the ideal of patient care, the nurse will probably spend less time at the bedside if the hospital rewards her for other activities. As a result, nurses almost universally express satisfaction in working with patients and

---

[2] See Chaps. 10 and 11.

just as often complain about the lack of opportunity for patient contact; yet, in at least one hospital, nurses did not take advantage of opportunities which arose to spend time with patients [50]. Administrative and professional roles seem to predominate in actual conduct and orientation to work. In many respects, the nurse is an obedient hospital employee whose job and success is dependent on the opinions of others, but she is at the same time a responsible hospital official whose very obedience is designed to win status and recognition within the administrative system.

In addition to being a public servant, humanitarian, and an employee and official of the hospital, the nurse is also a professional.[3] This creates other problems. Nurses, like members of other professions, seek to enhance their status by gaining a monopoly of scientific knowledge and maintaining high standards of competence [5]. Despite the professional claims of nurses, most of them do not actively support the professional movement. In fact, only a small, though influential group, primarily in university posts and state agencies, are vigorously attempting to redirect the nursing movement toward professionalism. In this respect, nursing bears a remarkable resemblance to other underprivileged groups—there is cleavage between a contented rank and file and a dissatisfied minority actively working to advance the competence and the professional status of the entire group. Only about 40 per cent of the nation's registered nurses are members of the American Nurses Association, the largest professional organization in the nation. The National League for Nursing, an organization for the improvement of education and services in nursing, has a membership of less than 23,000 nursing and lay personnel. Apparently, most nurses do not spend a significant amount of time reading professional literature: *The American Journal of Nursing*, for example, has 160,000 paid subscribers—not more than one-third of all active nurses. Only 1 per cent of all registered nurses hold master's degrees, and only 5 per cent hold baccalaureate degrees. Fewer than 1 in 10 nurses in administrative and staff positions in hospitals are college graduates [19, 49]. The absence of an identifiable body of knowledge which could be regarded as nursing science is another serious handicap. Nurses themselves do not perceive nursing as a distinct discipline; in one study, only 40 per cent of registered nurses regarded nursing as a discrete body of knowledge separate from medicine [22].

The confusion of nurses and the general public about the professional status of nursing is revealed in a study reporting that as many as 40 per cent of laymen in New York avoid using the term "profession" to describe the field of nursing; over one-fifth of them feel that the terms "semiprofes-

[3] The profession is also ideally dedicated to the service of the client for altruistic rather than commercial motives. The distinction between profession and humanitarianism is merely intended to highlight the dual prestige and service components of professional status.

sion" or "job" are more appropriate. The term "profession" is not used by over one-third of registered and student nurses, who substitute instead "calling"—a term which has certain religious connotations [22]. Nevertheless, most nurses regard their work as a profession.

Professionalization, it should be observed, usually is somewhat militant in character, a difficult position for many women to take overtly. The militant aspects include efforts to overcome lay control (represented by hospital administration) and to reduce subordination to physicians, which creates nurse-doctor conflicts.[4] Physicians have their intellectual roots in the physical sciences, while nurses have recently been more oriented to the social sciences. This creates another source of difference. Moreover, the physicians' authority in the hospital has been declining during precisely the same period that that of the nurses has increased, bringing the two groups into closer social contact and increasing the potential for friction. Today, the hospital is the domain of the nurse; she exercises informal controls over work on which the physician is highly dependent.[5]

Because conflict with doctors implies an infringement on the male status and on the professional autonomy of physicians, many nurses deny that any such conflict exists. In fact, there is evidence that they feel physicians are more ethical than nurses. One study indicates that most nurses are resigned to occupying a position officially subordinate to that of doctors; over three-fourths of the nurses, for example, agree that nurses should rise if a doctor enters the room [6]. In another study, one-fifth of the nurses agreed that the doctor performs the important tasks and that the nurse is merely a "maid on the job" [22]. Yet physicians, who expect obedience, apparently do meet some resistance. One observer reports that some nurses view themselves as a "cooperating brain" of the physician, but that the physician resents the presumption [47]. In another study, half of the nurses indicated that they have at times encountered doctors who are unfair to them; on the other hand, doctors complain of nurses being too "professional," distant, or sometimes even callous with patients. One of the major suggestions made by physicians for improvement of nursing service involved more precise compliance with doctors' orders [53]. The respect of nurses for physicians and their acceptance of formal subordination, contrasted with their simultaneous resentment of physicians, may parallel the ambivalence of socially mobile women toward men in general.

---

[4] See Chap. 11.

[5] The nurses' authority has also been derived as well from a *non*militant assumption of functions which physicians have discarded. Seventeen procedures, such as taking blood pressure and giving entradermal injections, which were formerly carried out by doctors, are now performed by nurses.

Recruitment

The attractiveness of the nursing profession to young women has been steadily increasing. The number of women active in nursing grew from 374,584 in 1950 to more than 460,000 in 1958—a 23 per cent increase [19]. More significant, the ratio of nurses to the general population has increased from 216:100,000 in 1940 to 268:100,000 in 1958—a 24 per cent increase over the general population growth during that period. The ratio of nurses to patients is currently 36:100; this represents only a slight decline over the 1945 nurse-patient ratio, despite the fact that hospital admission rates have more than doubled over the period [44]. Nationally, about 1 out of every 16 girls who graduate from high school enters nursing. In view of the growing range of vocational alternatives, the figures are impressive.

The existence of conflicting identities in nursing presents a difficult choice. In a highly specialized mass society, where young people cannot possibly have direct experience with most occupations, their assessment of a vocation necessarily depends largely on imaginary constructions about it. These vocational images are simplified versions of reality shared by various social groups. Nevertheless they are often the basis for appraising vocations. Accordingly, the popular image of nursing is undoubtedly a crucial element in the recruitment of nursing students.

The popular image of nursing is generally favorable. It is a vocation with high prestige for women. The majority of girls questioned in studies in at least two states agree that nursing is a calling which provides an excellent opportunity to render an important, often a sacred, service to humanity [57, 59]. Studies in two other states indicate that teaching outranks nursing in terms of prestige, but that nursing outranks social work; about one-fifth of the respondents in these studies rank the nurse higher than either the teacher or the social worker [5, 8]. Intellectually, nurses are probably not considered superior to women in most other professions, but neither are they regarded as intellectually inferior [6, 57]. Thus, the image of nursing encourages rather than repels.

High school girls also express favorable opinions about the standards of nursing education and the length of the training period.[6] But apparently a large proportion of girls are uncertain about whether these schools too closely supervise and restrict the social life of nursing students. This ignorance about the nursing school may turn students against the vocation to the extent that the immediate circumstances are given precedence over long-range advantages and disadvantages of the vocation.

The public too expresses reservations about nursing. Over 60 per cent of

---

[6] The following discussion is based primarily on references 8, 15, 22, and 57.

laymen believe that the work that nurses do is unpleasant and unappreciated. Laywomen are virtually unanimous in describing the nurse as a drudge; drop-outs from nursing schools, particularly, see nursing as a field for drudges.

The public also questions the amount of authority that nurses have on the job. In one study over half of the respondents looked upon nurses as special servants, although the other half thought of nurses as independent and self-directing in their work. The majority see the nurse taking orders in an employee role, and most believe that she has less control over her work than women in many other professions have. The public grants considerable responsibility to the nurse, but this responsibility is perceived as delegated by others who exercise primary authority over decisions. Nevertheless most high school girls believe the nurse to have an "ideal" amount of responsibility.

Many people have reservations about the financial advantages of nursing. On a nation-wide basis, the average monthly salary of general staff nurses is about $300 [19].[7] Although three-fourths of the high school girls in one study agreed that the pay received is satisfactory and reasonable, one-half of them doubt that the nurse's salary is above average for employed women. It is also significant that prospective nurses consider the cost of nurses' training "quite high." This perceived discrepancy between cost of training and postgraduate rewards is perhaps the crux of the financial difficulty.

Employed nurses also question the adequacy of their salary. In one study nurses were listed as at least equitably paid, while hospital administrators were considered to be overpaid [35]. But in another study, the complaints of almost three-fourths of a large sample of hospital nurses concerned pay and job grievances [38]. Also, one-fourth of the general-duty nurses in 37 Minnesota hospitals reported dissatisfaction with salary, and almost half of the nurses in another study expressed dissatisfaction with present salaries —over one-fourth of them wanted another $100 a month. Dissatisfaction with salary is even greater among younger nurses.

The favorable and unfavorable components of the nursing image form a reasonably clear pattern. The public is generally favorable toward nursing as an institution or profession within the general society; they perceive it as a prestigious and altruistic profession. The unfavorable views are associated with the employment characteristics of nursing, particularly with the working conditions within the hospital. This ambivalence seems to reflect the role conflicts within nursing: nurses themselves seem satisfied with their general status but dissatisfied with their particular job. As a member

[7] There is considerable variation. (The average weekly salary for general duty nurses in Atlanta is $65, and in Los Angeles, $89. Thirty-five per cent of the general duty nurses in New Orleans earn less than $3000 per year, while 57 per cent earn between $3000 and $4000 per year.

of the community, the nurse enjoys an unusual degree of prestige among women, but the conditions of her employment do not correspond to her high prestige. In the hospital setting, the nurse still bears the identity of a "servant," a competent and efficient drudge who is an extension of the doctor's right hand, an altruistic soul who perhaps merits more recognition than she receives.

The ideologies of prospective nurses are similar to those of the general population. They more frequently answer at the "extremely favorable" position on most of the issues already mentioned, and are less often undecided [57]. But by no means do they view every aspect of nursing with equal favor. Objections are principally focused on the education of nurses, their intelligence, their authority, the unpleasantness of the work and the physical demands of the work, as well as the comparative financial advantages.

The nursing shortage has increased the sensitivity of nursing leaders to the problem of recruiting nurses. In 1958, 11 per cent of budgeted nursing positions in this nation's hospitals were vacant. If nursing schools merely maintain current admission levels, the ratio of nurses to every 100,000 persons will drop from 268 to 246 by 1970. More than 550,000 nurses will be required by 1970 in order to maintain the present ratio. Over 600,000 would be needed to achieve the stated goal of 300 nurses for every 100,000 population by 1970. These figures indicate a need for a 20 per cent increase over the current level of supply; the rate of increase during the years between 1950 and 1958 was less than 15 per cent [19]. The sense of urgency represented in these facts gives both utilitarian and theoretical impetus to the problems of identifying the specific forces which lead young women into nursing.

Primary groups—*i.e.*, friends and relatives—are undoubtedly important, and in some cases, determining factors in career choice. One survey revealed that almost half of the student nurses sampled were encouraged to enter nursing by their relatives [39]. Haas reports that the nursing image of the mothers, fathers, siblings, and friends of twelfth-grade girls affected girls' decisions to enter nursing school [25]. In one study, four out of 10 high school girls reported that their impressions about nursing—the majority of which were favorable—were gleaned from relatives who were nurses or doctors [42].

Another one-fourth to one-half of the respondents reported that they received impressions about nursing—most of them favorable—from mass media. Over 10 per cent reported being influenced by one or more forms of the mass media, which suggests the potential influence of impersonal sources of encouragement.

To determine whether or not mailed brochures favorable to nursing can influence the vocational image, a longitudinal study was made of girls in

17 high schools [57]. In view of sociological theories which stress the effectiveness of personal relations over impersonal appeals, there was good reason to expect that the mailed brochures would not be effective. However, in view of widespread use of such impersonal recruiting appeals as posters, mailed brochures, and catalogues by nursing schools and professional associations, the problem is a relevant one. An analysis of the literature used by national and state nursing organizations and nursing schools disclosed three major career appeals: practical (utilitarian), service (altruistic), and professional (prestige). A series of brochures typical of each appeal was mailed to girls in four high schools, each school receiving a different appeal. Four other schools were used as "controls" and received no literature, while one school received all types of literature.

There was a general decline in the image of nursing held by all respondents between their junior and senior years. Appeals to practical employment considerations, such as social relations on the job, nature of the work, and financial security, had a favorable effect; the professional appeal, which emphasized prestige and the scientific nature of nursing, seemed to counteract the general decline in the nursing image; but the altruistic "service" appeal had a negative effect; among the girls who received it the image of nursing declined even further than among the girls who received no literature.

In many ways the study proved to be a classic example of the boomerang effect of an attempt to influence attitudes. Among prospective nurses (girls who had planned to enter nursing in their junior year), those who received any favorable literature developed less favorable images of nursing than those who received none (in fact, the images of the latter improved markedly). Again, the practical employment appeal created some favorable effect among prospective nurses, but not in the magnitude found among those who received no literature at all. The service appeal had the most negative effect on prospective nurses, traditional ideologies about the nurse's altruistic motives notwithstanding.

The ineffectiveness of the service appeal, as well as the effectiveness of the practical appeal for the total population of high school girls, might be explained in terms of secularization of society. The prestige, importance, and material rewards of American society now may lie elsewhere. Nevertheless the ineffectiveness of the service appeal for prospective nurses, compared to the relative effectiveness of the practical appeal, seems inconsistent with the altruistic motives generally attributed to nurses. While nursing prospects believe that nursing provides an excellent opportunity to put religious beliefs into practice, the fact remains that this did not seem to be a convincing argument for most prospective nurses. Studies of the reasons which nurses express for entering nursing almost universally conclude that they are more altruistic and religious than the general population [42], but this fact does not seem to warrant the assumption that altruism is their central motive. The character of a vocation, however, does not necessarily reflect the expressed motives of those who enter it; whether or not nurses behave altruistically depends on both the ability of the profession to control its members and the individual's motives for entering it.

Who Chooses a Career in Nursing

If there is a wide range of role conceptions in nursing, there is a correspondingly wide range of cultural backgrounds and expectations among girls whom it attracts. In the past, nursing apparently attracted highly dedicated women committed to the ideal of service to humanity, but today it recruits a heterogeneous group who selects nursing for a variety of reasons. Decisions to enter nursing tend to be made in the early part of life, long before high school and earlier than decisions to enter other vocations. One-fourth of the nurses who have been asked say they have wanted to be nurses since the age of thirteen or earlier; two-thirds since the age of fifteen; and 85 per cent since the age of eighteen [37, 59]. Only 10 per cent of the nursing students interviewed made their decision to become nurses after the age of seventeen, while 40 per cent of nonnursing students made their decision after that age [21].

According to a comparative study of the values of over 300 nursing and teaching students in Detroit, the occupational values of student nurses, compared to those of student teachers, emphasize good employment conditions and social relations. Nursing students are more interested in meeting people, being physically active on the job, advancing to a better paying job, securing a job quickly and easily if necessary, and being of direct service to people who need help. But student teachers rate as more important aspects of work in which authority and prestige figure predominantly: expressing one's own ideas and imagination, being one's own boss, having people look up to one, good working hours, and working with children [48].

One-fourth of all nurses have rural origins, but the percentage varies regionally in close approximation to the proportion of rural population [30]. By most criteria of religiosity, student nurses and nurses are more religious than the general population [59]. A study of prospective nurses in Minnesota indicates that an unusually large proportion of them would seek out social relations with other girls if they were to attend college, as opposed to attending cultural events there.

A large proportion of nursing prospects are daughters of nurses—evidence of vocational inbreeding.[8] One study, which held the father's occupation as the criterion, indicated that all socio-economic status groups are represented proportionately among nursing prospects [56]. However, other studies suggest that proportionately more lower and upper class girls enter nursing. The proportion of nurses who marry above their father's social class appears to have increased over the past three decades [6, 30, 59]. Yet, nurses are not particularly geographically mobile. They tend to work in the same area where they attended nursing school, although nurses from metropolitan areas are almost twice as likely as others to migrate [30].

There are also several studies which identify nurses by their psychological characteristics. As an example, one study found, in a comparison of graduate general duty nurses with college girls and student nurses, that graduate nurses are more self-conscious, more emotionally stable, less nervous, more objective, agreeable, and comparative than student nurses but, significantly, less inclined to social extroversion, depression, social acceptance, and cooperativeness than are college girls [29].

Training

Nurses' training is influenced by the structure of nursing schools which, in turn influences the commitment and identification of nurses to their profession. Although the fundamental causes of conflicting roles and images in nursing are to be found within the broad historical changes of the times, it is possible to locate specific forces which serve to maintain the variety of role conceptions that are passed down to each generation of nurses. The nation's many authorized schools of nursing undoubtedly play a crucial part in transmitting and shaping the variety of role conceptions within nursing. In school, the student learns to adjust herself to the discrepancies between the popular images of the nurse's work and the daily demands of the hospital.[9] This adjustment involves varying degrees of disillusionment.

There are three major types of training programs: three-year hospital administered schools, four-year collegiate schools, and two-year collegiate schools. In 1958, hospitals controlled three-fourths of all the nursing schools and enrolled nearly 80 per cent of the more than 113,518 student nurses, although enrollments in hospital schools, in comparison with those in college and university programs, have been declining [19]. All the hospital programs award a diploma in nursing at the end of three years of traditional, often practical, and specialized nursing courses taken in conjunction with a relatively heavy work schedule.

---

[8] See Chap. 7 for similar data regarding medical students.

[9] See Chap. 7 for discussion of the physician and his socialization.

Hospital and four-year college programs attract different kinds of students. One study reports that nearly half of the students of collegiate schools come from middle and upper class families, and that they are more likely to complete their nurse's training than are students from the lower class [36]. There are also marked differences in the preparation of the faculties of the two major programs. About one-quarter of nurses teaching in hospital schools do not have any degrees, while more than 99 per cent of those in collegiate schools do. About two-thirds of the faculty in collegiate schools hold master's or doctor's degrees; only one-fifth of those in hospital schools do [19]. The prestige of the degree schools seems especially attractive to unmarried, socially mobile nursing instructors. The faculties of collegiate programs seem to have broader and more heterogeneous training and probably images of nursing which differ from those in diploma schools.

Hospital and collegiate programs also differ philosophically on the importance and definition of apprenticeship in modern professional training. Formerly, students in hospital programs were apprenticed to nurses in the hospital in exchange for remission of tuition and were often used as cheap labor [7, 51]. The status of diploma students has greatly improved, but traces of this tendency to view the student as an apprentice rather than a student remain. The average work week of diploma schools approaches or exceeds 25 hours, which is longer than the average work week of collegiate programs. However, at the same time that state nursing boards are advocating a reduction in student clinical work loads, some nursing supervisors express concern that recent degree graduates are not sufficiently skilled to perform many nursing tasks competently. Other nursing educators question whether the nurse should be expected to be a completely skilled and competent nurse on the day of her graduation.

Diploma and degree programs are related to hospitals in different ways. Although there is considerable variation within each program, diploma schools of nursing are normally hospital programs, subordinate to the hospital administration which hires the faculty, pays their salary, and—by virtue of economic sponsorship of students—determines student academic and work schedules. The faculty of these schools are often products of the system who have stayed on to teach. Consequently, according to some observers, needs of the hospital and patients tend to take precedence over needs of students [7]. On the other hand, collegiate programs, while affiliated with hospitals, are only partly controlled by them. Relative autonomy from the hospital enables the faculty to advocate significant departures from the traditional humanitarian and employee conceptions of nursing endorsed in the hospital.

The differential outcomes of the two programs are suggested in the comments of faculty who have had experience with both programs. Compared to diploma students, degree students are frequently described as "more creative," "less dependable and efficient," "dissatisfied with the way things are," "questioning of authority," "more critical of nursing procedures and hospital rules," "more likely to make judgments for themselves," "in possession of a broader perspective of nursing," and "more objective." One comment of a collegiate teacher is telling: "We try to challenge hospital supervisors occasionally to keep them on their toes." According to one study, diploma seniors feel better informed than degree seniors, but there is more dissatisfaction with the diploma program. One study reports that more than twice as many diploma than degree students would change programs if they had it to do over again [21].

Competition between the nursing school faculty and hospital staff over control of the students' classroom and clinical experience probably reinforces some contradictions within nursing. These contradictions are more prominent in degree programs because of their relative autonomy from the hospital. Studies are now underway to determine the influence that official and unofficial relations between hospitals and schools have on the role conceptions which students learn there [56, 59].

The Self-Image

The more than 100,000 young women enrolled in nursing schools are expected to assume a new perspective toward the patient, the hospital, and the world. Many do, but there is considerable variation in the extent of emotional involvement which students display toward nursing. When Kuhn asked students in professional schools to describe themselves, only one-third of first-year student nurses mentioned their professional image in one of their first three statements, compared with about half of first-year law students, and first-year social workers. The professional identity, however, assumes increasing importance as the student advances through the school program; nearly three-fourths of the third-year students mentioned their professional identity [33].

The primary goal of nursing students is marriage rather than a full-time career. One-fourth of the students interviewed in one study expected or hoped to be married within six months after graduation and 6 out of 10 wished to be married within two years after graduation [36]. Nearly 60 per cent of more than 4000 student nurses in one study said that having their own careers is "very important," a much higher proportion than that found in comparative groups of laywomen; yet only one-fourth indicated that they would be very much displeased if they should marry and have a family without having had a chance to work at their career; less than one-fifth consider their career to be their first satisfaction in life [22]. The prospect of marriage and children permeates every aspect of nursing; no aspect of the profession can be completely understood apart from the influence of marriage plans and their frustration.

The difficulty which girls have in committing themselves to a professional career is reflected in nursing school attrition rates. About one-third of the nation's nursing students annually fail to complete their nursing program and the percentage has been increasing slightly over the past few decades [44]. According to several studies, the most frequently stated reasons for first year withdrawals are scholastic failure and matrimony [18, 42, 61].

In view of the rigorous testing programs required for admission to many nursing schools, however, it appears implausible that scholastic ability is not the major problem. Inability to sustain emotional relationships with patients is one factor which possibly needs more investigation; one writer blames idealistic goals and overwork as probable causes. Plain dislike for nursing is mentioned by some of the drop-outs, which suggests that the role of motivation in attrition should be investigated. In particular, the disparities between the image of nursing which brought the girls into school and the realities they find there may prove to be significant.

The students who remain also have problems. They must make transformations which may be emotionally difficult. These may include the surrender of some favorable preconceptions which brought them into nursing. There is evidence that disillusionment with the field of nursing begins early in the career as information about nursing increases. One unpublished study of transformations in the image of nursing reveals a general decline in favorableness toward the vocation between freshman and sophomore years. This decline reaches its peak in the junior year, a year devoid of intermediate goals [56]. Disillusionment is also indicated by doubts which some nursing students express about whether or not they have chosen the right vocation. According to some evidence, about 1 diploma student in 6 has serious doubts, with little change from year to year, while the number of degree students who have career doubts almost triples between the first and fourth year [21].

One author describes four types of nurses on the basis of their motives for entering nursing and their reasons for remaining. The happiest type of nurse appears to be the "converted" who entered nursing on negative grounds but found a love for it. She differs from the "dedicated" whose reasons for entering nursing were positive. The "disenchanted" on the other hand is one who becomes disillusioned with high expectations, but remains for negative reasons. The "migrant" has consistently the least investment in nursing, having entered it on negative grounds and remaining there for those reasons [50].

It seems likely that standard informal tactics are utilized by teachers in nursing schools in order systematically to control the novices' access to unfavorable information about the field. In interviews, nursing instructors have intimated that certain information is withheld until the senior year, "capping," or the first contact with patients. There is reason to believe that conflicts between school faculty and the nursing service of the training hospital, in particular, are withheld from students. The student culture also probably includes rationalizations and other defenses which help to minimize disillusionment [3].

Cultural Conflicts and Disillusionment

The socialization of the student nurse involves in part a reconciliation of nursing norms with the values of the broader culture. For example, students have difficulty reconciling the necessity of intimate male contact with social norms regulating relations between the sexes; the prominence of death in the hospital must somehow be compromised with the student's lack of previous contact with death; and the realities of physical illness and amputation must somehow be compromised with a cultural stress on youth and physical vigor [60]. Also, many expectations of students about patient relations are not met in nursing school. First-year students are especially ambivalent toward supervisory roles, in the second year they are easily hurt, and by the third year many of their ideals had given way to the conviction that nursing is just a job [32]. The first systematic contact with patients is often a time of disillusionment. Students early learn that the patient is not so willing to be helped nor as grateful as they had expected. Indeed, the patient often seems to present a challenge which unites students among themselves to secure control over him or avoid him. One study concludes, on the basis of respondents' preference for pictures, that beginning students in all types of schools are motivated by a desire to nurse patients unaided at the bedside (the "ministering angel" image), but by the second year the unaided patient relation has lost much of its attraction and in the terminal year it is no longer the majority response [41]. There is evidence that students like best those patients who conform to their expectations of an ideal patient [4].

By the nature of the pressures under which the nursing school exists, a completely realistic picture of the eventual career is not stressed. In their concern with improving nursing, teachers tend to overlook many less desirable employment characteristics of nursing. Teachers are prone to "preach an idealized version of hospital work" [31]. This idealism is not the result of a naive ignorance of complex realities but is an assessment of what is theoretically important enough to be stressed—common institutional characteristics of nursing as an occupation—and what is less relevant to the central nursing functions—the extreme variety of employment conditions, including differential salary scales, supervisory practices, and administrative chores such as ordering, filling out forms, and running errands.

Disillusionment accompanies the transition from school to work. A comparison of student and graduate nurses, for example, shows that both favorableness toward nursing and expressed job satisfaction is greater for students then for graduate nurses employed in hospitals. The greatest differences occur between students and nurses judged most successful by their superiors [11]. What seems to be involved is a discontinuity between the common institutional perspective of nursing which is stressed in the school and the unique expectations of employees which predominate in particular hospitals and which tend to compromise the institutional status. Not until she assumes full-time hospital employment does the student witness the full array of professional, humanitarian, business, medical employee and other norms which are not entirely congruent and must be compromised in the course of daily routines.

The type of nursing program undoubtedly influences the extent and nature of disillusionment after graduation as well as disillusionment that occurs during nursing school. In four-year college degree programs, the preferred relationship of terminal students was the sharing of the patient with co-workers, with the predominant orientation toward the patient. As girls progressed through three-year hospital diploma programs, on the other hand, they became increasingly oriented to technical-administrative relationships with fellow workers and "shared" patient relationships with co-workers, with the predominant orientation to co-workers. One consequence of shift in orientation of seniors in the hospital school was increased dissatisfaction with nursing [40].

There is some evidence that the training program determines students' role conceptions [14]. Degree students express less commitment to the bureaucratic role conception than diploma students do, are less certain of the role conceptions they express, and hold role conceptions which they themselves perceive to be different from nursing practice. Also, cross-sectional data comparing students and graduates suggest that discrepancies between ideal and perceived bureaucratic and professional roles increase for degree students, though not for diploma students, after graduation. Diploma graduates are more likely to adjust their professional and service role conceptions to present realities, while maintaining their initial loyalty to the hospital. But the reverse is true for degree graduates who maintain their initially high, unrealistic professional role conceptions in the face of disparities with reality, but adjust their bureaucratic role conceptions to the demands of the hospital [9]. It may be concluded that the process of identity formation during the nursing program may be disillusioning for significant numbers of nurses after graduation and full-time employment within the hospital.

Work and the Career

The difficulties which students express in committing themselves to the field of nursing are minor compared with the distractions of outside demands on employed graduates. There is little doubt about the ideological commitments of most nurses to the field of nursing as a vocation. Nearly all nurses think enough of nursing to recommend it to others [6, 22]. By almost any criteria, however, a substantial proportion of employed nurses are not personally committed to nursing as a full-time career. Over one-fourth of the nurses in a Wisconsin study preferred non-work situations for both personal satisfaction and informal group experiences, and 30 per cent of New York nurses interviewed are in doubt about continuing in the field [22, 46]. Nearly half of the nurses in a sample in Minneapolis estimated that they would not be working in three years [10]. Increases in the number of nurses employed part-time over the past few decades are also indicative of the way nurses view their career. Their number has risen from 8000 in 1942, which was less than 3 per cent of employed nurses at that time, to over 53,000 in 1958, which was nearly 12 per cent of all working nurses [19].

The turnover rate in nursing is also indicative of the transitory investment that many nurses have in their own career. Most nurses do not stay long in any one hospital: the annual turnover rate is between 40 and 70 per cent—nearly twice the estimate of most other industries [19, 34, 44]. This turnover costs hospitals nearly $100 million annually. Levine reports that turnover rates are especially characteristic of large hospitals. Turnover is also related to role conceptions: nurses who plan to seek a better job in another hospital or to work in nursing outside of the hospital hold high professional and service role conceptions [10].

The prospect and fact of marriage conditions most nurses' view of their career and prevents many of them from committing themselves to nursing as a primary identity, either while in nursing school or during their first years of employment. Throughout the history of nursing, those who have been most committed are the woman still unmarried in middle age. For many of these a career is probably a second choice, a compensation for the absence of successful marriage. They are among the most dedicated of nurses and the leaders of the professional nursing movement.

In view of the tentative nature of their careers, it is not surprising that the majority of nurses are content with their present positions and are not ambitious to achieve administrative rank or assume responsibility [5, 10]. Marital status is associated with mobility aspirations. While less than one-fifth of the unmarried nurses stated they would not consider promotion to head nurse or supervisor, nearly half of the married nurses gave this response [10]. The blocked-mobility pattern, which nursing shares with other professional groups in bureaucratic organizations, is another reason that the majority are not ambitious. Oddly enough, although patient care is an important aspect of most nurses' vocational image, the jobs which entail the most direct patient care have the lowest status and smallest rewards. Promotion removes the professional nurse from her special field of competence.

Most studies of nursing work roles reveal considerable dissent about who should perform which function among hospital work groups. A series of studies leaves no doubt about the extreme overlap of functions and existing disagreements between nurses and their subordinates, doctors, and patients. Staff and head nurses are doing work which they believe appropriate to subordinate personnel, while nurses fear that subordinates are assuming tasks which belong to nurses [13, 20, 37, 50]. Haas reports that nursing personnel cannot agree whether graduate staff nurses should report personnel problems to the head nurse, whether to caution colleagues about infractions of hospital rules, or whether the supervisor and head nurse should control all policy [24]. Haas also found that job consensus in hospital work groups influences the work relations of nurses. Role consensus was found to be inversely related to the number of "friction" incidents observed at nursing stations, and directly related to job satisfaction of persons in the work group. Persons with lower role consensus liked each other less and gave fewer complimentary ratings of one another's work.

In view of the transitory commitment to the career, low ambition levels, and disagreements on work roles, the extremely high morale of nurses is remarkable. Studies on the matter leave no doubt that nurses like nursing. Over 90 per cent of the 4000 tasks considered in one study were rated favorably by nurses [20]. Only 3 per cent of nurses in one study say they dislike their jobs, and 87 per cent would enter nursing again. Although nurses who desire more responsibility take a dim view of nursing, most are convinced that their choice of nursing was a wise one, would like to see their daughters become nurses, feel "needed" and think well of hospitals in which they are employed. They also think highly of their associates, peers, supervisors, and doctors; most are also satisfied with their working conditions and salaries [6].

While satisfied with their vocation as a whole, nurses are dissatisfied with specific conditions. The proportion leaving their job because of work dissatisfaction ranged from 3 per cent to 37 per cent in a five-state study. Sources of dissatisfaction were salary, work load, working hours, and relations with superiors. Another investigator reports that nurses complain about the structure of work—lack of management-employee trust, inadequate communication, and a poorly defined work situation [17, 38]. Nurses also often complain that they are overworked. In view of the nursing shortage, the truth of the complaint seems self-evident. Yet, without denying the accuracy of the complaint, complaints about overwork are perhaps overstated. Such complaints are a part of the nursing culture and often seem to refer more to the type of work than to the amount of work involved. The term "busy" has overtones of status and importance which cannot be ignored.

The ambivalence of nurses to their vocation is thus apparent. While they remain enthusiastic about nursing in general, they are dissatisfied—with the conditions of their daily employment. This dual perspective reflects their pattern of commitment: loyalty to the vocation, contrasted with transitory commitment to a career in it. Precisely because they are not committed to a life-long career, grievances about the job, even though widespread, are tolerable, because they do not immediately effect the generally favorable image of nursing in society. This contrast between the loyalty of nurses to their profession and their temporary commitment to their job in it, enables nurses to remain loyal to nursing in the face of unfavorable employment conditions. But those who do wish to make a career of nursing undoubtedly have a more difficult time reconciling their view of the field with their own conditions of employment.

Other Health Professions

Many of the problems which nursing currently faces are faced by all ancillary professions. These are the problems of social identity, a term used here to refer to the characteristics of a person's membership groups which determine the way he is placed by others. The vocational identity is a reflection of its ideological basis (the popular vocational images), its function (the roles it performs), and its societal position (its status). Accordingly, a central aim of much of the research on auxiliary medical professions has been the identification of practitioners and the popular images of them, of their status within the medical institutions, and their various roles within the work setting.

Several features of the nursing story highlight the problems of other ancillary professionals employed by hospitals. For example, nursing provides a model of the professionalization process. A small but active minority advocates increased professional standards and control over training. One nursing leader advocates that only nurses with baccalaureate and advanced degrees be called "full professional" nurses: the new identity is advocated only for the ambitious minority which sets itself apart from the majority.

The drive to gain full professional status and achieve a unique place of importance within the hospital's division of labor inevitably brings the group into conflict with the lay administration and the physicians, who are jealous of their prima donna status within the hospital scheme. As hospital employees, personnel in nursing and the so-called ancillary professions face the persistent threat that opinions of persons outside their profession will alter their own professional judgment and infringe upon what is considered their special competence. At the same time, the interdependence among all hospital professionals creates a need for supervision which offers every professional group the opportunity to gain control over one another.

If these dilemmas are apparent in nursing, despite that vocation's early association with hospitals and its relatively recent professional claims, then other ancillary health professions with more deeply ingrained traditions of autonomy which have only recently been employed in hospitals and other bureaucratic agencies must expect even more severe conflicts. Physicians themselves probably feel the status deprivations that accompany hospital and clinic employment.[10] Similar status losses are to be expected among ancillary professionals such as social workers who have had an independent professional footing before their employment in hospitals became widespread. Although medical social workers, like nurses, are predominantly women, they are perhaps less accustomed than nurses to subordination to other medical personnel.

Medical social work

The medical social worker offers another interesting group for analysis. The realization of the importance of the patients' social milieu by a few physicians about 40 years ago gave rise to the modern Social Service Department. However, as recently as 1947 a physician wrote, "Until recently, physicians have only slightly, if at all, concerned themselves with medical social work, and, unfortunately, many still do not. . . ." [43].

Some 30 years ago the International Conference of Social Work was told:

> The chief work of the social worker is to understand the patient and to make him understand what he especially needs to know in order that he may be properly cared for and, if possible, recover his health. Ideas, then, are the material in which the social worker chiefly deals. She is to gather ideas about the patient and to convey ideas to him. Her business is to understand him and to make him understand, so far as this is necessary to fulfill the hopes and desires with which he sought the hospital. What she aims to understand is especially (*a*) the patient's state of mind, (*b*) his economic, domestic, and industrial situation, and (*c*) these same facts as regards his family and those most closely connected with him in his school, his work, his recreations, and his religious life. When she aims to enlighten and assist the patient it is chiefly (*a*) by explaining to him the nature and the future of his own disease, (*b*) by explaining what is to be done for its palliation or its cure, and (*c*) as to what individuals or agencies outside the hospital can help him either by care or by cure [23].

[10] See Chap. 12.

Each of these responsibilities, however, overlaps with those of nurses and physicians, and may be regarded as an infringement on their professional sphere.

Actually, medical social work was crystallized into an organized hospital service as early as 1905. Social case work on behalf of the individual patient is a primary function of the medical social worker. Cooperating with the doctor and other members of the medical team, the social worker helps the team perceive the patient as a person who not only has a disease but reacts to illness in the context of his total situation. As a social worker, he is concerned with the patient's perception of his illness, with his ability to adjust to it, and with the social resources which he has to deal with it. He also tries to help the patient understand his situation. In this way the "difficult patient" can develop an attitude of cooperation which enhances the efforts of the medical team.

For example, a patient whom the doctor had instructed to construct an apparatus to exercise certain joints and muscles failed to cooperate in her treatment in the hospital because she did not know how to obtain or make the necessary apparatus. She knew her husband to be "all thumbs" and feared increasing the already strained relations between them by insisting that he attempt to construct the apparatus. When the social worker uncovered this problem and solved it to the patient's satisfaction, her improvement and dismissal followed rapidly. In other cases, the social worker's training in interviewing fits him for such activities as intake interviews at the time of admission and patient follow-up after discharge from the hospital. In still other cases, these skills, and a knowledge of the community's resources, help him to counsel with the patient and administration regarding arrangements for payment of hospital and medical expenses. The social worker is expected to provide increased understanding of the relationship of social and emotional factors as they relate to health and medical care [28].

Among the most frequent roles of the medical social worker then are those of consultant to the medical staff; interpreter to the patient, his family and his community; and cooperator in public health education. In each of these roles he tends to be subordinate to others in the medical profession, but brings to the field skills and knowledge in which he alone excels. Often his main problem is to gain a position on the team in which his skills will be fully utilized without threatening the status and prerogatives of other team members [2].

Public health educators

Public health educators have only recently become identified as a distinct professional group. The first training programs for this type of personnel were set up in 1943. Public health educators today are found in the voluntary health agencies, in school health programs, and in the public health service [28].

At the community level, public health educators see their functions as including the assessment of health education needs and potentials, organizing and promoting health education activities, and extending health information through the various communication media. At the state level, the health educator can perform similar functions and in addition he can encourage the recruitment and training of personnel, assist the medical, nursing, and sanitation personnel and others in their education programs, develop and maintain in-service training programs. They can perform similar functions on the federal level and in addition provide consultation services, serve as a clearinghouse for new ideas and materials, gather and interpret significant knowledge being developed in allied fields, prepare resource materials, and conduct research pertinent to the activities of the health educator.

References

1. Anderson, B. E., "Some Paradoxes in Nursing," *Teachers College Record*, 54 (December, 1953), 211.
2. Bartlett, Harriet, *Social Health Practices in the Health Field*, New York: National Association of Social Workers, 1961.
3. Becker, Howard S. and Blanche Geer, "The Fate of Idealism in Medical School," *American Sociological Review*, 23 (February, 1958), 50–56.
4. Berkowitz, Joanne E. and Norman H. Berkowitz, "Nursing Education and Role Conception," *Nursing Research*, 9 (Fall, 1960), 218–19.
5. Bixler, Genevieve Knight and Roy White Bixler, "The Professional Status of Nursing," *American Journal of Nursing*, 45 (September, 1945), 730–35.
6. Bressler, Marvin and William Kephart, *Career Dynamics*, Harrisburg, Pa.: Pennsylvania Nurses Association, 1955, pp. 23, 37, 85, 95, 102–103, 116.
7. Brown, Esther Lucile, *Nursing in the Future*. New York: Russell Sage Foundation, 1948, pp. 46–80.
8. Bullock, Robert P., *What Do Nurses Think of Their Profession?* Columbus, Ohio: The Ohio State University Research Foundation, 1954, 27–62.
9. Corwin, Ronald G., "Role Conception and Career Aspiration: A Study of Identity in Nursing," *The Sociological Quarterly*, 2 (April, 1961), 69–86.
10. ———, *Role Conception and Mobility Aspiration: A Study in the Formation and Transformation of Bureaucratic, Professional and Humanitarian Nursing Identities*. Unpublished Ph.D. thesis, University of Minnesota, 1960.
11. ———, Marvin J. Taves, and J. Eugene Haas, "Professional Disillusionment," *Nursing Research*, 10 (Summer, 1961), 141–44.
12. ———, "Social Requirements for Occupational Success: Internalized Norms and Friendship," *Social Forces*, 39 (December, 1960), 135–40.
13. Couey, Elizabeth and Diane D. Stephenson, *The Field of Private Duty Nursing*. Atlanta, Ga.: Georgia State Nurses Association, 1955, p. 245.

14. Deutscher, Irwin and Ann Montague, "Professional Education and Conflicting Value Systems: The Role of Religious Schools in Educational Aspirations of Nursing Students," *Social Forces,* 35 (December, 1956), 126–31.

15. Deutscher, Irwin, *Public Image of the Nurse* (Community Studies, Inc.). Part II, publication 96, Kansas City, Mo.: 1955.

16. Devereaux, George and Florence R. Weinder, "The Occupational Status of Nursing," *American Sociological Review,* 15 (October, 1950), 268.

17. Diamond, Lorraine and David J. Fox, "Turnover among Hospital Staff Nurses," *Nursing Outlook,* 6 (July, 1958), 388–91.

18. Dorffeld, Mildred E., Thomas S. Ray, and Theodore S. Baumberger, "A Study of Selection Criteria for Nursing School Applicants," *Nursing Research,* 7 (Spring, 1958), 67–70.

19. *Facts about Nursing,* American Nurses' Association, New York: 1960.

20. Ford, Thomas R. and Diane D. Stephenson, *Institutional Nurses: Role Relationships and Attitudes in Three Alabama Hospitals.* University, Ala.: University of Alabama Press, 1953.

21. Fox, David J., Lorraine K. Diamond, and Nadia Jacobowsky, *Career Decisions and Professional Expectations of Nursing Students,* Ithaca: Bureau of Publications, Cornell University, 1961, pp. 11, 25, 29.

22. Goldsen, Rose K. and Rodney F. White, *A Study of Professional Attitudes toward Work: The Case of Nursing.* Replicated study from U.S.P.H.S. Grant Number GN 44650, Cornell University, pp. 3–7.

23. Goldstine, Dora, *Expanding Horizons in Medical Social Work,* Readings in the Theory and Practice of Medical Social Work. Chicago: University of Chicago Press, 1954, p. 255.

24. Haas, J. Eugene, Marvin J. Taves, Katherine J. Densford, and Ruth V. Johnston, *Role Consensus on Hospital Stations.* Investigation supported by U.S.P.H.S. Grant Number GN 4647, Minneapolis: 1958.

25. Haas, J. Eugene, Marvin J. Taves, and David Shaw, "Primary Group Influence on Vocational Choices," *The Sociological Quarterly,* 2 (April, 1961), 87–97.

26. Habenstein, Robert A. and Edwin A. Christ, *Professionalizer, Traditionalizer, and Utilizer.* Columbia, Mo.: University of Missouri, 1955.

27. Haines, Anna J., "Nursing," *in* Edwin R. A. Seligman and Alvin Johnson, eds., *Encyclopedia of the Social Sciences.* Vol. 2. Toronto: The Macmillan Company of Canada, Ltd., 1933, 405–11.

28. Hanlon, John J., *Principles of Public Health Administration.* 3rd ed. St. Louis: The C. V. Mosby Company, 1960, pp. 466–69.

29. Healey, I. and W. R. Borg, "Personality Characteristics of Nursing School Students and Graduate Nurses," *Journal of Applied Psychology,* 35 (1951), 275–80.

30. Hughes, Everett C., Helen M. Hughes, and Irwin Deutscher, *Twenty Thousand Nurses Tell Their Story.* Philadelphia: J. B. Lippincott Co., 1958.

31. Hughes, Everett C., "The Making of a Physician—General Statement of Ideas and Problems," *Human Organization* (Winter, 1956), 21–25.

32. Ingmire, Alice E., "Attitudes of Student Nurses at the University of California," *Nursing Research,* 1 (October, 1952), 36–39.

33. Kuhn, Manford, "Self Attitudes by Age, Sex, and Professional Training," *The Sociological Quarterly*, 1 (January, 1960), 39–55.

34. Levin, Eugene, "Turnover among Nursing Personnel in General Hospitals," *Hospitals* (September, 1957), 50.

35. MacAndrew, Craig and Jo Eleanor Elliott, "Nursing Leadership in a Period of Change: A Case Study." Study conducted at UCLA under U.S.P.H.S. Grant Number GN 4552. Mimeographed.

36. McPartland, Thomas S., *Formal Education and the Process of Professionalization: A Study of Student Nurses.* Part V; publication 107. Kansas City, Mo.: Community Studies, Inc., 1957, pp. 27–29.

37. Martin, Harry W. and Ida Harper Simpson, *Patterns of Psychiatric Nursing: A Survey of Psychiatric Nursing in North Carolina.* Chapel Hill, N. C.: American Nurses' Foundation, Inc., 1956, p. 162.

38. Maryo, Joann S. and Julian J. Lasky, "A Work Satisfaction Survey among Nurses," *American Journal of Nursing*, 59 (April, 1959), 501–503.

39. Mayo, Adelaide A., R.N., ed., "Student Recruitment Is Underway," *American Journal of Nursing*, 49 (April, 1949), 242–45.

40. Meyer, Genevieve Rogge, "Conflict and Harmony in Nursing Values," *Nursing Outlook*, 7:7 (July, 1959), 298–99.

41. ———, *Tenderness and Techniques: Nursing Values in Transition.* Los Angeles: Industrial Relations Monographs of the Institute of Industrial Relations, No. 6, 1960, 9.

42. Middlewood, Esther L., "Why Do Students Drop Out?" *American Journal of Nursing*, 46 (December, 1946), 838–40.

43. *Modern Hospital*, 68 (May, 1947).

44. *Nursing Resources*, Department of Health, Education, and Welfare. Washington, D.C.: Government Printing Office, 1958.

45. Orzack, Louis, *Occupational Impressions, Occupational Preference and Residence*, Reprint Series of the Industrial Relations Research Center, No. 11. Madison: University of Wisconsin, 1960.

46. ———, *Work as a Central Life Interest of Professionals*, Reprint Series of the Industrial Relations Center, No. 8. Madison: University of Wisconsin, 1960, p. 127.

47. Pollak, Otto, Charles Westoff, and Marvin Bressler, "Pilot Study of Nursing Functions," *Nursing Research*, 2 (June, 1953), 15–22.

48. Ravitz, Mel J., "Occupational Values and Occupational Selection," *Nursing Research*, 6 (June, 1957), 35–40.

49. Reese, Dorothy E. and Stanley E. Siegal, "Educational Preparation of Nurses Employed in Non-Federal Hospitals," *Hospital Management*, 89 (April, 1960), 108–12.

50. Reissman, Leonard and John H. Rohrer, *Changes and Dilemma in the Nursing Profession.* New York: G. P. Putnam's Sons, 1957, pp. 50–80, 262–64.

51. Roberts, Mary M., *American Nursing: History and Interpretation.* New York: The Macmillan Company, 1954, p. 3.

52. Saunders, Lyle, "The Changing Role of Nurses," *American Journal of Nursing*, 54 (September, 1954), 1094–98.

53. Stewart, Donald and Christine E. Needham, *The General Duty Nurse.* Fayetteville, Ark.: University of Arkansas Press, 1955, p. 12.
54. Strauss, Anselm and Fred Davis, "The Development of Identities in Nursing." Research proposal, University of California.
55. Tantum, Julien Rundell, "Changing Roles of Professional Personnel in the Field of Medical Care," *Nursing Outlook,* 1 (January, 1953), 694–96.
56. Taves, Marvin J. and Ronald G. Corwin, "Role Conceptions in Nursing." Unpublished analysis: U.S.P.H.S. Grant Number GN 4647, C5.
57. ———, *The Image of Nursing among High School Girls.* Bureau of Business Research, Ohio State University (to be published).
58. Titus, Shirley, "Economic Facts of Life for Nurses," *American Journal of Nursing,* 52 (February, 1952), 1109–14.
59. Williams, Robin M., Jr., and Rose K. Goldsen, *Selection or Rejection of Nursing as a Career.* Ithaca, N. Y.: Cornell University Press, 1960, p. 12.
60. Williams, Thomas Rhys and Margaret M. Williams, "The Socialization of the Student Nurse," *Nursing Research,* 8 (Winter, 1959), 18–25.
61. "Withdrawal of Students," *American Journal of Nursing,* 49 (April, 1949), 248.

9

LIMITED, MARGINAL, AND QUASI-PRACTITIONERS

Walter I. Wardwell

Proliferation of technical knowledge in the field of health has resulted in the development of many medical specialties and in a variety of aides and technical assistants ancillary to the profession of medicine.[1] But there have also developed health practitioners who are independent of the medical profession. One such group of independent health practitioners are the *limited* practitioners whose health services are usually confined to particular parts of the human body. Still other health practitioners treat nearly the entire range of bodily functions and disorders, but

[1] See Chap. 8.

because they employ forms of therapy unacceptable to orthodox medical practice they are considered *marginal* practitioners. Finally, there are *quasi-*health practitioners—those whose ministrations to the sick are pseudo-scientific or incidental to another function, usually religious.[2]

Although limited practitioners, in the sense we employ the term, occasionally function as part of a medical team, share offices with physicians, or operate in a strictly medical setting, they usually deal directly with self-referred patients seeking a relatively specific service. Since they normally see such patients first, they assume responsibility for deciding which ones they will treat and which ones they will refer to physicians for conditions beyond their competence or jurisdiction. Hence they must exercise a degree of autonomous professional judgment that in this respect approaches medical diagnosis.

We can reach no final judgment concerning relationships between the various health professions, because social pressures toward change continually arise both within and outside these professions. For example, the former division of the medical fraternity into the warring camps of allopathy, homeopathy, and eclecticism has all but disappeared, and a rapprochement with osteopathy—until recently considered a "healing cult"—appears imminent [20, 33, 54]. The major stimulus to change is the dynamic nature of medical knowledge itself, which requires that physicians constantly adapt to scientific innovation; this is particularly true of major breakthroughs requiring reconceptualization of fundamental knowledge concerning basic life processes, *e.g.*, biochemistry, psychosomatic medicine, psychotherapy [14, 47]. The tendency toward exclusiveness and monopolization of discrete areas of practice, and the growing demand for specialized services not readily available from orthodox physicians (*e.g.*, psychotherapy) increase the importance of the newer professions.

Pressures toward professionalization, reinforced by licensing requirements, have raised the educational and ethical standards of the newer professions so that their public image, economic status, and social prestige relative to the medical profession have been greatly altered. In this constant shifting of ground new health professions appear as new modes of treatment are discovered (*e.g.*, psychology, audiology), some disappear as distinct groups (*e.g.*, homeopathy), and the most acceptable of them approach fusion with orthodox medicine (*e.g.*, dentistry, osteopathy). In the process of professionalization, a new health profession may leave behind a less professional and less competent nucleus which carries on extralegally or affiliates with an even newer, probably lower-status group with a somewhat different orientation toward illness and therapy. (See Table 9-1, pages 216–217.)

---

[2] Selected factual data pertaining to the principal health-related professions discussed in this chapter are presented in Table 9-1.

Pharmacy: A Special Case

The pharmacist, strictly speaking, is as subordinate (*i.e.*, ancillary) to the prescribing physician as is the nurse, but his over-all professional and social status is different. Although hospital pharmacists may indeed be as circumscribed in their functioning as other ancillary professions, retail pharmacists are not. Located apart from physicians, retail druggists supply commodities other than prescription medicines to their customers—a fact which casts them in an entrepreneurial as well as a professional role. Furthermore, druggists are often expected by their customers to suggest remedies for particular conditions that may not have been diagnosed by a physician and this expectation has been even more prevalent in the past—particularly in those parts of the country and in those social groups which lack easy access to physicians.

Pharmacy nevertheless is an adjunct to medicine: "All the responsibility and exercise of initiative and judgment belongs to the physician. . . . There is practically nothing he [the pharmacist] can do about a prescription if he is doubtful of it but get in touch with the doctor" [75]. The pharmacist's entrepreneurial role, however, and his frequent contacts with the public put him in a position of strength *vis-à-vis* physicians. Not only can he indirectly refer patients to particular physicians, but he can also effectively reward physicians who send patients to him—*e.g.*, a pharmacist "bought a downtown building with a corner location and put four physicians upstairs on a rent-free basis" [35], and other druggists have leased telephone lines from doctors' offices and have furnished doctors with prescription blanks on which a particular pharmacist's name appears. These are examples of unethical behavior that would most certainly be deplored by physicians and pharmacists alike. The very existence of such temptations, however, reveals the relatively strong position which the druggist occupies relative to the physician.

The principal source of ethical problems for the retail pharmacist arises from potential conflict between professional and commercial pressures [75]. Although there is a financial aspect to the practice of any profession the problem is more acute for the retail pharmacist, principally because he sells merchandise other than pharmaceuticals in a setting which resembles other retail establishments more closely than it does a professional office.

The professional training of the pharmacist emphasizes thoroughness, accuracy, cleanliness, and probity. It is a matter of professional pride, as well as a legal requirement, that the physician's prescription be filled with the utmost precision. Even if the physician has unnecessarily prescribed a trade-marked (perhaps more expensive) brand of a standard ingredient, the pharmacist should not substitute the standard ingredient

TABLE 9-1 COMPARATIVE DATA ON THE MAJOR HEALTH-RELATED PROFESSIONS

	Medicine	*Pharmacy*	*Dentistry*	*Podiatry*	*Optometry*	*Clinical Psychology*	*Osteopathy*	*Chiro-practic*	*Christian Science*
Number qualified to practice 1960	236,089	112,000	100,400	7,600	22,000	2,400	14,109	23,000	8,000
Number listed in the 1960 U.S. Census	229,590	92,710	83,268	—	16,081	—	3,951	14,360	—*
Degrees awarded	M.D.	B.S. in Ph.	D.D.S.; D.M.D.	D.S.C.; Pod.D.	O.D.; B.S. in Opt.	Ph.D.	D.O.	D.C.	C.S.; C.S.B.
Usual minimum number of years of college education	7	5	6	5	5	7	7	4	None
First college established in U.S.	1765	1821	1840	1912	1895	(A.P.A. founded in 1892)	1892	1897	1881 (none now)
First state regulatory law	1873**	1870***	1868	1895	1901	1945	1896	1913	None
First university affiliation of college	1765	1868	1867	1915 (none now)	1910	—	None	None	None
Number of U.S. colleges 1960	85	76	49	5	10	57	6	18	None
Rank on the North-Hatt Scale of Occupational Prestige (51)	93	—	86	—	—	85	—	—	—

TABLE 9-1—(Continued)

	Medicine	*Pharmacy*	*Dentistry*	*Podiatry*	*Optometry*	*Clinical Psychology*	*Osteopathy*	*Chiro-practic*	*Christian Science*
Jonassen's Interpolated Ranks in the North-Hatt Scale (39)	—	75	—	77	83	—	—	75	—
Reissman's Interpolated Ranks in the North-Hatt Scale (63)	—	79	—	—	75	—	79	75	—
James's Ranking of Acceptance as a Profession (37)	97	72	97	—	85	87	75	56	—
Hartman's Ranking of 25 Medical Specialties (30)	1 and 2	8	3	—	19	10	18	22	—

* "Therapists and healers (not otherwise classified)," which would include Christian Science practitioners, numbered 37,312.

** In 1760 New York attempted state regulation unsuccessfully, as did several other states during the colonial period. Effective licensing began only in the 1870's (69).

*** Earlier laws, beginning as early as 1808, were ineffectual (22).

for what is prescribed—even though it is a professionally approved goal to encourage physicians not to use brand names. How much substitution actually exists in such cases is not known, but Thorner implies that it occurs rather extensively.

The pharmacist is not authorized to diagnose or prescribe for medical conditions but only to dispense medicines that physicians have prescribed, or which, if not legally proscribed, customers may request on their own initiative. If the druggist is asked by a customer to recommend a medicine for a specific minor condition (*e.g.*, poison ivy) he usually can recommend a suitable remedy without difficulty. In such cases he has not actually diagnosed the patient's condition or prescribed for him. But if the patient merely states his symptoms (*e.g.*, dizziness, stomach pains), it would be unprofessional for the druggist to recommend a particular medicine. The line between the two cases is sometimes difficult for the pharmacist to discern.

Physicians naturally resent pharmacists who do more recommending of medicines than is necessary. Pharmacists, on the other hand, feel that physicians don't fully appreciate the knowledge and skill which a pharmacist must have in order to keep abreast of the latest scientific developments in pharmacology, and they resent the dispensing of pharmaceuticals for profit by physicians. *The General Report of the Pharmaceutical Survey, 1946–49,* concluded:

> Medicine, as a profession, maintains an attitude of condescending superiority toward pharmacy as a profession . . . . The ancient controversies involving the dispensing physician and the prescribing pharmacist remain as controversies [22].[2]

Social scientists have barely begun to study the fascinating profession of pharmacy. McCormack reported in 1956 that 85 per cent of the 117 freshmen entering one college of pharmacy saw themselves as future owners of retail drugstores [43]. Schwebel, using a sample of 450 New York State pharmacists who filled out the Strong Vocational Interest Blank, ascertained that "the typical pharmacist, as well as the typical satisfied pharmacist, has interests similar to those of the businessman" [68]. A more complete study of prescription pharmacists, based on a national sample of 450 druggists, was made by the National Opinion Research Center in 1955. In response to a question as to whether the general public regards the pharmacist mainly as a professional man or as a business man, 48 per cent answered "mainly professional" compared to 44 per cent

---

[2] Although salaried pharmacists who work in drug stores are not themselves entrepreneurs, they are subject to some of the same situational pressures as their employers. The problems of pharmacists engaged in research and teaching do not apply to retail pharmacists.

who answered "mainly business"; the remainder stated that they didn't know. Two-thirds of those who answered "mainly business," said that they would prefer to be considered professionals, while the rest said it didn't matter [11].

Remmers and Gage, using the Kuder Preference Record to study the abilities and interests of freshman pharmacy students, found that their preference for "persuasive activities" was far less than that of drug store managers and pharmacists, for whom the Kuder Test Manual provided norms. They concluded:

> It may be that a substantial number of the pharmacy freshmen will find themselves temporarily unfit for retail drugstore management because of insufficient interest in, and preference for, the persuasive type of activity for which, it appears, the typical drugstore manager has a strong preference [64].

The five-year program of preprofessional and professional training, which has been required since 1960, should further raise the level of professional competence of graduating pharmacists and may make them less satisfied with retail pharmacy as a profession. The opening up of opportunities in other phases of pharmacy, such as research and pharmaceutical manufacturing, provides new alternatives for those students psychologically not well adapted to retail pharmacy.

Limited Practitioners

Some health-related practitioners function independently of the medical profession but limit their area of practice to specified conditions and/or parts of the human body. In so doing they implicitly accept the authority of the physician over general conditions or systemic disorders. In the United States the best-established limited practitioners are dentists, podiatrists, optometrists, and psychologists. Other possible candidates for inclusion under this designation are speech pathologists (whose function does not conflict with that of organized medicine) [6], audiologists (those ancillary to medicine and those so-called retail audiologists who have barely started on the road to professionalization) [6], and midwives (who are disappearing in this country) [62]. Although the range of professional status of such limited practitioners is obviously very great, they all have attained, or have the potential for attaining, a fairly stable *modus vivendi* with organized medicine.

Dentists

Dentistry is fully recognized as a profession. It is the best established of the groups of independent health practitioners in terms of standards of professional training and requirements for licensure. Dental schools, almost without exception, are affiliated with universities—in many cases sharing their preclinical training facilities, instructors, and standards with the university medical school. From the very beginning, however, dental education and dental practice have been independent of medical control, owing partly to the almost complete lack of interest exhibited in dentistry by the medical profession [24]. The present course of professional training in dentistry requires at least two years of preprofessional college work, followed by four years in one of the 49 dental schools, for which the degree of Doctor of Dental Surgery (D.D.S.) or Doctor of Dental Medicine (D.M.D.) is awarded.

Dentistry is second only to medicine in public acceptance as a healing profession (see Table 1). Although Kriesberg and Treiman found that the public ascribes to the dental profession the same characteristics that it attributes to other high status occupations [41], Quarantelli reports that only 10 per cent of his sample of dental students felt that the public has a favorable image of the dentist [59, 60].

Podiatrists

Podiatry, sometimes called chiropody, is a well-established profession restricted to the diagnosis and treatment of certain types of foot ailments. Although podiatrists administer drugs, wield scalpels, and use casts and other appliances to correct various foot disabilities, they may not treat systemic ailments or perform amputations. First regulated by law in 1895 in New York, podiatry is licensed in all states and is accepted by organized medicine as an adjunct to medical care. With only 7600 practitioners, podiatry is still a relatively small field. Instruction is presently offered in the United States in only five colleges—none of which is affiliated with a university, although two have had university affiliation in the past. By 1938 all podiatric colleges required a total of five years of preprofessional and professional education for the Doctor of Surgical Chiropody (D.S.C.) or Doctor of Podiatry (Pod.D.) degree; beginning in 1964, all colleges will require a total of six years' training. Reed reported in 1933 that "on the whole the medical profession has used its influence to oppose the widening of the scope legally permitted the chiropodists," and that the president of the First Institute of Podiatry in New York City "has continued to maintain the position that the future of chiropody is that of a medical specialty and that, eventually, all who practice chiropody should be doctors of medicine" [62]. The difficulty facing the profession today appears to be that the formal course of training is nearly as long as that required for a medical degree but that podiatry does not carry the status and rewards of medicine. According to a thorough study of podiatric education made by a team of distinguished educators in 1961, all podiatric colleges are handicapped by limited financial support, part-time faculties, and inadequate facilities [58]. Furthermore, the study "disclosed that many of the students had undertaken professional studies previously in other institutions in such fields as dentistry, pharmacy, or veterinary medicine, and had demonstrated only limited success in their work prior to changing to a podiatry career."

Optometrists

Optometry is well-established now as an independent health profession. It is limited principally to making refraction and supplying eyeglasses and contact lenses to persons with defective vision. Licensed in all states since 1924, optometrists are trained at ten colleges in the United States (plus two in Canada), six of which are affiliated with established universities. The minimum number of years of preprofessional and professional college training is five, following which the student receives either a Bachelor of Science in Optometry or a Doctor of Optometry (O.D.) degree.

Relationships with ophthalmologists and oculists (both of whom are physicians specializing in treatment of the eyes), and with opticians (who grind lenses and make up spectacles in accordance with optical prescriptions), have been reasonably well clarified [1]. Optometrists should not diagnose or treat pathological conditions or use medicines to dilate the pupils of the eyes, but they may prescribe corrective exercises for such conditions as crossed eyes. Examination of medical and optometric literature, however, reveals that relationships between the two professions have not been resolved to the full satisfaction of both parties. Note the use of "skilled lay technicians" in this statement of the medical position:

> Optometrists who adhere to their proper field and do not attempt ocular diagnosis and treatment, or such basically medical procedures as the fitting of contact lenses, without supervision by ophthalmologists, may be considered skilled lay technicians who are acceptably engaging in the small segment of the field of eye care which they are permitted, by specific legal authorization, to share with ophthalmologists. They are entitled to ophthalmologic assistance and cooperation [46].

The attitude of organized medicine towards recognizing optometry and authorizing professional relationships with optometrists has wavered. One of the earliest courses of training was available at the Northern Illinois College of Ophthalmology and Otology, "a postgraduate school for physicians" which "in the early '90's permitted enrollment by opticians, lengthening its course to three months in 1895" [52]. Apparently "refracting opticians," as they were then called, were not at that time perceived by physicians as a threat to their authority. In 1934 the House of Delegates of the American Medical Association declared it "unethical for members of the American Medical Association to give lectures or courses of instruction before optometric groups or to consult with them." In 1950 it reversed its position, only to forbid collaboration again in 1955 [46]. Any physician, however, can legally prescribe glasses despite the fact that "the training received by medical students does not qualify them to do refraction" [62]. Optometrists stoutly maintain that they are fully qualified to recognize pathology, and that they often do a better refracting job than ophthalmologists do:

> About one fourth of the optometrist's education is devoted to study of the body, eye diseases, and symptoms of other diseases revealed in the eyes. Thus the optometrist is thoroughly trained in the detection of disease so that he can refer patients for whatever other professional care they may require [88].

Perhaps because they are not permitted to employ drugs, optometrists emphasize that "vision examinations without the use of drugs are preferable" and that they are concerned with "functional vision" [88]. The Committee on the Costs of Medical Care concluded as early as 1933: "The ophthalmologist who devotes his time to refraction is doing work for which he is overtrained" [19].

The principal current source of difficulty within the optometric profession concerns "the corporate practice of optometry" by commercial organizations, such as department or jewelry stores that hire optometrists to fit and sell optical products. The problem is that their relationships with patients are potentially more commercial than professional. But such optometrists constitute only a small minority of the profession.

There are no sociological studies of optometry except for Orzack and Uglum's overview of research possibilities in the field [53], but opinion surveys of occupational prestige confirm the public's acceptance of optometry as a profession. Indeed, James' study of the acceptance of professions found optometrists ranked above osteopaths, pharmacists, college teachers, and electrical engineers [37]. We may speculate that among the reasons for the high standing of optometry is that its practitioners must master the "hard" science of optics. Another reason may be that the eyes are symbolically a "good" and favorable part of the body compared with those parts of the body treated by dentists, podiatrists, and physicians. Eyeglasses may even serve as a status symbol associated with learned and prestigious occupations. No drugs or knives are found in optometrist's offices, and little emotion, pain, or anxiety is generally associated with refractions. Next to dentistry, optometry is the most numerous of the *limited* professions (about 22,000 practitioners in the United States in 1960), a fact which should make it better known to the public and therefore, perhaps better accepted. Finally, the scope of optometry is rather easily delimited by patient and optometrists alike, a characteristic which reduces ambiguity and confusion regarding the optometrist's function. This should also serve to make the optometric profession less threatening to organized medicine.

Clinical psychologists

Clinical psychology, another limited field of health practice, reveals its recent development in several ways. First, its practitioners do not receive their training in separate professional schools (as has sometimes been urged) but in the graduate departments of psychology of some 57 colleges of liberal arts and sciences [83]. Second, psychologists' opportunities for psychoanalytic training in the United States are now restricted by the fact that medical psychoanalytic institutes require that students already hold a medical degree or, alternatively, promise not to become practitioners. Third, certification and licensure of psychologists by state agencies, which did not begin until 1945, typically denies only the designation "psychologist" to the uncertified, and not their right to function as psychotherapists; the reason for this is the extreme difficulty of defining clinical psychology in such a way as to differentiate it from psychiatry and the pastoral counseling of clergymen [26].

Physicians and psychiatrists view psychologists as ancillary to medicine—*e.g.*, as capable only of performing psychometric or projective testing or limited psychotherapy following medical diagnosis—and are "strongly opposed to the independent private practice of psychotherapy by clinical psychologists" [29]. Actually relatively few psychologists are primarily engaged in independent private practice; Watson estimated in 1954 that the number was only about 400, with another 1600 clinical psychologists doing some private practice. By comparison, about 1,850 members of the American Psychiatric Association were wholly or partially engaged in private practice in 1952 [83]. Watson finds that in nonmedical settings, including psychological clinics, "cooperation, not subordination, is the basis of relationship with medicine," and "in schools, colleges, and agencies dealing with the relatively normal there is little need for medical collaboration and certainly not supervision" [83]. Goode states that in most clinical settings, the psychologist-therapist is not usually under real medical supervision: "Once a genuine team relationship is established, he works independently" [26].

Despite formal protestations, medicine appears to have given psychology *de facto* acceptance as a limited health profession rather than merely as an ancillary one. One reason for this may be that the psychologist does not touch the patient's body. Although mind and body are intertwined in any conceptualization of the malfunctioning of psyche or soma, the very concrete distinction between mere conversing and "the laying on of hands" permits drawing a clear line of professional responsibility which the psychologist has no desire to cross. An additional reason for medical acceptance of psychology has probably been the high standards of professional competence in psychology that have resulted from its historic locus in the graduate schools of established universities. Although psychologists have sometimes been criticized for having an inadequate clinical background, they have often been more intellectually alert and research-oriented than most practicing physicians or psychiatrists—probably as a consequence of their broad training in academic psychology and related subjects and because of the requirement that they submit a comprehensive research dissertation for the doctorate. For example, "in 1959, for the third successive year, the Hofheimer Award (for an outstanding research contribution) of the American Psychiatric Association was given by an all-psychiatric jury to a psychologist" [26].

In any case, clinical psychology appears to have gained high standing as a profession. On the North-Hatt scale of occupational prestige, psychologist is ranked 85, only one point below dentist [51], while James, studying professionalization, found that psychologist was ranked higher than clergyman, college teacher, electrical engineer, and osteopath [37].

Marginal Practitioners

Some practitioners, although they ordinarily treat nearly the whole range of human disease, have attained only *marginal* professional status because their whole approach to the problem of health and disease conflicts with that of orthodox medicine. Often referred to as members of *cults* or *sects*, they tend to reject such basic tenets of modern medicine as that disease is caused by bacterial agents which can be treated by drugs or prevented by inoculation, or they espouse a mono-causal theory of illness and therapy. In a fundamental sense they constitute a more serious threat to organized medicine than do limited medical practitioners, who typically do not advocate therapeutic principles contrary to those of medicine. For these reasons relationships between marginal practitioners and organized medicine are usually unstable, and the over-all professional standing of these groups tends to be ambiguous.

The best known marginal practitioners are the chiropractors, although osteopaths have historically also been considered cultists [20]. Naturopaths are very similar to chiropractors, and there have been several lesser known groups of marginal practitioners—*e.g.*, neuropaths, napropaths, vitopaths, mechanotherapists, spondylotherapists, and sanipractors. All share a tradition of hostility to the medical profession's liberal use of drugs (regarded as "foreign" or "poisonous" substances). This hostility toward drugs has by now been almost completely abandoned by osteopaths and has greatly weakened among those chiropractors who are designated "mixers."

Osteopaths

Osteopaths practice today as unlimited, nearly orthodox, medical practitioners in at least thirty-seven states [44, 54]. A few states still do not permit osteopaths to use certain drugs or to perform major surgery, while some states have two types of osteopathic licenses, one of which permits the licensee to perform major surgery [48]. By 1963 the six osteopathic colleges provided a high quality medical education and in addition taught traditional osteopathic theory and manipulative technique. To the dismay of many older osteopaths, today's young osteopathic graduate is more oriented toward allopathic medicine than toward body mechanics and manipulation, but the American Medical Association is in the process of welcoming osteopaths into the fold [40]. Its most recent change is to authorize state medical societies to determine how far physicians can ethically go in associating with osteopaths as professional colleagues, and which osteopaths are to be regarded as practicing scientific medicine: "The test should now be: Does the individual doctor of osteopathy practice osteopathy or does he in fact practice a method of healing founded on a scientific basis?" [54]. In 1961 the California medical and osteopathic associations formally voted to merge, with dissenting voices apparently coming only from die-hard "traditional" osteopaths, not from "allopathic physicians," as osteopaths choose to designate practitioners of medicine. Hence osteopathy has grown away from the principles of its founder, Andrew Taylor Still, who once proclaimed: "No system of allopathy, with its fatal drugs, should ever enter our doors. . . . Nor orificial surgery, with its torture and disappointments to the afflicted, can possibly find an abiding place in the minds of the true, tried, and qualified osteopath" [72]. The dilemma faced by osteopathic students developing a professional self-image has been sensitively studied by Peter New [49, 50].

Chiropractors

Since its beginnings in 1895, chiropractic has been beyond the medical pale [76, 79]. Whether or not it was "stolen" from Andrew Taylor Still's osteopathy, as has been charged [3], it has developed completely outside the field of medicine:

> Dr. Daniel David Palmer announced to the world a *separate, distinct,* and *independent* science, art, and philosophy of life. . . . Chiropractic holds nothing in common with any other system or health method. . . . If chiropractic bore any relation to medicine in any way, there would be no excuse for its existence. It is different, and in that difference lies its great success with cases given up by all other methods [9].

Organized medicine has stated almost as emphatically its disapproval of chiropractic [61]. Dr. Harvey Cushing is quoted as saying: "There is no pathological basis whatsoever for the theory of chiropractic, and it is silly to allude to it as a science" [7]. Constant repetition of such statements has intensified the hostility between medicine and chiropractic and has blinded physicians to certain basic facts about the chiropractic group. For example, one medical writer on chiropractic stated in 1939 that "legal status . . . so far has been denied to it in nearly all the states" [65]. In reality, however, the first state law licensing chiropractors was passed in 1913 and by 1931 thirty-nine states had given chiropractors legal recognition. Today about 23,000 practicing chiropractors are licensed in 46 of the 50 states; they are educated in four-year colleges which, while neither well-equipped nor known for scholarly research, prepare students to take state licensing examinations; in addition, students must have credits for two years of pre-professional college work to qualify for licensure in 23 states, and credits for one year of such work in three additional states; in 24 states they must pass the same "basic science" examinations as osteopaths, dentists, and physicians. These facts usually come as a shock to most physicians [34, 70]. But impressive as these requirements may be, they do not create anything like equality between chiropractic and medical education. Chiropractic clinical facilities are limited principally to ambulatory cases, hospital internships are practically non-existent, and the chiropractic philosophy of disease and its treatment remains suspect.

A small amount of sociological research on chiropractic has been published. In 1958 an extensive interview survey of over 500 California chiropractors was made by the Stanford Research Institute [2]. McCorkle has pointed to the congruence between chiropractic theories of illness and cultural values prevalent in rural Iowa [42]. The impact of his marginal status on the practicing chiropractor has been studied by Wardwell [81, 82], who distinguished several shared patterns of reaction which sometimes appear to contribute to the marginality of the role: (1) Chiropractors realistically unite to fight for self-protection, legal recognition, and public acceptance. (2) Chiropractors share such faith in their philosophy of illness and therapy that empirical evidence to the contrary threatens it very little, failures being explained as due to the lack of skill of the particular chiropractor or to the fact that the case didn't get to the chiropractor soon enough, with the result that irreversible pathology may have set in. (3) Chiropractors can feel that if their therapy is completely different from that of medicine they should not be expected to study the same subjects as physicians or meet the same licensing requirements; nor, if the two professions are completely different, need they feel inferior to the physician. (4) Chiropractors share what the writer has called an "ideology of an oppressed minority"—a comprehensive explanation for their inferior social standing and lack of professional acceptance. The ideology attributes organized medicine's disapproval of chiropractic to pecuniary motives and it righteously sanctions chiropractic's struggle against medical "oppression." The ideology gives the chiropractor in his daily practice a sense of carrying out an important mission—that of bringing help to the afflicted that medicine cannot cure.

Clark has criticized Wardwell's formulations, questioning whether chiropractors suffer problems of personal adjustment due merely to occupying a marginal social role. Using data derived from interviews with over 500 California chiropractors, he showed that those chiropractors who adhere most closely to the behavior patterns described by Wardwell as characteristic of the chiropractic group are no more satisfied with their community standing than are the chiropractors who deviate from the patterns [8].

The dilemma faced by organized medicine and by legislators is whether to continue to fight a rearguard action against the legal and social recognition of chiropractors, or whether to sanction legislation recognizing them and thereby help the chiropractic profession to raise educational standards and to eliminate incompetent practitioners [23, 80]. The American Medical Association acts as though chiropractors are nonexistent, or, if their existence must be recognized, as though they are out-and-out quacks rendering nothing but incidental psychological benefit to their patients. Organized medicine thus loses the good will of many patients who have received other than merely psychological benefit from chiropractors [*e.g.*, for sacroiliac strains]. Weiant finds extensive documentation in the literature of scientific medicine for benefits derived from chiropractic manipulation [84].

Current fears on the part of organized medicine that "chiropractic is attempting to evolve into the practice of medicine without restriction" [70] are probably exaggerated, since the vast majority of practicing chiropractors do not appear to want closer ties with medicine. Ideologically they are pretty well committed to a drugless, philosophy of *dis-ease,* as they spell it, and to a style of manipulative therapy which is their familiar stock-in-trade. There are strong vested interests—*e.g.*, the chiropractic schools—eager to keep chiropractic a separate and distinct healing profession. Hence it will be many years before chiropractic attains, if it ever does, the degree of professional recognition that osteopathy has achieved. Schools would have to be vastly improved, licensing laws would have to be broadened in scope and tightened up, the mono-casual philosophy of illness would have to become greatly attenuated, and at least a generation of chiropractors would have to be displaced before this could happen.

Medical acceptance of osteopathy might have the effect of impeding acceptance of chiropractic, for there would then be experts in manipulative therapy within the medical profession. On the other hand, the disappearance of osteopathy as a separate profession might bring about a gradual upgrading of the more progressive chiropractors (perhaps joined by dissident osteopaths), and the separation of a schismatic group of "straight" chiropractors into a sectarian and traditional association of drugless practitioners hostile toward physicians and chiropractic "mixers" alike. One can hypothesize that the cycle would then repeat itself, with the trend toward professionalization and scientific upgrading of drugless practitioners continually counterbalanced by the emergence of new cultistic groups adapting some variant of drugless therapy to the cure of mankind's ills.[3]

Quasi-Practitioners

A varied collection of nonmedical healers use methods that have not or cannot meet the criteria for empirical scientific validation. Some of these practitioners invoke the symbols and terminology of modern science and claim empirical validation for their therapy; others attribute their achievements to specifically nonscientific factors, such as religious faith, supernatural beings, or magical rites. In both cases the essential benefits which patients receive are clearly psychological although they are not conceptualized as such by the practitioners.

Psychotherapy can be intended or unintended. In his comparative study *Persuasion and Healing,* Frank offers a comprehensive definition of psychotherapy and states that its characteristics are common "also to methods of primitive healing, religious conversion, and even so-called brain-washing"; and that "the administration of an inert medicine by a doctor to a patient is also a form of psychotherapy" [21]. He lists physicians, osteopaths, chiropractors, naturopaths, clergymen, marriage counselors, parole officers, and group workers among those conducting psychotherapy. But it is essential to distinguish between those (including most quasi-practitioners) who conduct psychotherapy in this broad sense, perhaps unconsciously, and those whose therapy is conceptualized in terms of modern empirical psychology and who are scientifically trained in its theory and practice. It is of course possible for persons in other professions—*e.g.,* clergymen—intentionally to practice psychotherapy scientifically if they are trained to do so. The Academy of Religion and Mental Health exemplifies the overlapping interests of clergymen and psychotherapists [85].

Faith healers

One subgroup of quasi-practitioners is comprised of religious or faith healers. They ascribe to religious faith or supernatural intervention the benefits they confer on their patients. The means they employ are almost exclusively spiritual, such as prayer. Conventionally such healers are regarded as filling some other primary role—*e.g.,* that of clergyman or other religious specialist—rather than that of physician. Laws pertaining to

---

[3] The latest news pertaining to the chiropractic profession is a concerted movement toward unity of the "straights" and "mixers" and their respective associations, a development which made front-page news in *The Wall Street Journal* [5].

medical practice ordinarily exempt religious practitioners from their purview even where healing is their prime stock in trade and is done for a fee—*e.g.*, Christian Science practitioners.

Miraculous healing has been a potent Christian tradition. Healing shrines such as those at Lourdes in France and at Ste. Anne de Beaupré in Canada attract thousands of sick people, some of whom benefit from the emotional effect of the pilgrimages and the impressive ceremonies in which they participate with other believers [10]. The evangelist Oral Roberts conducts healing demonstrations before vast television audiences [36]. Christian Science, the most prominent contemporary American example of the link between religion and healing, has had its counterparts in "Jewish Science," "Divine Science," "New Thought," and the "spiritual healing" at one time emphasized by Jehovah's Witnesses [25, 28, 38, 55, 73].

Lesser-known groups combine religion with the occult, astrology, and pseudo-psychology for the purpose of eliminating all man's ills—not only physiological, but mental, spiritual, and financial. For example, the Foundation for Divine Meditation, in Santa Isabel, California—which shares quarters with the Academy of Self-Attainment and the National Institute of Christian Healing—offers to train practitioners in "instant healing," "psycho-metaphysics," or "suggestive passivity induction." From Indianapolis, the College of Divine Metaphysics offers correspondence courses in "metaphysical healing," "practical metaphysics," and "the psychology of business success." Its course in "metaphysical healing" includes lessons in "mental chemistry," "mental surgery," and "the mental cure" of numerous specific diseases and disorders. Completion of two such courses and payment of fees of $50 per course earns the student a Doctor of Psychology degree, authorizing him to enter practice immediately. One additional course merits the Doctor of Metaphysics degree, while another two courses are rewarded with the degree of Doctor of Divinity. Five courses and three doctorates for $250!

The Rosicrucians, who reportedly date from the fourteenth century, combine religion, astrology, healing, and vegetarianism in one package, offering instruction through correspondence or in residence. Their extensive list of publications includes one entitled, "Occult Principles of Health and Healing."

Primitive and magical healers

A second subgroup of quasi-practitioners not only invoke supernatural powers but also typically employ various material substances in conjunction with them. Hence they may be regarded as magical rather than as religious healers, although the line of demarcation is indistinct. In the magical group are included primitive healers (witch doctors, medicine men, shamans) [17, 66], specialized practitioners of folk medicine such as the Spanish-American *medicas* and *curanderas* in the southwestern United States described by Saunders [67], and other contemporary employers of magic.

Quacks

A third subgroup of quasi-practitioners comprises those who "pretend" to be scientific but are not. The word "pretend" is put in quotation marks because frequently the practitioner is himself deceived about the scientific merits of his procedure or equipment. This type of practitioner ascribes the benefits of his practice to "natural" rather than to "supernatural" forces. Prominent are mechanical devices of an electrical nature believed to emit beneficial impulses, waves, or radiations which somehow stimulate restorative processes in the patient's body. Some members of this subgroup, such as the famous Hoxsey Cancer Clinic in Dallas, Texas, dispense medicine or nostrums for which they claim special benefits not recognized by orthodox medical practitioners. Of course such practitioners sometimes actually do effect cures among those who believe. Faith can be as strong in the healing power of an unscientific technique (or for that matter a scientific technique!) as in the healing power of God. "Quackery" is the common term for such pseudoscientific practices, although historically it has sometimes been used for practices that were disapproved of in contemporary orthodox medical circles, but which later gained scientific acceptance [32]. In the field of psychotherapy "quack psychologists" are those who employ pseudopsychological principles in an untrained manner, as the practitioners of dianetics have been accused of doing [87]. Steiner's investigation of the variety of ill-trained persons to whom people "take their troubles" is a major empirical contribution to knowledge in this field [71].

These three subgroups of quasi-practitioners vary greatly in their therapeutic techniques, in their rationale for employing them, and in the degree to which they sincerely believe in their therapy. But in each case there is little doubt that the benefits derived by their patients are basically psychotherapeutic in nature although they may not be conceptualized or intended by the practitioner as *scientific* psychotherapy. As Frank has emphasized, suggestion is not absent from any type of therapy, including medicine. The psyche is always involved when the body suffers. The whole person is treated by any therapist even when the lesion is clearly somatic and the method wholly pharmacological. Thus all therapy is also psychotherapy.

Christian Science practitioners

Christian Science is examined here in the perspective of medicine, although it is obviously impossible completely to separate its medical aspects from its religious philosophy. It is well known that Christian Science denies the existence of matter, sin, death, and sickness, and asserts that all is mind, spirit, God, and good. "The word 'healing' as used in Christian Science extends to the healing of family and business problems, of social injustices, intellectual limitations, psychological tensions, and moral confusions" [18]. Despite prominent attention paid in Christian Science testimonials to the social and material benefits received by true believers, it is for its spiritual healing of disease that Christian Science is best known. Although the relatively large bibliography on Christian Science includes several unpublished sociological treatments, primary emphasis in such studies has been on its development as a religious sect rather than on its healing per se [13, 16, 31, 56, 57, 74, 77, 78].

The techniques of Christian Science healing are remarkably unlike those of other spiritual healing. Although the emphasis is on prayer and mental concentration, along with reading from the Bible and from Mary Baker Eddy's *Science and Health with Key to the Scriptures*, the group ceremonials and emotional ecstasy that accompany most primitive and contemporary faith healing are lacking. Even the function of the practitioner himself is minimized, for he does not have to be physically present with the patient, but can focus his mental energy on the patient's problem while remaining in his own home, or can be dispensed with altogether, since the patient is competent to attain correct belief by himself and is encouraged to do so through studying authorized writings. However, practitioners can help a person afflicted by a "claim" (*i.e.*, an illness) and practitioners play a significant role in most "demonstrations" (*i.e.*, cures).

Christian Science practitioners must take "primary class instruction" from a qualified teacher. Such instruction, which lasts about two weeks, is based on twenty-four questions and answers from the chapter entitled "Recapitulation" in Mary Baker Eddy's *Science and Health*. Pupils who have received primary class instruction may put C.S. (Christian Scientist) after their names and, if certain other requirements are met, may be officially listed in the *Christian Science Journal* as practitioners; such listing is the equivalent of certification as a qualified practitioner. Not all who take class instruction become practitioners, and some who practice do so only part-time. Some 6500 such practitioners are listed in the United States with another 1500 or so distributed around the world.

After three years of full-time practice, practitioners may apply for the Normal Course, which is given only once every three years to a limited number of pupils. The Normal Course usually lasts six days and merits the degree C.S.B. (Bachelor of Christian Science). A graduate of the Normal Class is certified as a "teacher" and may give primary class instructions to not more than 30 pupils once a year.

Class instruction of practitioners has always been surrounded by secrecy despite the fact that in principle any Christian Scientist can educate himself solely through study of the Bible, *Science and Health*, and other Christian Science texts. For example, note-taking in class has been either forbidden or severely restricted. Furthermore, "teachers are required to teach pupils to defend themselves 'against malpractice'" [86], for just as a practitioner's thought can produce benefit for a person, so also can it produce evil, intentionally or unintentionally. A conscientious practitioner avoids "promiscuous mental treatment." "Malicious mental malpractice"—*i.e.*, "malicious animal magnetism" (usually abbreviated "M.A.M."), presumably is employed only by the enemies of Christian Science, never by loyal members of the faith.[4]

A special feature of the system of qualification of Christian Science practitioners is that the bond between teacher and pupil is considered to be so close that if the teacher later falls out of favor with the Church authorities and becomes disqualified, all the pupils he has ever trained are disqualified as well. Only by being "retaught" by a teacher in favor with the Board (and again paying the instruction fee) can the pupil return to the privileged position of which he has been deprived through no fault of his own. Every teacher, then, not only has his own position and welfare to consider, but also must move with supreme caution lest his pupils be penalized for his actual or supposed defection [4]. Nevertheless, a number of Christian Science practitioners who have been excommunicated from the Church or whose names have been removed from the *Journal* for some other reason continue in practice.

The right of Christian Scientists to practice has been established in nearly all states. As one judge ruled: "I deny the power of the Legislature to make it a crime to treat disease by prayer" [4]. Additional recognition is shown in the fact that

> practitioners are authorized by statute to sign certificates for sick leave and for disability claims in seven states . . . and for federal employees. In health, accident, and hospitalization policies, some insurance companies today recognize the services of a Christian Science practitioner in lieu of a physician or surgeon [4].

But there is evidence that the climate of public opinion is changing, particularly where children are concerned, as shown by recent court rulings [4].

Women have always played an especially prominent role in Christian Science both as leaders and as members; and they have nearly monopolized Christian Science healing. In 1953 77 per cent of all practitioners were married women and another 11 per cent were single women—a total of 88 per cent [86]. Furthermore, practitioners tend to be of middle class or higher status and rather frequently have independent incomes.

---

4 In the very earliest days of Christian Science students were taught physical manipulation of the head and solar plexus "to produce a state of receptivity." Mrs. Eddy reasoned that since the belief to be rubbed out is located in the brain, "you lay your hands where the belief is to rub it out forever" [4].

The growth of Christian Science as a religious movement has been largely a result of the tireless dedication of its teachers and practitioners, the social characteristics of those affiliated with the movement, and the compatibility between the practical, this-worldly ethos of Christian Science and the American middle class ethic of the late nineteenth century. All observers agree that the center of social gravity of Christian Science has been in the urban middle classes. It is not difficult to see why "manual workers, factory workers, the poor, and the uneducated are not drawn to Christian Science, which demands something of a willingness to attribute poverty to the wrong set of mental attitudes" [86]. "To paraphrase Marx, it is an opiate for those whose lives are already sheltered" [13]. Thorner concludes: "Christian Science is the polar development of ascetic Protestant tendencies toward the transformation of the omnipotent and transcendental personal God of the Old Testament into a dependable impersonal and immanent force available for man's disposal"; the net result is a "toughly self-reliant and responsible" type of person who directs his energies in a pragmatic, this-worldly direction [74].

The Christian Scientist seeks empirical goals using nonempirical means. There is no question that the empirical goals sought are often attained; cases are even reported where physicians have sent patients to, or have themselves become, Christian Science practitioners. But there is no doubt that Scientific therapy is separate and distinct from scientific therapy. The problem concerns the efficacy of the means employed by Christian Science. How does Christian Science cure? "It has been estimated that sickness, suffering, sin, and death are denied at least three thousand times in the pages of *Science and Health*" [86]. "Efface from thought all forms and types of disease. . . . Avoid speaking aloud the name of the disease" [15]. During treatment the patient is told or tells himself repeatedly that sickness is not real and that he is well and whole. Such ritualistic denial of objective reality must carry great meaning not only for the patient but for the practitioner as well. Psychologically it suggests an almost schizoid withdrawal from reality. Denial probably occurs at several different psychological levels. First the practitioner denies his own weaknesses and inadequacies and finds opportunities to treat them nurturantly in patients. Secondly, when the Christian Scientist insists on man's inner perfection, goodness, and spirituality, he denies in effect his own aggressive (and other) impulses, which may then be projected according to well-known psychodynamic mechanisms onto others who are perceived as dangerous. Malicious animal magnetism (referred to, interestingly enough, as "the dragon") resembles nothing so much as paranoid delusions of persecution by imaginary enemies. Denial and projection to the "outside" of all hostility, sickness, and evil is a tenuous psychodynamic "solution" that needs continual reinforcement by repetitious denial of the reality of evil. Lacking the emotional ecstasy usually present in faith healing, Christian Science intellectualizes denial through an abstract and impersonal metaphysics.

In addition to the high proportion of women who are leaders and practitioners, there is a strong feminine orientation in general. The direction was initially set by Mary Baker Eddy, who referred to herself as "a God-like woman, God-anointed" [4], and who apparently considered herself the feminine representative in Christianity, as Jesus was the masculine representative. References to "Father-Mother-God" are carried out in the rewriting of the Lord's Prayer for Christian Science use. Identification of the church as feminine is not unusual in Christian denominations, for symbolically the church can be a mother as well as a pillar of strength; but the feminine emphasis seems strongest of all in Christian Science—in its founder, in its theology, in its practitioners, and in its overt repetition of loving sentiments in interpersonal relationships.

Emphasis on the gentle, more feminine virtues, and on the tendency to deny and project hostile impulses are both common in those strata in which Christian Science has attained its greatest success—the urban American middle classes in which, as Gorer and Mead have emphasized, there is much psychological dependence of men on women as well as considerable confusion over sex roles generally [27, 45].

Psychological factors in any religious affiliation are notoriously difficult to study, but those of Christian Scientists need more empirical investigation. Thus far, sociological studies of Christian Science have dealt mainly with such external factors as the growth of the movement and the social background of its adherents, paying little attention to the personal meaning of its therapy. Dakin has provided an excellent analysis of the meaning of the faith for Mary Baker Eddy herself [12]. It is high time for someone to analyze its meaning for other Christian Scientists.

Research Problems

Nearly all the types of research that have been done on the medical profession could be carried out on limited, marginal, and quasi-practitioners with great theoretical and practical benefit. In addition, comparative research on several of these types of professionals representing different degrees on scales of professionalization, prestige, or role marginality could ascertain the correlates of differential recruitment, adult socialization experience, professional self-image, choice of therapist by patients, and therapist-patient relationship. Other topics deserving investigation center on the social forces producing changes over time in the status or development of these professions: (1) the relationship between rational and nonrational factors in the acceptance or rejection of new modes of therapy; (2) the role of charismatic leadership in legitimizing therapeutic innovation and in establishing new health-related professions; (3) the effect of the activities of organized medicine and of state regulatory agencies on the establishment, evolution, and possible disappearance of limited, marginal and quasi-practitioners; and (4) comparative study of these professions in other societies for the light which cross-cultural investigation can shed on the forces and factors operative on the American scene.

References

1. *The Ancillary Worker in Ophthalmologic Medical Practice, Part I: The Optician.* Report No. 6 of the National Medical Foundation for Eye Care, 1959.
2. Barsalou, Frank W., *et al., Chiropractic in California.* Los Angeles: The Haynes Foundation, 1960.
3. Boyd, C. E., *The Cult of Chiropractic.* Shreveport, La.: American Medical Association and Louisiana State Medical Society, n.d.
4. Braden, Charles S., *Christian Science Today.* Dallas: Southern Methodist University Press, 1958.
5. Bush, Thomas W., "Chiropractors Climb," *The Wall Street Journal,* 158 (October 16, 1961), 1.
6. Carhart, Raymond, "Speech Pathology and Audiology," *Ashe, A Journal of the Speech and Hearing Association,* 2 (April, 1960), 99–102.
7. *Chiropractors and Naturopaths,* Committee on Legislation of the Medical Society of Virginia, 1947.
8. Clark, Alexander L., "Marginality and Induced Stress." Paper read at the St. Louis meeting of the Society for the Study of Social Problems, August 28, 1961.
9. Cooley, C. S., "Science Sidelights," *Journal of the National Chiropractic Association,* 19 (April, 1949), 35–38.
10. Cranston, Ruth, *The Miracle of Lourdes.* New York: The McGraw-Hill Book Company, Inc., 1955.
11. Croatman, Wallace and Paul B. Sheatsley, *The Prescription Pharmacist Today.* New York: Health Information Foundation, 1958.
12. Dakin, Edwin F., *Mrs. Eddy: The Biography of a Virginal Mind.* New York: Charles Scribner's Sons, 1930.
13. DeNood, Neal B., *The Diffusion of a System of Belief.* Unpublished Ph.D. thesis, Harvard University, 1937.
14. Dubos, Rene J., "Health and Disease," *Journal of the American Medical Association,* 147 (October 1, 1960), 505–507.
15. Eddy, Mary Baker, *Science and Health with Key to the Scriptures.* Boston: Christian Science Publishing Society, 1934.
16. England, R. W., "Some Aspects of Christian Science as Reflected in Letters of Testimony," *American Journal of Sociology,* 59 (March, 1954), 448–53.
17. Evans-Pritchard, E. E., *Witchcraft, Oracles, and Magic among the Azande.* London: Oxford University Press, 1937.

18. *Facts about Christian Science.* Boston: Christian Science Publishing Society, 1959.
19. Falk, I. S., C. F. Rorem, and M. D. Ring, *The Costs of Medical Care.* Summary of publications of the Committee on the Costs of Medical Care. Chicago: University of Chicago Press, 1933.
20. Flexner, Abraham, "A Layman's View of Osteopathy," *Journal of the American Medical Association,* 42 (June 6, 1914), 1831–33.
21. Frank, Jerome D., *Persuasion and Healing: A Comparative Study of Psychotherapy.* Baltimore: Johns Hopkins Press, 1961.
22. *The General Report of the Pharmaceutical Survey, 1946–49.* Washington, D.C.: American Council on Education, 1950.
23. Geiger, Arthur J., "Chiropractic: Its Cause and Cure," *Medical Economics* (February, April, June, and August, 1942).
24. Gies, William J., *Dental Education in the United States and Canada.* New York: The Carnegie Foundation for the Advancement of Teaching, 1926.
25. Goddard, Henry H., "The Effects of Mind on Body as Evidenced by Faith Cures," *American Journal of Psychology,* 10 (April, 1899), 431–502.
26. Goode, William J., "Encroachment, Charlatanism, and the Emerging Professions: Psychology, Sociology, and Medicine," *American Sociological Review,* 25 (December, 1960), 902–14.
27. Gorer, Geoffrey, *The American People.* New York: W. W. Norton & Company, Inc., 1948.
28. Griswald, Alfred W., "New Thought: A Cult of Success," *American Journal of Sociology,* 40 (November, 1934), 309–318.
29. Group for the Advancement of Psychiatry, Committee on Clinical Psychology, "The Relation of Clinical Psychology to Psychiatry," *American Journal of Orthopsychiatry,* 20 (April, 1950), 346–54.
30. Hartmann, George W., "The Relative Social Prestige of Representative Medical Specialties," *Journal of Applied Psychology,* 20 (December, 1936), 659–63.
31. Hoffman, Lois, "Problem Patient: The Christian Scientist," *Medical Economics,* 33 (December, 1956), 265–83.
32. Holbrook, Stewart H., *The Golden Age of Quackery.* New York: The Macmillan Company, 1959.
33. Holmes, Oliver Wendell, Sr., "Homeopathy and Kindred Delusions," *in The Writings of Oliver Wendell Holmes.* Cambridge, Mass.: Riverside Press, 1891, Vol. 9, Chap. 1.
34. Homewood, A. E., "Chiropractic," *University of Toronto Medical Journal* (February, 1961).
35. Hull, William H., *Public Relations for the Pharmacist.* Philadelphia: J. B. Lippincott Company, 1955.
36. Jacobs, Hayes B., "Oral Roberts: High Priest of Faith Healing," *Harpers' Magazine,* 224 (February, 1962), 37–43.
37. James, Warren E., *Differential Acceptance of Occupations as Professions.* Unpublished Ph.D. thesis. Ohio State University, 1957.
38. James William, *The Varieties of Religious Experience.* New York: Modern Library, Inc., 1902.

39. Jonassen, Christen, Robert Bullock, Jerome Folkman, William Kenkel, Alfred Clarke, and Russell Dynes, "Interpolations in the North-Hatt Scale." Unpublished ms.

40. Keesecker, Raymond P., *The Osteopathic Movement in Medicine.* Chicago: American Osteopathic Association, 1957.

41. Kriesberg, Louis and Beatrice R. Treiman, "The Public's Views on Dentistry as a Profession," *Journal of Dental Education*, 25 (September, 1961), 247–68.

42. McCorkle, Thomas, "Chiropractic: A Deviant Theory of Disease and Treatment in Contemporary Western Culture," *Human Organization,* 20 (Spring, 1961), 20–23.

43. McCormack, Thelma H., "The Druggists' Dilemma: Problems of a Marginal Occupation," *American Journal of Sociology*, 61 (January, 1956), 308–15.

44. McDowell, Harold D., *Osteopathy: A Study of a Semi-Orthodox Healing Agency and the Recruitment of Its Clientele.* Unpublished M.A. thesis. University of Chicago, 1950.

45. Mead, Margaret, *Male and Female.* New York: William Morrow & Co., Inc., 1949.

46. *Medicine, Optometry, and the Public Welfare.* The National Medical Foundation for Eye Care, 1957.

47. Menzel, Herbert and Elihu Katz, "Social Relations and Innovation in the Medical Profession: The Epidemiology of a New Drug," *Public Opinion Quarterly*, 19 (Winter, 1955–56), 337–52.

48. Mills, Lawrence W., *The Osteopathic Profession and Its Colleges.* Chicago: American Osteopathic Association, 1959.

49. New, Peter, "The Osteopathic Students: A Study in Dilemma," *in* E. Gartly Jaco, ed., *Patients, Physicians, and Illness.* New York: The Free Press of Glencoe, Inc., 1958.

50. ———, *The Application of Reference Group Theory to Shifts in Values: The Case of the Osteopathic Student.* Unpublished Ph.D. thesis, University of Missouri, 1960.

51. North, C. C. and P. K. Hatt, "Jobs and Occupations: A Popular Evaluation," *Public Opinion News*, 9 (September 1, 1947), 3–13.

52. *Optometry, the Profession: Its Antecedents, Birth, and Development.* A series of articles that appeared under the title "The Basis of Optometry's Public Relations" *in The Optical Journal and Review of Optometry* (October 1, 1945–January 1, 1947).

53. Orzack, Louis H. and John R. Uglum, "Sociological Perspectives of the Profession of Optometry." Monograph No. 230 of the *American Journal of Optometry and Archives of American Academy of Optometry* (August, 1958).

54. "Osteopathy: Special Report of the Judicial Council to the AMA House of Delegates," *Journal of American Medical Association*, 177 (September 16, 1961), 774–76.

55. Paulsen, Alice E., "Religious Healing," *Journal of the American Medical Association*, 86 (May 15, 22, and 29, 1926), 1519–24, 1617–23, 1692–97.

56. Pfautz, Harold W., "Christian Science: A Case Study of the Social Psychological Aspect of Secularization," *Social Forces,* 34 (March, 1956), 246–51.

57. ———, *Christian Science: The Sociology of a Social Movement and a Religious Sect.* Unpublished Ph.D. thesis, University of Chicago, 1953.

58. *Podiatry Education in the 1960's.* Special Commission on Status of Podiatry Education. Washington, D.C.: American Podiatry Association, 1961.

59. Quarantelli, Enrico L., *The Dental Student: A Social Psychological Study,* Unpublished Ph.D. thesis, University of Chicago, 1959.

60. ———, "The Dental Student Image of the Dentist-Patient Relationship," *American Journal of Public Health,* 51 (September, 1961), 1312–19.

61. Reed, Louis, *The Healing Cults.* Publication No. 16 of the Committee on the Costs of Medical Care. Chicago: University of Chicago Press, 1932.

62. ———, *Midwives, Chiropodists, and Optometrists.* Publication No. 15 of the Committee on the Costs of Medical Care. Chicago: University of Chicago Press, 1932.

63. Reissman, Leonard, *Class in American Society.* New York: The Free Press of Glencoe, Inc., 1959.

64. Remmers, H. H. and N. L. Gage, *Student Personnel Studies of the Pharmaceutical Survey.* Washington, D.C.: American Council on Education, 1949.

65. Riesman, David, *Medicine in Modern Society.* Princeton, N.J.: Princeton University Press, 1939.

66. Rivers, W. H. R., *Medicine, Magic, and Religion.* London: Routledge & Kegan Paul, Ltd., 1924.

67. Saunders, Lyle, "Healing Ways in the Spanish Southwest," *in* E. Gartly Jaco, ed., *Patients, Physicians, and Illness.* New York: The Free Press of Glencoe, Inc., 1958.

68. Schwebel, Milton, *The Interests of Pharmacists.* New York: King's Crown Press, 1951.

69. Sigerist, Henry E., "The History of Medical Licensure," *Journal of the American Medical Association,* 104 (March 30, 1935), 1056–60.

70. Stalvey, Richard M., "What's New in Chiropractic?" *New York State Journal of Medicine,* 57 (January 1, 1957), 49–59.

71. Steiner, Lee R., *Where Do People Take Their Troubles?* Boston: Houghton Mifflin Company, 1945.

72. Still, Andrew T., *Autobiography of A. T. Still.* Kirksville, Mo.: published by the author, 1908.

73. Stroup, Herbert H., *The Jehovah's Witnesses.* New York: Columbia University Press, 1945.

74. Thorner, Isador, *Christian Science and Ascetic Protestantism.* Unpublished Ph.D. thesis, Harvard University, 1950.

75. ———, "Pharmacy: The Functional Significance of an Institutional Pattern," *Social Forces,* 20 (March, 1942), 321–28.

76. Turner, Chittenden, *The Rise of Chiropractic.* Los Angeles: Powell Publishing Company, 1931.

77. Twain, Mark, *Christian Science.* New York: Harper & Row, Publishers, Inc., 1907.

78. ———, "Christian Science and the Book of Mrs. Eddy," *Cosmopolitan*, 27 (October, 1899), 585–94.

79. Wardwell, Walter I., "A Marginal Professional Role: The Chiropractor," *Social Forces*, 30 (March, 1952), 339–48.

80. ———, "Public Regulation of Chiropractic," *Journal of the National Medical Association*, 53 (March, 1961), 166–72.

81. ———, "The Reduction of Strain in a Marginal Social Role," *American Journal of Sociology*, 61 (July, 1955), 16–25.

82. ———, *Social Strain and Social Adjustment in the Marginal Role of the Chiropractor*. Unpublished Ph.D. thesis, Harvard University, 1951.

83. Watson, Robert I., *Psychology as a Profession*. Garden City, N. Y.: Doubleday & Company, Inc., 1954.

84. Weiant, Clarence W., *Medicine and Chiropractic*. New York: published by the author, 1958.

85. Westbeg, Granger, "Religious Aspects of Medical Teaching," *Journal of Medical Education*, 32 (March, 1957), 204–209.

86. Wilson, Bryan R., *Sects and Society: A Sociological Study of Elim Tabernacle, Christian Science, and Christadelphians*. Berkeley: University of Californa Press, 1961.

87. Winter, J. A., *A Doctor's Report on Dianoetics: Theory and Therapy*. New York: Julian Press, Inc., 1951.

88. *Your Eyes and Optometry*. St. Louis: American Optometric Association, 1958.

10

INTERPERSONAL RELATIONS IN MEDICAL SETTINGS

Sydney H. Croog

In many respects the hospital, like other complex formal organizations, presents both to casual observers and to employees an image of bustling, confusing, and sometimes mysterious activity. One means of approaching the study of the hospital is through the dimension of interpersonal relations. In recent years the character and potential utility of these relations have been receiving increasing attention in hospitals as well as in other types of formal organizations. Interest in the possibilities of systematically using interpersonal relationships for therapeutic ends has been responsible in part for the inaugurating of much recent sociological research in hospitals.

The character of interpersonal relations in formal organizations, as is well-known, is influenced by many elements. Social structural, cultural, and psychological factors operate to determine the content and structure of interaction. Thus, the structure of the hospital system, the cultural setting in which it exists, and the personalities of medical personnel are related to particular forms of interpersonal relations. The many variables that influence interaction within the hospital may be classified into two major overlapping categories: (1) those emanating from the external system, and (2) those which stem from the internal system. It is necessary to consider these multiple influences in order to understand interpersonal relations in medical settings and to control and direct their form and function.

The range of formal settings in which medical activities are carried out is relatively broad. They include the private office of the solo practitioner, various types of clinics, group practice situations, and hospitals.[1] Thus far the major portion of social science research on these settings has been concerned primarily with complex organization, notably hospitals. Of course, many of the same elements which determine the character of interpersonal relations in hospitals operate in an essentially similar fashion in other types of medical settings as well.

The modal type of hospital in the United States is the short-term general hospital. For various reasons, however, comparatively more social science research has been carried out in the mental hospital. Findings derived from research in mental hospitals will be reviewed here because they are useful in understanding the processes occurring in the general hospital.

One particularly important qualification must be mentioned. The use of small samples, the reliance on impressionistic evidence, the lack of controls, and the absence of replication indicate a need for a cautious approach in interpreting organizational studies. Generalizations about interpersonal relations in medical settings in this chapter should appropriately be viewed as tentative statements, subject to reformulation as the body of reliable information based on empirical investigation increases.

The Background of Research

Studies in varied settings

Hospitals can be classified in many ways: by type of service, type of management or control, type of financial support, physical size and type of facilities, staff composition, and numerous other features. In the United States there are approximately 7000 hospitals, about 5000 of which are of

[1] See Chap. 12 for a discussion of types of practice.

the nonfederal, short-term, general hospital type [46]. The number of persons involved in hospital settings is large. Hospitals of the United States employ an approximate 1.5 million full-time workers. About 25 million patients are admitted each year. In addition, many thousands of doctors, volunteers, visitors, and other categories of permanent and temporary personnel participate in various types of activities and relationships in these institutions for differing periods.

Sociological research in medical settings has thus far been concerned with phenomena at other levels than the generic "interpersonal" one. The explicit focus of most studies has been upon problems of social structure, authority, communication patterns, role theory, stratification, job performance, and similarly delineated dimensions. A large segment of this work, however, has relevance for problems of theory and practice involving interpersonal relations.

In turn, much of the research on interpersonal behavior in the general hospital has conceptual and methodological counterparts in studies undertaken in such settings as factories, school classrooms, prisons, and military posts. A pattern of mutual influence between studies in medical settings and those undertaken in other organizations has already begun to take form. Reports on the hospital, for example, may eventually take their place along with reports on other types of settings to constitute the empirical basis for a general theory of formal organization. At the same time, the theoretical and methodological contributions of research in other areas feed into and enrich the development of inquiry into structure and process in hospitals and other types of medically oriented milieux.

Interpersonal relations and therapeutic ends

During the past century the armamentarium of instruments and techniques available for patient care has been transformed by the contributions of science. In recent decades the view that the social milieu of an institution can be systematically utilized for therapeutic purposes has been put to pragmatic test in a number of mental hospitals. The theories underlying such an approach are at least as old as the temple-hospitals of Aesculapius in ancient Greece. In those settings patients were provided with recreational and religious facilities designed to provide rehabilitation and strengthening in the physical, emotional, and spiritual spheres.

The modern conception of the hospital as a total treatment milieu and the conviction that human relationships can be organized for maximum benefit to patients have led to the development and spread of "milieu therapy" and to systematic attempts at reorganizing the mental hospital as a "therapeutic community" [36, 37, 50]. As the apparent merits and successes of milieu therapy and related techniques have been disseminated, questions have arisen regarding the possibility of systematically utilizing interpersonal and social structural elements for therapeutic purposes in the general hospital and in nonpsychiatric settings.

Simmons and Wolff, for example, have made a notable attempt to conceptualize pertinent issues and to point up possible uses of the psychosocial environment of the general hospital [76]. Drawing upon concepts in psychosomatic medicine and the social sciences, they illustrate how treatment situations may themselves produce stress, complicate illness, and retard recovery. After calling for a focus of attention on the total physical and emotional stresses associated with the illness, they explore the possibilities and merits of a more intensive type of treatment than that now generally current. Thus, they remark:

> We begin to anticipate that, in addition to the medical specifics indicated for identifiable disease entities, . . . corresponding social specifics or methods of protecting the patient against or helping him cope with the stresses in his life, both individual and general, may come to be included more or less routinely in any therapeutic program [76].

Along somewhat similar lines, a recent monograph by Brown is concerned, as its subtitle indicates, with "The Use of the Physical and Social Environment of the General Hospital for Therapeutic Purposes" [9]. She reviews ways in which admissions procedures, dining room facilities, and patient lounges can be used to promote the development of a supportive climate for therapy. Furthermore, she evaluates the therapeutic potential which is available in the roles of chaplains, visitors, and fellow patients.

In the case of the mental hospital, milieu therapy and related efforts at utilizing relationships for practical ends appear as one stage in a long term trend. This trend involves movement from the conception of the hospital as "asylum" to a view of the institution as an agency actively using its total resources in behalf of patients.[2] In the case of the general hospital, the image has shifted also. The general hospital is no longer simply a place to be used as a last resort when patients cannot be cared for in the home. It is now an optimal location for active therapeutic intervention for a wide variety of ailments and disabilities.

Although proponents of milieu therapy approaches have reported favorable results in various experiments in mental hospital settings, a number of difficult questions regarding the specific processes and variables involved remain to be answered. These questions cross cut many fields and deal with some key issues for the understanding of social behavior, illness, and recovery. For example, what specific elements determine the form and structure of particular types of interpersonal relationships in hospital settings? What is the specific nature of the processes which occur at multiple

---

[2] See Chap. 6 for a discussion of mental illness and its treatment.

levels in social interaction? What is the nature of the linkage between patterns of interpersonal relations and physiological change? Current work in the various biological, psychological, and social sciences dealing with such questions as these may eventually lead to means of manipulating specific sets of elements in order to attain certain physiological and/or psychological ends.

The Hospital and Its External Environment

The influence of the external environment upon the internal system of the hospital is pervasive, affecting many aspects of the structure and content of the interpersonal environment within the institution. The external setting in which hospitals exist can be differentiated at a number of levels. At one extreme, hospitals can be seen in the context of vast divisions, such as Western society or Western culture. They can also be analyzed in relation to national, regional, or community contexts. At a more microcosmic level, the pertinent external environment of American hospitals can be seen as the county, town, and neighborhood. In the matter of supply of personnel, for example, the immediate local neighborhood may be the crucial area for determining the composition of the semiskilled and unskilled staff. On the other hand, the conditions in the state, region, or even the nation may constitute factors influencing the size, composition, and quality of the medical staff in a particular hospital.

Values and cross-cultural perspectives

The existence of the hospital is dependent upon such elements as the values, felt needs, and the level of technological development in a society. Humanitarianism, compassion, and belief in the worth of the individual are themes which historically have been associated with the founding and development of hospitals in Western countries [7, 25, 74]. Faith in science, belief in good health and the prolonging of life, and convictions about the power of rationally determined action are also important themes which are often ultimately reflected in the organization of activities in hospitals and in interpersonal relations within them.

In the United States, hospitals are organized to fill certain community needs, and their continued operation is dependent upon their ability to conform to the standards, expectations, and customs of the society outside. State and local laws specify that certain values will be fulfilled, particularly those relating to standards of professional practice, maintenance of the safety of life and property, and the prudent management of resources. Professional groups such as medical societies and nursing associations are among the many agencies outside the hospital which also have regulatory power over activities within it.

Numerous reports based on both research and random observation offer rich evidence of ways in which the interpersonal environment of hospitals may differ on a cross-cultural basis. Variations in the character of interpersonal relations in hospitals appear in many cases to be associated with the political, religious, economic, family, age-sex and status systems of each larger society as well as the prevailing conceptions of the nature of disease [12, 26, 32].[3]

As one consequence of the close interrelationship between the internal system of the hospital and the complex of social institutions of the larger society outside, changes in one area might eventually lead to changes in the other. Thus, the patterning of roles within the hospital may alter as the functions of a major social institution alter. More specifically, it has been suggested that the roles of doctor and patient as well as the more general mission of the hospital are all sensitive to changes occurring in the family system [61]. As some of the functions of the American family have been transferred to outside agencies, the hospital has become an adjunct to the home, a center for therapeutic activities which for various reasons can no longer be carried out in the family setting. These large institutional changes have many implications for the structuring of the traditional roles of doctor, patient, nurse, and other participants in hospital systems.

An instance of direct association between the governmental institution and aspects of doctor-patient relationships may be seen in a report by Field on medical practice in the Soviet Union [26]. Doctors providing services for factory workers are required to conform to a quota system: at any particular time only a limited number of persons can be certified as being ill enough to be excused from their jobs. By this means, the Soviet State is able to assure that a work force of predictable size will always be available for service. This same system of regulation, however, constitutes an effort by government to define the limits of morbidity in a substantial segment of the population. Field reports that workers use various maneuvers and even subterfuges to persuade physicians that they are sufficiently ill to merit being excused from labor. On the other hand, the physicians themselves are constrained to keep within the quota by the prospect of being penalized. Consequently, the interaction of doctor and patient in some cases involves subtle interplay whose content is influenced by the political structure as well as by the usual interpersonal elements associated with the seeking and supplying of medical care.

The status system of the external environment

Many of the influences upon interpersonal relations stemming from the external environment are inextricably intermeshed with social structural elements in the community. A formal organization such as the hospital

[3] See Chap. 16 for a discussion of cultural differences.

must rely entirely upon the external environment for personnel. The hospital competes with other formal organizations for staff, since there are limits to the size of the population potentially available and optimally qualified for service. The size and character of this population varies on a regional basis, and there are some marked differences between communities as well. The processes in the external environment which operate to bring people into the institution are critical in that they determine who will participate in the interaction systems within the hospital.

Numerous links exist between the status system of the community and the structure and content of the interpersonal environment of the hospital. In many cases, for example, the relative prestige of a hospital and the type of financial support it receives are related to its being identified with a particular segment or stratum of the community [23]. This identification, in turn, has implications for the staffing of the institution at various occupational levels. The most prestigious and respected hospitals in a community may have relatively less difficulty than low status institutions in attracting trustees, staff physicians, volunteer workers, and salaried employees.

Social status in the external community is also apparently related to position within the institution. Following an analysis by Hughes, Hall has observed:

> To a conspicuous degree, the hospital is so structured that it articulates neatly with the class structure of the community: the patrons are of upper class status, the functionaries belong to the professional group in society, and both act to help provide services for the clients who, by and large, belong to strata below both [40].

This statement is perhaps a more accurate portrayal of the voluntary hospital in the nineteenth century than it is of the modern prototype. The class origins of persons in professional groups in the hospital and those who are patients are not so distinctly at variance as is implied.

Nevertheless, it is well known that unskilled workers such as janitors and maids are at the lower end of the status scale, both inside and outside the hospital, while doctors enjoy an exalted status position in both areas. The phenomenon is probably more marked in more traditional, more rigidly stratified societies than the United States. In India, for example, occupation within the institution is associated positively with the position of the individual in the caste system of the society. Further, there are caste restrictions upon both interpersonal contacts and upon kinds of tasks which can be performed [32].

Hall, reporting on the multiple factors related to the appointment of particular physicians to particular hospitals in one community, indicates that considerations of ethnic origins, informal associations, and other types of social qualifications operate along with an evaluation of professional qualifications [38, 39]. More recently, on the basis of a study of Chicago hospitals, Solomon points out that "the ethnic and class segmentation and stratification of the city" play roles in determining access to particular hospital facilities. Thus, staff composition in part rests upon various social background characteristics including graduation from the "right" medical school, post-graduate training in the "right" type of hospital, and the sponsorship of key senior members of the staff [79]. Lieberson has also reported on the relationship between ethnic origins of the physician and the nature of medical practice [54].

The ecological distribution of patients and staff within the hospital is obviously a critical determinant of interaction systems. For example, in Southern mental hospitals similar to one described by Belknap, patients are distributed to specific ward areas not only on the basis of official diagnosis but on the basis of such criteria as race and, to a lesser extent, age [5]. The fact that in the Southern area of the United States Negro and white hospital patients are segregated is as much a product of community values as is the widespread segregation of adult patients by sex. In such instances, the standards of the external community rather than considerations of therapeutic potential are perhaps the more critical determinants of the nature of interaction systems.

Research on social structural factors in the external system and their consequences for the character of the experience of patients in the hospital has thus far been focused on mental patients. On the basis of a large scale investigation Hollingshead and Redlich point out the relationship between social class origins and such elements as length of hospitalization, type of diagnosis, and the nature of the hospital in which the mental patient is treated [45]. A study of mental hospital patients in New York State was carried out by Hardt and Feinhandler as a partial replication of the Hollingshead-Redlich work, and it confirmed the general hypothesis that the social class level of the patient is inversely related to the risk of continuous long-term hospitalization [42]. The specific context of staff and patient groups, the duration of contact of members, and the amount of therapeutic interaction of patients with physicians and psychiatrists also appear to vary, depending upon the segment of society from which the mental patient comes.

Patterns of deference current in the community outside the hospital are often carried over into the institution, although the transfer is not comprehensive or consistent in all cases. A study of nurses in Pennsylvania by Bressler and Kephart offers some suggestive findings in regard to degree of juxtaposition between the system of stratification in the hospital and that in the outside community [8]. On the basis of responses to questions concerning deference to physicians, nurses were classified into groups showing "high," "medium," or "low" deference. The social class position of each married nurse was determined through reference to the occupation of her husband. It was found that the higher the class status of the nurse, the less willing she was to show deference to the physician.

While hospital staff members perceive each other in terms of formal occupational characteristics, they also respond to one another according to their perceptions of each other's "latent social identities" [34]. Sexual, ethnic, class, and religious identities of staff members are attained outside the institution, and they are commonly prescribed as theoretically irrelevant to status in the hospital. But as Gouldner has demonstrated, latent social identities intrude upon and influence behavior in the organization in many ways. In the United States, the role performance of female physicians, for example, is often colored by problems involving these social identities [85, 86]. The relations of female doctors with their male peers, with subordinate workers, and with patients are complicated by relative importance of female status as opposed to professional status. Much hortatory literature in nursing education stresses the therapeutic importance of recognizing and appropriately responding to the latent social identities of patients.

Some indications of the relevance of criteria from the external system for the structuring of staff-patient interaction can be seen in the results of a study by Graham [35]. A group of student nurses was asked to select a registered nurse for service in a hypothetical hospital situation, and they were required to make a forced choice from a list of nurses of varying national origins. Eighty-five per cent of the students selected either the "English" or the "German" nurse. Their reasons for choices and rejections all showed marked stereotype reactions concerning national character and its relation to the presumed performance of the nurse.

The fact that status criteria of the external community can influence interaction patterns within the hospital has some direct implications for administrative attempts to manipulate the social milieu for therapeutic ends. Some effects of these extra-hospital criteria have been explored in the context of formal groups of patients in mental hospital settings. In a study of a patient-government organization in two "open" psychiatric wards, Croog found that the degree of participation and the nature of the leadership structure were associated with educational level, occupational status, and ethnic origins [16]. This finding regarding participation is consistent with observations made in other types of settings, such as jury sessions [82].

In the situation of the "closed" wards of the mental hospital, however, it appears that other variables may be more highly associated with degree of participation. Rosenberg reports, for example, that in a patient-council group composed of seriously disturbed patients in the closed ward of a "total institution," participation had special appeal to low status patients [68]. The organization was regarded by professional personnel as one instrument for counteracting severe withdrawal by patients. In a sense, patients were able to indicate their progress in recovery through demonstrating their social affiliative skills in the council. In this context, status criteria of the external community were apparently less salient than in the "open" ward milieu.

Cultural subsystems, differential participation, and interpersonal relationships within the hospital

In recent years it has become increasingly apparent that certain strains and difficulties in hospitals can be traced to differential participation in the larger society on the part of personnel. The origins of many problems involving mutual misunderstandings, failure in communication, and failure in the fulfillment of role expectations lie in the differential internalization of norms and values by members of various subcultural groups. Interpersonal relations in the hospital may be profoundly influenced by the tendency of individuals to respond to similar stimuli in ways conforming to the social class, ethnic, or religious sub-cultures in which they have been socialized.

Evidence from many sources indicates that the meaning of illness, evaluation of symptoms, and attitudes toward the hospital vary greatly among the societies of the world and among groups within a single society [15, 62, 70]. Within the patient population of a hospital there may be found a number of distinctive conceptions of illness and sets of beliefs regarding behavior appropriate to the sick role. Thus, Zborowski discovered that Italian and Jewish patients in a Veterans Administration Hospital were far more expressive regarding their symptoms and suffering than were patients of Irish and "Old American" ethnic origins [88]. He concludes that variations in reaction to pain, attitudes toward disease, and perceptions of the physician may be linked to such elements as time-orientation among ethnic groups, child-rearing practices, and the configuration of the "ideal pattern" to which members of particular subcultural groups are expected to conform.

Various practical problems in quality of care can arise from differences in the value systems of hospital personnel and patients. For example, the patient who conforms to the norms of his own groups by describing his symptoms in great detail may be regarded as a hypochondriac and a nuisance by doctors and nurses who were socialized in cultural settings where stoicism and a "stiff upper lip" are regarded as the intelligent responses to illness. They may prefer to deal with the patient down the hall who has exactly the same disease but who is silent and uncommunicative about his symptoms. In such a case the medications and routine therapeutic procedures prescribed for the two patients might be exactly the same; however, the quality of care received by each might be very different.

The hospital and changes in the external environment

Other types of influences upon interpersonal relations within the hospital derive from trends and changes in the larger society outside. Thus, the concept that the most effective work unit is a "team" has recently been given wide currency in industry, government, the armed services, and educational institutions. It has also diffused into hospitals, particularly by departments of nursing. At one level, attempts to develop the team principle in the hospital may be seen as a reflection of the needs of the system for the effective organization of work. At the same time, however, the attempts appear to represent one form of adaptation to problems of labor shortage. Emphasis on the importance of teamwork in the hospital may serve as a device for attracting and holding workers, as it stresses the value of the individual (regardless of his formal occupational status) to the system.

The social, economic, and ideological changes which have led to the burgeoning hospitalization insurance in the United States constitute another type of extra-hospital influence upon the ecology of patients and upon the structure of interaction situations. Decades ago there were two major categories of patients in many hospitals: a marked social gulf existed between the groups classified as "ward patients" and "private patients," reflected in part by differences in facilities, cuisine, and visiting privileges. The spread of hospitalization insurance, however, has served to reduce the number of "ward patients," and, in most general hospitals, patients of diverse social status in the community are located in close proximity. In a sense, the semiprivate room has become a melting pot of patients from diverse social backgrounds.

The external environment, personality, and the internal system

Thus far, this discussion has been concerned primarily with social structural and cultural elements which derive from the external environment of the hospital and which influence the character of relationships within the system. Other critical sets of determinants are those associated with the personality structures of the participants in the system. Although it is widely assumed that there are associations between types of personality structure and the particular constellations of interpersonal relations that exist in the context of formal organizations, relatively few empirical studies have dealt with this problem.

Some evidence relevant to the question of modal personality types among hospital personnel may be found in the literature on occupational choice [31, 67]. In regard to the general problem of relationship between personality structure and choice of vocation, Levinson and Inkeles point out that certain types of occupations may attract people with particular personality traits and that the strength of those traits influences the character of their adaptation to the requirements of occupational roles [6, 48]. Can characteristic personality types be differentiated among hospital personnel? More certainty exists in folklore than in the findings of empirical studies reporting on personality traits and occupational choice. In regard to medical students, a group which has been the subject of much recent research, Merton remarks that there is little evidence of association between personality and the choice of different kinds of medical careers [58].

Problems arising from conflict between formal role requirements in the hospital and personality needs have been given the most extensive research attention in the case of the nurse.[4] Much of the current concern within the nursing profession about dissatisfaction and turnover among nurses is based on observations and assumptions about the presence of a particular set of affective needs in those women who choose to enter nursing. The expression of those needs is molded by the demands of the nursing role, one which is characterized by many contradictory elements. Devereux and Weiner, in an article dealing with the occupational status of nurses, point out that nurses bring to their work a number of distinctive emotional needs, fantasies, and expectations [18]. The work situation and the status system of hospitals, however, limit the satisfaction of these emotional needs. As they put it, perhaps too strongly, the nurse is "systematically discouraged from displaying foresight, initiative, imagination, and feeling."

Schulman observes that "the mother surrogate exists as the basic psychological orientation of the nurse," and he remarks that increasing emphasis on technology and administration in nursing has brought a number of problems to the profession [72]. Some nurses who are promoted to ever higher administrative posts feel guilt and discomfort, since they are thereby deprived of the opportunities for affective expression presented by bedside care. One systematic attempt at appraising the limits set by organizations upon the expression of personality "predispositions" of workers is found in the work of Argyris [2, 3].

Role groups and personality structure

The existence of linkage between personality type and particular forms of interaction or social structure is widely assumed by hospital personnel. Thus, social scientists carrying out research in general hospitals may be informed that the personality of the head nurse sets the tone of a ward. Or they may be informed by physicians that the way to understand the institution is to study the character of the chiefs of the various professional services, for the chiefs determine the nature of the organization. Widespread stereotypes exist which portray doctors as independent individualistic people. Such traits are presumed to limit their capacity for being integrated into the ward team and are presumed to make them rebellious against administrative regulation [10]. There are also widely disseminated stereotypes of psychiatric tinge which portray such specialists as surgeons, pediatricians, obstetricians, and proctologists as each having differing kinds of unconscious needs.

---

[4] See Chap. 8 for a discussion of nursing.

Another common bit of folklore circulated among employees themselves is that hospital people are "different" from those who work in other types of settings. When expressed by a sympathetic observer, this usually refers to an assumption that those who choose to work in hospitals are somehow more sympathetic, altruistic, and humane than workers in industry or in business. As in the case of much folklore and stereotyping, beliefs about personality types and patterns often form the justification and basis for behavior on the part of members of various role groups of the hospital. For example, as Merton has pointed out, in their choice of future medical specialty, medical students are influenced in some degree by their beliefs regarding modal personality among such varied specialists as surgeons, internists, and psychiatrists [58].

On the whole, attempts at delineating personality characteristics of particular groups of hospital personnel have represented one portion of larger studies seeking to examine personality in relation to such elements of organizational life as job satisfaction, task performance, or ideological commitment. For example, personality characteristics of attendants in mental hospitals have been the subject of recent research. Studies carried out by Gilbert, Levinson, and Pine have been concerned in part with the investigation of relationships between the ideology of the attendant regarding the nature of mental illness and regarding the aims and policies of the hospital and certain aspects of his personality. One segment of the research effort centered on the association between "authoritarian" or "equalitarian" personality types and the holding of distinctive ideologies which the authors characterize as "custodialism" and "humanism" [30]. They found a significant association between custodial ideology and personal authoritarianism as measured by the "F" scale. A study by Carstairs and Heron in a British mental hospital replicated the American research in part, reaching conclusions which differed in a number of respects but which pointed in the same general direction [11].

Personality of the "patient," disease syndrome, and interpersonal relations

Turning to the influence of the personality of the patient upon the hospital interpersonal environment, issues of a somewhat different order may be seen. The hypothesis that certain modal personalities or personality profiles are associated with particular ailments has stimulated much research on the relations between emotional state and physical illness or disability.[5] The question of which personality characteristics are associated with particular illnesses is currently the subject of much controversy, and the optimum mode of conceptualizing the particular pattern has yet to be

---

[5] See Chap. 4.

determined [76]. Nevertheless, research in psychosomatic medicine has provided increasingly strong evidence of apparent linkage between disease type and personality type [1, 21, 76]. Such findings have many implications for the understanding of the structure and emotional tone of interpersonal relations involving patients and hospital personnel. For example, if patients with peptic ulcer do indeed exhibit marked dependency traits, as has often been suggested in the psychiatric literature, then it is likely that the emotional tone of the interaction systems in which such patients participate will be distinct from those in which patients with other types of personality structure take part.

One aspect of the patient role which has been the subject of recent research and theoretical commentary is the nature of response to illness and the ward situation. The entrance of professional and paramedical workers into their occupational roles is largely a "voluntary" one, while entrance into the role of patient is determined by social definition as well as by physiological, affective, and cognitive processes within the person who becomes ill. The patient enters the hospital with a set of conceptions regarding the institution, his illness, and his body. His experiences in the institution and his subjective perception of those experiences help to determine the nature of his conduct in situations of interpersonal relations [27, 60, 76].

Entrance into the patient role is often accompanied by many shades of stress and anxiety. Moving into the alien atmosphere of the hospital away from the familiar things of home and family represents one sort of strain. The requirements of adopting the dependent, infantilized behavior patterns which are forced upon adults who become hospital patients represent another. Besides those stresses involving unfamiliar social setting and role, many hospital patients must deal with dangers to life itself. Cancer, heart disease, and the host of other ailments with potentially terminal consequences are real and frightening entities which can stimulate primitive psychological response. Even minor ailments can have threatening and anxiety-laden aspects whose consequences can be as serious as those associated with major illnesses.

The contingencies of unconscious processes upon the structure and content of interaction involving patients are many. For example, as Dunbar has pointed out: ". . . the meaning of disease varies according to the personality structure. For some patients it will activate a well-concealed neurotic or psychotic trend and for others it may seem a happy solution to a situation of intolerable stress" [21]. The course of convalescence may be profoundly influenced by the emergence of differing types of defenses which have been developed in early life. On superficial observation these defenses might appear to be rational responses to the ward situation. But complaints about treatment or expressions of well-being on the part of patients may depend not so much on the real character of the ward as upon the way in which the realities are perceived by the patient and the ways in which they mesh with his unconscious needs [21].

In an article on psychiatric aspects of medical practice in a general hospital, Bibring reviews the types of behavior patterns exhibited by four patients with tuberculosis. These patterns constitute modes of adjustment to stress, and they had been developed by each patient over the course of his life. Though all are suffering from the same physical disease, each patient brings to the ward situation distinctive techniques for handling anxiety. To ward personnel and to fellow patients, one of the four would seem overconcerned and worrying, another would appear self-willed and independent, and so forth [6]. An intensive psychoanalytic study of the reactions of a woman who experienced surgery was carried out by Janis, and one area of research interest was the relationship between the patient and the surgeon [49]. It was seen that the patient's postoperative perceptions of her relationship with the surgeon were linked to unconscious components such as her emotional dependency and certain regressive reactions heightened by the stress situation.

Other important influences on the complex area of interpersonal relations are the unconscious adaptive mechanisms which the staff members bring into the hospital situation. For example, staff members may also react to those fears of death, disability, and mutilation which affect patients at deep levels. Furthermore, in the course of interacting in accordance with the requirements of formal role, both staff members and patients may be acting out on an unconscious level certain roles and conflict situations characteristic of their own individual family life [75]. In such instances, a ward or business office may constitute a symbolic family or quasifamily situation, and both staff members and patients may be using this milieu to work out at an unconscious level some unresolved personality problems involving parent-child or sibling relationships. The complex interplay of conscious and unconscious responses on the part of both patients and staff can be eventually reflected in the quality of interpersonal relationships and in the social forms characteristic of life in the general hospital.

The Internal System and Interpersonal Relations

Thus far in this discussion the primary focus of attention has been upon the external system of the hospital and upon those variable elements which participants in the organization bring with them from the outside. In this section the focus turns to the internal system of the hospital. Social structural forms, cultural traits, and some psychological processes are examined in terms of their influence upon the character and quality of interpersonal relations within the organization.

Social structure and the hierarchy of authority

The general hospital is one of the most highly stratified and rigid of formal organizations. Like other large bureaucratic institutions, it works toward the achievement of its goals through reliance upon such structural devices as a complex system of division of labor, an elaborate hierarchy of authority, formal channels of communication, and sets of policies, rules, and regulations. Although arrangements in formal structure enable the institution to attain a relatively high degree of efficiency and speed in the performance of its major functions, at the same time those arrangements have multiple consequences in many areas.

In the general hospital, as Smith has pointed out, a system of dual authority is utilized as a basic device for controlling and directing the activities of diverse types of personnel [77]. One line of authority, the administrative one, runs from trustees down to hospital workers. The second is the line of professional authority, one in which the primary power figures are the physicians. The system of professional authority permits the physician to exercise power throughout the hospital structure.

Inevitably, conflict between the two systems of authority permeates many aspects of hospital life. Lay and professional lines of authority come into conflict, for example, since they tend to have overlapping jurisdiction over certain areas and certain personnel. Each system is oriented to a different set of values, one emphasizing the maintenance of the operation of the organization, the other emphasizing the provision of service. Much of the stress and tension occurring at the interpersonal level in hospitals can be traced to varying types of clashes between the two systems of authority. Thus, as Smith remarks, "Value differentials may so distort the understanding of common problems shared by administration and professional departments that each may tend to see the other's position as possible only for a fool or a rascal" [78].

Henry has also pointed out various consequences of certain administrative arrangements in hospitals, particularly in regard to the areas of interpersonal relations and communication [43, 44]. For example, where the authority system operates through multiple subordination, one worker is subject to directions from many chiefs, and certain powerful stresses result. The performance of tasks becomes complicated by problems of inconsistent orders, overlapping of responsibility, and inadequate coordination of activities. The difficulties stemming from structural arrangements become associated with interpersonal stresses, the level of morale, and with the attitudes of staff members toward one another.

In a report on administrative arrangements in the medical and surgical wards of a large general hospital, Coser illustrates ways in which two different types of authority structure affected role behavior and the relations of role groups with one another [14]. She points out that in the medical ward there was consistent delegation of authority downward through levels in the medical hierarchy. In the surgical section, there was little delegation of authority, and decision was made by fiat. One effect in the surgical ward, for example, was the development of a "colleague type of relationship between nurses and doctors." Since only little authority could be exercised by assistant surgical residents and interns, "they could not be consistently superior to the nurse," and this condition was associated with the development of relatively equalitarian relationships between resident, intern, and nurse.

Change in the system of formal authority may have dramatic and extensive consequences, as Lentz has demonstrated. In the business office of one hospital, the replacing of one supervisor with another led to movement from a relatively authoritarian type of regime to a relatively democratic and liberal system of management. The new supervisor rearranged work patterns in ways which stressed individual responsibility. This and related innovations contributed to the creation of a social climate which discouraged turnover, increased output, and raised the level of morale of the workers [52].

Status and stratification

As Smith has pointed out in reference to the phenomenon of "blocked mobility," the hospital consists of a series of relatively discrete occupational groups. Personnel cannot be promoted from one occupational status level to another [77]. Movement from one level to another can be accomplished only if an individual in one group leaves the system, obtains training outside, and re-enters at a different level. Occupational groups tend to be discrete from one another, not only in terms of function, but in their patterns of association, in their values, and in their perceptions of the institution and of each other.

The effects of social structural elements upon interpersonal relations and more specifically upon job performance are perhaps more generally assumed than measured. A series of recent studies by Seeman and Evans represents one of the few attempts thus far to relate specific social structural features to performance of medical tasks [73]. In one article, the authors conclude that the stratification system of the hospital does make a difference in medical performance. They report, for example, that "where staff stratification is low, the communication to and about the patient appears to be, relatively speaking, full and clear . . . and the teaching function is said to be well-performed. The reverse, of course, holds on the high stratification wards." Moreover, they remark that attitudes toward stratification on the part of the intern seem to be related to his performance in patient care. Thus, interns who appear to prefer highly stratified ward situations tend to be those who report spending less time than their fellows in giving psychological support to patients.

Assigned position in the status hierarchy of the hospital is not accepted with equanimity by all workers and staff members. Some resent both the system and their own position within what they perceive as a caste-like structure. Lentz reports that white-collar workers who had formerly been employed in industry reacted with bitterness to the relatively low prestige they were accorded as members of the administrative branch of one hospital [52].

Formal roles and interpersonal relations

The continuing operation of a complex organization such as a hospital is contingent upon the differentiation of tasks, the assignment of tasks to particular occupational groups, and the performance of those tasks by members of each group in a routine manner which fulfills the expectations of other personnel. Formal occupational roles serve to channel and control interaction in ways which assure that the major functions of the organization will be performed. At the same time they appear to divide the institution into groups with relatively distinctive associational patterns and frames of reference.

Goffman, alluding to the mental hospital as a type of "total institution," indicates the significant degree to which staff and patients live in separate social worlds [33]. Wessen has noted some consequences of the hierarchical structure in terms of the patterns of interaction which occur on the wards of one general hospital [84]. He reports that on the ward the doctor is three times more likely to speak to another physician than to a nurse, and his interaction with personnel in other occupational groups is minimal. Similarly, the frequency of conversational interaction of a nurse with other nurses on the ward is approximately twice that of a nurse with other types of co-workers. The channelizing of interaction among personnel of various occupational levels along the lines noted is assumed by numerous observers to have dysfunctional consequences for patient care. The flow of communication upward regarding the condition of patients and the effects of administrative policies is inhibited, and the social barriers between occupational groups may tend to limit the development of a team approach [41].

Along with patterns of limited interaction among hospital personnel of varying ranks, differential interaction involving members of the same occupational group is a common feature of large hospitals. Persons within the same status, who share common interests and often the same departmental affiliation, tend to affiliate themselves in formal groupings and cliques. For example, in line with this tendency, surgeons are most likely to have lunch with other surgeons in the hospital cafeteria, rather than with doctors in other specialties [10, 84]. Patterns of differential association tend to promote solidarity within in-groups, and they may have numerous other functional consequences as well. However, they may at the same time constitute a type of divisive influence. The tendency of physicians in the same specialty to associate with one another may raise barriers against the informal exchange of information concerning patients, and thus may limit the opportunities for members of one specialty to maintain familiarity with the viewpoints, approaches, and technical advances in other fields.

Some interesting work has been carried out on the relationship between the nature of interaction patterns and the numbers and types of potential participants from diverse role groups. Kandler, *et al.*, on the basis of research in the ward of a mental hospital, report that interaction between patients and nurses increases as more nurses are added to the setting. However, there appear to be limits to the pattern. When more than five nurses are present, their rate of interaction with each other increases, and the rate of interaction with patients decreases [51]. New and Nite have found a similar pattern [59].

Social structural sources of influences over the quality of doctor-patient relationships have been described by Daniels [17].[6] In particular, the hospital system operates to control the modes of affective involvement of the doctor or medical intern with the patient. Thus, medical interns recognize that the performance of their professional roles would be obstructed by an intense empathic identification with their patients. Such identification would handicap them in their efforts to achieve the technical efficiency and rational control which doctors must possess. Further, tendencies toward intense affective involvement are limited in part by such situational factors as heavy patient load and the inherent, structured brevity of the intern-patient relationship.

Lack of conformity to role expectations constitutes one of the sources of interpersonal strain in hospitals, as it does in other types of institutions. Relations between staff members and patients are notably susceptible to stresses arising from this source. Persons in the various role groups of the hospital, as acculturated functionaries of the system, have explicit expectations in regard to patient behavior. But people who enter the hospital or clinic as patients are likely to have differing conceptions of staff with which they come in contact. Or if they are aware of the formal requirements of the role, they may be unwilling or unable for various reasons to conform. As Reader, Pratt, and Mudd have pointed out, differences in expectations may lead directly to difficulties and misunderstandings in relations between patients and staff, and this may be expressed in both manifest and covert ways [65]. Degree of conformity to role expectations is a particularly critical matter for patients in the mental hospital [55, 63]. At least one measure of

---

[6] See Chap. 11.

improvement in the condition of mental patients consists of the evaluation of their capacity to conform to the role expectations of staff. Unless patients meet these expectations adequately, they may never be discharged.

Role groups, perceptions, and attitudes

In recent years much attention has been devoted in organizational studies to the analysis of relationships between group productivity or efficiency and such variables as cohesion, consensus, morale, and job satisfaction. Research in hospital settings also deals with issues of this sort. One rationale for many of these studies is the assumption that the feelings and perceptions of group members exert important and complex influences upon job performance and upon the quality of interpersonal relations. From the evidence now available in the literature on hospitals, it appears that members of the major role groups in these institutions tend to have divergent perceptions and attitudes in a number of areas. Wessen, for example, found that although members of the various role groups in a hospital displayed high agreement on the importance of patient care as a basic goal, they perceived the aims and nature of the institution in essentially differing terms [84]. Ideological differences on such fundamental issues as hospital aims and policy were indicative of other types of divisions and tension areas among hospital occupational groups, and the many differences in attitudes and viewpoints tended to limit the degree to which cohesion might develop. Along similar lines, Solon, *et al.*, have noted variations among staff members in an out-patient department in regard to their perceptions of the patients and the ways in which those patients made use of the clinic [80]. The nature of these perceptions appeared to be associated with the staff member's professional identification and his role in the organization. Thus, doctors, nurses, and social workers expressed diverse views in regard to whether or not clinic patients were able to afford private care as well as in regard to the apparent educational and intellectual level of the persons coming to the clinic. The authors suggest that differential perceptions and assumptions on the part of personnel may be reflected in the kinds of reception which they give to the clinic patients.

A study by Dodge revealed a number of divergences between doctors and nurses in regard to their attitudes toward patients and toward each other [20]. For example, nurses in the sample population tended to have higher scores than doctors on instruments measuring levels of idealization of and identification with patients. Further, it appeared that those doctors given high rating by nurses were also those who scored highest in identifying with and idealizing the patient. At the same time, those nurses who attained high scores on the idealization and identification scales were those who were judged inferior by the doctors.

Informal organization

Side by side with the formal organizational structure of hospitals there exists informal organization, an apparently universal component of complex social systems. Informal organization has norms, goals, leadership structure, and traditions of its own. It is characterized by intimate relationships and normative controls, and it may support or subvert organizational functioning and the achievement of formal goals. Informal organization constitutes a network of relationships of considerable size and complexity, and it has long been recognized as constituting a powerful influence in bureaucratic systems.

Hospital studies dealing with aspects of informal organization have typically focused upon its implications for therapy. In the case of the mental hospital, as Caudill and others have demonstrated, membership by patients in cliques which are antagonistic to the institution can do much to negate the therapeutic aims of the institution [13]. In his report on a state mental hospital, Belknap has illustrated ways in which individual ward areas in one state mental hospital are controlled through informal punishment and reward systems by the psychiatric attendants [5]. Patients who wish to avoid electric shock therapy and who wish to move toward discharge from the hospital behave in terms of an awareness that the immediate power figure whom they must please is the ward attendant. This apparent usurpation of power by the attendants occurs even though the formal regulations of the hospital dictate that decisions regarding therapy and discharge are the responsibility of staff psychiatrists. In this case informal organization in the wards operates in ways which are at variance with the formal program of methods and goals laid out by the hospital. Similar processes have been noted by others [71].

The functioning of informal organization in the context of the general hospital has been subjected to extensive analysis by Fox [27]. In the small metabolic ward where she carried out her research, patients suffered from chronic and debilitating diseases which were only imperfectly understood and only partially controllable by physicians at the time. The patients were the objects of research and experiment, and the character of life on the ward was influenced to a considerable extent by universal recognition of the seriousness of the diseases and the uncertain outcome of therapy. In this context, informal organization among patients played an important role in enabling individuals to come to terms with their precarious life chances. Patients shared a deep mutual commitment and interest in one another, and they utilized as means of stress reduction a number of socially patterned responses, such as shared humor, prayer, friendly competition for recognition as a distinctive case, and the development of close, colleague type relations with their physicians. So integrated and close-knit was this group that for some patients it served at least partially to impede the formal therapeutic goals of the ward. Some became reluctant to leave and to adjust anew to life on the outside, and some suffered severely when the condition of another member of the ward community took a negative turn.

Intraorganizational conflict and strain

It has often been observed that individual departments, units, and professional groups in hospitals vie with one another for increased recognition, new privileges, and for more advantageous positions in the power system. Some of the stresses have been associated with the pressures for change exerted by so-called "emergent professions." It is widely known, for example, that changes in the role of nursing and social work departments have been accompanied by periods of resentment and stress. Macgregor, in attempting to account for the "dim view" taken by a "great many physicians" toward recent trends in nursing, remarks that "some see it as an attempt by nurses to usurp some of the doctor's functions or to become pseudo-physicians" [57]. Wilson, in discussing changes in the traditional role of the physician in the hospital, has shown that the rise of hospital administration to the status of a profession has resulted in strains and in readjustments in the nature of work and authority relationships between doctors and administrators [87].

The recent trend involving the entrance of departments of psychiatry into the general hospitals provides a case in point at the physician level [29]. Smith observes that psychiatrists believe one mission of their field is to introduce concepts and change current patterns of thought among non-psychiatric physicians [78]. He reports, however, that efforts at reform by members of this department, new to general hospitals, are met with strong reactions and often with considerable hostility by other fields and departments.

Tenure and the turnover within role groups

When it is viewed as a total social system, the hospital can be seen as a structure through which various personnel groups move at differing rates of speed. The degree of stability differs within such major categories of personnel as trustees, physicians, nurses, patients, and business office workers. Hospitals, like other large organizations, may be characterized as consisting of (a) a "core group" of relatively stable personnel with a high degree of commitment to the institution and (b) a highly transient population which in many ways is distinctive in orientation, commitment, and life goals. The core group in the nursing population of hospitals has sometimes been described as the "home guard" [47].

Although rates of turnover have been reported for individual institutions, most studies have focused turnover rates for specific occupations, particularly those of the professional nurse, the aide, and the attendant [19, 53]. Stability in job tenure has been found to be associated with a number of variables. High turnover rates are most commonly evident in large hospitals, particularly those with schools of nursing. Turnover is greatest among nurses in the youngest age groups, and rates for staff nurses exceed those for supervisory personnel. High occupancy rates and low staff-patient ratios appear to be positively associated with high rates of voluntary turnover among the professional nurses [19]. This latter finding suggests that the amount of pressure placed on the nurse may be a factor in her decision to terminate her employment.

Personnel flow has at least several major effects upon the nature of interpersonal relations. It has important influence upon the quality of relationships in that it may hinder the development of primary group feeling among ward workers. Personnel in areas of high turnover must devote more effort toward integrating their activities than those in areas where long-established relationships exist and where sets of mutual expectations are well-established. In the general hospital the workers who have most contact with patients are usually at the junior levels of the nursing staff and it is in this group that a high proportion of turnover occurs. Consequently, patients constantly come into contact with workers who are still in the process of learning the norms and values of the hospital.

Flow and turnover are basic to the life process of organizations. Nevertheless, because job instability and geographic mobility appear inordinately high in certain employee groups, there is widespread concern among hospital administrators and leaders in the nursing profession about the impact of turnover upon the effective operation of hospitals and the providing of optimal patient care. The potential disintegrative effect of turnover has been limited, however, by the fact that it occurs according to predictable patterns and by the fact that it is of relatively minor proportions within key role groups such as the medical staff and the trustees.

Hospitals v. *individual subcultural systems*

Each institution has an individual history, sets of formal regulations and informal customs, and a fabric of traditions and folklore which render it distinctive. Further, individual departments, subdepartments, units and subunits may develop traditions and customs of a sort which cause them to appear as microcosmic cultural systems within larger systems. To some extent, each is characterized by a jargon or a code language of its own, and new staff members must learn the special meanings of these words as they become enculturated [5, 10, 22, 64].

One trait common to the culture of hospitals is the informal system of classifying patients. Patients are commonly evaluated by various levels of staff in terms of such characteristics as manageability, personality traits, types of disease or disability, and their potential interest as teaching material. Thus, in a teaching hospital the patient with the rare disease or mysterious disorder often stands in a high position in the hierarchy of ratings, and the patient who is considered a "crock" occupies a low position. In the mental hospital, the degree of manageability of the patient is an especially important criterion in informal ratings [5]. Long before student nurses and medical students enter the hospital for training, they are aware of the value system relating to patients and have begun to internalize it [58]. The differential evaluation of patients is often reflected in specific behavior patterns on the ward, and the relationships of "crocks" with staff members are likely to be distinctive from those experienced by the more highly rated types of patients.

As in the case of the larger cultural systems of which they are a part, the individual cultures of hospitals are characteristically marked by conflicts in values. Many of these value conflicts are reflected in problems of interpersonal behavior, and they may have direct implications for the administrative management of patients. Rapoport, in his report on a planned mental hospital community, deals at length with problems of values and the multiple implications of conflict between them [64]. For example, in the hospital which he studied, "permissiveness" was a major theme. A number of hospital policies were based on the assumption that reduction of bureaucratic restrictions and the encouraging of expression by patients would have certain therapeutic, diagnostic, and rehabilitative benefits. At the same time, the staff of the hospital remained legally responsible for the safety of patients and property, as well as for the orderly maintenance of the organization. Thus, there were necessary and real limits to permissiveness. Situations were constantly arising in which administrative and system maintenance values came into conflict with the permissiveness value. Autocratic administrative action then became necessary to reinstate controls.

Another example of conflict in values is presented by Gallagher and Albert in an analysis of a critical incident in a humanistically oriented mental hospital [28]. On one occasion a lecturer came to the hospital to present a talk on patient art. The apparently open meeting was attended by patients as well as by staff. In that institution both staff and patients were committed to values relating to working through problems of therapy on the basis of a type of colleague relationship. At the same time staff members believed that it was also desirable to maintain the status lines between themselves and patients. Hence, many of the staff members present felt uncomfortable because of the presence of patients at the lecture, a feeling which was heightened because of their own ambivalence about the situation.

As in the case of other cultural systems, some of the customs which are frequently practiced in hospitals are essentially contradictory and even non-rational in nature. For instance, in tuberculosis hospitals, sets of regulations based on an elaborate belief system commonly prescribe procedures for controlling contagion through the use of protective clothing and masks. However, in at least one hospital, the incidence of use of such clothing by staff members in contact with patients appeared to be related to occupational status levels and to the nature of the interaction. Staff members of high rank were particularly likely to avoid wearing gown and masks. Moreover, the wearing of protective clothing by a staff member appeared to be related in part to whether or not the interaction involved formal business or informal socializing [69].

Unconscious mechanisms and social process: insights from mental hospital settings

In recent years a number of social scientists have been exploring some of the relationships between unconscious mechanisms and structured social behavior in the hospital. The bulk of this work has been carried out in mental hospital settings rather than in the general hospital or in other types of medical settings. One conceptual product to which many authors have contributed is the delineation of the phenomenon of "collective disturbance." In periods of such disturbance, feelings of unrest and agitation sweep through a ward area and sometimes throughout an entire hospital. These feelings are communicated in considerable part by affective, nonverbal means. Although the origins of such feelings are obscure, their effects are obvious, and such episodes represent a major problem for management [13, 81]. Their regular patterning has led at least one observer to characterize them as "oscillations" [64]. In many mental hospitals recognition of a shift by patients toward the manic side is often given expression in such comments by staff members as "The ward is high today."

On the basis of his study of a small psychiatric ward, Caudill points out that primitive instinctual behavior of mental patients can become accepted and integrated into the ward social system [13]. Consequently, the social subsystem in which patients participate may come to contain elements of insulated regressive behavior which can frustrate the purposes of formal organization. He has also postulated the existence of "covert emotional structure" which underlies overt formal and informal structure in the hospital. Stanton and Schwartz have developed a "staff consensus" hypothesis which holds that periods of disagreement among staff members of a mental hospital will tend to lead to episodes of disturbed behavior among patients [81].

The exact nature of these phenomena remains to be clarified and tested through replication in multiple settings, not only in psychiatric hospitals but in general hospitals as well. At least one recent attempt at testing a version of the Stanton-Schwartz hypothesis on staff consensus has been made [83]. This yielded essentially negative results, for the authors could find no significant statistical relationship between the direction of change in staff consensus concerning the individual mental patient and the direction of change in the level of disturbance in the patient. However, further work can be expected which will explore the dimensions of the influences of unconscious processes upon interaction in hospital settings.

Conclusion

Consideration of the forms of interpersonal relations in medical settings and the elements which determine those forms leads into problems of an exceedingly complex nature. While some impressive beginnings have been made in identifying critical variables which influence these relationships, it is apparent that only rudimentary information exists and that the general hospital in particular is still virtually a virgin area for the development of rigorous and systematic empirical research by social scientists.

In view of the many lacunae in scientific knowledge about the nature of processes involved in the interrelations between individual behavior and organizational structure, current attempts at milieu therapy and sociotherapy in mental hospitals in many ways represent courageous experiments. At present, no sizeable set of systematic, empirically-tested generalizations is available to lead such experiments toward specific therapeutic ends, although the social science literature already provides insights to serve as guides. Such experiments, as they are developed and applied in general hospitals as well as in mental hospitals, offer much promise for advancing theories of interpersonal and organizational behavior while they pursue practical and applied ends.

Fortunately, insofar as the development of theory is concerned, much of the work currently being developed in other types of organizational settings has relevance for the understanding of interpersonal relations in hospitals. At the same time, the general hospital represents in many ways a unique type of organization, one which requires research oriented both in theory and method to its special characteristics. Such research will have many rewards. It is apparent, for example, that the clarification of many problems regarding interpersonal relations in the hospital can be achieved through acquiring an understanding of the social structural and cultural context in which they exist. Conversely, of course, the understanding of many aspects of formal organization can be promoted through insight into the forms and processes of interpersonal behavior.

References

1. Alexander, Franz, ed., *Psychosomatic Medicine*. New York: W. W. Norton & Company, Inc., 1950.
2. Argyris, Chris, *Diagnosing Human Relations in Organizations: A Case Study of a Hospital*. New Haven, Conn.: Yale University Labor and Management Center, 1956.
3. ———, *Understanding Organizational Behavior*. Homewood, Ill.: The Dorsey Press, 1960.
4. Back, Kurt W., *et al*., "Public Health as a Career in Medicine: Secondary Choice within a Profession," *American Sociological Review*, 23 (October, 1958), 533–41.
5. Belknap, Ivan, *Human Problems of a State Mental Hospital*. New York: McGraw-Hill Book Company, Inc., 1956.
6. Bibring, Grete L., "Psychiatry and Medical Practice in a General Hospital," *New England Journal of Medicine*, 254 (February 23, 1956), 366–72.
7. Bockoven, J. Sanbourne, "Some Relationships between Cultural Attitudes toward Individuality and Care of the Mentally Ill: An Historical Study," *in* Milton Greenblatt, Daniel J. Levinson, and Richard H. Williams, eds., *The Patient and the Mental Hospital*. New York: The Free Press of Glencoe, Inc., 1957, pp. 517–26.
8. Bressler, Marvin and William M. Hephart, *Career Dynamics*. Philadelphia: University of Pennsylvania, 1955. Reported *in* Everett C. Hughes, Helen MacGill Hughes, and Irwin Deutscher, *Twenty Thousand Nurses Tell Their Story*. Philadelphia: J. B. Lippincott Company, 1958, pp. 63–64.
9. Brown, Esther Lucille, *Newer Dimensions of Patient Care*. New York: Russell Sage Foundation, 1961.
10. Burling, Temple, Edith M. Lentz, and Robert N. Wilson, *The Give and Take in Hospitals*. New York: G. P. Putnam's Sons, 1956.
11. Carstairs, G. M. and Alastair Heron, "The Social Environment of Mental Hospital Patients: A Measure of Staff Attitudes," *in* Milton Greenblatt, Daniel J. Levinson, and Richard H. Williams, eds., *The Patient and the Mental Hospital*. New York: The Free Press of Glencoe, Inc., 1957, pp. 218–29.
12. Caudill, William, "Around the Clock Patient Care in Japanese Psychiatric Hospitals: The Role of the Tsukisoi," *American Sociological Review*, 26 (April, 1961), 204–14.
13. ———, *The Psychiatric Hospital as a Small Society*. Cambridge: Harvard University Press, 1958.
14. Coser, Rose Laub, "Authority and Decision-Making in a Hospital," *American Sociological Review*, 23 (February, 1958), 36–63.
15. Croog, Sydney H., "Ethnic Origins, Educational Level, and Response to a Health Questionnaire," *Human Organization*, 20 (Summer, 1961), 65–69.
16. ———, "Patient Government—Some Aspects of Participation and Social Background on Two Psychiatric Wards," *Psychiatry*, 19 (May, 1956), 203–207.

17. Daniels, Morris J., "Affect and Its Control in the Medical Intern," *American Journal of Sociology*, 65 (November, 1960), 239–67.

18. Devereaux, George and Florence R. Weiner, "The Occupational Status of Nurses," *American Sociological Review*, 15 (October, 1950), 628–34.

19. Dodge, Joan S., "Why Nurses Leave—and What to Do about It," *Modern Hospital*, 94 (May, 1960), 116ff.

20. ———, "Nurse-Doctor Relations and Attitudes toward the Patient," *Nursing Research*, 9 (Winter, 1960), 32–38.

21. Dunbar, Flanders, *Psychiatry in the Medical Specialties*. New York: McGraw-Hill Book Company, Inc., 1959.

22. Dunham, H. Warren and S. Kirson Weinberg, *The Culture of the State Mental Hospital*. Detroit: Wayne State University Press, 1960.

23. Elling, Ray H. and Sander Nalebsky, "Organizational Differentiation and Support," *Administrative Science Quarterly*, 6 (September, 1961), 185–209.

24. Etzioni, Amitai, "Interpersonal and Structural Factors in the Study of Mental Hospital," *Psychiatry*, 23 (February, 1960), 13–22.

25. Faxon, Nathaniel W., ed., *The Hospital in Contemporary Life*. Cambridge: Harvard University Press, 1949.

26. Field, Mark G., *Doctor and Patient in Soviet Russia*. Cambridge: Harvard University Press, 1957.

27. Fox, Renée C., *Experiment Perilous*. New York: The Free Press of Glencoe, Inc., 1959.

28. Gallagher, Eugene B. and Robert S. Albert, "The Grelbdorf Affair," *Psychiatry*, 24 (August, 1961), 221–27.

29. Gardner, George E., "The Establishment of Child Psychiatry Programs in a Children's Hospital," *American Journal of Orthopsychiatry*, 28 (July, 1958), 523–33.

30. Gilbert, Doris C. and Daniel J. Levinson, "Role Performance, Ideology, and Personality in Mental Hospital Aides," *in* Milton Greenblatt, Daniel J. Levinson, and Richard H. Williams, eds., *The Patient and the Mental Hospital*. New York: The Free Press of Glencoe, Inc., pp. 197–208.

31. Ginzberg, Eli, *et al.*, *Occupational Choice: An Approach to a General Theory*. New York: Columbia University Press, 1951.

32. Glaser, William A., *Some Topics for Cross-National Research about Hospital Organizations*. New York: Bureau of Applied Social Research, Columbia University, March, 1960.

33. Goffman, Erving, "Characteristics of Total Institutions," Symposium on Preventive and Social Psychiatry, 15–17 April 1957, Walter Reed Army Institute of Research. Washington, D.C.: Government Printing Office, pp. 46–47.

34. Gouldner, Alvin W., "Cosmopolitans and Locals: Toward an Analysis of Latent Social Roles—I," *Administrative Science Quarterly*, 2 (December, 1957), 281–306.

35. Graham, Thomas F., "Stereotypes of Nationalities by Student Nurses," *Journal of Clinical Psychology*, 14 (July, 1958), 324–26.

36. Greenblatt, Milton, Richard H. York, and Esther Lucile Brown, *From Custodial to Therapeutic Patient Care in Mental Hospitals*. New York: Russell Sage Foundation, 1955.
37. Greenblatt, Milton, Daniel J. Levinson, and Richard H. Williams, eds., *The Patient and the Mental Hospital*. New York: The Free Press of Glencoe, Inc., 1957.
38. Hall, Oswald, "The Informal Organization of Medical Practice in an American City." Unpublished Ph.D. thesis, University of Chicago, 1944.
39. ———, "The Stages of a Medical Career," *American Journal of Sociology*, 53 (March, 1958), 327–36.
40. ———, "Sociological Research in the Field of Medicine: Progress and Prospects," *American Sociological Review*, 16 (October, 1951), 639–43.
41. Hamburg, David A., "Therapeutic Aspects of Communication and Administrative Policy in the Psychiatric Section of a General Hospital," *in* Milton Greenblatt, Daniel J. Levinson, Richard H. Williams, eds., *The Patient and the Mental Hospital*. New York: The Free Press of Glencoe, Inc., pp. 91–107.
42. Hardt, Robert H. and Sherwin J. Feinhandler, "Class and Mental Hospitalization Prognosis," *American Sociological Review*, 24 (December, 1959), 815–21.
43. Henry, Jules, "The Formal Structure of a Psychiatric Hospital," *Psychiatry*, 17 (May, 1954), 139–51.
44. ———. "Types of Institutional Structure," *Psychiatry*, 20 (February, 1957), 47–60.
45. Hollingshead, August B. and Frederick C. Redlich, *Social Class and Mental Illness*. New York: John Wiley & Sons, Inc., 1958.
46. *Hospitals*, 35 (August 1, 1961). Guide Issue.
47. Hughes, Everett C., Helen MacGill Hughes, and Irwin Deutscher, *Twenty Thousand Nurses Tell Their Story*. Philadelphia: J. B. Lippincott Company, 1958.
48. Inkeles, Alex and Daniel J. Levinson, "National Character: The Study of Modal Personality and Sociocultural Systems." *in* Gardner Lindsey, *Handbook of Social Psychology*. Reading, Mass.: Addison-Wesley Publishing Company, 1954, pp. 977–1020.
49. Janis Irving L., *Psychological Stress: Psychoanalytic and Behavioral Studies of Surgical Patients*. New York: John Wiley & Sons, Inc., 1958.
50. Jones, Maxwell, *The Therapeutic Community*. New York: Basic Books, Inc., 1953.
51. Kandler, Harriet, *et al.*, "A Study of Nurse-Patient Interaction in a Mental Hospital," *American Journal of Nursing*, 52 (September, 1952), 1100–1103.
52. Lentz, Edith, "Morale in a Hospital Business Office," *Human Organization*, 9 (Fall, 1950), 17–21.
53. Levine, Eugene, "Turnover among Nursing Personnel in General Hospitals," *Hospitals*, 31 (September 1, 1957), 50ff.
54. Lieberson, Stanley, "Ethnic Groups and the Practice of Medicine," *American Sociological Review*, 23 (October, 1958), 542–49.

55. Loeb, Martin B., "Role Definition in the Social World of a Psychiatric Hospital," *in* Milton Greenblatt, Daniel J. Levinson, and Richard H. Williams, eds., *The Patient and the Mental Hospital*. New York: The Free Press of Glencoe, Inc., 1957, pp. 14–19.

56. MacEacharn, Malcolm T., "History of Hospitals," *in Hospital Organization and Management*. Chicago: Physician Record Company, 1957, pp. 1–28.

57. Macgregor, Frances Cooke, *Social Science in Nursing*. New York: Russell Sage Foundation, 1960.

58. Merton, Robert N., George C. Reader, and Patricia L. Kendall, *The Student Physician: Introductory Studies in the Sociology of Medical Education*. Cambridge: Harvard University Press, 1957.

59. New, Peter Kong-ming, Gladys Nite, and Josephine M. Callahan, *Nursing Service and Patient Care: A Staffing Experiment*. Kansas City, Mo.: Community Studies, Inc., Publication No. 119, November, 1959.

60. Parsons, Talcott, *The Social System*. New York: The Free Press of Glencoe, Inc., 1951.

61. ———, and Renée Fox, "Illness, Therapy, and the Modern Urban American Family," *Journal of Social Issues*, 8 (1952), 31–44.

62. Paul, Benjamin D., ed., *Health, Culture, and Community*. New York: Russell Sage Foundation, 1953.

63. Polansky, Herman A., Robert B. White, and Stuart C. Miller, "Determinants of the Role-Image of the Patient in a Psychiatric Hospital," *in* Milton Greenblatt, Daniel J. Levinson, and Richard H. Williams, eds., *The Patient and the Mental Hospital*. New York: The Free Press of Glencoe, Inc., 1957, pp. 380–481.

64. Rapoport, Robert N., Rhona Rapoport, and Irving Rosow, *Community as Doctor*. London: Tavistock Publications, 1959.

65. Reader, George G., Lois Pratt, and Margaret C. Mudd, "What Patients Expect from Their Doctors," *Modern Hospital*, 89 (July, 1957), 88–94.

66. Reissman, Leonard and John H. Rohrer, *Change and Dilemma in the Nursing Profession*. New York: G. P. Putnam's Sons, 1957.

67. Roe, Anne, *The Psychology of Occupations*. New York: John Wiley & Sons, Inc., 1956.

68. Rosenberg, Larry, "Social Status and Participation among a Group of Chronic Schizophrenics," *Human Relations*, 15 (1962), 365–377.

69. Roth, Julius A., "Ritual and Magic in the Control of Contagion," *American Sociological Review*, 22 (June, 1957), 310–14.

70. Saunders, Lyle, *Cultural Difference and Medical Care*. New York: Russell Sage Foundation, 1954.

71. Scheff, Thomas J., "Control over Policy by Attendants in a Mental Hospital," *Journal of Health and Human Behavior*, 2 (Summer, 1961), 93–105.

72. Schulman, Sam, "Basic Functional Roles in Nursing: Mother Surrogate and Healer," *in* E. Gartly Jaco, ed., *Patients, Physicians and Illness*. New York: The Free Press of Glencoe, Inc., 1958, pp. 528–37.

73. Seeman, Melvin and John W. Evans, "Stratification and Hospital Care: I. The Performance of the Medical Interne," *American Sociological Review*, 26 (February, 1961), 67–80.

74. Shryock, Richard H., *The Development of Modern Medicine*. New York: Alfred A. Knopf, Inc., 1947.

75. Simmel, Ernest, "Psychoanalytic Treatment in a Sanatorium," *International Journal of Psychoanalysis*, 10 (January, 1929), 70–89.

76. Simmons, Leo W. and Harold G. Wolff, *Social Science in Medicine*. New York: Russell Sage Foundation, 1952.

77. Smith, Harvey L., "Two Lines of Authority: The Hospital's Dilemma," *The Modern Hospital*, 84 (March, 1955), 59–64.

78. ———, "Professional Strains and the Hospital Context," *in* Milton Greenblatt, Daniel J. Levinson, and Richard N. Williams, eds., *The Patient and the Mental Hospital*. New York: The Free Press of Glencoe, Inc., 1957.

79. Solomon, David N., "Ethnic and Class Differences among Hospitals as Contingencies in Medical Careers," *American Journal of Sociology*, 65 (March, 1961), pp. 463–71.

80. Solon, Jerry, *et al.*, "Staff Perceptions of Patients' Use of a Hospital Out-Patient Department," *Journal of Medical Education*, 33 (January, 1958), 10–21.

81. Stanton, Alfred H. and Morris S. Schwartz, *The Mental Hospital*. New York: Basic Books, Inc., 1954.

82. Stredtbeck, Fred L., Rita M. James, and Charles Hawkins, "Social Status in Jury Deliberations," *in* Eleanor E. Maccoby, Theodore M. Newcomb, and Eugene L. Hartley, eds., *Readings in Social Psychology*. New York: Holt, Rinehart & Winston, Inc., 1958, pp. 379–88.

83. Wallace, Anthony F. C. and Harold A. Rashkis, "The Relation of Staff Consensus to Patient Disturbance on Mental Hospital Wards," *American Sociological Review*, 24 (December, 1959), 829–35.

84. Wessen, Albert F., "Hospital Ideology and Communication between Ward Personnel," *in* E. Gartly Jaco, ed., *Patients, Physicians, and Illness*. New York: The Free Press of Glencoe, Inc., 1958, pp. 448–68.

85. Williams, Josephine J., "The Woman Physician's Dilemma," *Journal of Social Issues*, 6 (1950), 38–44.

86. ———, "Patients and Prejudice: Lay Attitudes toward Women Physicians," *American Journal of Sociology*, 51 (January, 1946), 283–87.

87. Wilson, Robert N., "The Physician's Changing Hospital Role," *Human Organization*, 18 (Winter, 1959–60), 177–83.

88. Zborowski, Mark, "Cultural Components in Responses to Pain," *Journal of Social Issues*, 8 (1952), 16–30.

11

PATIENT-PRACTITIONER RELATIONSHIPS

Robert N. Wilson

"*In every* medical action there are always two parties involved, the physician and the patient, or in a broader sense, the medical corps and society. Medicine is nothing else than the manifold relations between these two groups. The history of medicine, therefore, cannot limit itself to the history of the science, institutions, and characters of medicine, but must include the history of the patient in society, that of the physician, and the history of the relations between physician and patient" [21].

If the relations between physician and patient are the crux of medicine, as Sigerist contends, then the patterned content of interaction exhibited by this relation is clearly of immense interest to the student of medicine as a social institution. It is thus appropriate to think first of doctor and patient as participants in an unique mutuality, as actors in a therapeutic drama who fulfill well-rehearsed social roles with respect to one another. The welter of behaviors and expectancies subsumed under "the physician's role" or "the patient's role" does not, however, transpire in a vacuum. Rather, these roles are exquisitely sensitive to the environing frame of cultural values, of nonmedical activities, of the tempo and tenor of the community around them. Just because health and illness are such salient human problems, the effort to cope with them through doctor-patient interaction is especially exposed to the influences of the time and place in which the effort occurs.

There seem to be two particular dangers which the analyst of doctor-patient relationships must avoid. First is the temptation to adopt a narrow and sociologically incorrect notion of "role," conceiving of role only as the set of deliberate activities embraced by doctor or patient singly. Social role is better viewed as consisting of these activities plus the configuration of expectations directed by each party to the transaction toward the other and toward himself. The physician's role is then partly defined by what patients expect of him; the patient's role, of course, is partly defined by what physicians expect of him. The juxtaposition of such anticipations and predictions about one another's behavior is the essence of the role relationship. When the juxtaposition is imperfect there is a "problem" in human interaction, whatever the causal history of the imperfection.

A second special hazard, one which can be avoided to some extent by cognizance of historical and cross-cultural variation, is found in the tendency to embrace an idiosyncratic model of patient-practitioner relationships as the correct definition and to treat all alternative arrangements as deviations. Several such particular models have at times appeared to physicians, patients, and other observers to be ordained and exclusively reasonable. In the United States, examples might be the model of classical psychoanalysis and the model of the fee-for-service general practitioner. We must be alert, then, to varieties of patient-practitioner relationships, to a range of possible interpersonal models conditioned by type of illness, specificities of role definition, the characteristics of medicine as science and as art, and the prevailing sociocultural matrix.

The Social Role of the Patient

With the possible exception of certain severe congenital defects, no one is "born" as a patient. Nor can he expect to assume the patient's role as a consequence of a normal developmental sequence, as the result of schooling in patienthood. The role is usually temporary, only loosely circumscribed by accepted definitions of its content, and ascribed to the individual rather than achieved by him. It is not consciously sought by many persons in any society, although the secondary gains of illness—especially the security of a protected dependency—may lead some persons to an unconscious desire to be ill. The decisive element in assuming the role of patient is probably not the sheer fact of sickness or accident, but the recognition by the affected individual and/or certain other people of a particular need for help in coping with the condition.

Even within a single culture, the definition of conditions requiring assistance varies widely. Mental illness is perhaps the clearest example of this ambiguity and vagueness; indeed, some psychiatrists propose that an operational definition of a "case" is precisely the involvement in a therapeutic relationship, rather than any intrinsic state of the ill person. Thus a patient is a person in contact with a psychiatrist or other helping agent [26]. Yet the mental diseases are only the most extreme instances of inexact correspondence between an ill state and the decision to adopt the role of patient. As Koos found in Regionville [16], a plethora of physical symptoms may be differentially viewed with respect to whether they do or do not need medical attention. The decision to become a patient, whether it is autonomous or imposed, is conditioned by many factors including the urgency of symptoms, degree of experience with the sick role, and availability of help. A poignant statement by one of Koos's respondents illustrates the dilemma of potential transitions from being ill to becoming a patient:

> I wish I really knew what you mean about being sick. Sometimes I've felt so bad I could curl up and die, but had to go on because the kids had to be taken care of, and besides, we didn't have the money to spend for the doctor—how could I be sick? . . . How do you know when you're sick, anyway? Some people can go to bed most anytime with anything, but most of us can't be sick—even when we need to be.

The recognition of illness and the disposition to seek aid in recovering from it is thus the key prerequisite to the establishment of a patient-practitioner relationship. These processes of cognizance and search may range from the tentative self-diagnosis and self-referral of the medically sophisticated person to the entire passivity of a tuberculosis sufferer uncovered by public health authorities. The chain of events involved in becoming a patient has been fairly thoroughly examined for certain disease entities and certain categories of ill persons [4, 17]. Most generally stated, the pattern seems to consist in a combination of subjective feelings of discomfort, initial searching by the affected individual, counsel by family members, friends, or other informal advisors such as pharmacists, and final confirmation of the ill state by a medical practitioner. This general pattern, however, may be distorted by the omission of links in the chain because of ignorance of appropriate pathways or disinclination to assume the patient's role.

Although becoming a patient is a complex series of behaviors, and one deserving much fuller research attention, there appear to be critical problematic stages. It may be observed that the problems at each of these stages are exacerbrated in the case of the chronic illnesses which are increasingly important in American society; they may, indeed, constitute typical problems for an aging population in which communicable disease and acute trauma are elegantly controlled by medical technique. The first problem concerns the perception of symptoms as serious enough to merit help. If immediate physical or emotional discomfort is not extreme—and in the chronic ills it often is not—the afflicted person may simply fail to take the first step in defining himself as a patient. Despite widespread, if superficial, medical knowledge and the exhortation of health professionals, substantial numbers of persons do not attach significance to painless or minor indicators of disease; the lump of cancer is only the most notorious example. Because the indicators may be subtle and imperceptible to the individual, he may need help in the stage of earliest recognition. Chest X-rays and cervical smears demand the voluntary collaboration of an apparently healthy person. The individual is required, in some sense, to think of himself as a "pre-patient," and this of course is in itself an implicit threat.

Once some recognition has occurred, there remains the problem of discovering pathways to care. The individual may commonly not know what resources are available to him. Or, knowing them, he may resist approaching them because of the potential economic consequences of patienthood. A further reason for avoiding care is often overlooked by highly rational students of behavior: this is the plain fact of disturbance in customary life patterns, the "trouble" involved in seeking care. It may take a good deal of time and energy to become a patient, and the best intentioned helping agents must combat a basic inertia. The individual must be moved and motivated, quite apart from financial hazards or psychological resistance.

There is, finally, the basic tendency to refuse categorization as a patient because assumption of the ill state is destructive of a cherished self-image and a settled configuration of social roles. In a society of the well, the ill person is singled out, restricted, reduced comparatively to a condition of psychological and social servitude. To be a patient is to be a man but not quite a man, to be human without the full responsibilities and privileges of humanity. Physical disease is a reminder that we are all animals under the skin, that the veneer of culture is precariously vulnerable to the imperatives of physiology. Mental disease calls back the helplessness of childhood, the unsettled perceptual stance of the naked infant in a universe of chaos.

Sociologically viewed, the patient is a deviant individual. The onus implied in his deviance is clearly more forceful in mental than in physical illness, but is in any case considerable—especially if the state of illness is prolonged. The essential reason for his being labeled a deviant is not obscure: a patient is by definition an individual whose incapacity thwarts his performance of the social roles with which he is normally charged. His illness diminishes the body social by one, and in a tightly integrated society the withdrawal of particular persons from full functioning may have a pervasive effect. It is thus eminently reasonable to believe with Parsons that a society cannot long afford an endemic or epidemic taking of the patient's role; that society must construe this role as undesirable, temporary, and basically disruptive.

Parsons' analysis of the structure of the sick role is perhaps the most incisive exploration of the social meaning of the patient's situation [22]. His discussion is peculiarly relevant to American society, or to any highly industrialized, rational social system. He notes that the sick role is institutionalized, is delimited in such a way that the well population is "insulated" from the contagion of the ill. The ill person is defined as "needing help," as obligated to accept this help and to cooperate with the therapeutic agent. The patient is made dependent on the non-sick society:

> 1. This incapacity is interpreted as beyond his powers to overcome by the process of decision-making alone; in this sense he cannot be "held responsible" for the incapacity. Some kind of "therapeutic" process, spontaneous or aided, is conceived to be necessary to recovery.
>
> 2. Incapacity defined as illness is interpreted as a legitimate basis for the *exemption* of the sick individual, to varying degrees, in varying ways, and for varying periods according to the nature of the illness, from his normal role and task obligations.
>
> 3. To be ill is thus to be in a partially and conditionally *legitimated* state. The essential condition of its legitimation, however, is the recognition by the sick person that to be ill is inherently *undesirable*, that he therefore has an obligation to try to "get well" and to cooperate with others to this end.
>
> 4. So far as spontaneous forces, the *vis medicatrix naturea*, cannot be expected to operate adequately and quickly, the sick person, and those with responsibility for his welfare, above all, members of his family, have an obligation to *seek competent help* and to cooperate with competent agencies in their attempts to help him get well; in our society, of course, principally medical agencies. The valuation of health, of course, also implies that it is an obligation to try to prevent threatened illness where this is possible [22].

In a society which is marked by an interdependent series of highly complex social roles, the patient is under particularly heavy pressure to regain capacity. In keeping with the emphasis on the value of health in American culture, and in Western European culture generally, the patient has the corresponding advantage of a developed scientific armamentarium and a host of helping agents. The ill person, then, recognizing his illness or having it enunciated by others, prepares to define himself as a more or less compliant partner in a therapeutic relationship. At this point in his career as patient, he typically confronts some helping agent—often, but not always, a physician. He has assumed the patient's role, but the assumption is laden with ambivalence and ambiguity. Unless he is a veteran patient repeating a familiar sequence of actions, he faces a primary uncertainty. What will be the treatment? The duration of illness? The contingencies of interpersonal relations with the practitioner? The probability of complete or partial recovery? It should be stressed, too, that this initial foray into patienthood circumscribes only a vital fragment of the total sick role. The role will change and proliferate as the individual moves from the nadir of ill-being toward recovery—or toward dissolution. In its most exacting guise, the sick role may become permanent; its duration may connote invalidism, in which case the individual is caught up in a role quite different from that ideal asymmetry sketched by Parsons.[1]

In any event, the social role of the patient is a complicated and various affair. It merits the closest scrutiny by social research. One of the most rewarding directions for such research would seem to be that followed by Goffman [11] in his examination of the "moral career" of the mentally ill. Goffman has tried, with notable success, to trace the patient's subjective experience of induction into a particular kind of sick role and progressive adaptation to it. This investigation of the natural history of patienthood might well be emulated for other types of illness, other therapeutic settings, and other cultural circumstances. It could be supplemented by techniques which might lend extra force to this model of sensitive empathic analysis, such as psychological testing, observation of small-group interaction, attitude surveys, and structured interviewing. A current effort to tackle the meaning of the patient's experience in a general, rather than mental, hospital has been made by Duff and his associates in New Haven.

The Social Role of the Practitioner

Having defined the patient as a social deviant, it is natural to think of the practitioner first as an agent of social control. He is implicitly charged by society with the job of returning the affected person to full functioning, of reversing the tide of withdrawal so that the patient may again take up the threads of social obligations. The practitioner is the representative of dominant cultural values, and although there is increasing sophistication and self-consciousness—especially at certain junctures in psychotherapy—about the way in which he expresses these values, they are ordinarily intrinsic and need no deliberate articulation. That is, the practitioner is the symbol of the well and normal, of the non-ill encountering the ill. It might

[1] See another discussion of the sick role in Chap. 4.

be guessed that his role as symbol of health is actually equal in importance to—and indeed inseparable from—his role as a technically-equipped curative agent.

The practitioner's intimate relationship to key values in his society is perhaps best demonstrated by the ancient association of medicine and religion. In the priestly origins of healing, the same person was responsible for ultimate social goals (religion) and proximate enabling goals (health). Today, in secular Western society, when health itself has become something of a religion in keeping with our veneration of efficiency, the medical professions are superbly aligned with major cultural phrasings of conduct and decorum.[2] Altruism, technical expertness, and pragmatic efficacy are embodied in the physician, who stands on a peak of prestige; he may in the sweep of history be as characteristic a figure of the age as the engineer or physicist or advertiser.

Although practitioner and patient are engaged in a process of mutual role definition, and the behavior of each is shaped by the expectations of the other, there is as a rule no question as to where the initiative in the relationship lies. The patient originates the relationship and has a greater or lesser voice in its course and termination, but the practitioner has a nearly exclusive monopoly of psychological and social leverage. Thus on balance the practitioner has more to do with defining the patient's role than vice versa. It is a curious fact that in order to act as a rehabilitation agent who presses for the return of the patient to active functioning, the physician must first separate the ill person from his society. One might say that he not only validates the individual's role as patient, but that he enforces a measured seclusion from complete social involvement. The dramatic isolation of quarantine or mental hospitalization may obscure by comparison the no less critical separation a practitioner routinely imposes on the patient. The crux of this separation is found in the doctor-patient relationship itself: the patient must offer a special and abnormal allegiance to the practitioner; he must relinquish a degree of autonomy; he must often forego specified portions of his accustomed labor and leisure. As potent wielder of social control, the physician's directive role may be epitomized in the popular deferential phrase: "You're the doctor."

Doctor and patient obviously bring different things to their confrontation. At the very heart of their perceptual discrepancies is probably the imbalance of attention intrinsic to the situation: the patient's illness is understandably the most significant thing in the world to him at this time, while the physician must see this individual and his symptoms as one among many. No one can be so absorbed in suffering as the sufferer; quite apart from the therapeutic necessity of the physician's maintaining a

[2] Compare with the discussion on medicine in other cultures in Chap. 16.

scrupulous distance, of his renouncing a crippling empathy, there is the fact that he simply cannot feel what the patient feels or assign his trouble the same enveloping priority.

Overlying this fundamental difference are the many ways in which the two parties' preparations for the situation have been at variance. The patient has been inadvertently thrust into a hopefully temporary and partial role. The physician has been recruited into a lifelong professional concern, and the therapeutic situation is to him a normal and agreeable working context rather than a threatening skirmish. The physician has freely chosen a specific model of professional behavior; the patient has had a role imposed upon him for which he is typically ill-prepared and which he is reluctant to assume. Given these disparities, it is obvious that a considerable portion of the practitioner's role must be devoted to teaching the patient how to be a patient, to a tutorage—explicit and implicit—in a certain pattern of interaction. Most interactive situations contain elements of guidance exercised by the party whose sphere of competence is most directly involved: even the shoeshine boy tells his customer how to place his feet. But very few roles—that of parent being perhaps the chief exception—require as much continuous educative effort as that of the medical practitioner. Broadly speaking, the doctor is active, doing something for and to the patient, while the patient is passive, asking that something be done for him. These diverse stances may prefigure a congenial reciprocity, but they also insure that the value systems of practitioner and patient will differ in detail despite their presumed agreement on the ultimate goal of cure.

Possession of the initiative and of recognized competence imply power. They also imply a correlatively heavy burden of responsibility. Although the patient too has important obligations—especially the central one expressed by Parsons as "to try to get well"—it is the practitioner who must act. He is hourly engaged in what is probably the most difficult of human tasks—decision-making—and in a setting where the consequences of error are quite often irreversible and very dangerous. Entrusted with the most precious of assets, the living body and mind, the practitioner must chart a course of therapy; he does so, moreover, in a situation of relatively great uncertainty, hostage to a science which still contains large increments of art and improvisation.

All practitioners are professionals and all patients are amateurs. (Although in some sense the hypochondriac and the chronically ill may be regarded as "professional patients.") They thus begin their relationship with varying orientations toward the patient's illness. The difference in context and attitude is perhaps inevitable. Compounding this difference may be a variety of factors; when they are substantial in number and weight, the relationship may be sabotaged almost before it has begun. For many reasons the two parties may inhabit quite separate universes of discourse. Most obvious in this separation is the barrier of language and frame of reference between sophisticated and lay conceptions of health and disease. Education, social class, proximity to medical culture, experience with illness—all may affect the extent to which physician and client may be said to be talking about the same thing. The language of medicine, essential to precision, aggravates the situation of two strangers speaking of matters sacred to the one and necessarily profane to the other. Although research has shown expectably that the most deprived and culturally alien sectors of the population fail to understand much of the standard medical vocabulary [27], it is likely that all communication between therapist and patient is flawed to some extent by the failure of the patient to understand.

The strictly referential meaning of words is probably not the most hazardous problem, however. More vital is the gulf which may exist in assumptions of value, total style of life, and level of verbal abstraction. Primary to these considerations is the difference between social class of physician and patient within a single culture, and patterned value distinctions between physician and patient of different cultures. It is often taken for granted that the differing values and experiences of physician and patient, when they come from widely separated social backgrounds, cripple communication and render therapy—especially psychotherapy—problematic. This assumption is not, however, especially well-documented. Qualifications are clearly in order on at least two scores: the type of illness involved suggests that valuative consensus need be more or less complete—a Harley Street practitioner can presumably deal as competently with a Cockney fracture as with an Oxbridge one, although he might be utterly stymied by a Cockney psychoneurosis; further, our understanding of the structure of therapy is still tentative, and it may well be that in some instances compatabilities of personality between therapist and patient can offset seeming distances anchored in group-membership characteristics.

Conflicting value systems based upon social class patterns are thought to be particularly destructive of the close relationship essential in psychotherapy. A good deal of indirect evidence shows that successful nonorganic treatment is quite rare if therapist and patient are ill-matched in socioeconomic status [15]. Responsibility for this non-meeting of the minds is ordinarily assigned to the lower-class patient who confronts an upper-middle class psychiatrist. The patient is able to conceive of illness solely in somatic terms; he lacks both the habit of introspection and the conceptual tools to abstract and objectify elements of the mental life; he may be less firmly wedded to values of individual responsibility, initiative, and achievement than is the striving professional; contrary to popular stereotypes, he may be gripped by a morality too rigid to accommodate (for example) the incursion of analysis into sexual behavior. Although these and other factors undoubtedly operate strongly, it is seldom proposed that social class lacunae might be bridged by the therapist's flexibly searching out a common ground of discourse. At least one researcher-clinician, making such an effort, has found that with ingenuity and persistence the unreachable may be at least more closely approached.

If mental illness has seemed to be the primary field in which value differences based on class interfere with the patient-practitioner relationship, the interference is by no means confined to these illnesses. The out-patient clinic or emergency room of a general hospital is daily the scene of misunderstandings imposed by conflict between the orientations of hospital personnel and patients. Suspicions of malingering, failures to follow treatment directives, financial ambiguities, chasms between life-styles all tend to complicate the therapeutic process [2]. Preventive medicine and public health, too, are often subject to the special difficulties inherent in the "conversation between the classes"; a recent instance is the variable willingness of parents to participate in the administration of polio vaccine to their children [5].

Value conflict is still more damaging to the relationship when practitioner and patient act within quite separate cultural frameworks. Here the disparities may be so deep that the fundamental perceptions of the nature of health and illness are not commensurate; there may be disagreement over the most general definition of the roles of patient and therapist. The most vivid illustrations of such conflict are drawn from the attempts to bring Western scientific medical care to populations living within non-Western configurations of value.[3] Much thought and research has been devoted to the basic problem of fitting modern health care into widely-varying traditional frameworks of belief and conduct [24]. A major conclusion reached by the many students of intercultural medical practice is that the practitioner must come to know the values of his patients—and respect them—if he is to be an effective curative agent. He must not only be alert to the particular conception of the patient's role with which he is dealing, but must be able to view the therapeutic interaction in the context of a total culture whose major patterns affect health behavior in manifold ways. Lyle Saunders has provided perhaps the clearest and most comprehensive statements of what cultural differences mean for the social role of the practitioner:

> When the practice of medicine involves the application of elements of the institution of medicine in one culture to the people of another, or from one subculture to members of another subculture within the same cultural group, what is done or attempted by those in the healing roles

[3] See Chap. 16 for a discussion of health in other cultures.

> may not be fully understood or correctly evaluated by those in the patient roles. Conversely, the responses of those on the patient side of the interaction may not conform to the expectations of those on the healing side. To the extent that this occurs, the relationship may be unsatisfactory to everyone concerned.
>
> When persons of widely dissimilar cultural or subcultural orientations are brought together in a therapeutic relationship, the probability of a mutually satisfactory outcome may be increased if those in the healing roles know something of their own culture and that of the patient and are aware of the extent to which behavior on both sides of the relationship is influenced by cultural factors. An even higher probability of satisfaction may result if the professional people are willing and able to modify elements from their medicine so as to make them fit the expectations of the laymen with whom they are working [28].

Of all the sub-cultural differences that may divide practitioner from patient within a given society, the sub-culture of the medical profession itself may well be the most critical. It is patent that a reciprocal role relationship hinges on certain fundamental divisions between the parties. That is, it is essential for the medical professional to entertain a definite perceptual set toward the patient and his illness; only thus can the extent of both his technical fund and curative leverage be realized. And this perceptual stance must be clearly distinguished from that of the patient. If differences of opinion make horse races, differences of perspective as surely make education and/or therapy possible. Yet the advantages of professionalization in the physician's role are balanced in some degree by negative divisive factors. The very technical proficiency on which his efforts rest may be a barrier to sympathetic understanding of the patient as a human being; his advanced specialization in modern medicine may make him unable or unwilling to regard the whole patient; his range of concerns may be narrowed to the patient-as-organism, with slight attention to the patient as family member, worker, full social being. Medical schools today are of course attempting to counteract this tendency by emphasizing preventive care and family-centered treatment.

The professional attitude toward the patient has many facets, but its core is probably to be found in what Parsons has termed "affective neutrality." This orientation is the vital distancing mechanism which prevents the practitioner from becoming the patient's colleague in illness, from entering an emotional compact whose mute provisions would destroy his objective judgment and his therapeutic-educative leverage. Affective neutrality constitutes the physician's prime safeguard against the antitherapeutic dangers of countertransference. (In the type-case of psychoanalytic countertransference, Freud warns the male physician against returning the erotic overtures of a neurotic female patient [6].) The practitioner's neutral posture does not mean that he is resolutely unfeeling—although the medical student may undergo a stage of flamboyant callousness in his struggle to adopt professional norms of conduct.[4] It does mean that his primitive emotive response is controlled and complicated, that his feelings are at least partially prevented from affecting his technical judgment. Strictly speaking, one might say that the ideal practitioner exhibits sympathy but not empathy, intuitive understanding without full-scale involvement; he should understand the patient's feelings without feeling them himself. There are many ways in which this ideal of measured neutrality may be disturbed. It may be the most artificial as well as the most essential element in the professional role, and one of the hardest aspects to be "learned" during professional education.

Two other important dimensions of the professional attitude have been isolated by Parsons, who terms them the orientations toward "universalism" and "functional specificity." The universalistic theme connotes the practitioner's tendency to treat all patients alike; this does not, of course, mean the prescription of identical therapies, but rather the viewing of patients as in some sense equal members of a universe of health and illness. Criteria which lie outside the field of health are considered to be irrelevant to the treatment process; judgment is guided by technical medical factors, and these are invariably applied to cases arrayed according to rational modes of classification. Again, a compelling adherence to universalistic norms is not easy to achieve; it may be summarily vitiated not only by the intrusion of ideally extraneous factors, such as the patient's ethnicity or financial capacity, but by problematic junctures in medicine itself. The efflorescence of social medicine, psychosomatic medicine, and psychiatry, with their emphases on family context and total social configurations in which the client is implicated, now calls into question both traditional schemes of disease classification and traditional models of uniform orientation toward patients.

The norm of functional specificity impels the professional to limit his attention and activities to a rigidly circumscribed sphere—to those things which are strictly "medical." The practitioner is not expected to be expert at religious or political counsel, or to intrude into the patient's private affairs any further than the medical problem demands. Functional specificity is clearly most characteristic of Western medicine; it rests on the fine-grained division of labor found in industrial societies and on the development of a comprehensive science of medicine. There are significant currents working for and against this norm in modern professional life. Specialization, which is the butt of so much humor and the object of so much genuine concern, sometimes carries the mandate of specificity to extreme lengths. On the other hand, the increasing stress upon the whole patient and all his psychosocial circumstance means that the practitioner

[4] See Chap. 7 for a discussion of medical education.

may become legitimately interested in a wider range of factors. In programs of total medical care, ancillary professionals such as the social worker may make the physician indirectly privy to a much more detailed case history than seems appropriate to the model of functional specificity. The line separating the medical sphere from the nonmedical is, then, a shifting one; especially in psychotherapy, the practitioner may at times be drawn into a set of global concerns more nearly comparable to those of the priest-healer than those of the hospital technician.

The social role of the practitioner, like that of the patient, is thus not a fixed pattern of attitudes and capacities. It is rather a process, subject to constant redefinition as expectations change. The role is lively, growing, debatable, and debated; it is exposed to changes in types of illness, organization of medical care, medical sophistication, and in the society at large. There is no single practitioner's "social role." In the exceedingly complex arrangements of contemporary medical care, there is instead a continuum of roles embracing varieties of physicians, nurses, administrators, technicians, and so on.

The Patient-Practitioner Relationship as a Therapeutic Subsystem

Although sensitive physicians have for centuries been alert to the importance of their interpersonal bond with the patient as an element in the course of illness and recovery, the self-conscious examination of this bond is a characteristically modern concern. An interest in the dynamics of the interpersonal flow probably dates from Freud and his absorption in the structure of the therapeutic process [7]. Secondarily, there has been a pronounced sociological tradition which supplements the Freudian orientation by paying special attention to the social roles of the two parties and the norms governing them. Here, the classic formulation of the physiologist and social scientist, L. J. Henderson [14] and the analytical model of Parsons [22] have been pre-eminent.

There are several basic ideas about therapeutic action. Not every student of the relationship would subscribe to all of them, but they do afford some framework for exploration. The first and most significant is that the relationship is a dynamic one, that doctor and patient are implicated in a moving pattern of initiative and response rather than a static frieze of habitual postures. Clinical activity therefore rests upon an attentive grasp of the unique events which transpire in the given relationship. The personalities and the individual styles of doctor and patient are intrinsic to the relationship, and operate against the possibility of the patient's being seen as merely one in a series of mechanical problems or of the doctor's being seen as merely a stock representative of medical culture.

A peculiar affective pattern—that comprehensive emotional investment of patient in physician usually termed "transference"—is thought to be imperative to full therapeutic efficacy. Transference, which is essentially the transformation of a contemporary social relationship so that it recapitulates a childhood relationship, is firmly rooted in general medical practice because of the patient's customary regression under the stress of illness. This regression appears to be a normal response to fear, to the dependency of patient on doctor, to the doctor's privileged (hence parent-like) access to the body and its secrets. Freud terms positive transference, "the vehicle of success in psychoanalysis exactly as it is in other methods of treatment" [7], thus emphasizing its applicability to the general medical situation. Positive transference affords the physician a leverage which is usually considered essential to successful treatment, although the extent of transference clearly rests on the severity and duration of illness. Negative transference (or resistance in the psychoanalyst's terms) clearly inhibits treatment; however, it is perhaps less crucially involved in general medical practice, except in cases of chronic disease, than it is in analytic therapy. A significant difference between the psychoanalytic doctor-patient relationship and all others is that transference is brought to explicit awareness in analysis but is seldom so deliberately regarded in other contexts.

In addition to the concepts of dynamics, personality boundaries, and transference, the therapeutic subsystem is conditioned by prevailing cultural definitions of the roles of doctor and patient and of the nature of illness. These prevailing definitions set limits to the system. To note only the most obvious examples, the relationship is governed by legal codes, professional codes, and the contemporaries of both parties—the patient's family and the physician's colleagues. It is governed as well by the specific context of therapy: hospital, office, home, or wherever.

Although the therapeutic situation is unique, it shares vital characteristics with a number of other intense two-person interchanges. It is intimate, salient to deep interests of both persons, stylized but vulnerable to personality and situational exigencies, and integral to the successful maintenance of the larger social system. In the heightened dependence of one party on the directing other, it most nearly resembles the pairings of parent-child, priest-supplicant, or teacher-student. Under the fee-for-service model of American practice, the therapeutic relationship also is like the seller-buyer dyad, despite the fact that its "market" dimensions are deliberately subdued. Again like all of these comparative subsystems, it is ordered to an ideal pattern, a normative structure which is highly significant in guiding the participants regardless of the gap between ideal image and actual behavior. Finally, therapy is an exchange relationship in which both parties have something to gain and something to give; the balance of reciprocity is sure to be uneven, but the notion of the practitioner as solely "donor" and the patient as solely "recipient" constitutes a distortion of the therapeutic process—and indeed of any interpersonal nexus [20].

One of the most revealing angles of approach to therapy is the comparison of this relationship with that of parent and child, with the socialization process as elaborated most thoughtfully by Parsons [23]. Socialization and therapy have interestingly similar characteristics as processes of social control, as asymmetrical relationships, as emotionally laden and directed toward a terminus in which the dependent party has become independent as a fully-functioning member of his society. The emotional relearning of psychotherapy comes closer to the model of socialization than does general medical practice, but therapy of any sort is illumined by the comparison. Four major features of the relationship are singled out for analysis; these features have the activity of parent or therapist as their point of reference. They are: support, permissiveness, manipulation of reward, and denial of reciprocity. Briefly, they entail:

support the therapist expresses his obligation to be of assistance, to provide a stable figure on whom the patient may lean. He will be available, helpful, nurturant toward the patient's needs for dependency. It is understood, however, that the support is temporary and contingent on the patient's continuing efforts to get well.

permissiveness the therapist allows the patient to express feelings and indulge in actions which would not be acceptable in a nontherapeutic relationship. Again the dispensation is temporary and rooted in the idea that patient or child is for the moment unable to adhere strictly to ordinary norms of social intercourse. Permissiveness is granted with the justification that the patient, by reason of his illness, "can't help" doing certain things and cannot be held to usual expectations of responsibility.

manipulation of reward the therapist exerts leverage on the ill person by controlling certain rewards which are especially significant to the dependent party. As in child-rearing, the primary reward is probably approval, which can be offered or withheld at the discretion of the socializing or therapeutic agent. Rewards are given for doing the "right thing," for trying to "grow up" or to "get well."

denial of reciprocity the therapist, as a condition for the granting of support and permissiveness, withholds from the patient his own full interpersonal responsiveness. He keeps the relationship asymmetrical by refusing either to feel all the patient feels or to allow the patient access to his, the therapist's, true feelings. He will not meet fire with fire, irritation with irritation, adoration with adoration; for to do so would be to sacrifice the independent terrain on which he stands, and with it the potential for helping the other.

Assuredly the patient and child are not the same thing; one departs from a disturbed maturity, while the other is by definition immature. Doctor and parent are unlike in the magnitude of their involvement with the dependent party, the depth of their emotional linkage, the range of their concerns for the other. Yet the processes of inducting an individual into society and of returning him to a full and sanctioned functioning in society are remarkably parallel. In particular, the patient's being as a child seems to be inseparable from the physical and emotional insult of illness, and the physician's being as a parent seems intrinsically commensurate with his superior knowledge and experience in the domain of health.

The sanctity of body and mind are matters too important to be submitted to an utterly rational calculus of anticipation and behavior. Doctor and patient are entrapped in the mysteries of life and their intercourse partakes of a religious flavor: no patient in extremity of suffering and anxiety can regard the physician as of like substance with himself; the curative path and the curative agent are necessarily endowed with transcendent qualities and approached with ardent faith rather than cool resolve. There are at least two salient sets of reasons why the doctor-patient relationship is pervaded by mystical-religious elements. The first involves the peculiar dependence of patient on physician, the giving over by one individual to another of critical decisions affecting not only the course of life but in some instances the possibility of survival. In order for this extraordinary transaction to occur, the patient must view his doctor in a manner far removed from the prosaic and the mundane. He thus more or less consciously regards him as the possessor of charismatic qualities, of a magnetic and profound gift for leadership in affairs of health. There is of course a very great distance between the faith invested in a Navaho singer or a Caribbean spiritualist and the faith invested in a clinician at a university medical center; yet every healing relationship contains a substratum of nonrational awe, and every healer is endowed with at least a minimum of magical attributes.

A second root of the mystical and the religious lies in the character of medicine itself. Although the scope of phenomena which are amenable to empirical explanation and control in medicine has steadily been enlarged, especially during the first half of the twentieth century, the plethora of unanswered and presently unanswerable questions generates precisely the kind of basic uncertainty which underlies the religious impulse.[5] Art and religion both attempt to hint at the ineffable and to bring pattern into the inexplicable flux of existence. Medicine remains an art-science, and one must be dubious about the proposition that clinical intuition will give way entirely to electronic computation of syndromes. The increasing relevance of psychotherapy to medicine in general, and perhaps particularly to the run of chronic ailments, probably means that the domain of the incompletely formulated, the spontaneous, and the intuitive will remain large and may in some instances even expand.

[5] See the discussion of Christian Science in Chap. 9.

Practitioner and patient as minister and communicant are further illumined by the patterns of gesture and speech which they rehearse in their interaction. The case history and the confession; the physical examination and the laying on of hands; the prescription and the injunction to live in the paths of righteousness—all these and more speak to the parallels. The element of the sacred in medical ritual is of first importance as a clue to religious overtones. Perhaps the aseptical rigor of the surgery has a function of symbolic purification for the participants which matches its technical rationale [32].

The privacy of the two relationships is again significant. It is assumed that in dealing with salvation or healing an intimate compact is required. The self-revelation so vital to any exploration of the soul or the self necessarily demands a protected situation; the physician's consulting room may well be the appropriate modern analogue of the inviolable sanctuary of the medieval cathedral. Legal medicine, and especially forensic psychiatry, have as one set of considerations precisely the limits of this inviolableness, the boundaries which society may wish to put on "privileged communications." Although both the medical and the religious relationships have the characteristic of privacy, and offer the possibility of some refuge from the importunities of this world, they are fundamentally allied in social control. The radical essence of religious vision is only a slight portion of the total social meaning of religious institutions. In general, the priestly function tends to buttress prevalent cultural values and the return of the prodigal is as much a return to cultural conformity as to a state of grace. Both medicine and religion "understand" deviance, but in neither sphere is comprehension necessarily forgiveness. Rather, the protected atmosphere and avuncular tone are directed to the acceptance of the sinner in his sin or the patient in his illness only as a first step toward rehabilitation. Patient and supplicant withdraw temporarily from worldly affairs only as a prelude to a fit return.

Although the economics of health care is a highly complex and controversial field,[6] there are some features of the patient-practitioner relationship which are directly tied to its nature as a market transaction. The fact that the practitioner must be in some way compensated for his efforts—and compensation itself is not at all unique to the American system—leads us directly to the mutuality of the relationship. Medical relationships represent a double exchange. There is first the reciprocity of emotion and intellect centered on the illness itself; in this the patient's gains are apparent, but the physician too receives the rewards of interpersonal responsiveness and of intrinsic pleasure in problem-solving. Secondly, of course, the physician receives a strictly economic return in kind or in cash. It is clear that this monetary exchange affects the motivations and satisfactions of both

[6] See Chap. 14.

parties; it adds sobriety to the interaction, especially in that the patient sacrifices something of value in return for a hoped-for good. Yet the model of fee-for-service relationship in contemporary American practice seems to imply considerable ambivalence in both roles. In the case of the patient, monetary tribute may preclude the possibility of ever forming a therapuetic relationship, or may sour a once-formed relationship with anxiety and resentment. Bill collection may, to the physician, profane a partly sacred relationship; as a professional the practitioner is ideally supposed to embody the tradition of the gentleman whose first interest is not self-aggrandizement. *Noblesse oblige*, however, requires a sufficient economic basis for *noblesse*.

The therapeutic subsystem is by definition a temporary arrangement, but one whose termination is problematic rather than fixed. In the simplest case of minor physical injury, consensus about breaking off the relationship may be relatively easy to reach; the suitable end is the point at which symptoms are relieved and/or bodily functioning is restored. Most chronic diseases, however, and especially the mental illnesses, do not lend themselves to such a ready agreement on the completion of care. The decision itself is not clearly in the province of one party or the other. Probably neither physician nor patient commonly announces the rupture of therapy in explicit terms. Instead, the typical path is more likely to be a form of "withering away" of the therapeutic state as the patient's need becomes less urgent and the practitioner's interest less pronounced. Psychoanalytic therapy raises perhaps the most intriguing questions concerning the death of the relationship: in the voyage of exploration and self-discovery, who is to decide the safe harbor? How is the intimacy of concord which has been fostered in the service of therapy to be dissolved without harm to the patient? Is prolonged dependency a favorable omen for the individual's future as a mature being? Freud, of course, addressed one of his last clinical papers to just these dilemmas [3]. Again, traditional general practice and the panel system current in Britain, as well as some types of group medicine in the United States, pose the issues in somewhat different form. Here the problem is not so much outright termination of the relationship as its maintenance at a lowered threshold of intensity, or better, at variable thresholds, over lengthy time periods.

The Doctor-Patient Relationship in Different Social Settings

As with all dramas, the therapeutic process is influenced by the stage on which it is enacted. There are three primary settings for the doctor-patient relationship and each has its characteristic implications for the relationship. In most of the world at most times, the favored setting has probably been the patient's home; nursed by his family and emotionally supported by the circle of kin, the patient has entertained the healer as an expert consultant whose talents—however great—are seen as supplements to folk therapy, and whose services are often sought only as a last recourse [18, 19]. Yet the home environment is in many ways the most limiting and least advantageous to the physician, for it is a setting controlled by the patient and family. On this home ground the visitor-physician must not only cope with a variety of family members in addition to the patient, but he is in a certain sense always on trial in showing his therapeutic wares to an assembled and highly involved audience. He intrudes on a scene whose management is out of his hands, although his prestige and manipulative skills may enable him to achieve dominance fairly early in the course of therapy. The importance of this type of clinical experience is thought to be so great that family care, involving a long series of home visits, is now being systematically introduced to the medical curriculum. It is possible that the current emphasis on viewing the family group as the locus of illness, and the notion that this group may be most "naturally" observed in the home, will lead to a greater frequency of home therapy in Western scientific medical culture than there has been in recent years. An increasingly strong conviction that the way an individual lives is exceedingly relevant to the way in which he falls ill may reverse the trend of thinking which has held the rigorously ordered hospital environment to be therapeutically ideal [12]. Such a reversal in medical theory has, too, very important implications for the introduction of Western medicine to nonliterate societies in which the patient's home is the accepted setting of healing.

The practitioner's office is in modern Western society the prototypical medical setting.[7] Although expanded use of hospital facilities has meant that for many conditions the doctor's office is the scene of diagnosis rather than therapy, the bulk of patients begins the experience of patienthood here. In chronic diseases, minor ills, and psychotherapy, the office may be the setting for the entire healing process. The physician is more clearly in control here than in any other treatment setting. He determines timing, spatial arrangements, lighting, the inclusion or exclusion of third parties such as nurse or relatives, and so on; it is quite significant that the patient waits for the doctor, since this means the physician has the initiative and can stage the therapeutic process at will. The office is thus the place for supreme exercise of the skills of "impression management," for an elaborate dramaturgy of healing which is beautifully susceptible to Goffman's scheme of interpersonal analysis [10]. The physician can disclose to the patient as much or as little of himself and of medical culture as he chooses; he is free to make a deliberate statement of his own role and its boundaries,

[7] See Chap. 12 for a discussion of arrangements of practice.

as well as to structure rather precisely the content of the patient's role. A seldom-remarked feature of this setting is the opportunity it affords for implicit communication of medical culture. The nurse or receptionist, and the other waiting patients, school the neophyte in proper behavior. Interior decoration casts an aura of professional substance and well-being. The inevitable spate of reading material provides the patient not only with a chance to catch up on past issues of *The Saturday Evening Post* but with a rapid and not at all subtle introduction to medical ideology—notably the official economics of private professional enterprise. For the office is the arena of the doctor as independent entrepreneur, as miraculous healer and rugged businessman coalesced into the very model of twentieth century careerism.

The hospital setting is in some sense neutral ground for physician and patient. Both are "guests" of an institution which has its own organization and its own corporate life. The purity of the patient-practitioner relationship is inevitably adulterated by the presence of a host of ancillary personnel and by the bureaucratic imperatives of a multipurpose organization. For the doctor, the hospital is an environment well attuned to all the technical requisites of medical care; it affords him an ideal therapeutic facility in terms of the scientific armamentarium and the resources of supporting members of the medical team. At the same time, it increasingly requires him to develop a highly specialized bureaucratic role—subject to administrative and collaborative desiderata—which is in certain important respects at variance with the traditional image of the healer as charismatic generalist [32]. One might say that the hospital setting facilitates an extraordinary perfection of the physician's role, but that in so doing it tends to restrict the scope of that role. Here the doctor is one healer among many, and although his prerogatives are great his control is far short of the absolute dominance he can exercise in the office setting. He must cope with the exigencies of large-scale organization, a task for which his clinical experience may have afforded little preparation [2, 30].

The doctor-patient relationship is further colored in the hospital by the enforced passivity of the patient. Their unequal relationship is compounded as the patient loses his clothes and his opportunity for discretionary action, his full personal identity and his grasp of the initiative in interpersonal relations. The patient is subject to the physician's (and the organization's) regimen, and treatment may be enhanced by his entire exposure to therapeutic dicta. On the other hand, he is a stranger and afraid; stripped of the costuming of his normal social roles, having become a full-time patient, he may be less well able to mobilize his own recuperative assets. In some instances doctor and patient may draw closer together under the impress of the hospital environment: the doctor may be the patient's sole anchorage, his one familiar bridge to the world he relinquished when he entered the doors of the hospital. The patient may feel he is in league with the doctor against organizational demands, and may use his relationship to his physician to manipulate other hospital personnel.

Patienthood in the mental hospital, usually much longer in duration than that in the general hospital, poses special problems for the doctor-patient relationship. Perhaps the most salient of these is the fact that a long stay allows the generation of several informal social systems which compete with, and complicate, the therapeutic dyad. Although the philosophy of the "therapeutic community" explicitly recognizes this, and is designed to take advantage of the total system as a healing agent, there is no doubt that the existence of the "other twenty-three hours" drastically alters the one-to-one tie between practitioner and patient. The company of patients is probably the chief difference between the two kinds of hospital settings; mental patients can and do form a community of the ill, while the general hospital does not as a rule provide either the time or the motivation for such a growth [3, 30].

The Future of the Relationship

This discussion has systematically distorted the nature of contemporary medical practice by its enforced concentration on a single model of doctor-patient relations. It has focused on the therapeutic pairing which consists of the independent medical professional *vis-à-vis* one patient, whether it be in the context of general medicine or of psychotherapy. There are today many other models in effect, and one may discern a variety of future alternatives.

The most pronounced shift in the traditional Western therapeutic dyad is probably a departure from the dyad itself. Increasingly the patient is involved not in an isolated two-person social system, but in a medical team effort in which the physician is first among equals rather than unique healer. A paramount issue of the future may be the redefinition of the doctor's role as a collaborative one, and the patterning of team medicine for maximum therapeutic efficacy. The future of medical practice will probably rest on a detailed meshing of medicine, nursing, social work, administration, perhaps even social science [25].

Complementing the apparent break-up of the exclusive one-to-one relationship from the practitioner's side, there is a growing disposition to involve other family members and significant figures in the patient's life space. Although this disposition is of course most obvious in psychotherapy, following the lead of child-guidance clinics which treat families rather than disturbed children, it is also relevant to general practice.

Balint [1], Galdston [9], Halliday [13], and others are now beginning to discern a model of social medicine in which the practitioner, with the help of auxiliary specialists, will try to unite psychological, social, and biological orientations in therapy. They envision a patient-practitioner relationship which will monitor the patient's ill and healthy life course, rather than limiting itself to the treatment of specific disease entities.

References

1. Balint, Michael, *The Doctor, His Patient and The Illness.* New York: International Universities Press, Inc., 1957.
2. Burling, Temple, Edith M. Lentz, and Robert N. Wilson, *The Give and Take in Hospitals.* New York: G. P. Putnam's Sons, 1956.
3. Caudill, William, *The Psychiatric Hospital as a Small Society.* Cambridge, Mass.: Harvard University Press, 1958.
4. Clausen, J. A. and M. R. Yarrow, eds., "The Impact of Mental Illness on the Family," *Journal of Social Issues,* II (1955).
5. Deasy, L. C., "Socio-Economic Status and Participation in the Poliomyelitis Vaccine Trial," *American Sociological Review,* 21 (1956), 185–91.
6. Freud, Sigmund, "Observations on Transference—Love" (*Further Recommendations on the Technique of Psychoanalysis,* III), *in* James Strachey, ed., *The Complete Psychological Works of Sigmund Freud.* Vol. XII. London: The Hogarth Press, Ltd., 1958. See especially pp. 165–66.
7. ———, "The Dynamics of Transference," *in* James Strachey, ed., *The Complete Psychological Works of Sigmund Freud.* Vol. XII. London: The Hogarth Press, Ltd., 1958, p. 105.
8. ———, "Analysis Terminable and Interminable," *International Journal of Psychoanalysis,* 18 (1937).
9. Galdston, Iago, *The Meaning of Social Medicine.* Cambridge, Mass.: Harvard University Press, 1957.
10. Goffman, Erving, *The Presentation of Self in Everyday Life.* Edinburgh: University of Edinburgh Social Science Research Centre, 1958.
11. ———, "The Moral Career of the Mental Patient," *Psychiatry,* 22 (1959).
12. Goss, M., "Change in the Cornell Comprehensive Care and Teaching Program," *in* Robert K. Merton, George B. Reader, and Patricia L. Kendall, eds., *The Student-Physician.* Cambridge: Harvard University Press, 1957.
13. Halliday, James L., *Psychosocial Medicine.* New York: W. W. Norton & Company, Inc., 1948.
14. Henderson, L. J., "Physician and Patient as a Social System," *New England Journal of Medicine,* 212 (May 2, 1935), 318–23.
15. Hollingshead, August B. and Frederick C. Redlich, *Social Class and Mental Illness.* New York: John Wiley & Sons, Inc., 1958.
16. Koos, Earl L., *The Health of Regionville.* New York: Columbia University Press, 1954.
17. Kutner, B. and G. Gordon, "Seeking Care for Cancer," *Journal of Health and Human Behavior,* 2 (1961).
18. Leighton, Alexander H. and Dorothea C. Leighton, *The Navaho Door.* Cambridge, Mass.: Harvard University Press, 1944.

19. Leighton, Alexander H., "Gregorio, the Hand-Trembler: A Psychobiological Personality Study of a Navaho Indian," *Papers of the Peabody Museum of American Archeology and Ethnology*, Harvard University, 40 (1949).
20. Lennard, Henry L., Arnold Bernstein, Erdman B. Palmore, and Helen C. Hendin, *The Anatomy of Psychotherapy*. New York: Columbia University Press, 1960.
21. Marti-Ibanez, Felix, ed., *Henry E. Sigerist on the History of Medicine*. New York: M.D. Publications, Inc., 1960, p. 26.
22. Parsons, Talcott, *The Social System*. New York: The Free Press of Glencoe, Inc., 1951, pp. 428–73.
23. ——— and R. Fox, "Illness, Therapy, and the Modern Urban Family," *Journal of Social Issues*, 8 (1952), 31–44.
24. Paul, Benjamin D., ed., *Health, Culture and Community*. New York: Russell Sage Foundation, 1955.
25. Pollak, Otto, *Integrating Sociological and Psychoanalytic Concepts*. New York: Russell Sage Foundation, 1956.
26. Redlich, F. C., "The Concept of Health in Psychiatry," *in* Alexander H. Leighton, John A. Clausen, and Robert N. Wilson, eds., *Explorations in Social Psychiatry*. New York: Basic Books, Inc., 1957.
27. Samora, J., L. Saunders, and R. Larson, "Medical Vocabulary Knowledge among Hospital Patients," *Journal of Health and Human Behavior*, 2 (1961).
28. Saunders, Lyle, *Cultural Differences and Medical Care*. New York: Russell Sage Foundation, 1954, p. 8.
29. Smith, H., "Two Lines of Authority Are One Too Many," *Modern Hospital*, 85 (1955), 48–52.
30. Stanton, Alfred H. and Morris S. Schwartz, *The Mental Hospital*. New York: Basic Books, Inc., 1954.
31. Wilson, Robert N., "The Physician's Changing Hospital Role," *Human Organization*, 18 (1959–60), 177–83.
32. ———, "Teamwork in the Operating Room," *Human Organization*, 12 (1954), 9–14.

Part III

SOCIOLOGY OF MEDICAL CARE

12

THE ORGANIZATION OF MEDICAL PRACTICE

Eliot Freidson

Medicine is practiced in privacy. In the other established professions, work goes on in the publicity of the court, the church, and the lecture hall as often as in the office; the work of the doctor is characteristically conducted in the consulting room or the bedchamber. Furthermore, the physician usually renders personal services to individuals, rather than to congregations or classes. Perhaps because of these characteristics medicine is more likely than other established professions to be seen as a simple practitioner-client relationship.[1] But it is much more than

[1] For an extensive treatment of the doctor-patient relationship, see Chap. 11.

that: medicine is practiced in an organized framework which influences both doctor and patient. Indeed, at present in the United States, the framework of practice seems to be moving toward more elaborate forms which may be expected to change the doctor-patient relationship.

The Consolidation of Professional Authority

Only recently has the physician had widespread professional authority. Until the nineteenth century, he had too little sure knowledge and technique to sustain the authority he sought. As L. J. Henderson put it, it was not until about the year 1910 or 1912 in the United States that a random patient with a random disease consulting a doctor chosen at random stood better than a 50–50 chance of benefiting from the encounter. Certainly until the latter half of the nineteenth century, the physician was used by a rather small proportion of the population, and in the United States he was fighting—often unsuccessfully—for licensing laws [49].

Generally speaking, the physician had neither *de jura* nor *de facto* control over the practice of healing: even his "science" was unpopular, as the various healing movements and the thriving patent medicine business of the century will testify. Without a truly scientific foundation and without basic standards in the training of physicians, how could medicine justify its desire for occupational monopoly and lay submission? Certainly not by success, nor by ethics, nor by reference to superior education. In prosecuting Jacoba Felicia de Almania, the medical faculty of the University of Paris had to content itself with the claim—which now appears ludicrous—that she should not practice because she was not instructed in medieval theory. She never made promises, she asked for a fee only in the event of success, she cured cases which physicians could not, but she was too "ignorant" to practice [31].

By the end of the nineteenth century, however, the physician's monopoly over healing was fairly well established. Unlike the lawyer and clergyman [27], he was rising in public esteem. By the time medical education in the United States was reformed, the physician was in the virtually unprecedented position of being the symbol of healing to people in all the social classes. While a few early medical specialties were in direct competition with folk specialties, the general medical practitioner acquired wholesale the clientele of a variety of folk specialists. The nostalgic and sentimental image of the old-fashioned family doctor who was all things to all men is based upon the fleeting period in history when folk practice had declined but medical specialization was still in an incipient stage.

The Fragmentation of Medical Responsibility

During earlier times, the physician could learn most of what he needed to know during his training period: if he was wise and creative, he could temper his sparse formal education by continually reflecting on his experience with past cases. Furthermore, significant advances in medical knowledge subsequent to formal training were few. Equipped with a small shelf of basic technical books, the early physician could conceivably work in total isolation as efficiently as the knowledge of his age would permit, occasionally watching the work of an itinerant surgeon or dentist, or glancing through one of the few medical journals of the time. By and large, he could handle as well as the next man any ailment that presented itself to him. By the time the general practitioner had reached his peak of authority in the public eye, the development of medical science had led to the training of specialized men who seized fragments of his domain. Specialization as such was hardly new. The Hippocratic oath itself implied a specialty involving lithotomy (or, as Nittis argued [38], castrating slaves for the eunuch market). Indeed, in the eighteenth and nineteenth centuries, there were perhaps as many "specialties" among folk practitioners as now exist among physicians. Witness the specialist bone-setters, blood-stoppers, baruchers, wart-doctors and others cited by Jones [29]. What was new was the refinement of knowledge and technique underlying specialization, and its growth within the control of a single profession.

In addition to specialists, there arose diagnostic and therapeutic tools which, unlike the instruments in the hallowed black bag, were too expensive for any individual to own and use at his own convenience, and too complex for him to operate even if he could afford them. The hospital came to serve as a locus for such capital equipment, and new specialists like radiologists and pathologists became essential personnel in treatment centers. The physician came to depend upon the hospital and upon the new specialists for access to the new medical technologies.

Clearly, with the rise of modern medicine it became difficult to practice alone and, what is more, positively unrealistic to attempt to handle the whole range of human ills. Over the past 40 years, general practice has declined and practice limited to particular organs, specific illnesses, or special procedures has increased remarkably. In 1923, for example, only 11 per cent of all physicians were engaged in limited practice. By 1957, however, the proportion had risen to 42 per cent [52]. Of the physicians who completed medical school in 1950, only 25 per cent were in general practice a few years after graduation [54].[2]

---

[2] See Chap. 7.

The Growing Problem of Coordination

The displacement of the general practitioner by the specialist renders continuity and comprehensiveness of care difficult, if not impossible. First, members of the same family are less and less likely to be able to go to one physician—for general problems, children go to a pediatrician, and the adults to internists. For anything uncommon, both children and adults go to other specialists. This has led to the fragmentation of the individual patient. When the various parts of the individual have been examined by those with specially competent knowledge of those parts, how are they to be put together again? Without someone with continuing responsibility for the patient through all his consultations with specialists, the parts are unlikely to be put together at all. In many cases there is no doubt that the parts need not be put together, sentimentalists notwithstanding, but in those fairly common disorders which seem beyond the germ theory, it does seem necessary to see and treat the patient as a whole. The idea of comprehensive care expresses the prevailing uneasiness in medical educational and policy circles about the lack of continuous and well-rounded communication between patients and their doctors.

When more than one doctor is handling a case, each must communicate with the other if the case is to be handled efficiently and well. The hospital has become a place where many physicians are brought together around the same bed, and consequently where communication about the patient and coordination of his regimen is facilitated.[3] Conceivably too, the hospital outpatient department may provide a milieu for such communication. But in the United States, the bulk of patient care is provided by medical practice outside the hospital. It is precisely in extra-hospital practice that the greatest problems of coordination and communication seem likely to occur as the general practitioner disappears.

Solo Practice: Myth and Reality

Symbolically, the typical mode of medical practice in the United States is "solo practice." This involves a man working by himself in an office which he secures and equips with his own capital and with patients who have freely chosen him as their personal physician and for whom he assumes responsibility. Stereotypically he lacks any formal connection with colleagues.

The phrase "solo practice" is as often used in an ideological as in a descriptive mode. It is, as Evang put it, a "sacred cow" to the medical

[3] For a more detailed discussion of communication within the hospital, see Chap. 10.

profession in more than one country [14]. The ideological connotation has interesting analytical implications. One of the central themes is independence—the notion of "professional autonomy"—in which a man can do as he pleases. For autonomy to exist, the practitioner must work alone and must have no long-term obligation to his clients: he must be able to sever the relationship to his client at any time and vice versa. In this sense, a fee-for-service rather than a contractual financial arrangement is likely to encourage autonomous practice.

A truly autonomous fee-for-service solo arrangement is inherently unstable, however: it is eventually bound to fall under the control of either patients or colleagues. In a system of free competition the physician may neither count on the loyalty of his patients (with whom he has no contract) nor on that of his colleagues (with whom he has no ties and who are competing with him). Since his colleagues are competitors, he is not likely to solicit their advice or trade information and he certainly will not refer his patients to them for consultations. Under these circumstances, he is quite isolated from his colleagues and relatively free of their control—but at the same time he is very vulnerable to control by his clients. To keep them, he must give them what they want, or someone else will attract them away by doing so. Obviously, conscientious practice under these conditions is difficult and frustrating, as Samuel Sorbière's rather bitter *Advice to a Young Physician* testifies [41]. It is hardly right to describe it as "autonomy" [18].

Simple restriction of competition by banding together against the tyranny of the client choice substitutes the tyranny of colleague choice. Realistically, "total autonomy" can result only under very special circumstances. It is plausible to think that when the supply of physicians is sufficiently restricted to fail to meet demand, control by the client may be avoided. If in addition to a scarcity of physicians and other potential competitors, no large capital is required for initiating a practice, no consultations, and no extra-consulting-room institutions like hospitals are necessary for its pursuit, control by colleagues can be avoided and "total autonomy" approached.

In the United States today, the supply of physicians in many areas is such that client control can be avoided; but, increasingly, colleague control cannot. Dependence on colleagues in one way or another is the rule today in the United States, for consultations, hospitals and capital equipment are essential to modern practice. In short, present practice is not really solo: it embraces a large variety of organized relationships, most of which currently emphasize colleague rather than client controls.

Sources of Cooperative Arrangements among Practitioners

How do cooperative arrangements develop? Let us start with an ostensibly "solo" fee-for-service practice in a situation where the supply of physicians is reasonably restricted. Under such circumstances practice is only partially secure because the continual entrance of younger men into a system which does not include predictable retirement of the older practitioner always presents some threat of competition. In answer to the threat, one keeps his patients to himself, but to do this involves a deadly grind of perpetual availability for service. In order to take an evening or a weekend off or a vacation, in order to be sick, one's practice must be "covered" by colleagues who can be relied on to avoid "stealing" patients. A cooperative arrangement is necessary.

The need for such organization becomes even more pressing when specialization is involved. Patients who must see more than one physician in the normal course of obtaining medical care might become particularly attracted to any one of them. The danger of losing patients by referring them to a young internist seems to have led at least some general practitioners to avoid referring patients at all. In one study of Negro doctors, it was found that some refer patients to white rather than Negro consultants, assuming that the former do not want to keep Negro patients [43]. Effort to prevent referrals is patently unsatisfactory, however, since the conscientious practitioner on one occasion or another knows that his patient needs help he cannot give himself. He can send some, but not all, patients to a clinic or an out-patient department whose staffs presumably will not "steal" them. A rather natural and conventional arrangement is to work out a fairly definite reciprocal arrangement: the general practitioner habitually refers his patients to a limited number of specialists who may be trusted to act "ethically" by eventually returning his patients to him, and who, in turn, will refer patients needing general services to him.

The time has passed in the United States when the general practitioner was in a strong enough position to be the key "feeder" to a network of specialists. As the patient has developed more sophistication and the number of accessible specialists has increased, the patient circumvents the general practitioner and seeks out his own specialists. Indeed, the general practitioner's place is being taken by the internist and the pediatrician, and nonprofessional referrals are the major source of patients in urban settings for the average opthalmologist, otorhinolaryngologist and orthopedist, if not the obstetrician-gynecologist, allergist, and dermatologist.

Since there has ceased to be a single key "feeder" in the division of labor, there is danger of considerable confusion and irregularity in the disposition of the patient. Fairly well-integrated arrangements among physicians become important not only as a way of gaining and regulating access to patients but also as a way of establishing regular channels of communication about the patient and his illness. The "colleague network" described by Hall may be used as the prototype of such an informal but well-integrated arrangement in American solo practice [23, 24, 25]. Indeed, one may suspect this network is a strategic mode of regulating recruitment and access to work in all occupations in which objective criteria are not available to assess performance. Certainly the colleague network is very important in the academic and legal worlds.

The Colleague Network

Hall provides a lucid description of the colleague network:

> In so far as the doctors of a given community are established and possess relatively loyal clienteles, they form a system. This system can effectively exclude the intruding newcomer. On the one hand they have control of the hospital system through occupying the dominant posts therein. On the other they tend to develop, in the course of time, through association, a sort of informal organization. Rights to position, status, power become recognized and upheld; mechanisms of legitimate succession and patterns of recruitment become established.
>
> The provision of medical facilities in a given community, in so far as a system or an order has been established, depends heavily on such an organization. As a matter of fact, the two matters discussed above, *i.e.*, institutions and clienteles, are intimately related to the working of the informal organization. The allocation of positions in the institutions, the pace at which one receives promotions, the extent to which one has patients referred to him, all hinge on the workings of the informal organization. . . .
>
> Sponsorship is not necessarily a one-sided process. It permits the newcomer to share in the established system of practising medicine, but it also imposes responsibilities upon him. It obligates him to fulfill the minor positions in the institutional system. Where he needs expert advice or assistance it obligates him to turn to his sponsor. And if he is designated as successor to an established member of the profession he necessarily takes over the duties and obligations involved there. Hence the protégé is essential to the continued functioning of the established inner fraternity of the profession [23].

The kind of network Hall describes is more likely to exist in localities where there is a variety of hospitals and other medical institutions ordered hierarchically. It is much less likely to be so definite and articulated in small cities where hospitals are virtual open community institutions. And even in large cities, the municipal and proprietary institutions at the bottom of the prestige hierarchy provide fairly free access to physicians irrespective of their location in colleague networks [25, 51]. For this reason we can assume that the sociometric studies of Coleman, Katz and Menzel portray the looser, more common form of colleague network in the United States [7, 8].

Elementary Forms of Cooperative Practice

Because it is entirely informal, the colleague network represents the most elementary type of cooperative practice. But it has sufficient weakness to make it uncomfortably vulnerable to collapse. Under the solo system of practice, patients and hospitals are not always completely monopolized. Often the colleague network cannot completely control the treatment environment and so may lack the reliable patronage necessary to gain the cooperation of hungry young men. Furthermore, the good faith among peers upon which an informal system depends may break down in petty jealousies and antipathies.

The large solo practice in the United States has developed some formal techniques of protecting itself. The successful physician may, as Hall suggested, send his overflow to a young physician in whom he takes an interest but he may and often does avoid sending out any cases at all by hiring the younger man to work in his office, handle the routine cases and make the grueling house and emergency calls. This lightens his burden while it reduces the danger of permanently losing patients. The employer-physician's position is particularly strong when the man he hires is not fully qualified to practice on his own (as is the case with some English medical assistants) or when it is very expensive or otherwise difficult to set up a practice (as is the case where practices must be bought or where competition is severe).

When the junior is in a position to break away and be a competitor, however, the hiring physician is very vulnerable. Each young man he introduces to his patients may leave and take some of those patients with him. One way to prevent that is to draw up a legal document whereby the younger man agrees not to set up an independent practice in the same community. Another way, which by no means rules out the first, is to take the young man into partnership, sharing expenses and profits according to some prearranged schedule, and thereby giving him a direct stake in the maintenance and growth of the practice.

The most common type of formal cooperative arrangement among peers is not the partnership, but what might be called the association—an arrangement whereby physicians have their own patients from whom they collect their own fees, but share the expense of maintaining such common facilities as offices, equipment, assisting personnel, and the like. In addition, it is possible that when one physician is away the other will cover him by seeing his patients in his absence. In one form or another, this rudimentary type of formal cooperation is very widespread in the United States, particularly in city "professional buildings" with fairly elaborate suites and in "medical centers" owned by the resident physicians.

From the association it is a short though by no means simple step to the small legal partnership—sharing profits from fees as well as overhead expenses. The division of pooled fees is likely to be a constant bone of contention, however, since the practices of the partners, though overlapping, are not identical. This is particularly the case when specialties are involved, for one specialist may feel he brings in more money than the other and so deserves a larger proportion of the profits.

If those problems can be overcome, however, the partnership is more reliable and more calculable than simpler forms of cooperation. In the colleague network doctors can arrange trustworthy coverage for each other so as to be able to enjoy leisure hours in spite of unpredictable patient demand. In the simple association this virtue is carried over, but the sharing of overhead costs reduces the ordinary expenses of practice per person and makes it possible to have more laboratory and diagnostic equipment. The partnership adds to these virtues increased long-term financial security. Where practitioners of different ages are involved, the younger man may see more patients at a time when otherwise he would have few, and considerable income at a time when he could expect little. The older man may have a higher income at a time when patients would be retiring him or when he himself would be forced by his decreasing energy to relinquish patients. Moreover, where more than one specialty is involved, each can function as a referring agent to the other, with mutual advantage: the dubious ethics of fee-splitting, often functional in informal cooperative forms, becomes regularized in the partnership without raising an ethical problem. It not only constitutes some protection against the competition of practitioners outside the cooperative arrangement, but also creates a situation where communication among practitioners about the patient is facilitated.

Bureaucratic Practice

One requirement common to all these forms of cooperation is access to a fairly large number of patients. Cooperative practice is comparatively large-scale in character, and involves the ordering of expenses, referrals, consultations and—in the case of partnerships—profits, into a system which meets the needs of a larger number of people than one man alone can handle. The more formal the arrangement, the more systematized and rational it becomes. At a certain point in the expansion of scale, however, a qualitative change in the form of cooperative practice occurs. It is this point where "group practice" occurs.

"Group practice" is very often used to designate a form of association that goes beyond the scope connoted by the two-man partnership, but definitions have not been very helpful in delineating such difference. The value of the term, like that of "solo practice," is limited by its ideological overtones. Rather than autonomy and independence, it is "groupness" and interdependence which are emphasized. But if "medical group practice is a formal association of three or more physicians providing services in more than one medical field or specialty, with income from medical practice pooled and redistributed to the members according to some prearranged plan" [28], it is hard to see how it differs from the partnership except as such partnership does not involve more than one specialty. The difference between a two- and a three-man partnership does not seem significant. Since 57 per cent of the medical groups recently surveyed by Pomrinse and Goldstein had only three to five full-time physicians, obviously a large proportion of what are called "medical groups" are on the surface insignificantly different from partnerships [42].

If numbers are to be used to define group practice, Jordan's suggestion of the minimum number of five full-time physicians seems reasonable [30]. Five full-time physicians—not all of them giving day-to-day routine medical care—can serve an ordinary population of anywhere from 5,000–20,000, depending on the proportion of general practitioners, internists, and pediatricians, the financial arrangements with patients and the general style of practice. As the number of patients and doctors increases further, it seems likely that, modified somewhat by the strength of the doctor's bargaining position, some of the technical characteristics of bureaucracy will emerge: hierarchical organization, extensive division of labor, systematic rules and procedures, and the like.

The Third Party

Large-scale, bureaucratic practice is not widespread in the United States, but it is becoming more common [42] and its potential impact is great. It has been growing out of two quite different sources. One is the traditional entrepreneurial basis of professional practice: like a successful business, the successful practice may expand by hiring or by taking into partnership many other practitioners. Some of the most famous clinics in the United States grew this way. The other source is the increasingly important role being played by agencies which assume responsibility for the welfare of a population. This is the so-called third party. Some agencies have organized and staffed large-scale bureaucratic practices to serve a particular clientele. Others have provided, in the form of health insurance, the large-scale financing which makes entrepreneurial bureaucratic practice practical.[4]

On occasion in the past, governments have sought to provide medical care for their citizens, as have employers for their employees and con-

[4] For a more detailed discussion of utilization of health services, see Chap. 14.

sumer groups for their members [11, 45, 50]. In some instances, the doctor contracted to provide care to a population for a flat salary. In other instances, he was paid a retainer by a city in order that he would stay in the locality and make himself available, free nonetheless to charge each patient a fee. Many physicians in rural, "underdoctored" areas in the United States are in a position similar to that of the "public physician" of ancient Greece [5]—attracted to a town by its promises of guaranteed income, housing, and well-equipped medical facilities.

Recent developments in third party care in the United States represent an enormous increase in scale and scope. The rise of the centralized nation-state committed to a modicum of welfare service for its citizens and empowered to mobilize physicians for the public good is of patent significance, though as yet less in the United States than in Europe. In the United States much the same role is being performed by the giant corporations, insurance companies, and trade unions which, though lacking political power to mobilize physicians, nonetheless possess sufficient economic power to negotiate the terms of the practice of medicine. Even the voluntary hospital seems to be becoming something of a third party, mediating between the lay community supporting it and the physicians who depend upon it.

There are two ways in which the role of the third party is important. First, the third party might be seen as a force which offsets an imbalance. As has been noted, with the development of the modern medical profession has come greater control of the practitioner by colleagues than by clients. The third party at its best has the client's welfare in mind and, unlike the client himself, also has available expert guidance in determining a policy which advances the health of community members. Thus, it can be better equipped than individual clients ever could be to counterbalance the material interests of the practitioner without detracting from the scientific quality of practice. The problem is, does it work out that way? This problem leads to the second point of third party significance: its influence over the nature of medical practice [16].

A third party can simply arrange some scheme for paying the doctor for his services, or—less commonly—can go so far as to set up medical practice units of its own. The arrangement which has the least influence on the organization of practice continues the fee-for-service tradition: the doctor claims from the third party a standard fee for each service he renders a client. Obviously, all that is added to practice is some paperwork and a somewhat less flexible fee schedule than ordinarily. But while the fee-for-service method is desirable to the physician, it has not been considered desirable administratively: it is too "open-ended" and too difficult to supervise [2, 9]. More acceptable, administratively, is paying the physician a given sum for each patient to whom he renders services over a period of time (a capitation system) or putting the physician on salary. In short, a method of easily predictable payment, subject to little fluctuation except by negotiation, is most desirable to the third party. Even in the United States the number of salaried practitioners and practitioners paid on a capitation basis seems to be growing [11, 52];[5] beyond that, the increasingly large role of the third party seems likely to introduce an element of greater economic regularity into the foundation of practice. The net effect, varying with the precise role of the third party, seems to be that much of the physician's traditional entrepreneurial freedom is being lost.

The scanty evidence that exists suggests that a restriction on the physician's entrepreneurial freedom does not necessarily impinge upon his freedom of judgment. Certainly in England, where the government pays capitation fees to most general practitioners, few physicians feel any particular loss of freedom to diagnose and prescribe as they see fit [13, 53]. And in the Soviet Union, where medical practice units are organized as well as financed by the State, it does not appear that physicians feel particularly oppressed even though, as Field observed, government manpower policies can sometimes influence the physician's behavior when he is confronted by a request to grant sick leave to an industrial worker [15]. On the whole, there seems to be no imperative reason why the mere existence of a third party need influence diagnosis, prescription, or therapy in medical practice. Indeed, it has been argued that the existence of a responsible third party allows the physician to devote himself wholly to his art, without having to preoccupy himself with business.

The Different Forms of Practice

Thus far we have sketched a number of forms of practice and some of their functional characteristics. The variety may be seen to distribute itself between two logically but not numerically important extremes. At one end there is a rarity, true solo practice. Empirically, it is unstable, merging into more common, loose forms of informal cooperation with colleagues. The colleague network represents a tighter but still informal type of cooperative practice. The "association" represents a simple variety of formal cooperation, while the small partnership and then the group practice are tighter and more complex forms. Finally, there is the tightest and most formal variety of practice, which may be called organizational or bureaucratic. We can divide all these types of practice into two groups, and roughly parallel the common-sense distinction between solo and group practice. The former

[5] Weiskotten's survey of the medical class of 1950 obtained evidence contradicting the common belief that there is a trend toward salaried practice in the United States [54]. When the graduating class of 1960 is surveyed, the existence of a trend can be more accurately determined.

includes true solo and all types of informally cooperative practice; the latter includes, from the "association" on, all types of formally cooperative practice. Using this simple distinction, we may make the comparisons which are perhaps most important for social policy.

Form of Practice and the Quality of Care

The foremost policy question about such a pursuit as medical practice is its technical consequences—the quality of service it provides. It is, unfortunately, the question about which there is least information. The opinion is fairly widespread that a physician cannot practice the best possible medicine without easy access to modern diagnostic and therapeutic facilities. In this sense, it is reasonable to assume that the solo practitioner who lacks access to such facilities is least likely to do the best for his patient. Formal cooperative arrangements, whether simple or complex, are more likely to provide the capital to buy an extensive amount of equipment.

Furthermore, the isolation of the practicing physician from his colleagues is believed to be a significant element in the quality of care. It is presently believed that a physician must continually keep abreast of advances in scientific knowledge, relying less on the questionable but ubiquitous "education" of drug manufacturers and their representatives [36] and more upon the "education" of colleagues and colleague associations.[6] As we have seen, solo practice as such cannot readily be classified as more or less isolated. A considerable degree of informal but nonetheless real and important interaction can take place among loose networks of practitioners. Much of it, as Peterson observed, is bound to be about fishing, bridge and golf, but some is certainly about medicine [40]. But the fact that isolation in solo practice is *possible* marks it off from "group practice," whether a small partnership or a large-scale medical group. In this sense, group more than solo practice contains within it conditions that may encourage a quality of care. Indeed, Peterson reported a tendency for those in group practice to give a higher quality of care than those working alone [40].

In addition, care by a variety of specialists is held to be necessary these days. While solo practice does not preclude the use of specialists, group practice facilitates frequent consultation and exchange of professional information. Where a number of physicians of varied specialties work together within the same organization, it is not only easier to refer patients, but also to communicate and coordinate information about them. Coleman, Katz, and Menzel have demonstrated the importance of colleague relations to one facet of care—prescribing drugs [7]. Thus, it is to be ex-

---

[6] See Chap. 7.

pected that in group practice the fragmentation of care following upon specialization can be compensated for and that so-called comprehensive care is more likely to ensue.

Finally, there is the element of supervision, the quality of which Seeman and Evans have shown influences medical performance [46, 47]. The most reputable medical institutions—*e.g.*, medical school clinics and teaching hospitals—are characterized by doctors working in close association with each other and by fairly systematic supervision of work by chiefs of service, tissue committees, and the like. Except in a purely educational context, where it is ideologically acceptable, the nature of supervision in such medical bureaucracies has received little attention, but it is indubitable that at least some formal administrative supervision almost always exists [21]. Furthermore, the cultivation of a medical records system and the continuous accumulation of information in records is in itself supervisory, for while the records may not be subject to routine inspection, they may always be examined if some doubt arises about a physician's work. If, as Peterson assumes, systematic and complete records are an important element of competent medical care, bureaucratic practices—which are far more likely to encourage record keeping—can to this extent provide a higher quality of care.

In theory, then, formal and cooperative rather than informal arrangements are more likely to provide good medical care. However, there are only scattered bits of evidence to support this theory. A reflection on the system of solo practice predominant in the United States might be noted in the finding that somewhat less than half of all surgical in-hospital procedures performed in the nation during 1957–58 were by men certified to practice surgery [26], but this is not direct evidence that the quality of care in group practice is higher. Comparative studies are necessary.

One of the rare comparative studies in this area was made by the Health Insurance Plan of Greater New York, in which the hospitalization and perinatal mortality of a population served by medical groups under contract with the insurance plan compared favorably with that of the New York City population [10, 48]. That study, however, was concerned with an additional element in the arrangement of medical care—the prepaid service contract. It is believed that when people can be insured so that no financial barrier stands between them and medical care, they will not hesitate to use services and so can obtain the care they need early in the course of illness, thus preventing complications. Consequently, a comprehensive prepaid service contract is believed to be—of itself—conducive to better medical care. With insurance and organization variables undifferentiated, the influence of either on quality of care is difficult to establish.

The same difficulty holds when the mode of compensating the physician is undifferentiated from organization. A study by Densen and his associates compared the hospital utilization of members of a single union who were under two different medical insurance plans—one involving medical group practice compensated on a per capita basis, and the other solo fee-for-service practice [12]. Hospital utilization in the former proved to be lower, even though the comprehensiveness of insurance was much the same. But it is difficult to tell whether the lower utilization resulted from group practice, as such, or from the fact that the group plan provided no additional compensation to the group physician for in-hospital surgery. Clearly, present evidence is inadequate.

Form of Practice and Patient Satisfaction

Whether or not people are deeply involved emotionally with their doctors, they must in any case be sufficiently happy with the care they receive to use physicians. Patient satisfaction assumes additional importance when medicine becomes a political issue. In a number of national sample surveys in the United States, most people have expressed general satisfaction with medical services which typically are organized on only a loosely cooperative fee-for-service basis: and the solo general practitioner is part of the national folklore. In spite of this, fairly large proportions of the population cite grounds for dissatisfaction. They complain that doctors keep them waiting too long, are difficult to reach on nights and weekends, and don't give enough time to them. Koos' studies report the largest proportions of dissatisfaction, while the Gaffin study showed that people are less likely to complain about their own doctors than about doctors in general [19, 32, 33].

This material, however, like the data on in-hospital surgery, bears on solo practice only insofar as it is the most common and most characteristic form in the United States. Again, comparative studies provide the most useful evidence. Anderson and Sheatsley compared two groups of socioeconomically equivalent insured patients, one being served by solo physicians compensated by an insurance organization on a fee-for-service basis, the other by physicians in medical groups, paid on a per capita basis [1]. The finding was that the solo fee-for-service program elicited more patient satisfaction than did the capitation group practice. Patients of the latter were prone to complain of lack of personal interest, insufficient explanation of their condition by the doctor, waiting in the office, and difficulty in getting house calls. In Freidson's study, where patients contrasted their experience with these two types of practice, there was also a tendency to feel that sense of "personal interest" was more likely to be obtained in solo fee-for-service practice than in capitation group practice. But there was some feeling that medical care of a technically higher quality could be obtained from the medical group [18]. In both studies, however, solo fee-for-service practice is compared to capitation group practice, and no way is provided to control the financial variable and compare forms of practice as such.

Plainly, the material on patient satisfaction is equivocal, but none contradicts the idea that emotional satisfaction on the part of the patient seems more likely to be gained from a physician who is in a position to be more immediately responsive to the patient than are group physicians who have obligations to a work organization [18]. The English population seems as satisfied with its solo capitation practice as is the American with its solo fee-for-service practice; it seems that the arrangement of payment is less important than the organization of work [17].

Form of Practice and Job Satisfaction of Physicians

Physician satisfaction too may be more influenced by the arrangement of work than by the arrangement of payment. In assessing job satisfaction, however, we must first recognize that it is much easier for the physician to "freelance" than for the professor or the minister, both of whom require congregations rather than an assortment of successive individuals, and neither of whom can count on the fairly strong motivation provided by illness. This alone means that even in an environment where the state sets the terms of work for the average practitioner (*e.g.*, Britain, the Soviet Union), it is possible for the physician to be able to stay outside the scheme if he wishes. In this sense, a physician in any organized scheme of practice always has an alternative.

It may be noted furthermore that job satisfaction is inevitably a function of the career alternatives which exist at any particular time, and the symbolic and material rewards of these alternatives. In the United States today, for example, the symbolically valued form among physicians is the successful solo fee-for-service specialty practice. The general practitioner may genuinely enjoy the procession of minor cases (called "garbage" by specialists), the laying-on of hands and the genial calls at humble homes—the human rather than the scientific side of medicine [6]. But in depressed moments, he may realize that he is not a social success because he is not a "scientific" specialist with limited practice and prominent clients. Thus environment must be considered a partial influence on satisfaction, both in the way it defines any form of practice and in the way it offers alternative possibilities [35].

No matter what the tyranny of the patient, solo practice has the quality of potentially complete autonomy. The physician working in the privacy of his own consulting-room can examine, diagnose, prescribe, and treat as he sees fit. There is no one to soften patient pressure to honor lay prejudices, of course, and when practice is insecure it is likely that the doctor will feel obliged to do what he does not really want to do, but theoretically, the solo physician may dismiss his patient rather than give in to him. Autonomy perhaps more extensive than in any other profession thus exists, at least *in potentia,* in solo practice [14]. This is what was stressed by medical students in response to survey questions on why they would reject salaried positions in organizations [4].

In contrast to this apparently gratifying side of solo entrepreneurial practice are a number of potential handicaps—isolation from one's colleagues and their information and support, the necessity to be preoccupied daily with the financial basis of practice, the leanness of early and late stages of the career and chiefly, the difficulty of controlling and regularizing work hours. These are the very things which are said to be solved by group practice—indeed, medical students who preferred salaried positions stressed opportunities to work in close association with colleagues, to obtain a regular income, and to work regular hours [4].

On the whole, one should expect that a doctor-owned, fee-for-service partnership or group practice would provide most of the gratifications of both and fewest of the deficiencies of the two extremes—solo practice and bureaucratic practice. It seems to allow the greatest amount of room for self-determination without in turn sacrificing the major virtues of cooperative practice. It is a very popular form in the Midwest and Southwest of the United States [42]. The 1956 survey of a "cross-section of American male students in all four years of the entire group of approved medical schools in the United States" by Cahalan and his associates reported that of those who preferred a nonsalaried form of practice, only 26 per cent preferred solo practice to group practice, partnership, or some other form of formally cooperative practice [4]. Since more freshmen than seniors preferred solo practice, we can assume that interest in cooperative forms increases as the medical student comes closer to being a physician. However, students who preferred group practice were less likely to expect their preference would be realized than were students preferring the solo form. Testimony to the realism of their expectation is provided by Weiskotten's finding that 64 per cent of those in the class of 1950 engaged in private practice were practicing alone [54].

Research Needs

Systematic and reliable information about medical practice in the United States is incredibly scanty: the extraordinary bulk of published material is composed almost entirely of special pleading or unsystematic individual impression; the only reliable body of extensive information bears on the financing, distribution, and utilization of health services. From any point of view two research tasks as yet unperformed are fundamental—

study of the polar extremes of purely solo practice and bureaucratic practice. The former is important both for its persistence and its symbolism, the latter for its reputed but as yet undemonstrated potentialities.

Sociologically, solo practice represents a very peculiar way of organizing skilled work. It is based on the almost ludicrous assumption that a long period of professional training develops such stable professional values in the physician that his work—entirely escaping observation by colleagues—will be performed adequately even under the most harrowing or tempting circumstances [37]. Structurally, it is on the surface a one-man "organization": it is more accurately a case in which one man forms the focus for an "organization" composed of himself and prospective clients, an "organization" whose boundaries blur as they merge into the surrounding community. As modern organizations go, solo practice is a primordial form which, in spite of the community of professional identity presumed to fortify it [20], grows by becoming part of the lay environment. Careful and systematic examination of the way in which the true solo practitioner captures and organizes segments of the environment—and is in turn captured and organized by it—would be valuable indeed.

Ideologically, solo practice implies full professional autonomy; bureaucratic practice limits autonomy [3]. Indeed, bureaucracy, with its essential reliance on the authority of office, seems to contradict the idea of the "authority" of knowledge [21, 22, 39]. The physician, with his high social status, his strong subjective sense of importance, and the immediate fateful consequences and the privacy of his daily work seems better able to resist bureaucratic authority than any of the other professionals. Consequently, careful study of bureaucratic practice should shed much light on the varieties of influence and authority which can exist in a bureaucratic organization and can demonstrate some of the limits of professional freedom in a bureaucratic setting.

References

1. Anderson, Odin W. and Paul B. Sheatsley, "Comprehensive Medical Insurance," *Health Information Foundation Research Series,* 9 (1959).
2. Armstrong, Barbara N., *The Health Insurance Doctor, His Role in Great Britain, Denmark and France.* Princeton, N.J.: Princeton University Press, 1939.
3. Ben-David, Joseph, "The Professional Role of the Physician in Bureaucratized Medicine: A Study in Role Conflict," *Human Relations,* 11 (1958), 255–74.
4. Cahalan, Don, Patricia Collette, and Norman Hilmar, "Career Interest and Expectations of U.S. Medical Students," *Journal of Medical Education,* 32 (August, 1957), 557–63.
5. Cohn-Haft, Louis, *The Public Physician of Ancient Greece.* (Smith College Studies in History, 42.) Northampton, Mass.: Smith College, 1956.

6. Coker, Robert E., Norman Miller, Kurt W. Back, and Thomas Donnelly, "The Medical Student, Specialization and General Practice," *The North Carolina Medical Journal,* 21 (March, 1960), 96–101.
7. Coleman, James, Elihu Katz, and Herbert Menzel, "The Diffusion of an Innovation among Physicians," *Sociometry,* 20 (December, 1957), 253–70.
8. ———, "Social Processes in Physicians' Adoption of a New Drug," *Journal of Chronic Diseases,* 9 (January, 1959), 1–19.
9. Colling, Joseph, "General Practice in England Today," *The Lancet,* 258 (March 25, 1950), 525–602.
10. Committee for the Special Research Project in H.I.P., *Health and Medical Care in New York City.* Cambridge: Harvard University Press, 1957.
11. Davis, Michael M., *Medical Care for Tomorrow.* New York: Harper & Row, Publishers, 1955.
12. Densen, Paul M., Ellen W. Jones, Eve Balamuth, and Sam Shapiro, "Prepaid Medical Care and Hospital Utilization in a Dual Choice Situation," *American Journal of Public Health,* 50 (November, 1960), 1710–26.
13. Eckstein, Harry, *The English Health Service.* Cambridge: Harvard University Press, 1958.
14. Evang, Karl, *Health Service, Society and Medicine.* London: Oxford University Press, 1960.
15. Field, Mark G., *Doctor and Patient in Soviet Russia.* Cambridge: Harvard University Press, 1957.
16. ———, "The Doctor-Patient Relationship in the Perspective of 'Fee-for-Service' and 'Third Party' Medicine," *Journal of Health and Human Behavior,* 2 (Winter, 1961), 252–62.
17. Fox, T. F., "The Personal Doctor and His Relation to the Hospital," *The Lancet,* 268 (April 2, 1960), 743–60.
18. Freidson, Eliot, *Patients' Views of Medical Practice.* New York: Russell Sage Foundation, 1961.
19. Ben Gaffin Associates, "What Americans Think of the Medical Profession," American Medical Association brochure, n.d.
20. Goode, William J., "Community Within a Community: The Professions," *American Sociological Review,* 22 (April, 1957), 194–200.
21. Goss, Mary E. W., "Influence and Authority among Physicians in an Outpatient Clinic," *American Sociological Review,* 26 (February, 1961), 39–50.
22. Gouldner, Alvin W., "Organizational Analysis," *in* Robert K. Merton, Leonard Broom, and Leonard S. Cottrell, Jr., eds., *Sociology Today.* New York: Basic Books, Inc., 1959, pp. 400–28.
23. Hall, Oswald, "The Informal Organization of the Medical Profession," *Canadian Journal of Economics and Political Science,* 12 (February, 1946), 30–41.
24. ———, "The Stages of the Medical Career," *American Journal of Sociology,* 53 (March, 1948), 327–36.
25. ———, "Types of Medical Careers," *American Journal of Sociology,* 55 (November, 1949), 243–53.

26. Health Information Foundation, "Physicians Who Perform Surgery," *Progress in Health Services*, 10 (June, 1961).

27. Hofstadter, Richard, *The Age of Reform*. New York: Alfred A. Knopf, Inc., 1955.

28. Hunt, G. Halsey and Marcus S. Goldstein, *Medical Group Practice in the United States*, Public Health Service Publication No. 17. Washington, D.C.: Government Printing Office, 1951.

29. Jones, Louis C., "Practitioners of Folk Medicine," *Bulletin of the History of Medicine*, 23 (September–October, 1949), 480–93.

30. Jordan, Edwin P., ed., *The Physician and Group Practice*. Chicago: Year Book Publishers, Inc., 1958.

31. Kibre, Pearl, "The Faculty of Medicine at Paris, Charlatanism, and Unlicensed Medical Practices in the Later Middle Ages," *Bulletin of the History of Medicine*, 27 (January–February, 1953), 1–20.

32. Koos, Earl Lomon, *The Health of Regionville*. New York: Columbia University Press, 1954.

33. ———, "Metropolis—What City People Think of their Medical Services," *American Journal of Public Health*, 45 (December, 1955), 1551–57.

34. Lieberson, Stanley, "Ethnic Groups and the Practice of Medicine," *American Sociological Review*, 23 (October, 1958), 542–49.

35. McElrath, Dennis C., "Perspective and Participation of Physicians in Prepaid Group Practice," *American Sociological Review*, 26 (August, 1961), 596–607.

36. May, Charles D., "Selling Drugs by 'Educating' Physicians," *Journal of Medical Education*, 36 (January, 1961), 1–23.

37. Merton, Robert K., "Some Preliminaries to a Sociology of Medical Education," *in* Robert K. Merton, George G. Reader, and Patricia L. Kendall, eds., *The Student-Physician*. Cambridge: Harvard University Press, 1957.

38. Nittis, Savas, "The Hippocratic Oath in Reference to Lithotomy," *Bulletin of the History of Medicine*, 6 (July, 1939), 719–28.

39. Parsons, Talcott, "Introduction" in Max Weber, *The Theory of Social and Economic Organization*. New York: Oxford University Press, 1947, pp. 58–60.

40. Peterson, Osler L., Leon P. Andrews, Robert S. Spain, and Bernard G. Greenberg, "An Analytical Study of North Carolina General Practice, 1953–1954," *The Journal of Medical Education*, 31 (December, 1956), Part 2.

41. Pleadwell, Frank Lester, "Samuel Sorbière and his *Advice to a Young Physician*," *Bulletin of the History of Medicine*, 24 (May–June, 1950), 255–87.

42. Pomrinse, S. David and Marcus S. Goldstein, "Group Practice in the U.S.," *Group Practice*, 9 (November, 1960), 845–59.

43. Reitzes, Dietrich, *Negroes and Medicine*. Cambridge: Harvard University Press, 1958.

44. Rorem, C. Rufus, "Pattern and Problems of Group Medical Practice," *American Journal of Public Health*, 40 (December, 1950), 1521–28.

45. Sand, René, *The Advance to Social Medicine*. London: Staples Press, Ltd., 1952.

46. Seeman, Melvin and John W. Evans, "Stratification and Hospital Care: I. The Performance of the Medical Interne," *American Sociological Review*, 26 (February, 1961), 67–80.

47. ———, "Stratification and Hospital Care: II. The Objective Criteria of Performance," *American Sociological Review*, 26 (April, 1961), 193–204.

48. Shapiro, S., L. Weiner, and P. M. Densen, "Comparison of Prematurity and Perinatal Mortality in General Population and in Population of Prepaid Group Practice," *American Journal of Public Health*, 48 (February, 1958), 170–87.

49. Shryock, Richard H., *The Development of Modern Medicine*. New York: Alfred A. Knopf, Inc., 1947.

50. Sigerist, Henry N., *A History of Medicine*. New York: Oxford University Press, 1951.

51. Solomon, David N., "Ethnic and Class Differences among Hospitals as Contingencies in Medical Careers," *The American Journal of Sociology*, 66 (March, 1961), 463–71.

52. Somers, Herman Miles and Anne Ramsay Somers, *Doctors, Patients and Health Insurance*. Washington, D.C.: Brookings Institution, 1961.

53. Taylor, Stephen, *Good General Practice*. London: Oxford University Press, 1954.

54. Weiskotten, Herman G., Walter S. Wiggins, Marion E. Altenderfer, Marjorie Gouch, and Anne Tipner, "Trends in Medical Practice—An Analysis of the Distribution and Characteristics of Medical College Graduates, 1915–1950," *Journal of Medical Education*, 35 (December, 1960), 1071–1121.

55. Williams, Josephine J., "Patients and Prejudice: Attitudes towards Women Physicians," *American Journal of Sociology*, 51 (January, 1946), 283–87.

13

THE COMMUNITY OF HEALTH ORGANIZATIONS

Sol Levine
Paul E. White

A *considerable* volume of health services are not rendered within hospital settings or the offices of individual practitioners but are dispensed by a complex network of health agencies or organizations. Although these agencies vary in size, form, function, autonomy, and professional composition, they interact with each other and comprise a health agency system serving the general community and the myriad of individual recipients.

The Spectrum of Health Agencies

In attempting to classify the agencies within the health system, such sociological variables as size, function, professional composition, and locus of authority could be employed, but in the daily parlance of health professionals there is a readymade system of classification which may serve as a more useful point of departure. There are four main types of health organizations which are of interest: (1) official or public agencies; (2) voluntary or nonprofit agencies; (3) hospitals and nursing homes, and (4) health-related organizations.

Official agencies

Within most medium or large size communities in the United States, there are official health oriented agencies which, like other governmental organizations, depend upon tax funds and operate within clearly specified legal limits and regulations. Official agencies are organized on several levels: federal, state, county, and city.

Federal agencies, for the most part, affect the local community only indirectly. Most federal health agencies (where "the most confused organizational picture in the United States is found . . ." [28]) operate primarily through state agencies, but occasionally branches of these agencies directly serve local communities. The United States Public Health Service is the most important of these agencies: among its many important and encompassing activities are research, demonstration projects, and financial grants-in-aid to states. Another significant agency is the Children's Bureau, which, like the Public Health Service, is part of the Department of Health, Education, and Welfare. One of the main functions of this agency is that of encouraging the improvement and extension of services to mothers and children on the state and local level. This is accomplished by financial assistance, sponsorship of health programs, demonstration projects, and extensive research and educational activities. A third agency with considerable significance for the local scene is the Bureau of Vocational Rehabilitation which makes grants-in-aid to states for the purpose of rehabilitating vocationally handicapped persons with physical or mental disabilities. Another organization is the Veterans Administration which operates hospitals and out-patient departments and administers various kinds of training benefits for former members of the armed forces. These are only a few of the federal agencies whose activities have import for and are intertwined with the services offered by other agencies on the local level.

The pattern of official health organizations on the state level is a highly complex arrangement which varies markedly from state to state. "A study made by the Public Health Service in 1950 indicated a total of sixty different types of state agencies contributing in some way to state health programs . . ." [28]. Direct health or health-related services are offered by a vast array of state departments, and the same health service is often the focus of the activities of a number of agencies. The organization of primary concern on the state level is the department of health, in which responsibility for public health services is invariably invested.

Personal health services provided by state health departments vary greatly in kind and magnitude but, in general, tend to be confined to the provision of mobile personnel and equipment to specific localities at periodic intervals. In this manner, for example, many dental services, diagnostic X-rays, and other health services may be made available to selected parts of the population. In those areas where full-time local health departments are lacking, however, the state health department may offer a greater volume of direct health services on a more permanent basis. In fact, one of the main functions of the state health department is to promote the establishment of full-time health departments in areas where there are none and, perhaps even more important, to assist existing health departments in the planning and execution of their programs. In order to fulfill this latter objective, the state health department may grant considerable financial aid to local health departments and provide them with various kinds of personnel resources, including consultative and specialized services and in-service training programs.

Local public health agencies have traditionally carried out six fundamental services: (1) recording and analysis of vital statistics; (2) control of communicable disease; (3) maintenance and supervision of environmental sanitation; (4) public health laboratory services; (5) maternal and child health services, and (6) health education of the general public [28]. The types and number of personnel necessary to carry out these services vary, of course, with the size of the jurisdiction served by the health department—but all usually have the full-time or part-time services of a health director and at least the part-time services of nursing personnel, sanitary engineers or other sanitary personnel, and office workers.

In recent years, there has been increased concern with the role and scope of the health department [28]. As the morbidity pattern in the United States has changed, existing programs have been re-examined and health leaders have attempted to chart new ones. With the decrease in the incidence of communicable diseases, public health programs have been developed to control cancer, heart disease, mental illness, and accidents; administrators have placed increased emphasis upon early detection, prevention, comprehensive care, and rehabilitation and have initiated new activities such as cancer detection clinics, glaucoma screening programs, accident control programs, and services involving ambulatory and home care of the patient. There has been a corresponding influx into the larger public health agencies of such new public health personnel as medical social workers, health educators, nutritionists, and even social scientists. For some time now, policy leaders and teachers of public health have spoken increasingly in terms of a "team approach" to public health problems, intentionally distinguishing the practice of public health from that of private medicine [35].

The scope of programs conducted by a local public health department depends in large part upon the training of its administrator, the health officer. The large proportion of local health agencies throughout the country are under the direction of physicians who have not had formal training in public health methods. Others are administered by untrained laymen. The ideal of the public health profession is to have local public health units under the full-time direction of physicians with graduate training in public health. In the changing curriculum offered by schools of public health for prospective health officers, stress is placed on community organization and social science in addition to the usual spectrum of laboratory courses.

In addition to rendering different kinds of direct services to the public, official health units also have shown increasing concern with coordinating the activities of the many and diverse types of community health agencies and thereby trying to reduce the gaps and overlaps in the services provided by these organizations. Since the local public health unit is the agency with the greatest legal responsibility for the health of the population, the belief has grown among public health professionals that the task of achieving maximal coordination of these various health and health-related agencies should reside in the local health department.

Voluntary agencies

Existing side by side with official agencies are a multitude of nongovernmental or voluntary health agencies which are legally incorporated as nonprofit organizations on the local, state, or national level and which are supported by funds solicited from the public. What large community does not have a chapter or affiliate of the American Cancer Society, The National Foundation, The Visiting Nurse Association, or The Tuberculosis and Health Association? Other organizations are associated with the more esoteric illnesses or conditions but are rapidly becoming embedded into the voluntary health activity of communities across the country: *e.g.*, Muscular Dystrophy, Cystic Fibrosis, Multiple Sclerosis and so on. There is great variation in these agencies not the least of which is reflected in their executives who may range from nurse, social worker, or community organizer, to interested layman. Some agencies are small, consisting only of a part-time director and a secretary; others are larger than many official health departments.

Voluntary agencies vary considerably in the services they perform and the activities in which they engage. A good number of them, such as Muscular Dystrophy and Cystic Fibrosis, raise funds to sponsor research; others, such as the American Cancer Society, not only raise funds for research but also distribute considerable educational material and, in some cases, give financial assistance to special classes of patients; still others, such as the Tuberculosis and Health Association, engage in case finding and assist in the rehabilitation of the afflicted. A few, such as the Visiting Nurse Association, provide direct services to a large number of patients.

The degree of voluntary health agency activity in the United States is extensive and involves the time and energy of hundreds of thousands of laymen serving on boards and committees as well as literally millions of volunteers. Personnel and laymen associated with these agencies tend to express the general belief that voluntary agencies possess advantages which are not shared by their official counterparts. For example, it is often said that voluntary organizations are more flexible, more free to experiment, and more able to pioneer in the health field and that they supplement the activities of and provide a needed stimulus to tax-supported agencies. On the other hand, voluntary health leaders generally grant that official agencies, because of their greater resources in money and personnel, are better equipped to undertake longer-range and more broadly based direct service programs. Whether these are indeed respective advantages of the two types of organizations is worthy of systematic research. For example, it would be desirable to document the kinds and magnitude of experimental programs undertaken by voluntary agencies [26].

Hospitals

Hospitals are the major treatment centers of the community. Some of them are official, and some voluntary; some are addressed to a specific disease syndrome, others are more general in their scope; some do not have out-patient facilities, others offer a wide range of services through their out-patient departments and other extra-hospital programs.[1]

The changing morbidity picture, the growing philosophy of comprehensive care, the heightened efforts at decreasing in-patient hospital utilization, and the gradual extension of health insurance to cover medical costs outside the hospital setting have combined to cause many hospitals to go beyond the mere provision of in-patient services and to expand the scope of existing out-patient departments [51, 61]. Over the years, the services of out-patient departments have been broadened to include a wide range of diagnostic and therapeutic services to ambulatory patients in the general community. The new functions assumed by the out-patient clinics have established them more firmly in a network of relationships with other hospitals and community agencies.

[1] For a detailed description of the structure of the hospital, see Chap. 10.

Health-related organizations

Side by side and overlapping with the complex of health agencies is a constellation of welfare and social agencies. While these agencies are not primarily devoted to health, they do perform a number of important health or health-related activities. One such agency is the official welfare department, which exists everywhere on the state level and can also be found as an autonomous agency on the local level in most medium-sized communities. Although the welfare department has historically been associated exclusively with relief for the indigent and such concomitant activities as the administration of alms-houses and the operation of orphanages, it has drastically expanded its scope and services in recent years. The Social Security Act of 1935 heralded the inauguration of significant new programs for older people, the disabled, and dependent children. "The Act also contains provisions for unemployment compensation, old age pensions, care for the crippled, maternal and child welfare services, venereal disease control, and other activities. . . ." [53]. Subsequent provisions also included federal grants to states to defray the costs of preventative, therapeutic, and rehabilitative services to the indigent [53]. The welfare department subsidizes the cost of much of the medical care given by other agencies to welfare recipients and is one of the main sources of referrals to agencies offering direct health services to the community.

The activities of the educational system overlap at many points with those of the health agencies of the community. Although administrative arrangements vary, most schools are required by law to have some kind of health program for their students which inevitably brings the school into contact with the health department, as well as with other official or voluntary agencies. In addition, school counseling or guidance programs have reciprocal contact with special community agencies serving children and their families. In some cases, special student health problems may produce heavy referral traffic between the school and agencies offering such specialized services as speech therapy, remedial reading, or other forms of aid to handicapped children.

There are also a large number of private agencies devoted to social welfare or social service activities—among them, the Salvation Army, the Family Service Society, the YMCA and the Travelers' Aid Society. Many of these agencies had their "start in religious groups, in settlement houses or in efforts by citizens to deal with the mass migrations of the past" [53]. In recent years, these agencies have extended their collective scope to encompass such diverse activities as financial assistance, rehabilitation, counseling, recreational activities, and varied types of help to needy parents and underprivileged children. Other health-related agencies which may supplement the health agencies are the courts, commercial organizations, and religious associations.

The Sociological Study of Health Agencies

The various health agencies, despite their complexity and heterogeneity, are amenable to logical classification and analysis. Drawing upon the general field of organizational sociology and specific studies of the health field, the spectrum of health agencies can be analyzed under the following main subject areas:

1. The internal structure of the health agency
2. The organization and its community environment
3. Vertical relationship with parent bodies
4. Interagency relationships

The internal structure of the health agency [2]

The components of each organizational structure are basically the same and consist of the board, the executive director, and the staff. There are variations and elaborations of these components, to be sure, as in the case of some official agencies which have no boards. Moreover, the boards of official agencies are responsible to civic authorities and are less immune to direct sanctions than their counterparts in voluntary agencies are. In general, however, and especially with regard to voluntary agencies, these organizational components are remarkably consistent from agency to agency.

The boards are the formal policymakers of the organizations and, within limits imposed by their respective organizational affiliations, are commissioned to formulate and modify the charter and bylaws of the organization and allocate its expenditures. Boards vary in size but are generally composed of up to 30 or 40 individuals drawn mainly from the business and industrial sectors of the community, sometimes from the professional groups and rarely from the lower income levels of the population [13, 37, 72]. Board members are appointed for terms usually ranging from three to six years. An institutionalized mechanism of rotating membership generally requires members to retire from the board for a period of one term after having served two or three terms. This is intended to prevent the board from becoming "self-perpetuating," but desirable members are often asked to resume membership after periods of token retirement.

Since large boards are often unwieldy, decision-making power is frequently delegated to an executive committee. The executive or paid direc-

---

[2] Much of the ensuing discussion is based on a three-year study of some 130 health and welfare agencies and their interaction patterns in four northeastern communities. The project is sponsored by the Social Science Program of the Harvard School of Public Health and was supported by Grant 8676 from the National Institutes of Health. Sol Levine is the principal investigator of the project and Benjamin D. Paul, former director of the Social Science Program, is co-investigator.

tor of the agency is responsible to the board and acts within the limitations it imposes. Once the basic functions and scope of the organization are determined, the executive may exercise a good deal of latitude in administering the operations of the agency and supervising his staff. Moreover, because the executive is frequently a professional and is the person most knowledgeable about the day-to-day occurrences within the agency, the information he conveys to the board may be the main basis on which its policy decisions are formulated. While all executives appreciate the value of having influential citizens on their boards, which serves as an indication of the climate of the dominant community and potential receptivity of the population, some executives view boards as barriers to the achievement of imaginative programs. One of the main tasks of the energetic executive is that of continually educating his board and enlisting its support for desirable programs.

In the case of official agencies, the board is sometimes appointed by the relevant governmental unit—city, county, state—or, at other times, is governed by a committee of the members of the elected governmental body itself. Consequently, the executives of official agencies normally must contend with board members who are less committed to the agency itself than are members of the boards of voluntary agencies. Another variation in the executive-staff relationship is found in hospitals because, in many instances, a good number of staff physicians are not employees of the hospital. In these cases the executive deals with the physicians as a group, usually through a committee. The physicians are not individually responsible to the executive except for adhering to administrative procedures in connection with the treatment of patients and the utilization of hospital facilities. Otherwise, the individual phyiscian retains control over the disposition of his private patient within the hospital. Smith has drawn attention to the fact that two lines of authority—lay and professional—exist within the hospital structure, a condition which he demonstrates constitutes a dilemma for hospital personnel [62].

Each organization, depending on its functions, contains a range of professional positions. Many of these may be occupied by persons without formal training; one of the reasons for this is the acute shortage of trained personnel in this field [1]. Interviews with executives in some 130 agencies indicated the organizational problem most frequently mentioned is staff shortage; the next is budgetary difficulties [38].

Most community health organizations, particularly the voluntary agencies, also have part-time volunteer workers who perform varied services without remuneration and thus supplement the work of staff and board members. It is the part-time volunteer who helps substantially in carrying out the basic organizational chores including clerical work, home visits, sundry clinic duties, and door-to-door fund raising. Although there have been various studies of volunteers in different types of voluntary organizations, the only intensive investigation of volunteers in a health agency is to be found in Sills' study of the National Foundation [60]. Starting with the assumption that the characteristics of an organization are determined largely by the social character of its membership and the gratifications of participation, Sills intensively examines who are the volunteers, why and how they were recruited, and the psychological satisfactions they derive from participating. He also describes a series of organizational devices by which the Foundation maintains membership interest and avoids goal-displacement. An interesting finding is that although authority in the Foundation is delegated from the national to the local level, about half of the volunteers perceive the organization as a federation of local chapters which are serviced by a national office [60].

Although the characteristics of participants in voluntary agencies have been studied, the agencies themselves have rarely been the object of sociological investigation, other than Sills' work and a few case studies of individual national health agencies [8, 15, 21]. As Rosen and Wellin point out, no organizational study of an official health agency has been reported [52].[3] The few sociological studies of health organizations have focused first on hospitals, and then upon out-patient departments, to the relative exclusion of other types of agencies. Studies of out-patient departments seem to focus largely on the relationship between the norms and characteristics of a profession and the demands of the organization. Thus, in a study of an out-patient department, Goss addresses herself to the problem of how individual authority required by physicians is reconciled with the hierarchical demands of the larger organization [22]. Possible strain is avoided by having each physician act autonomously in the professional sphere. Supervision is exercised, if at all, by physicians and often takes the form of advice. Goss also finds that the usual influence of the norms of subordinates or superordinates is less operative for physicians within the out-patient department where their behavior is mainly determined by the professional norms established prior to affiliation with the formal organization.

That health agency environments are appropriate settings for the testing and refinement of sociological hypotheses is evidenced in a study by Bennis and his associates in which they employed the concepts of "locals" and "cosmopolitans" in classifying nurses in several out-patient departments. It was expected, for example, that "locals" would show greater in-group loyalty and involvement in organizational goals and that "cosmopolitans" would be more interested in outside groups. But the findings were con-

[3] Professors Sydney H. Croog and Benjamin D. Paul have recently completed a comprehensive study of the structure and operation of official health agencies.

trary to expectations. "Cosmopolitans" maintained in-group loyalties and shared organizational goals and "locals" revealed less in-group loyalty and were more interested in groups external to the out-patient setting, such as nursing associations. The authors interpret these surprising findings in the light of the distinctive nature of the nursing profession and its intra-organizational environments. They suggest that the anticipated local-cosmopolitan schema tends to hold less in settings where organizational goals are unclear, where individual success is not dependent upon the organization and "where the main body of the membership perceives the profession chiefly as embodying ultimate values rather than criteria for skills, research, and the development of a body of knowledge" [2].

Another study of the out-patient department by Solon and his co-workers focuses on staff perceptions of patients and their use patterns. Distinct differences appear in the perceptions and attitudes of physicians, nurses, and social workers. Solon suggests that these may be related to the values and experiences of the different professional groups [63]. In brief, the physician, with an outlook anchored in his private practice, seems to be least sympathetic of the various practices and utilization patterns of the patients such as "shopping around" for medical care and receiving free care. The social worker, on the other hand, shows a strong identification with the patient while the nurse appears ". . . to articulate her strong concern for the patient with a strong organizational identification" [63].

Considerable work has already been done on communication patterns among personnel in hospital settings [9, 49, 65]. There is also need for intensive studies of communication within and across other health agency settings. Some headway in this direction has been made by Berkowitz and Bennis, who present some tentative findings based on their studies of nurses [3]. Chiefly, they report that interaction involving the transmission of organizational material is directed more to superordinates; peers are the greatest recipients of interpersonal interaction and subordinates are the lowest recipients of task content, though the authors themselves question this last finding and offer alternative explanations. They also describe a relationship between the status of the recipient and the satisfaction and importance of the interaction.

The agency and its community environment

The promotion of health and the prevention and cure of disease constitute the ideal orientation of the health agency system. Few, if any, agencies possess access to all the resources they need to enable them to attain their objectives fully. Under the realistic conditions of scarcity, organizations must limit their activities and select particular functions that permit them to achieve certain ends as fully as possible. "By function is meant a set of interrelated services or activities that are instrumental, or believed to be instrumental, for the realization of an organization's objectives" [36]. In more operational terms, "function" consists of the services offered and the specific categories of recipients or population groups served. The functions selected by an agency represent its decision as to allocation of resources to serve its community environment. By characterizing organizations by their primary functions, some order and clarification can be introduced into the otherwise diverse array of agencies in the community.

The nature of the disease involved and the existing medical technology partially determine the range of services which an organization may offer to the community. The disease process itself usually has a natural history and forms a sequence of organic reactions within the individual which provides the health specialist with specific opportunities for intervention. The functions of an organization represent its mode of intervening with respect to the disease or illness. There are seven main functions which an organization may perform: (1) *education*—the transmission of medico-scientific information intended to produce behavior reducing the risk of illness; (2) *prevention*—the employment of scientific technology to make the individual impervious to diseases; (3) *treatment*—the utilization of medico-scientific technology to control the disease in its acute stage, and to restore the individual so far as it is possible to his previous state of functioning; (4) *rehabilitation*—the application of medico-scientific technology to restore the organism to maximum functioning after the illness has struck and had some irreversible effects; (5) *resource-giving*—the facilitation of the receipt of medico-scientific technology by the removal of financial and other impediments; (6) *research*—the building of medico-scientific knowledge and technology with regard to a specific illness, and (7) *coordination*—the integration of medico-scientific resources of different agencies.

These functions, with the exception of the last two are services rendered directly to specific population groups. Although there are various possible ways by which the recipient populations might be classified, age and illness are the main bases of discrimination.

Classification by age parallels the divisions which are found in the larger society. The customary age breakdown within the health system in the United States is: (1) infant and preschool; (2) school; (3) adult; and (4) elderly. The first group is generally supervised by a parent or guardian; the second is in school at predictable times; the third group, especially its male members, is at a place of employment; and the fourth is fairly sedentary, either at home or in hospitals, nursing homes, or other institutions.

Income is another differentiating characteristic within the system of health agencies which cuts across age and illness. People are classified as either self-supporting, medically indigent (not indigent but unable to afford necessary health services) and the financially indigent who not only cannot afford medical services but are even unable to pay for the other necessities of life. Some other more specialized bases of classification may be adopted by sectarian or church-sponsored agencies whose services may be aimed mainly at specific racial, ethnic, or religious groups.

But an agency may not adhere rigidly to these criteria; indeed it may depart drastically from them at any time for all kinds of reasons—a diminishing case load, an unclear or changing agency policy, lack of knowledge and the whim of its personnel [24]. Then, too, an agency may screen clients referred by certain agencies but automatically accept others referred by a specific agency with which it enjoys an established and favorable relationship. In general, however, these criteria—illness, age and income—constitute the framework by which agencies order the client or patient world around them.

The goals and related functions of an organization not only determine its services to the community but also affect what the organization needs and seeks to obtain from its community environment. An organization requires three main elements: patients or clients, personnel, and such nonhuman resources as money, space, equipment, and information [36]. Although these elements may be obtained form other health agencies, it is the general community as a source of elements which concerns us here.

Elling and Halebsky have studied the factors affecting the support received by governmental and voluntary hospitals [16]. They report that voluntary nondenominational hospitals receive more financial support than do their official or governmental counterparts. A similar relationship obtains when patient channelling (referrals) is used as a measure of support and when the criterion of community participation is considered (but the authors have no comparative data on the composition of hospital volunteers). They point out that as hospitals evolved in the present century:

> voluntary hospitals tended to draw business, industrial and society leaders on to their boards and did not leave any channel of formal control open to the public. City and county hospitals, on the other hand, have remained the 'people's' hospitals in the sense that popular control and identification has been partially retained through the election of governmental officials [16].

They also suggest that the higher prestige assigned to voluntary hospitals may possibly explain, in part, the greater support they receive.

That voluntary hospitals do tend to enjoy higher prestige than governmental hospitals, is supported by data obtained in studies of health agencies in four communities based on ratings by agency executives, board members, and community leaders [39]. It is this respect that Perrow's comment on the importance of organizational prestige is most pertinent:

> One of the ways of controlling dependency is to create and maintain a favorable image of the organization in the salient publics. If an organization and its products are well regarded, it may more easily attract personnel, influence relevant legislation, wield informal power in the community and insure adequate number of clients, customers, donors, or investors . . . [47].

In addition to funds, voluntary health agencies still have need for recruits—either as board members who link the agency to the community or as volunteers who perform the daily activities of the organization. As Sills points out, voluntary health agencies do not have the alternatives of other kinds of organizations for recruiting members:

> Unlike a church, for example, a voluntary health association cannot depend upon the occupational structure for recruits; . . . unlike a military organization, it has no such coercive mechanism as conscription legislation; unlike a government bureaucracy, a business firm or a professional or trade association, it cannot depend upon the occupational structure for recruits . . . [60].

It tends therefore to make use of other interpersonal relationships. Of all volunteers recruited by the National Foundation, 52 per cent joined at the invitation of one they knew personally; 20 per cent were asked to join by some other community member; 18 per cent were invited by an organizational or work colleague, and only 10 per cent joined on their own initiative [60]. It is in this respect that the typology of voluntary agencies offered by Gordon and Babchuck is most relevant [21]. They characterize agencies by whether they are mainly expressive or instrumental, by the social status they enjoy, and their accessibility. Voluntary agencies in general would appear to be organizations of relatively low accessibility, despite their obvious need for membership. Sills, in his interesting study of members recruited by the Foundation focused on the typology of joiners, the acquisition of new interests and attitudes as a result of membership, and the psychological gratifications in participation [60]. Comparable information on volunteers in other voluntary agencies would be most desirable.

The financing of health agencies has been the object of considerable attention and controversy in recent years. With the exception of proprietory hospitals, nursing homes, or special clinics, none of the agencies of the health system is a profit-making organization. The three main sources of funds for health agencies are: public tax funds, contributions from the general community, and fees for service from individual clients or recipients.

Most government agencies rely almost entirely upon tax funds for their support. Theoretically, an official agency is only required to submit a budget to the appropriate allocating group, either an administrative or a legislative body, for review and approval. Agency executives usually expect that some budgetary items invariably will be deleted or decreased and they are known to exaggerate their needs accordingly. A good number of executives of official agencies also confide that they find it easier to obtain funds for projected services which are likely to yield concrete results than for services having less tangible consequences—*i.e.*, education.

Were the concerns of agency executives limited to just satisfying the vote-oriented objectives of the legislators, their task would be difficult enough. In some communities, however, the fund procurement problems of official agency executives are further complicated by other factors which arise mainly from the relationship of official agencies to the political patronage system. Agency executives who adhere to the norms of the patronage system are more likely to be successful in their requests for funds, whereas those who fail to conform are more likely to encounter difficulties.

Historically, the voluntary health agencies depended mostly upon private philanthropy and individual contributions. Charitable funds, often in the form of bequests, together with the personal services of volunteers, enabled an appreciable part of the voluntary health system to operate. As population grew, the volume of health services increased. Most of the roles in the health system became professionalized, diminishing the importance of many of the volunteer services and creating the need for more funds in order to hire new professionals. Simultaneously, technological developments in medicine necessitated the procurement of costly machinery and physical plant.

Philanthropy itself has accommodated to changing community conditions [26]. With the demise of individual fortunes in many communities, the paternalistic system with its "Lady Bountiful" became less prevalent and less capable of supporting the wide gamut of health services. The rise of national corporations also affected the system of local philanthropy, as local branches of these corporations gradually replaced locally-owned industry. These local branches are more prone to have charity quotas which are allotted more or less impartially to the whole array of voluntary agencies in the community. Agency reliance on large individual donations, therefore, has gradually been superseded by more effective fund raising approaches which are more carefully organized and community-wide in scope. The two predominant modes of soliciting funds are: independent fund raising on the part of the agency itself and membership in a community chest or fund organization.

Independent fund raising takes three general forms: special offers—often from board members and their friends—to obtain large individual contributions from a few well-to-do persons, mail solicitation of the general public, and door-to-door canvassing. The calendar year has been divided into fund raising seasons, each one the domain of a particular agency. Usually the national or parent bodies of the local organizations determine when fund raising is to take place. Thus the TB Association claims Christmas with its seals, Crippled Children monopolizes Easter. Other organizations do not necessarily synchronize their fund raising with holidays, but may publicize a special period such as Mental Health Week or Heart Sunday, when they concentrate their efforts on programs which will "educate" the public as to the value of their special endeavors. The campaign then concludes with an appeal for donations. There seems to be no general rule for determining which kinds of agencies will conduct which sort of campaign.

There is a real difference, however, between those agencies that conduct independent campaigns and those that solicit through the community chest or fund. Community chests and funds originated as a response to the gradual proliferation of fund-raising agencies. They were initiated primarily by the business and industrial segments of various communities in order to expedite the collection of funds by decreasing the number of solicitations to which a given business enterprise might be subjected. The intent was to consolidate fund drives into a single one, so that the community would be approached but once a year and the money apportioned among the various community agencies.

The plan has succeeded to some extent. A great proportion of the funds solicited in the community are collected through the community chest or fund, although monies acquired through independent fund drives are also considerable [26]. It is those agencies with proportionately large local expenditures of local funds that tend to belong to the community chest or fund. Sometimes both chests and funds and other times only one or the other is found in a city. The financial arrangements of organizations vis-à-vis fund or chest are most varied. The arrangements in one city may be cited to illustrate the complexity of arrangements. In this city, upon joining the chest, an agency is generally guaranteed an annual income for a stipulated number of years which is equivalent to its yearly budget prior to membership in the chest. In subsequent years, expenditures become subject to revision and funds for specific purposes may be deleted from the agency budget. After this initial period of financial adjustment, an agency's budget is normally approved automatically so long as the agency does not modify its services. If the chest should fail to meet its fund raising goal, the budgets of member agencies are usually decreased in proportion to the fund raising deficit.

The fund is a financial partnership. The budgets of member agencies usually are not subject to review or revision, and the member agencies usually receive relatively fixed proportions of the proceeds of the fund drives. Fund member agencies tend to be those which could well conduct independent fund drives. They derive their strength either from their strong appeal to a particular group, or from the fact that they solicit from a wide area or region of which the community is only a part. In most cases, fund membership is a compromise with local pressure groups. It concedes to the integrated fund drive but rejects local control. In some areas, both a chest and a fund exist. In such cases, chest agencies as a whole constitute one member of the fund.

Those agencies which conduct independent fund drives almost exclusively concentrate on single specific disease syndromes, with some noteworthy exceptions such as the Red Cross and the Salvation Army. These agencies are often prohibited from participating in the community chest or fund by the national parent bodies. Several considerations underlie these national policies. The reason most frequently elicited from specific disease agency personnel is that membership would result in the loss of their "agency identity"; they would become submerged in the mass of chest agencies and the special appeal of their agency would be forfeited. However, there are other reasons as well. Specific disease agencies often concentrate on research, for the diseases they concentrate on are usually incurable. These agencies consequently wish to centralize their funds in research endeavors and to achieve this end they must delimit the programs of the local affiliates in order to drain off as few funds as possible. The independent fund drive is advantageous to these research-oriented agencies; it frees them of any stipulations which a local community chest might impose and thereby permits them to expend their funds in accordance with their own goals.

The conflict between proponents of independent and federated fund raising represents the greatest source of friction within the health and welfare agency world [26]. Community chests and united funds have exerted pressure on the independent agencies at the local level in an attempt to induce them to adopt federated fund raising. The controversy stems mainly from the different goals of the two types of agencies—*i.e.*, the federated agencies are mainly concerned with serving local interests whereas the independent drive agencies are geared to accomplishing national objectives. United funds and community chests recently have established a number of local "research and health foundations," often as a means of competing with the research appeal of independent national voluntary agencies [26]. On the other hand, independent voluntary agencies, in order to capitalize on the public appeal of direct service, have attempted to indicate that their efforts also bear fruit on the local level.

Aside from tax funds and contributions to the public, some agencies finance the costs of their operations through fees for service. This is particularly true of voluntary hospitals which tend to charge a fixed fee for services to patients. One important recent development in hospital financing is the growth of such voluntary health insurance plans as those of the Associated Hospital Plan and private insurance companies. Under these plans, payments to hospitals are, in essence, still made on a fee-for-service basis, though frequently with some stipulation in the contract as to the amounts to be paid for specific services and as to the particular method of payment. Most other agencies which charge fees for service utilize a "sliding scale," *i.e.*, they bill the patients or clients according to his income and family size.

Organizational Goals

All organizations, including health agencies, operate within a changing environment and are faced with the recurrent need to reappraise their goals and objectives and to establish new ones [4, 57, 58, 66]. In general, the products of health agencies would appear less tangible than, for example, those of business organizations and, accordingly, the task of goal reappraisal would be rendered more difficult [66]. But organizations do not respond merely to the changing environment; they often produce the very changes in the environment which in turn command their adaptation. A dramatic case in point is the development of the Salk vaccine which heralded the eventual disappearance of polio—the major goal of the National Foundation [60]. When the goals of a health agency, particularly voluntary agencies, are realized, there are two main available courses it may follow: it may disband as an organization, or it may develop new goals or objectives. The more usual course is the latter—which Blau defines as the "succession of goal." It is vital for the organization to have its new goals, like the old ones, legitimatized by the rest of the health agency system and/or the general community, for the goals represent the agency's claim to basic elements without which it cannot survive. The National Foundation is an excellent case in point of a large voluntary health agency which is presently attempting to redefine its goals in the midst of a changing environment which it itself helped produce [60].

Vertical relationships with parent bodies

Sills' intensive study of the National Foundation offers a stimulating case analysis of how a national voluntary organization may exercise control over its local affiliates so that it undergoes a minimum of goal displacement [58, 60]. He distinguishes between two types of national voluntary organizations: corporate organizations which delegate authority downwards from the national to the local level, and federated organizations which delegate authority upwards from the local to the national level. In the corporate type structure, the local units tend to have been formed at the initiative of the national body. In a federated organization, the local affiliates tend to have created the national unit as a coordinating body [7]. Examples of corporate organizations are the American Red Cross, the

American Cancer Society, and the American Heart Association; examples of federated structures are the Visiting Nurses Association, the National Tuberculosis Association, and United Cerebral Palsy. Corporate and federated national health and welfare organizations tend to differ in the stipulations or requirements they establish for their local affiliates or chapters. In contrast with federated organizations, corporate agencies tend to forbid the local to incorporate or own property. The explanation here seems to be that the more permanent the local structure the more it is able to exist independently of national support, and, consequently, the more independent it is of national direction [7]. Local affiliates of corporate agencies are also required to give a greater percentage of the funds they raise to the national organization and are also more restricted in how they use whatever funds they retain on the local level.

Corporate agencies seem less interested in having professionally trained persons as executive directors or staff on the local level. The few agencies that do indicate the desirability of having professionally trained staff on the local level are of the federated type [7]. This is in line with a study of one community which reveals that none of the executive directors of corporate agencies are professionally trained, whereas a considerable proportion of the heads of federated agencies do have graduate training in one of the health or health-related professions such as nursing, social work, or health education. Of course, types of personnel are related to other organizational characteristics (*e.g.*, function) but it is to be noted that by not having professionals as members of the permanent staff, corporate agencies minimize the threat of goal displacement. Nonprofessionals seem to display "local" patterns of behavior with greater interest in and allegiance to the organization, per se. Professionals, however, approximate the "cosmopolitan" who is bound by the norms of his profession and may achieve job mobility by moving to other organizations. Professionals, hence, would appear to be less dependent upon national parent bodies and, under certain circumstances, more ready to question national policy.

There is some evidence, on both national and local levels, that an organization's functions are correlated with its structure. Single-disease agencies tend to have a corporate structure and to state as their primary goal that of "finding a cure." Federated organizations are more likely to state as their major objective "prevention" or "maximum relief of suffering" [7]. Although most local affiliates tend to perform some services in their communities to justify their fund raising, these services do indeed seem to vary in accordance with the structure of the national organization. As expected, there is a greater tendency for federated organizations to operate clinics or other programs which entail cooperation with other agencies, whereas the health services of corporate agencies are more often confined to educational programs or the payment of individual medical bills incurred elsewhere [7].

The variation in the degree of control exerted by a national organization over its local chapters, as Johns has noted, can be characterized as (1) high degree of control; (2) mixed-local national control, and (3) local control [33]. Some of the sanctions which national organizations exercising high degree of control may employ to effect conformity are: withholding charters; failing to provide field services; excluding local units and staff members from official rosters; and restricting the participation of workers in personnel services and pension plans. In organizations characterized by mixed control, national plans and policies are submitted to local chapters as required actions or recommendations. These policies are generally arrived at through regular meetings with local representatives and considerable leeway is permitted in adapting local policy to local conditions. Among organizations where local control prevails, the role of the national organization is limited to making recommendations and to arranging meetings where mutual problems may be discussed and experiences exchanged [33].

Similar patterns are evident among official agencies, as well. For example, in an official state rehabilitation organization with a corporate structure whose main objective is to return to employment persons who have suffered a serious illness, the local branch of the state organization, to justify its existence, must demonstrate to its parent body or state legislators that the "right" number of persons have been successfully rehabilitated. The local agency, therefore, must be selective in the persons it admits as clients. Consequently, other community organizations often are unable to persuade the official agency to accept the more seriously debilitated clients for rehabilitation. The local official agency is unable to commit its resources to the consuming task of rehabilitating what seem to be "poor risks." While the local agency may share the values of the other community agencies, and want approval from them, it is the parent agency and other officials on the state level on whom it relies for its financial support [36].

Two important research opportunities are afforded in studying national-local relationships. The first pertains to learning the processes by which pressure is exerted on the local chapter by the community environment and by the national agency [69], and the types of accommodation achieved by the local unit in resolving these conflicting pressures. The second involves ascertaining the impact of a change in agency function (*e.g.*, a shift from research to direct service) on the total structure of an organization and the processes by which the organizational structure may evolve.

Relations among health agencies

In highlighting the need to study the organization in relation to its environment, Etzioni has specified the area of interorganizational relationships as one requiring further empirical study [17]. March and Simon suggest that interorganizational conflict is very similar to intergroup conflict within organizations but present no supporting data [41]. Health and welfare agencies on the local community level offer an excellent opportunity for exploring and locating the dimensions of relationships among organizations. An appreciable number of these organizations exist in any medium-sized American community. Within most community settings, various kinds of relationships exist among health and welfare agencies. Thus, for example, the welfare department may refer clients to an out-patient department, or information on the status of families may be shared by such voluntary organizations as the Visiting Nurse Association and the Red Cross. Johns and de Marche suggest the following dimensions around which interagency relationships may be classified: (1) those involving "furthering acquaintance with other agency leaders"; (2) those resulting in the exchange of information; (3) those which "in addition to furthering acquaintance and exchanging information, have resulted in specific consultation with representatives of other agencies"; (4) those which "in addition to those above, have resulted in definite planning with representatives of other agencies"; and (5) those which "have also resulted in definite operating responsibilities with representatives of other agencies" [33].

The typology set forth by Johns and de Marche centers largely on the cooperative process or the intensity of the relationship. Levine and White, on the other hand, focus largely on the goods or elements—*i.e.*, clients, personnel, and nonhuman resources—which are exchanged. Organizational goals or objectives which are derived from general health values define the organization's ideal need for these elements. Because elements are scarce, organizations are compelled to restrict their activity to limited special functions. However, even the fulfillment of these limited functions requires access to certain kinds of elements which an agency may seek to obtain through exchanges with other organizations. "Theoretically, then, were all the essential elements in infinite supply there would be little need for organizational interaction and for subscription to cooperation as an ideal. Under actual conditions of scarcity, however, interorganizational exchanges are essential for goal attainment" [36].

The interdependence of agencies within the health system and their exchanges with one another are seen as contingent upon three related factors: (1) the objectives of each agency and the particular functions it selects which, in turn, determine the kinds and number of elements it requires; (2) the access which each organization has to necessary elements from sources outside the health system which may determine an agency's dependence upon other parts of the health system; and (3) the degree to which there is domain consensus between the agencies. Organizational domain in the health field refers to the area the organization stakes out for itself in terms of disease covered, population served, and services rendered. Before two organizations can exchange elements with one another, there must at least be minimal consensus between them regarding their respective domains. Obviously, there can be little exchange between two agencies that do not know of each other's existence or are completely unaware of each other's functions. On the other hand, intense competition may occur between two agencies offering similar services, especially when other agencies have no clear criteria for referring patients to one rather than the other. In some cases, the conflict situation may be resolved by having the two agencies involved handle the same category of patients but at consecutive stages. For example, one agency may assume responsibility for patients when they are bedridden and the other when they become ambulatory. Another means of removing conflict and achieving consensus is to divide the population segments among the agencies in question. For example, in one case, where three agencies were involved in providing rehabilitation services, conflict among them was resolved by having one agency serve preschool children, another school children, and the third, adults.

Although administrators have expressed considerable concern for reducing barriers to cooperation and achieving greater coordination among health and welfare agencies, the problem itself has received little systematic attention. While there is little empirical evidence that interagency cooperation, per se, is necessarily related to organizational effectiveness, there is good reason to believe—for various direct service agencies at least—that some organizational objectives would be furthered by greater cooperation with other agencies. The comparatively little research which has been done on interagency cooperation has relied largely on assessments by staff rather than on more objective data. Johns and de Marche compiled a long list of conditions presumed to be barriers to interagency cooperation [33] which includes such factors as lack of knowledge of the work or objectives of other agencies, personality conflicts, differences in professional philosophy, "vested interests," lack of funds, and the influence of national agencies.

Attention should be drawn to the possible consequences of interorganizational exchange: it may affect future exchanges with the three main sources of elements—other agencies in the health system, parent bodies, and the general community. A dramatic illustration is found in the apprehension of a good number of agencies to develop relationships with Planned Parenthood, since they may be ostracized by other agencies or significant segments of the community, and thereby forfeit access to necessary elements [48]. While the community may at times intrude on the interaction processes within the health agency world, these are usually rare and dramatic occurrences. As noted, there are indeed crucial points of articulation between the community and the agencies: the allocation of funds and other resources by the community which establishes limits within which the health system operates; the role of boards as policymakers who legitimatize specific agency functions and delineate organizational domains; and so on. Once the objectives and the implementing functions of an organization are established, however, these functions seem to exert their influence autonomously on health agency interaction. Other organizational variables, in turn, appear to affect interaction within the limits established by the function variable. Much of the interaction of the health system appears to proceed in relative insulation from the surrounding community environment.

Miller's observations on interinstitutional conflict as a major impediment to delinquency prevention are most relevant for our understanding of barriers to interagency cooperation [44]. Although the institutions with which he is concerned—the courts, the police, correctional institutions and psychiatric agencies—extend beyond the health and welfare system and are less bound by a unifying value system than are the health and welfare agencies, the differences among them with regard to treatment approaches throw light on the problem of domain conflict. Differences were found to exist regarding such issues as: (1) the etiology of crime (morality versus pathology and individual locus versus social locus); (2) methods of dealing with offenders (restriction versus rehabilitation); (3) the approach priority (action versus research); (4) methods of organizing preventive programs (localization versus centralization); and (5) the appropriate status of personnel (lay versus professional). Miller concludes that the interinstitutional conflicts stem from the differing philosophies of the respective institutions and result in blocking community action. He suggests that there is need to shift research efforts from those focusing on the relationship between the agencies and the recipient population to those concentrating on the relationships among the agencies themselves [44].

An interesting note on interagency cooperation is offered by Form and Nosow in their study of a disaster situation [18]. The authors report that whatever interaction did take place during the emergency period was spontaneous and fortuitous and rested on informal and implicit arrangements. They observe that "organizational cooperation was facilitated among organizations with similar internal structure" [18] and that smooth cooperation is dependent upon congruent expectations among organizations in the disaster system. The authors conclude that "first and foremost . . . a disaster system must rest upon a pre-disaster plan of coordinated organizations" [18].

This suggests the possible need of an individual or agency whose explicit role would be that of assessing community health needs, and attempting to achieve more effective coordination among the health and welfare agencies. Such a person or agency would have to be very familiar with community organization and with the scope of the various health professions and must be able, whenever necessary, to negotiate with relevant persons and agencies outside the local community. The public health physician with graduate training in public health would seem to be one likely candidate for this role. As a city government official, he would enjoy relatively easy access to health offices, hospitals, and court offices and other relevant official heads (*e.g.*, welfare, education, and so on). As the leader of a "team" comprising such different professionals as nurse, social worker and sanitary engineer, he would have some familiarity with the orientations of each of these professionals. In some communities the most appropriate person might well be the head of the community council, or the director of the welfare department, or the head of a large community hospital. It is also conceivable that some committee consisting of a public health director and one or two other health administrators might also be feasible.

Although many public health directors feel that they are coordinating the work of other community agencies, there is little evidence that this is actually the case, nor is there any clear agreement on the part of the rest of the health agency system as to what types of coordination are desired or whether the responsibility for coordination should reside in the health officer. Given the diverse array of health agencies, with varying goals and loci of authority, the task of achieving more effective coordination challenges the wisdom and skills of the public health professional, the community organizer and the sociologist [45].

Conclusion

The problems and activities of health and welfare agencies comprise one sector in the health field to which the sociologist should be able to make a clear and unmistakable contribution. In relating to other problems in the health field (*e.g.*, etiology of illness), the sociologist, regardless of the merit of his potential contribution, must take into account the special experience and competence of the physician. But in the area of health and welfare organizations the physician usually has little expert knowledge and if anyone can lay claim to this particular province, it is the sociologist. While the study of health agencies may entail the usual resistance by members of a system who are being scrutinized, it should not be difficult to convince the practitioner that the sociologist possesses the necessary equipment and preparation to function in this area. The diversity of the health and welfare agency system affords a fertile and relatively untapped field which, if properly explored, should eventually rebound to the enrichment of organizational sociology.

References

1. Albee, George W., *Mental Health Manpower Trends*. New York: Basic Books, Inc., 1959.
2. Bennis, Warren G., Norman H. Berkowitz, M. Affinito, and M. Malone, "Reference Groups and Loyalties in the Out-Patient Department," *Administrative Science Quarterly*, 2 (March, 1958), 481–500.
3. Berkowitz, Norman H., and Warren G. Bennis, "Interaction in Formal Service-Oriented Organizations," *Administrative Science Quarterly*, 6 (June, 1961), 25–50.
4. Blau, Peter M., *The Dynamics of Bureaucracy*. Chicago: University of Chicago Press, 1955.
5. ———, "Formal Organization: Dimensions of Analysis," *American Journal of Sociology*, 63 (July, 1957), 58–69.
6. Boulding, Kenneth E., *The Organizational Revolution*. New York: Harper & Row, Publishers, 1953.
7. Briggs, Jean L. and Sol Levine, "Control over Local Affiliates by National Health Agencies." Paper delivered at annual meeting of the American Sociological Association, St. Louis, September 1, 1961.
8. Carter, Richard, *The Gentle Legions*. New York: Doubleday & Company, Inc., 1961.
9. Caudill, William, Frederick C. Redlich, Helen R. Gilmore, and E. B. Brody, "Social Structure and Interaction Processes on a Psychiatric Ward," *American Journal of Orthopsychiatry*, 22 (April, 1952), 314–34.
10. Caudill, William, *The Psychiatric Hospital as a Small Society*. Cambridge: Harvard University Press, 1958, pp. 266–303.
11. Chapin, F. Stuart and John E. Tsouderos, "The Formalization Process in Voluntary Associations," *Social Forces*, 34 (1956), 342–44.
12. Clark, Burton R., "Organizational Adaptation and Precarious Values," *American Sociological Review*, 21 (June, 1956), 327–36.
13. Covert, C., "No 'Common Man' on Hospital Boards," *The Syracuse Herald-Journal* (October 20, 1959).
14. Dimock, Marshall E., "Expanding Jurisdictions: A Case Study in Bureaucratic Conflict," *in* R. K. Merton *et al.*, eds., *Reader in Bureaucracy*. New York: The Free Press of Glencoe, Inc., 1952, pp. 282–91.
15. Dulles, Foster R., *The American Red Cross: A History*. New York: Harper & Row, Publishers, 1950.
16. Elling, Ray H. and Sandor Halebsky, "Organizational Differentiation and Support: A Conceptual Framework," *Administrative Science Quarterly*, 6 (September, 1961), 185–209.
17. Etzioni, Amitai, "New Directions in the Study of Organizations and Society," *Social Research*, 27 (Summer, 1960), 223–28.
18. Form, William H. and Sigmund Nosow, *Community in Disaster*. New York: Harper & Row, Publishers, 1958.
19. Fox, Sherwood D., "Voluntary Associations and Social Structure." Unpublished Ph.D. thesis, Harvard University, 1953.

20. Goldhamer, Herbert, "Voluntary Associations in the United States," *in* Paul K. Hatt and Albert J. Reiss, Jr., eds., *Reader in Urban Sociology*. New York: The Free Press of Glencoe, Inc., 1951, pp. 505–506.
21. Gordon, C. Wayne and Nicholas Babchuck, "A Typology of Voluntary Associations," *American Sociological Review*, 24 (February, 1959), 22–29.
22. Goss, Mary E. W., "Influence and Authority among Physicians in an Out-Patient Clinic," *American Sociological Review*, 26 (February, 1961), 39–50.
23. Gouldner, Alvin W., "Reciprocity and Autonomy in Functional Theory," *in* Llewellyn Gross, ed., *Symposium on Sociological Theory*. New York: Harper & Row, Publishers, 1959.
24. Gurin, Gerald, Joseph Veroff, and Sheila Feld, *Americans View Their Mental Health*. New York: Basic Books, Inc., 1960.
25. Hamlin, Robert H., "The Role of the Voluntary Agency in the United States—Present and Future." Address at the opening session of the 1961 annual meeting of the National Tuberculosis Association, Cincinnati, Ohio, May 22, 1961.
26. ———, *Voluntary Health and Welfare Agencies in the United States*. New York: The Schoolmasters' Press, 1961.
27. ———, "The Role of Voluntary Agencies in Meeting the Health Needs of Americans," *The Annals of the American Academy of Political and Social Science*, 337 (September, 1961), 93–102.
28. Hanlon, John J., *Principles of Public Health Administration*. 2nd ed. St. Louis: The C. V. Mosby Company, 1955.
29. Hollander, Sidney, *Toward Improved Chest–Council Agency Relations*. New York: Association Press, 1951.
30. Homans, George C., "Social Behavior as Exchange," *American Journal of Sociology*, 63 (May, 1958), 597–606.
31. Hunter, Floyd, *Community Power Structure*. Chapel Hill: The University of North Carolina Press, 1953.
32. Johns, Ray E., *The Cooperative Process among National Social Agencies*. New York: Association Press, 1946, p. 199.
33. ——— and David F. de Marche, *Community Organization and Agency Responsibility*. New York: Association Press, 1951.
34. King, C. Wendell, *Social Movements in the United States*. New York: Random House, 1956, p. 114.
35. Leavell, H. R. and E. Gurney Clark, *Textbook of Preventive Medicine*. New York: McGraw-Hill Book Company, Inc., 1953.
36. Levine, Sol and Paul White, "Exchange as a Conceptual Framework for the Study of Interorganizational Relationships," *Administrative Science Quarterly*, 5 (March, 1961), 583–601.
37. ———, "Characteristics of Board Members of Voluntary Health and Welfare Agencies." (Mimeo.)
38. ———, "Problems of Voluntary Health and Welfare Agencies." (Mimeo.)
39. ———, "Differential Prestige of Health and Welfare Agencies." (Mimeo.)
40. Long, Norton, "Local Community as a System of Competing Games," *American Journal of Sociology*, 64 (November, 1958), 251–61.

41. March, James G. and H. A. Simon, *Organizations*. New York: John Wiley & Sons, Inc., 1958.

42. Messinger, Sheldon L., "Organizational Transformation: A Case Study of a Declining Social Movement," *American Sociological Review*, 20 (February, 1955), 3–10.

43. Miller, Paul A. *et al., Community Health Action*. East Lansing: Michigan State University Press, 1953.

44. Miller, Walter B., "Inter-Institutional Conflict as a Major Impediment to Delinquency Prevention," *Human Organization*, 17 (Fall, 1958), 20–23.

45. Morris, Robert, "Basic Factors in Planning for Coordination of Hospitals and Institutions for Long-Term Care." (Mimeo.)

46. Parsons, Talcott, "Suggestions for a Sociological Approach to the Theory of Organizations—I," *Administrative Science Quarterly*, 1 (June, 1956), 63–85.

47. Perrow, Charles, "Organizational Prestige: Some Functions and Dysfunctions," *American Journal of Sociology*, 66 (January, 1961), 335–41.

48. Rein, Martin, "An Organizational Analysis of a National Agency's Local Affiliates in Their Community Contexts: A Study of the Planned Parenthood Federation of America." Unpublished Ph.D. thesis, Brandeis University, 1961.

49. Reissman, Leonard and John H. Rohrer, eds., *Change and Dilemma in the Nursing Profession*. New York: G. P. Putnam's Sons, 1957.

50. Roemer, Milton I. and Rodney F. White, "Community Attitudes toward the Hospital," *Hospital Management*, Part I (January, 1960), Part II (February, 1960).

51. Rogatz, Peter and Guido M. Crocetti, "Home Care Programs—Their Impact on the Hospital's Role in Medical Care," *American Journal of Public Health*, 48 (September, 1958), 1125–33.

52. Rosen, George and Edward Wellin, "A Bookshelf on the Social Sciences and Public Health," *American Journal of Public Health*, 49 (April, 1959), 441–54.

53. Sanders, Irwin T., *The Community: An Introduction to a Social System*. New York: The Ronald Press Company, 1958.

54. ———, "The Community Social Profile," *American Sociological Review*, 25 (February, 1960), 75–77.

55. Saunders, J. V. D. and J. H. Bruening, "Hospital-Community Relations in Mississippi," *Rural Sociology*, 24 (March, 1959), 48–51.

56. Seeley, John R., R. Alexander Sim, and E. W. Loosley, *Crestwood Heights*. New York: Basic Books, Inc., 1956.

57. Selznick, Philip, "An Approach to a Theory of Bureaucracy," *American Sociological Review*, 8 (February, 1943), 47–54.

58. ———, *TVA and the Grass Roots*. Berkeley: University of California Press, 1949, pp. 258–59.

59. ———, *The Organizational Weapon*. New York: McGraw-Hill Book Company, Inc., 1952.

60. Sills, David L., *The Volunteers: Means and Ends in a National Organization*. New York: The Free Press of Glencoe, Inc., 1957.

61. Silver, George A., "Social Medicine at the Montefiore Hospital—A Practical Approach to Community Health Problems," *American Journal of Public Health*, 48 (June, 1958), 724–31.

62. Smith, Harvey L., "Two Lines of Authority: The Hospital's Dilemma," *in* E. Gartley Jaco ed., *Patients, Physicians and Illness*. New York: The Free Press of Glencoe, Inc., 1958, pp. 468–77.

63. Solon, Jerry, Cecil G. Sheps, Sidney S. Lee, and Maeda Jackowitz, "Staff Perceptions of Patients' Use of a Hospital Out-Patient Department," *Journal of Medical Education*, 33 (January, 1958), 10–21.

64. Sower, Christopher, John Holland, Kenneth Tridke, and Walter Freeman, *Community Involvement*. New York: The Free Press of Glencoe, Inc., 1957.

65. Stanton, Alfred H. and Morris S. Schwartz, *The Mental Hospital: A Study of Institutional Participation in Psychiatric Illness and Treatment*. New York: Basic Books, Inc., 1954, pp. 193–243.

66. Thompson, James D. and William McEwan, "Organizational Goals and Environment: Goal Settings as an Interaction Process," *American Sociological Review*, 20 (April, 1955), 206–10.

67. Truman, David B., *The Governmental Process*. New York: Alfred A. Knopf, Inc., 1951, p. 118.

68. Tsouderos, John E., "Organizational Change in Terms of a Series of Selected Variables," *American Sociological Review*, 20 (April, 1955), 209.

69. Warren, Roland L., "Toward a Typology of Extra-Community Control Limiting Local Community Autonomy," *Social Forces*, 34 (May, 1956), 338–41.

70. White, Paul E. and Sol Levine, "Cost as a Factor in Interorganizational Exchange." (Mimeo.)

71. Willie, Charles V. and Herbert Notkin, "Community Organization for Health: A Case Study," *in* E. Gartley Jaco ed., *Patients, Physicians and Illness*. New York: The Free Press of Glencoe, Inc., 1958, pp. 148–58.

72. ———, "Community Leadership in the System of Health and Welfare Services." (Mimeo.)

14

THE UTILIZATION OF HEALTH SERVICES

Odin W. Anderson

From the standpoint of sociology, statistics on utilization of health services can be used as indices of certain kinds of population behavior: they reveal how much health services are expected to cost under certain circumstances; from the standpoint of medical care, they may show to what extent a population is receiving medical care. In other words, utilization of health services reveals varying patterns of significance to a wide range of interests.

It is reasonable to assume that patterns of utilization are not quixotic; in different contexts there are patterns of utilization dependent on such factors as illness levels, age and sex composition of the population, presence or absence of health facilities, family income, residence, and the perceptions of providers and recipients of health services. All of these are important, but some have more bearing on utilization than others. Further, their relative importance—except for age and sex—varies with circumstances.

So far, statistics on utilization by various kinds of biological and social variables are straightforward and simple. There is an abundance of data relating use of various types of health services to factors such as family income, residence, ethnic group, and so on. These are necessary as a base for formulating hypotheses and planning more complex research into the interrelationships of social factors and use of health services.

Components of Health Services

The various individual components of the health services used as units of measurement differ greatly according to level of use, expenditures, and meaning to the population and the providers of services. For example, the general hospital is a very different entity from the mental hospital; dental service reveals patterns of use quite different from those of physicians' services; use of drugs shows variations not similar to that of other goods and services, and so on.

Health services are usually divided into two broad categories: personal and public, and they are so divided largely as a result of historical development, differences in methods of coping with health problems, and the administrative patterns and sources of funds today. By far the larger category is that of personal health services. These are normally received by people as individual patients. Public health services traditionally are those provided for the population as a group without special regard for individual differences and initiative. The better known public programs, for example, are those established to assure a sanitary environment, and pure water, food, and atmosphere. Others control communicable disease through mass immunization. The essential difference between personal and public health services is fairly obvious—in the first, the service must be initiated by individuals—or, in the case of children, by their parents; in the second, the services can be carried out with only the passive participation of the population, without its knowledge, or even—if necessary—with its enforced compliance.

Within the category of personal health services, a division is usually made between general hospitals and those intended only for the treatment of long-term chronic diseases, such as mental illness and tuberculosis. It is obvious that these two major types are involved in very different medical problems and need to be distinguished for statistical reporting purposes.

Personal health services are usually divided by the following components of service listed below. They comprise the usual units for reporting of expenditures and gross measures of utilization:

A. General Hospital Services
   1. *Days*
      (a) Number of days per stay
      (b) Number of admissions
   2. *Type of case*
      (a) Medical
      (b) Surgical
      (c) Obstetrical
   3. *Type of accommodation*
      (a) Private
      (b) Semiprivate
      (c) Ward
   4. *Ancillary services*
      (a) Operating room
      (b) Delivery room
      (c) Drugs and medications
      (d) Laboratory
      (e) Radiology
B. Physicians' Services
   1. Site of service—home, office, hospital, clinic
   2. *Type of Service*
      (a) Surgical
      (b) Medical
      (c) Obstetrical
   3. *Specialization*
      (a) General practice
      (b) Range of specialties
   4. *Type of practice*
      (a) Solo
      (b) Partnership
      (c) Various types of groups
C. Drugs and medications
   1. Number of prescriptions
   2. Prescription and nonprescription drugs
D. Dentists' Services
   1. Number of visits to dentist
   2. General practice and various specialties
   3. *Types of services*

(a) Extractions
(b) Fillings
(c) Crowns, bridges, dentures
(d) Prophylaxis

E. Nursing Home Services
   1. Number of days per stay
   2. Number of admissions

F. Other
   1. Appliances—glasses, hearing aids, trusses
   2. Private duty nursing

These are the main measures of quantity and—to some degree—the quality of personal health services. They can be crossclassified by a great variety of variables such as age, sex, residence, and diagnosis. It is also possible to employ expenditures as a measure of use, although admittedly this is a relatively crude measure; however, expenditure data are usually recorded whereas information on use is recorded far less commonly.

Factors Related to Use of Services

The primary variables related to use of service are age and sex, because morbidity and mortality rates are directly related to them as inherent parts of the biology of the human organism and life cycle. Comparative studies of use of health services by income, residence, education, and other factors must then allow for possible age differences in the populations studied. At most, however, these variables provide some idea of patterns and variations of utilization. Except for age and sex, they do not reveal why the variations exist, and further research into the context in which health services are used is then necessary. This context then becomes the frontier of social research on the use of health services.

There are a host of social-psychological factors that can be studied—*e.g.*, perceptions of health and health services in different situations, general life values, the priorities families place on how they spend their incomes, knowledge of diseases, and many others. Studies of use also can be made in relation to sources of money for health services. Are there differences in use when services are paid for by government, by voluntary health insurance, and by families? What are the relationships in given situations between the number of hospital beds, physicians, dentists, and the use of these services? Are there differences in use between various methods of organizing and providing services, such as physicians in a group-practice prepayment plan who are paid a salary as compared with solo practitioners in a prepayment plan who are paid on a fee-for-service basis? It is obvious that research in these areas touches directly on problems of public policy. It should also be clear that there are many sociological problems dealing with institutions and organizations that can be explored simultaneously.[1]

In the absence of data on use of services, the value of expenditure data increases. Such data are used extensively today, because they are regarded as being "hard" and "making sense." They can be easily weighed against family income, government budgets, and fringe benefit negotiations in labor-management bargaining. And their "reality" is undeniable. However, their significance for an evaluation of use is limited unless information on volume and quality of services becomes available.

Nationwide data on total expenditures according to the main components of services outlined above are published annually by the Department of Commerce. These data reveal the relative financial importance of the various components and provide a rough index of "countervailing forces" in the health field. The main components are, in fact, autonomous—a spontaneous financial equilibrium evolves between them, little influenced by direct administrative rules and regulations.

Patterns of Use and Expenditures

Volume of use of health services reveals a considerable range in time and place, even among areas with relatively similar standards of living and accessibility to care. Today, for example, annual hospital admission rates[2] in Great Britain, Saskatchewan, the United States, and Sweden vary from 88 to 200 per 1000 population; the number of physicians' visits per person per year varies between less than three to five; the proportion of people who see a dentist at least once a year ranges between 16 and 34 per cent—all without readily discernable reasons. There are, indeed, probably greater differences within areas than between areas.

Although there are great variations in use, a repetition of patterns occurs, regardless of time and place within various ranges. Use of services basically is a function of age and sex. Available age and sex rates indicate that utilization is lower for males than for females—and increases with age. This parallels morbidity patterns by age and sex. It would seem, then, that where use varies at different times and places, the differences are a function of the contexts in which health services are used—family income, educational level of health of household, absence or presence of health

[1] For a more detailed discussion of these topics, see Chaps. 4, 12, and 13.

[2] In this chapter, the discussion is limited to admissions to general hospitals. This is not to deny the importance and magnitude of admissions to long-term and chronic disease hospitals, including mental hospitals. See Chap. 6 for a discussion of hospitalization for mental illness.

insurance, and the organizational structure of the health services establishment.[3]

General hospital care

In 1935, the admission rate to general hospitals in this country was 59 per 1000 population; in recent years it has been approximately 130 [22]. An increase has taken place throughout the entire Western world. In England and Wales the rate is now 88 per 1000; in Sweden, 128; in Saskatchewan, 200. In the course of time, a very high proportion of the population is admitted to general hospitals. One nationwide population survey revealed that 75 per cent of American adults had been in a general hospital within ten years prior to the interview [17]. In order to obtain admission rates by age and sex, a systematic population survey is required because health agencies seldom compile such data regularly. Table 14-1 is an

TABLE 14-1 Admission Rates to General Hospitals for a 12-Month Period, United States, 1952–53, by Age and Sex

	Both sexes	*Male*	*Female*
All persons	12%	9%	15%(10)*
Under 6	8	8	8
6–17	8	8	8(7)
18–34	16	6	25(10)
35–54	12	10	14(12)
55–64	12	10	13
65 and over	13	11	15

* Figures in parentheses exclude hospitalized deliveries.
Source: Odin W. Anderson and Jacob J. Feldman. *Family Medical Costs and Voluntary Health Insurance: A Nationwide Survey,* New York: McGraw-Hill Book Company, Inc., 1956, p. 180.

example of patterns of hospital admissions by age and sex. From the limited data it appears that if utilization rates were available by age and sex in European countries or in Australia, for example, the same pattern of use by age and sex (as distinct from volume) would be found. Systematic data from Canada supports this assumption [7].

Past admission rates to hospitals varied considerably by family income—*i.e.*, the lower the income, the lower the rate. This has changed, however, and admission rates by income are now virtually uniform (Table 14-2). This uniformity may not prevail in other countries, but it does represent an important shift in use of services in the United States. Admission rates by residence show variations, but not according to the usual presupposi-

[3] The data to follow may seem incomplete and fragmentary because their paucity does not make possible detailed comparisons of use of services for time and place by many desired variables. The data for the United States as a whole are as complete as for any country, but for international, inter-regional and inter-city differences one can at best produce over-all averages without detailed breakdowns.

TABLE 14-2 Admission Rates to General Hospitals for a 12-Month Period, United States, 1952–53, by Family Income

	Per cent
All incomes	12%
Under $2,000	12
$2,000–3,499	12
$3,500–4,999	12
$5,000–7,499	12
$7,500 and over	11

Source: Anderson and Feldman, *op. cit.*, p. 183.

tions of urban and rural differences. Table 14-3 shows that urban utilization is lower than rural.

TABLE 14-3 Admission Rates to General Hospitals for a 12-Month Period, United States, 1952–53, by Residence

	Per cent
All areas	12%
Urban areas of 1 million and over	10
Other urban	11
Rural nonfarm	14
Rural farm	12

Source: Anderson and Feldman, *op. cit.*, p. 184.

One constant pattern of differences in admissions to hospitals is the presence or absence of hospital insurance. Regardless of age, sex, family income, and residence, families that have some type of hospital insurance are admitted to hospitals more often than those without insurance. Nationwide averages show that members of families with hospital insurance are admitted to hospitals at a rate of 14 per cent, compared with 9 per cent of those without hospital insurance. Data from a similar survey conducted in 1958 show that this difference has narrowed.[4]

In Western countries, the admission rate to general hospitals has increased and the average length of stay has decreased. There seems to be a constant relationship between admission rate and average length of stay. Where the admission rate is relatively high, the length of stay is relatively short. During the 1930's in this country, the admission rate per 1000 population was 59, and the average length of stay was 15 days. Currently, the admission rate is 130, and the length of stay is between 7 and 8 days. The common sense reason for this shortened stay is the increase in admissions of patients with relatively minor conditions. Also, surgical and

[4] Unpublished data from the survey conducted by the Health Information Foundation and the National Opinion Research Center show a rate of 13 per cent for insured and 10 per cent for uninsured.

obstetrical cases have a shorter stay than formerly because of changing concepts of medical practice.

For comparative purposes, the differences in admission rates and length of stay between the United States, England and Wales, and Sweden may be contrasted. As reported earlier, the admission rate in the United States is 130; in England and Wales, 88; and in Sweden, 128. The average lengths of stay respectively are less than 8, 15, and 14 days [41]. Sweden has an admission rate as high as that in the United States, and an average stay almost twice as long; England and Wales have an admission rate much lower than that of the United States and Sweden, with an average stay about the same as that in Sweden. Present information does not permit easy explanation for these differences. Because the mortality patterns by cause in these countries are quite similar, very similar morbidity patterns may be assumed. Accordingly, the context in which medicine is practiced must be examined.

Physicians

Americans are seeking physicians' services much more frequently than they did a generation ago. During 1928–31, 2.6 out-of-hospital physician visits per person in a year were reported [13]. During a 12-month period extending from 1957–58, there were 5.3 physicians' visits per person per year [43].

As seen in Table 14-4, physicians' visits by age and sex follow morbidity

TABLE 14-4 Number of Physician Visits Per Person Per Year Out of Hospital, By Age and Sex, United States, July 1957–June 1958.

Sex and age	*Visits per person*
All ages	5.3
Under 5	6.4
5–24	4.2
25–64	5.4
65 and over	6.8
Male	4.5
Female	6.1

Source: U.S. National Health Survey. Health Statistics. Selected Survey Topics, July 1957–June 1958. Washington, D.C., Public Health Service, 1958. U.S. Public Health Service Bulletin No. 584–85.

patterns. Younger people reveal a relatively high rate of acute disease episodes (chiefly respiratory and infectious), and upper age groups have a high rate of long-term and chronic diseases—hence a *U* shaped curve. The differences in the average number of physician visits by sex reflects the higher illness rates reported for females, excluding conditions associated with childbirth.

A nationwide survey in 1950–51 showed that Canadians used physicians' services much less than did persons in the United States; the number of out-of-hospital physician visits per person per year was less than 2 [7]—lower than the United States figure in 1928–31. Great Britain, several years after the establishment of the National Health Service, showed a rate of use of physicians' services similar to that in the United States, which has never had a universal health service system. But, in Sweden—with a near-universal health insurance system—physicians are seen only two-thirds as often as in the United States or Great Britain.[5]

Perhaps as significant a measure of use of physicians' services as the number of per person visits is the percentage of those in a population who do not see a physician during a year. This percentage varies considerably in time and place, and by age and sex. During the period 1928–31, for example, approximately 60 per cent of the population in the United States did not seek physicians' services during a given year; 25 or so years later, 60 per cent of the population did [1, 13].

The variations for the latter period in the United States can be seen by age and sex in Table 14-5. Those in the age group under 6 are most

TABLE 14-5 Per Cent of Persons with No Out-Of-Hospital Physician Visits, For a 12-Month Period, United States, 1952–53, by Age and Sex

Age and sex	*Per cent with no visits*
All persons	40%
Under 6	28
6–17	48
18–34	37
35–54	41
55–64	42
65 and over	35
Male	45
Female	35

Source: Anderson and Feldman, *op. cit.*, Table A-97, p. 196.

likely to see physicians at least once during a year, and the age group from 6–17 is least likely to do so. It is of interest that those under 6 are more likely to see physicians than those 65 and over. And in Canada in 1950–51, 57 per cent of the population did not see physicians in a year [7].

Utilization of physicians' services by family income shows that the higher the income, the greater is the number of physician visits per person, although the disparity between number of physician visits per person and family income is not as great now as it was a generation ago [24].

A subdivision of physicians' services that receives a great deal of attention because of its importance as a health insurance benefit and the ease with which it can be recorded is surgery. Surgical procedures account

[5] Richard Sterner, unpublished data from studies made by the Sickness Insurance Fund in Sweden.

for 20 per cent of the expenditures for all physicians' services in the United States. Table 14-6 shows that 7 per cent of the people in the United States undergo surgery during a year. Although there is a generally higher utilization of personal health services by the aged, this is not true for surgery. Obviously, these figures do not reveal the variations of types of

TABLE 14-6 Surgical Procedures * per 100 Person-Years for a 12-Month Period, United States, 1952–53, by Age and Sex

	Per cent
All persons	7
Under 6	4
6–17	6
18–34	6
35–54	8
55–64	8
65 and over	8
Male	6
Female	8

* Includes all cutting procedures (including Caesarean but not normal deliveries) or setting of a dislocation or fracture. Does not include circumcision of newborn infants and suturing of wounds.

Source: Anderson and Feldman, *op. cit.*, Table A-94, p. 193.

surgery in different age-groups. Females have a constantly higher utilization of all types of personal health services, including surgery.

Over the years, the differences between rates of surgical procedures and family income have been converging so that at present they are small. In fact, among the insured portion of the population, low-income groups experience a much higher rate of surgical procedures than do high-income groups.

Dentists

Relative to other personal health services and goods and considering the overwhelming need for dental care in the population, the utilization of dental services is low. This is true even for upper-income groups. During the last generation there has been only a slight increase in use of dental services as measured by the proportion of people who see a dentist at least once during a year.

As shown in Table 14-7, 34 per cent of the population of the United States sees a dentist at least once during a year. The familiar sex differentials persist—*i.e.*, higher utilization by females than by males. There is a precipitous drop-off among those 65 and over. The proportion of persons in each income group that saw a dentist at least once during the year is reported in Table 14-8. The proportion of the population that sees a dentist rises as income rises, but even in the highest income group—$7500 and over—44 per cent of the people did not consult a dentist at least once a year. A study in Canada reveals very similar patterns of use of dental services [8].

TABLE 14-7 Per Cent of People Consulting Dentists at Least Once During a Year for a 12-Month Period, 1952–53, United States, by Age and Sex

Age and sex	*Per cent of persons*
All persons	34%
Under 6	10
6–17	44
18–34	44
35–54	39
55–64	25
65 and over	13
Male	31
Female	36

Source: Anderson and Feldman, *op. cit.*, Table A-98, p. 198.

TABLE 14-8 Per Cent of Persons Consulting Dentists Annually, by Family Income for a 12-Month Period, 1952–53, United States

Family Income	*Per cent of persons*
All incomes	34%
Under $2,000	17
$2,000–3,499	23
$3,500–4,999	33
$5,000–7,499	44
$7,500 and over	56

Source: Anderson and Feldman, *op. cit.*, Table A-100, p. 200.

Patterns of expenditures

Patterns of expenditures for personal health services by source of payment, divisions between the components of services, and family income, age, sex, and so on reveal many significant facets. Sixty per cent of the expenditures for all personal health services in the United States are made by families and individuals; 20 per cent are paid for by some form of voluntary health insurance; and 20 per cent by various levels of government. In other words, 80 per cent of all expenditures are made outside the governmental sector. The governmental sector is concerned with medical care for recipients of public assistance, members of the armed forces and their dependents, with the operation of mental and tuberculosis hospitals, public health programs, veterans' care, and similar traditional responsibilities of government in the United States. This 20–80 ratio is by no means static and, therefore, is a significant statistic for the student of public policy formulation.

Each component of service in the private sector may be shown as a percentage of the total, as in Table 14-9. These components are relatively autonomous entities, and the proportions shown have emerged from a spontaneous play of forces in terms of use and price. Further, the breakdown indicates roughly the financial resources of each component of service and the relative degrees of public involvement with them.

TABLE 14-9 COMPONENTS OF SERVICES IN THE PRIVATE SECTOR

	Percentage
Hospital care	23%
Physicians' services	34
Medicines	20
Dentists' services	15
All other	8

In a nationwide survey of families conducted for a 12-month period in 1957–58, it was found that families spent an average of $294 for the full range of personal health services; individuals spent $94. By age groups, the average expenditures for those under 6 was $48, rising to $177 for those 65 years of age and over. As expected, females had higher expenditures than males ($111 compared with $77).

On a family basis, expenditures came to 5.5 per cent of annual income. The lower the family income, the lower was the absolute expenditure, but the higher was the percentage of income laid out in a year. Families with incomes of $2000 or less laid out on an average of $165, or 13 per cent of their incomes, compared with families with incomes of $7500 and over that laid out $411, or 3.9 per cent of their incomes [3].

The distribution of family expenditure by magnitude covers a tremendous range. In the same nationwide survey, 20 per cent of the families had expenditures of less than $50 or more during the year, and 4.6 per cent had expenditures of $1000 or more. These patterns (not necessarily the same magnitudes) repeat themselves by age, sex, residence and income in studies conducted 25 years ago. In the 1928–31 study of the Committee on the Costs of Medical Care, and in the two surveys of Health Information Foundation and National Opinion Research Center in 1953 and 1958, it was found that approximately 10 per cent of the population make 40 per cent of all expenditures for personal health services in a year [5, 13].

Utilization in Various Contexts

So far no attempt has been made to relate such patterns of utilization to well-defined situations in which they are found. But why are hospitals and physicians' services used at different rates in various countries, regions, and cities? While this question cannot be answered from present data for lack of well-controlled and comparative studies, it is believed that there is now a sufficient volume and variety of utilization data to permit the formulation of research aimed at elucidating why such variations exist. This necessitates a research design rigid enough to control many of the important factors involved in utilization patterns.

In this country there is a great deal of concern over hospital utilization rates and to some extent, surgical procedure rates. As already noted, use of hospitals during the past twenty years has increased greatly and at the same time cost per day has quadrupled. The twin factors of increased use and cost have pushed hospital insurance premiums to such an extent that they are now a subject of public discussion and debate.

Statistics on hospital use show various patterns among consumer or labor sponsored group practice plans, health insurance plans sponsored by private insurance companies, and hospital and medical society sponsored Blue Cross and Blue Shield plans. Studies so far do not permit generalizations that one type of approach necessarily results in higher utilization than another. In one effort to study this problem, Health Information Foundation and National Opinion Research Center surveyed two populations in the same area that were enrolled in different comprehensive physicians' service plans [5, 11]. One of the plans was based on group-practice units and the other on traditional free choice of physician and fee-for-service method of payment. These plans were Health Insurance Plan of Greater New York (HIP) and Group Health Insurance (GHI) also in New York. In HIP there were 6.3 hospital admissions per 100 members; in GHI there were 11.0. Hospitalized surgery rates were 4.3 per cent and 7.6 per cent respectively. Nevertheless, the HIP population consulted physicians just as often as did the GHI population. Persons in both groups saw physicians outside of hospitals six times a year. The HIF-NORC study indicated a difference in hospital use although it did not determine why these differences existed.

Recently, however, the results of two major studies were published. One compared utilization and many other factors between a Blue Cross-Blue Shield type of plan, a plan with a low deductible and coinsurance, and a group-practice plan. The use of hospitals in the three plans was virtually identical [36]. The other study, done in New York City, was of two groups of union members with hospital insurance under a union-administered plan but with physicians' services under two different arrangements—a group practice type and a union-administered fee-for-service plan. There was no difference in hospital admission rates between the two groups [12].

There is probing in other contexts as seen in studies conducted in King County, Washington, and Windsor, Ontario. Both have medical-society-sponsored physician service plans providing comprehensive physicians' services with free choice of physicians practicing on a fee-for-service basis. In King County, the hospital admission rate was 114 per 1000 population; in Windsor, Ontario, it was 118. These rates are lower than the national average in the United States [10, 40].

A few years ago the utilization of physicians' service by a sample of the population of HIP was compared with that by a sample of the population of New York City. It was found that the HIP population had a higher rate of utilization. This was not unexpected, but there was some surprise that the differences were not greater [9].[6]

There are those who feel that the very presence of health facilities, such as hospitals, leads to their use because medical "need" is very elastic [35]. In a rough way it does seem that the rate of use varies with the presence of hospital beds, particularly when patients do not pay directly for hospital care.

It is common knowledge that hospitals have become an extremely important part of medical care. Nevertheless, it should be realized that about 60 per cent of medical practice, as measured by expenditure, is conducted outside of the hospital. The number of hospital beds has kept pace with the increase in population since World War II, but the number of physicians has not. If this trend continues, inevitably the pattern of use must change. There are, however, no objective standards with which to establish the proper ratio of hospital beds and physicians—not to mention other types of facilities and personnel—to population. These ratios must emerge out of a context of effective demand, family income, and appreciation of health services. The foregoing studies of particular situations are literally all that have been done so far.

Finally, there is the question of the influence of insurance on use of services. All comparative studies have shown that insured families use more services and spend more for services than do families without insurance. The obvious conclusion is that insurance encourages use (many say unnecessary use), but it is of great interest that persons with insurance are also more likely than the uninsured to seek dental care and spend more money for drugs, even though those services are not commonly covered by insurance. Easy explanations, then, are not possible.

Psychological and Sociological Factors

Literature on the psychological and sociological aspects of use of health services is not extensive or systematic. It is not possible therefore, to present a detailed and coherent picture of how people behave regarding health services. A few basic generalizations may be made that perhaps sound like the rankest truisms, but do show an increasing level of sophistication regarding the importance of social and psychological factors in the use of health services.

It is now realized that personal income is only one of many factors that

---

[6] See Chap. 12.

must be considered. As recently as 30 years ago it was assumed that those who did not receive "adequate" health services could not "afford" them. This concept still lingers: the term "financial barrier" is standard jargon in medical care literature.

But as health insurance became more widespread and family incomes increased, the economic factor became less and less important as a reason for not seeking services; consequently, other factors were clearly at work. Koos, in his classic study, demonstrated the relationship of social class to use of services. He showed an interrelationship of factors: the lower the class and the lower the income, the lower the perception of symptoms needing care and the lower the use [30].

Anthropologists show the importance of cultural differences in the attitudes toward and use of services [35].[7] Consequently in their study of the populations enrolled in HIP and GHI in New York City, Sheatsley and Anderson standardized for ethnic composition, knowing that there were differences in use between ethnic groups which had no necessary relationship to family income.

While the concept of the economic man has been diluted in studies of use of health services, we still struggle with an equally unrealistic concept which might be called the "health man." Professionals in the health field seem to insist on a concept of ideal health behavior which they believe a rational human being would follow. The person they have in mind sees his doctor early, but not too early; uses health facilities, as needs arise, but does not overuse them; follows all the health rules; spends just the right amount of money for health services in relation to his total needs, and so on. We continue therefore to try to learn why human beings persist in doing what is not good for them. For example, a study shows that over 80 per cent of an adult sample of the population of this country believe annual physical checkups are a good thing, yet fewer than 30 per cent had had such examinations in the year preceding the interview—and, in most instances, such examinations had been required for life insurance, employment, or other purposes. The same was true for annual visits to the dentist. Eventually, as systematic research continues, we may evolve theories of human behavior with reference to health supported by factual data. But the fragmentary facts may be noted, with no attempt at ex post facto explanations.

1. The National Health Service in Great Britain is one of the most comprehensive health services for the population ever devised. Yet in a study of a representative sample of families in London, 37 per cent of the families (as reported by the mothers) had a member suffering pain or discomfort and not being treated. A visit to a physician is free of charge [33].

---

[7] See Chap. 16.

2. From a survey of a representative sample of adults in the United States, 8 per cent reported that 12 months prior to the interview they had not carried out physicians' recommendations for hospitalization. Only 20 per cent mentioned expenses as the reason for not following the recommendation [18].
3. From the same survey cited in item 2 it was noted: "It appears that most people who have not seen a dentist regularly have not done so simply because, in one way or another, they don't believe such visits to be necessary" [17].
4. From a study of approximately 500 families in Hackensack, New Jersey, Weeks reported that income was an important factor in putting off medical or dental care among low-income families, but upper-income families more frequently said they were too busy or gave other reasons. And, regardless of income, family habits were important: Families that can be categorized as buying on time, buying on impulse, or budgeting their expenses were more likely to put off care than families that cannot be so classified [46].
5. Finally, here is an observation by Feldman from the study of attitudes of a national sample of adults referred to above: "All other things being equal, a person who views doctors as having few faults should utilize their services more frequently than a more antagonistic person. Well, we have correlated attitudes toward doctors with the number of times a doctor was seen during the past year, controlling by a rather refined index of perceived medical needs. This partial correlation still turns out to be remarkably close to zero. In general, it seems that if a person recognizes that he is ill he will generally consult a doctor no matter what he thinks of the profession as a whole" [14].

Observations and Suggestions for Further Research

These data indicate that there is quite a bit of information on patterns of utilization in different contexts, but that very little is known about the reasons for the differences in these patterns. Accordingly, there is a range of sociological and social psychological variables to which further research should be directed—utilization of services and social class, and the perceptions of and attitudes toward health and health services on the part of the general public and the providers of service. There are potential relationships here that need a great deal of unraveling.

Further research on utilization of services—that is, hospital and physicians' services—should be conducted in well-defined operating situations. Otherwise, we will simply continue to accumulate more interesting data that are difficult to relate to specific contexts. A specific problem which has both practical and theoretical application is the apparent difference between hospital admission and surgical rates in group medical practice associated with insurance and the prevailing type of solo practice, fee-for-service method of payment associated with insurance. These two types respectively represent relatively tight and loose social systems of great interest to sociology. They also represent competing systems of great interest to medical care generally, and so far evaluations have been inadequate.

Finally, it is hoped that sociologists can contribute to more sophisticated —*i.e.,* realistic—thinking in the medical care field. There is a tendency among many in the medical care field to assume that there is no limit to the amount of hospital or physicians' services people would use if facilities were available and services were free and there were no deliberate controls of any kind. There seems to be no concept of an equilibrium of use—and it is this concept which can usefully be explored by sociologists to serve both sociology and medical care.

References

1. Anderson, Odin W. and Jacob J. Feldman, *Family Medical Costs and Voluntary Health Insurance: A Nationwide Survey.* New York: McGraw-Hill Book Company, Inc., 1956. Table A-97, p. 196.
2. Anderson, Odin W. and the Staff of the National Opinion Research Center, *Voluntary Health Insurance in Two Cities: A Survey of Subscriber-Households.* Cambridge: Harvard University Press, 1957.
3. Anderson, Odin W., Patricia Collette, and Jacob J. Feldman, *Family Expenditure Patterns for Personal Health Services, 1953 and 1958,* Nationwide Surveys, Research Series No. 14. New York: Health Information Foundation, 1960.
4. Anderson, Odin W. and Monroe Lerner, *Measuring Health Levels in the United States.* Research Series No. 11. New York: Health Information Foundation, 1960.
5. Anderson, Odin W. and Paul B. Sheatsley, *Comprehensive Medical Insurance—A Study of Costs, Use, and Attitudes under Two Plans,* Health Information Foundation Research Series No. 9. New York: Health Information Foundation, 1959.
6. California State Department of Health, *Health in California.* Berkeley: The Department, 1956.
7. Canada, Department of National Health and Welfare and Dominion Bureau of Statistics, *Illness and Health Care in Canada.* Canadian Sickness Survey, 1940–51. Ottawa: The Department, 1960.
8. Canada, Department of National Health and Welfare, Research and Statistics Division, *Health Care Series Memorandum No. 12. Hospital Care in Canada: Recent Trends and Developments.* Ottawa: The Department, 1960.
9. The Committee for the Special Research Project in the Health Insurance Plan of Greater New York, *Health and Medical Care in New York City.* Cambridge: Harvard University Press for the Commonwealth Fund, 1957.
10. Darsky, Benjamin J., Nathan Sinai, and Solomon J. Axelrod, *Comprehensive Medical Services under Voluntary Health Insurance: A Study of Windsor Medical Services.* Cambridge: Harvard University Press, 1958.

11. Densen, Paul M., Ellen W. Jones, Eve Balamath, and Sam Shapiro, "Prepaid Medical Care and Hospital Utilization in a Dual Choice Situation," *American Journal of Public Health,* 50 (November, 1960), 1710–26.
12. Densen, Paul M. and Sam Shapiro, "Comparison of a Group Practice and a Self-Insurance Situation," *Hospitals,* 36 (November 16, 1962), 63–65.
13. Falk, I. S., Margaret Klem, and Nathan Sinai, *The Incidence of Illness and the Receipt and Cost of Medical Care Among Representative Families.* Chicago: University of Chicago Press, Committee on the Costs of Medical Care No. 26, 1933.
14. Feldman, Jacob J., "What Americans Think about Their Medical Care." Paper read at the annual meeting of the American Statistical Association, Chicago, December 27–30, 1958.
15. Forsyth, Gordon and Robert F. L. Logan, *The Demand for Medical Care: A Study of the Care-Food in the Barrow and Furness Group of Hospitals.* London: Oxford University Press, 1960.
16. Freidson, Eliot, *Patients' Views of Medical Practice—A Study of Subscribers to a Prepaid Medical Plan in the Bronx.* New York: Russell Sage Foundation, 1961.
17. ——— and Jacob J. Feldman, *The Public Looks at Dental Care.* Research Series No. 6. New York: Health Information Foundation, 1958.
18. ———, *The Public Looks at Hospitals.* Research Series No. 4. New York: Health Information Foundation, 1958.
19. Great Britain, Ministry of Health and General Register Office, *Report on Hospital In-Patient Enquiry for the Two Years, 1956–1957.* London: Her Majesty's Stationery Office, 1961.
20. Health Information Foundation, "The Growth of American Hospital Facilities," *Progress in Health Services* (September, 1960).
21. ———, "The Distribution of American Hospital Facilities," *Progress in Health Services* (December, 1956).
22. ———, "The Changing Pattern of Hospital Use," *Progress in Health Services* (May, 1958).
23. ———, "Trends in Use of General Hospitals," *Progress in Health Services* (October, 1959).
24. ———, "The Increased Use of Medical Care," *Progress in Health Services* (October, 1958).
25. ———, "Hospitalized Mental Illness," *Progress in Health Services* (October, 1959).
26. ———, "Hospitalized Mental Illness in the United States," *Progress in Health Services* (October, 1960).
27. ———, "Families with High Expenditures for Health," *Progress in Health Services* (November, 1960).
28. ———, "Hospital Use by Diagnosis: A Study in Contrasts," *Progress in Health Services* (January, 1961).
29. Hoffer, Charles R. *et al., Health Needs and Health Care in Michigan.* East Lansing: Michigan State College, 1950, Agricultural Experiment Station, Special Bulletin No. 365 (June, 1950).
30. Koos, Earl L., *The Health of Regionville: What the People Thought and Did About It.* New York: Columbia University Press, 1954.

31. Lerner, Monroe, *Hospital Use and Charges by Diagnostic Category: A Report on the Indiana Study of a Blue Cross Population.* Research Series No. 13. New York: Health Information Foundation, 1960.
32. ———, *Hospital Use by Diagnosis: A Comparison of Two Experiences.* Research Series No. 19. New York: Health Information Foundation, 1961.
33. Political and Economic Planning, *Family Needs and the Social Services.* London: George Allen & Unwin, Ltd., 1961.
34. Roemer, Milton I. and Max Shain, *Hospital Utilization under Insurance.* Hospital Monograph Series No. 6. Chicago: American Hospital Association, 1959.
35. Saunders, Lyle, *Cultural Difference and Medical Care: The Care of the Spanish-Speaking People of the Southwest.* New York: Russell Sage Foundation, 1954.
36. School of Public Health and Administrative Medicine, Columbia University, with the cooperation of the National Opinion Research Center, University of Chicago. *Family Medical Care under Three Types of Health Insurance.* New York: Foundation on Employee Health, Medical Care, and Welfare, Inc., 1962, p. 152.
37. Shain, Max and Milton I. Roemer, "Hospital Costs Relate to the Supply of Beds," *Modern Hospital,* 92 (April, 1959), 71–73.
38. Shanas, Ethel, *Medical Care among Those Aged 65 and over—Reported Illness and Utilization of Health Services by the "Sick" and the "Well."* Research Series No. 16. New York: Health Information Foundation, 1960.
39. Sheatsley, Paul B., "Public Attitudes toward Hospital," *Hospitals* (May 16, 1957).
40. Shipman, George A., Robert J. Lampman, and Frank Miyamoto, "The Administration of Medical Service Corporations in the State of Washington," Health Information Foundation, *Progress in Health Services* (June, 1960).
41. Sweden, National Board of Health, *Public Health in Sweden, 1958.* Annual Report, Stockholm, 1960, p. 34.
42. Trussell, Ray E. and Jack Elinson, *Chronic Illness in a Rural Area: The Hunterdon Study.* Vol. III of *Chronic Illness in the United States.* Cambridge: Harvard University Press for the Commonwealth Fund, 1959.
43. United States Public Health Service, *National Health Survey, Health Statistics, Selected Survey Topics, United States, July 1957–June, 1958.* United States Public Health Series Bulletin No. 684–85.
44. ———, *National Health Survey, Health Statistics, Selected Characteristics by Area, United States, July, 1957–June, 1959.* Series C-No. 6.
45. ———, *National Health Survey, Preliminary Report on the Volume of Physician Visits, United States, July–September, 1957.* Series B-1.
46. Weeks, H. Ashely, *Family Spending Patterns and Health Care.* Cambridge: Harvard University Press, 1961.

15

PUBLIC HEALTH IN THE COMMUNITY

Irwin T. Sanders

The community may be viewed in three ways, each of which has special relevance to health; first, as a place; second, as a collection of people; and third, as a social system. After considering the community in general, attention will be devoted to health as a major community system, relating it briefly to other local institutional complexes. Important community factors such as power, leadership, and decision-making; the action programs and community issues; and, finally, the problem of community change will also be considered.

Three-Dimensional View of the Community

The community as a place

"Place" is important to health in at least three aspects. One is the epidemiological, which partially relies upon mapping to locate and explain the incidence and spread of various types of illness—an important topic but not within the purview of this discussion.[1] Place is important secondly because it can be used to reveal the availability and utilization of health services [41]. For instance, it is common practice to regard a population of 1000 per physician as a reasonable ratio, but many rural counties have as many as 3000 persons or more per physician. As Hoffer notes, health facilities are unevenly distributed and "where medical service is available, people follow approximately the same pattern for health services as for trade" [31]. Harden's study of communities in central Illinois also supports the assumption that population and goods and services increase together [31], while Price and Hitt noted a direct correlation in Louisiana between urbanization and the facility with which people can obtain the services of doctors, dentists, and nurses [61]. But Larson and Hay found no support in two New York counties for the hypothesis that utilization of private health resources by rural people is closely related to the availability of these resources within the county. They suggest that some relationship may exist, but that county indices are poor measuring devices for this purpose [44]. Hamilton, in studying the locational factors related to physicians in Wisconsin, found the ratio of physicians to population to be twice as high in the metropolitan as in the nonmetropolitan areas [27]. In a similar study of the Southern Appalachian area, however, Hamilton found less difference between the metropolitan areas (1,185 persons per physician) and nonmetropolitan areas (1,824 persons) [28]. The contrast between availability of hospital facilities in rural Wisconsin and the Southern Appalachians is also very marked. He indicates that in Wisconsin the nonmetropolitan communities compared favorably with the metropolitan communities in number of hospital beds per 1000 population, but somewhat unfavorably in hospital days per 1000 population [29]. By contrast, 57 counties of the Southern Appalachian region have no hospitals of any kind and 27 of these counties have populations of more than 10,000 [27]. It is clear therefore that the location of the community has much to do with the health facilities and services available there.[2]

But place also refers to the physical environment in which man lives, some of it natural and some of it manmade, but all of it part of the visible

---

[1] See Chap. 3.
[2] See Chap. 14 for a discussion of utilization of health services.

community—the tangible signs of communal living. The physical community includes among other things, the problems of traffic flow, sewage disposal, stream and air pollution, as well as the question of safe and adequate housing.

Although earlier social reformers such as Jacob Riis had written about the slums, it was not until the 1930's that many city health departments conducted studies of the problem areas in their cities. They found a close connection between deteriorated housing and such problems as crime and delinquency, illegitimacy, venereal disease, and tuberculosis. Such studies, excellently summarized by Rumney [65], revealed that far more public funds were spent in these blighted areas than were received in tax revenues from the property owners there. These studies, however, did not establish any causative relationships between bad housing and these social conditions. It is an important point to bear in mind for, if bad housing were the cause, then housing reform would resolve the resultant conditions—which, of course, it does not. Chapin, Johanson, and Johnson suggest that in the borough of Manhattan low rentals are followed by a high percentage of crowding [12]. One of the most penetrating critics of these earlier studies was Dean who, in an article entitled "The Myths of Housing Reform," grouped what he termed the nonrational defenses of housing reform under four headings: (*a*) appeals to the subjective evaluational roots of housing standards; (*b*) myths surrounding the complex relationship of slums to social disorder; (*c*) myths about the social effects of rehousing, and (*d*) myths about the financial liability of slums to the municipality [16].

A further difficulty in dealing with housing as a social problem is the accurate determination of what is good, adequate, or bad housing. The members of different communities as well as specific segments within a single community differ in their judgements of adequacy, as well as about the courses of action to be taken in improving situations which are generally recognized as bad. Twichell [75], Wirth [83], Chapin [11], and Brunsman [10] all address themselves to the research aspects of this problem and provide helpful leads.

Slums, whether rural or urban, may be thought of as "areas containing housing which is in an advanced stage of physical decay or which, because of poor planning, disagreeable surroundings, or bad sanitary facilities, is likely to produce diseased physical or social lives for its inhabitants" [42, 82]. Without the help of municipal or real estate authorities, a single property owner cannot hold back this deterioration; only collective action can bring sufficient social pressure upon recalcitrant landlords or tenants to arrest the process of decay or blight.

If bad housing is associated with bad health, how can better housing be obtained? One answer has been slum clearance, which views the elimination of bad housing as a primary necessity, particularly with the corollary provision of cheap public housing in the same or some other location. More recently, the stress has shifted from slum clearance to urban renewal, which has broadened the concern from attack on residential areas alone to the problem of economic decline in the downtown center. This has led to many efforts by city governments to halt what is considered urban blight by requiring landlords to bring their property up to a certain standard and maintain it there. In places such as Cleveland, Ohio, this is called a Neighborhood Improvement Program; it relies more upon a public informational campaign and voluntary cooperation than upon enforcement of comprehensive housing codes [78].

As city authorities gain experience with what might be called community organization techniques, they are also learning that the past emphasis upon the physical aspects of urban renewal must take into account social and economic aspects as well. This is the plea of such commentators on the current urban scene as Jacobs, who thinks that a variety of social contacts and economic services must be maintained in any area that is rehabilitated even though it means that some preferred orderly, aseptic spatial designs may have to be scrapped [37].

The community as a collection of people

Concern with the physical community is important in the comprehensive planning for good health, but planning must not stop there. What about community size? Has it been increasing or decreasing over the years? If increasing, has natural increase or immigration been largely responsible? What has been happening to death rates and length of life?

Related to these is the question of population density. Nagi has stated that "certain sources of sociological stresses such as complexities in life situations and role conflicts are characteristic of urbanization, which is highly associated with the density of population" [54].[3] This holds true for the Zulu of South Africa as well [70].

Population composition—whether viewed in terms of sex, age, occupation, or marital status—is also related to many health factors. Finally, morbidity rates, days of disability and confinement in bed, as well as infant mortality rates all serve as indicators of health and disease.

But people are more than statistics; they are carriers of traditions and cultural values, as Paul [58] and Straus [74] point out. We find these traditions and values clearly expressed when we compare the differences in response on the part of various ethnic groupings to health programs [15]. For example, Lieberson has shown that ethnic identification of physicians significantly influences their pattern of medical practice [46]. Wellin finds

---

[3] See Chap. 4 for a discussion of stress.

that local culture affects public health in three ways: it affects the objective profile, or the ecology, of health and disease; it creates its own, or subjective, picture of health and disease; and it influences the progress of health programs [80]. Certainly it is not stretching Wellin's analysis to point out that these same effects apply to subcultures within the communities as well as to the composite local culture.

People in a local community differ not only in terms of value orientations and beliefs about health, but also in terms of social class. In some communities these classes may be so amorphous that only those at the extremes of top and bottom can be pointed out by the average citizen; in other communities, the social distinctions may be so clearly drawn that most people know just where they stand in the social scale. Many studies of social stratification have shown a differential class distribution in utilization of health services, in educational opportunities, and in associated patterns of recreation, employment, religion, and political behavior. Kantor and her associates have cited some of these, showing a relationship between socioeconomic level and the incidence, prevalence, and treatment of mental illness [39]. Reeder has shown a connection between perception of community status and blood pressure groups [62], Freeman and Simmons have presented data on social class and posthospital performance levels of the mentally ill [21], and Koos has found statistically significant differences in the symptoms reported by members of different social classes of a small rural community [43].

Thus it is clear that communities vary in the kinds of people who make them up, and that different kinds of approaches have to be used in reaching different ethnic groups.

Communities also differ in size. The problems of a city health department, which deals primarily with the lower socioeconomic groups in the downtown population, may be of a different order from those in smaller suburban communities where living standards and incomes are higher. Furthermore, the people in one community may move much more frequently than do those in another community, either changing houses within the community or leaving it, to be replaced by newcomers. Communities may double in size over a 10- or 15-year period and develop a marked "oldtimer-newcomer" cleavage that is reflected in the reception which is accorded public health programs.

The quality of the population, as measured by its educational attainment, occupational skills, and physical fitness, may also influence community attitudes toward public health. A community that has a disproportionately large number of elderly people and children because of the out-migration of those in the income-producing ages has to make adjustments different from those with a high concentration of working adults.

The community as a social system

A third way to view a community is as a social system. This assumes that every community has a variety of patterns of action which have grown up around the satisfaction of important local needs with specialization of function and of personnel. The community as a system, therefore, may be viewed as the totality of the interaction among these major systems, of which health is one.

The economy, for example, can be broken down into component social networks (or subsystems) which consist in large part of the formal groups and associations clustered together around a significant common interest: finance, industry, commerce, agriculture, transportation. Some of these groups represent management, some labor, some the public, but they make up the content of the subsystem. Such groups, when studied individually, are seen to be sets of social relationships: among officers, among members, between officers and members, or between different groups. Relationships, in turn, can be reduced to the persons or units who fill the appropriate statuses in a given situation and carry out the expected roles. In such a way, the economy—a major system—is an abstraction which can be traced to the patterned behavior of the individuals in a community who, during part of the day at least, are filling economic statuses as opposed to familial or recreational statuses. Whether one studies the community at the analytical level of organizations, or of subsystems, or even of major systems will depend upon the purposes the study is to serve and the appropriateness of a given level for that kind of study [66].

Many efforts are currently being made to define a community in such a way as to describe its communal properties, which are to be distinguished from behavior which happens to occur within the community's geographical area. Sutton and Kolaja [75], Reiss [63], Parsons [56], Mercer [49], and Nelson, Ramsey, and Verner [55] have tried to put this problem in clearer focus. Arensberg has taken a fresh look at community studies from the anthropological point of view [3], and the present writer [66] and others—such as Loomis [48]—have elaborated the concept of social system, applying it to a local community. Warren [79], Sills [71], and Levine and White [45] have called attention to the conflict between the vertical and horizontal axes of health organizations such as the Red Cross, which must serve national purposes and yet receive local support. Anyone seeking to view the community as a social system, and attempting to fit the health system into such a context, must be aware of the developing theory and the clarification of concepts currently taking place.

Health as a Major Community System

A major community system, whether it be education or the economy, has identifiable characteristics, such as (1) a structure, or a related series of agencies, organizations or establishments; (2) a set of functions, both manifest and latent; (3) functionaries, or persons charged with the responsibility of promoting the interest of the system or major segments of it; (4) ideology or rationale, which provides the justification for the continuation of the system; (5) paraphernalia, or the necessary equipment and material resources for carrying out the expected activities; and (6) linkages with other systems within and without the community.

The organization or structure of the health system

Everyone connected with health has certain roles he is supposed to carry out. This applies not only to the physician, dentist, sanitary engineer, public health educator, but also to the hospital orderly, the patient, and even the patient's family.[4] Health services are provided through a definite network of social relationships which have been built up over many years but which survive because the members of each new generation learn to perform the roles expected of them in situations involving health. And the concept of "social situation" is very important, for social roles can be performed only in the presence of other people. This calls for activities in groups, whether in the small group (patient-doctor-nurse in an office visit) or in the large associations which range from organizations such as the local medical association to the entire bureaucracy of a hospital.

The concept of major system provides a means of taking all of these diverse patterns and organizing them into a theoretical scheme, similar to but not necessarily exactly like that which one finds in any given community. In American communities, for instance, there are five types of health structures or subsystems, closely intertwined, but nevertheless distinct enough to be analyzed separately.[5] First, there is the private office practice of the professional health persons, which would include the small clinics where specialists work in proximity to take advantage of laboratories, X-ray equipment, and joint consultation on troublesome cases. Private practice traditionally has included home visits, but this is shifting to the requirement that the patient come to the office wherever possible, or even to the hospital when the physician deems the case to be too serious for home care. Embedded in this subsystem is the almost sacred belief about the individuality and inviolability of the doctor-patient relationship.

---

[4] See Chap. 7, 8, 10, 11 for specific discussions of these parties.

[5] See Chap. 12 for a detailed discussion of the organization of health services.

A second subsystem might be termed group health care. People, by virtue of employment or membership rights, have access to medical and other health services in facilities set up by factories, stores, business or governmental agencies, schools, or labor unions, and the like.

A third subsystem is the "world" of the large hospitals, clinics, and health agencies.[6] Although medical professionals can move easily from office to hospital and back again in the performance of any day's duties, the shift by a patient from his job or home to the hospital represents a tremendous reorganization of roles for him and his family.

A fourth subsystem is public health. In general, its personnel do not "practice" in the customary sense of the word. They protect, administer, and perform services. Public health people detect but most often do not treat; they refer patients but do not diagnose; they immunize to reduce incidence of disease, they inspect to prevent epidemics, they educate so as to raise the patient's understanding of health care for himself and his family, they make home visits to check on communicable disease, and they visit work sites to enforce standards protecting the workers' health. The structure of public health, then, consists of a set of roles different from those found in the other subsystems and its personnel usually find themselves in social situations different from those in the doctor's office, the hospital operating room, or the emergency room of a factory [4]. They are truly public in the sense that they are at the contact points between local people and health needs, frequently in a nonmedical setting.

A fifth subsystem, peripheral but necessary, is that of the pharmacist and those who sell materials and appliances required by and usually purchased individually by the patient.[7] The health system in the United States makes use of the free enterprise system as the mechanism through which such drugs and appliances are provided to the individual. The pharmacist who owns and presides over a mercantile emporium, with stock ranging from antibiotics and aspirin to school supplies and ice cream, is essential to both the economic system and the health system. As a registered pharmacist, his role is limited to that of filling doctor's prescriptions and selling nonprescription remedies. Communities differ in the extent to which those in the private practice subsystem tolerate the offer of medical advice by the pharmacists. In some communities, the pharmacists remove from the doctors' shoulders the responsibility for prescribing for a cold, a backache, or constipation; in other communities, pharmacists carefully advise patients to give their doctor a ring. But since the majority of the people in most American communities do not have a "doctor of their own," they purchase remedies on the basis of hearsay, advertisement, packaging, or price.

---

[6] See Chap. 13 for an intensive analysis of this system.

[7] See Chap. 9 for a detailed discussion.

The structure of each of these subsystems differs because the requisite group situations vary. Obviously, the drug store is no place for a physician's diagnosis, nor is the office of the public health director a suitable place for an operation. Each requires a different network or organized activity, which constitutes the structure of the subsystem. One begins to understand the nature of the health system, then, as one examines these important components—individually and in relation to each other. It is the totality of their roles, social relationships, and groups that comprises the major health system of any community.

A *set of functions*

The health system has certain functions which distinguish it from the other systems—education, local government, religion, economy, recreation, welfare—which the community supports. Some of these are what Merton calls *manifest*, or stated and obvious; others are *latent*, not so readily discerned. Two manifest functions are readily apparent. The first is to cure the sick. Illness is always a crisis experience for any individual and for his immediate kin and close associates; widespread illness—whether endemic or epidemic—is a crisis experience for a community. The health system has developed to take care of these individual and community crises. Within the United States the concept of illness differs among regions, communities, or social classes within the communities. This, of course, can lead to variations in what is meant by "curing the sick."

A second manifest function of the health system is to keep people well. It is significant that this is usually considered a less important function than curing the sick, when from a logical point of view it should be more important. In American communities, illness is personalized and good health taken for granted; the tendency is to accentuate the curative rather than the preventative. Again, there is great debate throughout the United States over just how much effort should go into keeping people well. Is this a personal or a community responsibility? Is this an invasion of the sphere of the private practitioner? To what extent should people be forced to adopt measures that research has shown to be in the interests of better health? Should all efforts at keeping people well be delegated to local, state, and national governments with an occasional assist from the private practitioner? Although answers to all of these questions are not always available, there is general agreement that some communitywide efforts at keeping people well should be made.

There also are latent functions performed by the health system. One of these is the offsetting of the impersonality of mass society by giving people a chance to talk intimately with health personnel about matters that trouble them. The psychiatrists are those most quickly thought of in this connection, but anyone familiar with the health field realizes that health personnel of all types are viewed by those in need as confidants or as competent to give advice. Although recent studies show that there is more neighboring and more informal social activity in urban areas than previous writers had supposed, there is still a great need in such communities for people to use the safety valve of talk. Most Americans consider health personnel to be the appropriate people to talk to—even for a fee.

Another latent function of the health system is the introduction of some degree of rationality into everyday life. Its practitioners supposedly deal with cause-effect relationships, many of which are subject to empirical test. To the extent that people become better educated about health, to that extent do they accept scientific explanation in place of erroneous folk beliefs. The health system is a major way of confronting individuals with scientific facts at the point at which they must respond in terms of personal choice. The fact that it has not proven as successful as hoped in this regard (witness the fluoridation battles) does not minimize the importance of this latent function.

The health system is also charged with a third task, which is more often latent than manifest: that of preserving an efficient labor force. In the opinion of some, workers are to be kept well not for the sake of health alone but for the sake of the economy. It is considered a national scandal when a large proportion of draftees are rejected because of failure to meet the physical standards [24]. Perhaps one reason why the recent attempts at national programs of physical fitness have not excited more popular support is the fact that they are not being channeled through the health system, where it would seem to belong, but through the educational system and its peripheral personnel of football coaches and calisthenics experts.

The members of a community tend to have a picture of how specific tasks related to these functions should be distributed among the subsystems previously described. Brower, in his study of Cortland County, New York, identified those specific tasks that the private doctor, the county health department, and the school were each most frequently expected to perform. Interestingly enough, methods of payments were supposed to differ: direct reimbursement for the doctor, taxes for the public health department and the school—although the school (representing the group health subsystem) was the agency most frequently expected to render its services without being reimbursed [9].

Functionaries

Just as the other community systems have their functionaries (the economy, the Secretary of the Chamber of Commerce; religion, the clergymen; education, the school superintendent; local government, the mayor or party leader), so the health system has its functionaries. These are distributed throughout the community subsystems: the officers of the local medical or dental association; the executives of the group health arrangements supported by insurance company officials concerned with actuarial details; the hospital managers and the presidents of their boards of directors; the public health officer; and the spokesmen for the local pharmacists; the public relations personnel of the drug companies. This listing of functionaries, partial though it is, shows that the health system—as is true of most major systems in American communities—has no single spokesman who represents the entire field; instead, there are different functionaries for each subsystem. To understand public health and the community, therefore, one must identify these functionaries and determine the degree to which their roles complement or conflict with each other.

A growing body of literature discusses the changing roles of these functionaries [13, 83]. Many studies deal with the relationships among different functionaries—such as that between physician and nurse—or with the division of labor among the professionals in a public health department.[8] In contrast to these roles related to the internal workings of the health system are some with marked community implications. Hassinger and McNamara have studied the relationships of the public to physicians in a rural setting in Missouri [32], and Saunders and Bruening have described hospital-community relations in Mississippi. The second study finds that the hospital administrator is the key to the hospital's community relations [68]. Because many of the roles are yet ill-defined, the functionaries representing competing health interests occasionally make contradictory pronouncements about the same topic. In such cases many citizens become sadly confused and tend to downgrade all health agencies or programs.

Ideology and rationale

One of the difficulties those in the health field face is the lack of widespread acceptance of the rationale behind their efforts. What can the health functionaries present as their chief reason for existence? In the case of the private practitioner or those presiding over the large clinics and hospitals, or even in the case of the pharmacists, the problem is not very acute. Direct services are rendered upon demand of individuals or groups. But public health usually means intervening in the lives of people, often against their will. To date, those in public health have not succeeded in developing for themselves or conveying to the general public an ideology of intervention which jibes with the more widely-accepted beliefs about individual rights and the general distrust of government involvement in daily affairs. Not unexpectedly, the demand for and support for health is outstripping the development of its rationale, but the existence of this lag between performance and justification prevents a steady progress toward stated public health goals.

[8] See Chap. 10.

Paraphernalia

Every occupation uses tools which come to be identified symbolically as well as practically with that trade. The paraphernalia of health, whether it is in the simpler equipment for diagnosis or the much more complex laboratory equipment for running difficult tests, is expensive. Hospitals are expensive to build, furnish, and operate; public health programs involving large populations are also costly. The paraphernalia of the health system, designed to render specific services, is not as extensive as that of the economy, which concentrates upon many kinds of services, yet some visitors from abroad stress the dependence of American physicians upon their paraphernalia. It is true that the health system, like other major systems in our society, is intricately linked with the technological side of our culture, many times producing almost miraculous results because of the aid of some specialized instrument.

The identification of the medical man with his paraphernalia distinguishes him from the old country doctor who was judged according to his performance as a person as well as a physician, and not as a specialist highly trained in the manipulation of equipment. The public image of the doctor, therefore, is undergoing a change, perhaps becoming less sympathetic and less favorable—just at the time when one disease after another is being brought under control.

Linkages with other systems

The very nature of community life dictates that no major system can exist in isolation, each is inextricably tied in with most of the other systems. Whereas the subsystem of private practice is most closely connected with the ideology and folkways of the economy, the public health subsystem is most closely allied with the ideology and folkways of local government. The former stresses the rights of the individual, the latter is directed toward collective needs. Although a service motif, at the surface at least, runs throughout all our major systems, it is particularly emphasized by many in the health field.

The links between the health system and other systems in a given community must be traced if the full picture of the health field is to be obtained. An analysis of indigent disability, for example, indicates the close coordination required between the health and welfare systems if this problem or any similar problem, is to be dealt with effectively by the community [18].

These few points relative to health as a community system and to the subsystems of which it consists are based on "the presumptions that there are relations of interdependence between the more detailed phenomena which are subject to intelligible analysis; the antithesis is the conception of randomness of relative variability, so that knowing the pattern of variation of one subphenomenon gives no clue whatever, even in the form of imposing some limitation to the variability of the other" [57]. The interdependence seems obvious.

Some Community Factors Affecting the Health System

A discussion of health and the community, necessarily limited in space, must be suggestive rather than definitive in scope. Its main contribution lies in presenting a relatively simple scheme for the analysis of social phenomena which relate to health and its community context. In applying such a scheme, however, there are at least three factors of community life which need to be taken into account. The first of these has to do with community power, leadership, and decision-making; the second deals with action programs and community issues; while the third is directed at the problem of change within the community.

Community power, leadership, and decision-making

The American's yen for gimmicks has implications for the complex field of social relationships. One of comparatively recent vintage is the "power clique" gimmick which has been given much attention in education, social welfare, public health, and many other fields where the community is the base of operations. In its naivest, simplest terms this blandly states that (1) every community has an identifiable power clique, and (2) that if you get the members of this clique on your side, all of your problems will be solved. There is of course a considerable element of truth in these two points, but what is even more important is what is not said.

The first difficulty frequently lies in an unrealistic definition of power in the community. One can agree on a general definition of *power* as referring "to the ability or authority of individuals or organizations to control, effectively guide, or influence other individuals or groups" [26], but such definitions give little clue to the structuring of power. There goes on in an actual community, as Long has pointed out, an ecology of games. He speaks of what one could call subsystems as a variety of games: banking, newspaper publishing, and so on, and claims that these games give structure, goals, roles, strategies, tactics, and publics to the players. Players in each "game" make use of players in the other "games" for their particular purposes, and the totality of their interaction produces unintended but systematically functional results for the community. He sees an overall leadership and social frame as providing a vague set of community-shared values that promotes cooperation in the system though it does not provide a government [47].

This picture of community interaction shows that there is a distribution of power throughout the whole system, with each "game" possessing power in that players in other "games" must depend upon it to accomplish their own goals. This introduces the idea of functional necessity as an element in power; you have power if you are needed—a fact which labor unions discovered long ago. Though we often think of power as absolute and relative, it is perhaps more correct at the community level to think of it as *relevant* and *irrelevant*. Some players who are powerful in their own "game" or subsystem have no power in other "games," for what they have to offer has no relevance to that "game." This is an important distinction for health workers wishing to enlist the support of "power figures" in behalf of a program. Some of these figures are relevant, and should be approached; others are irrelevant, and will turn down requests for assistance on several grounds—but the fundamental reason is their irrelevance.

The "power clique" gimmick fallaciously assumes that if one is powerful he can do whatever he would personally like to do to help a cause. In fact, power is often circumscribed. The health official who dabbles in politics, the clergyman who tries to tell businessmen how to conduct their affairs, the school superintendent who poses as an authority on welfare problems—all are examples of functionaries who are moving beyond their circumscribed sphere. The same holds true for the nonprofessionals identified with one or more systems, particularly if their claim to fame rests with only one system, organization, or agency.

In one respect, however, the gimmick is realistic: there is an unequal distribution of power in the community, though it is probably not as concentrated as is implied. After all, the ordinary citizen with no pretense to power does have more than is often realized: he has a vote on many issues, he can buy or not buy a product, he can watch or not watch a television program, and he can participate or not participate in a host of community activities. His choices may be somewhat predetermined by those with more power than he, but he is not altogether powerless. To understand the distribution of power in American communities, it is necessary to draw up some typology of leadership, recognizing that each type has certain power attributes that are identified with its structural position. Such a typology may have some "power slippage"—that is, it may not account for all conceivable types of control, effective guidance, or influence over other individuals or groups as set forth in the earlier definition of power. But such a typology is operational in that it traces the flow of influence and can be used practically in planning for and conducting various kinds of action programs. The paradigm presented below relates the type of leader to the total community system in terms of the number of systems or analytical levels at which he is concerned; it indicates the range of his power as well as its duration. Some leaders have a broader range of power than others, and some occupy indeterminate positions which are not limited to regular terms of office.

PARADIGM I A TYPOLOGY OF COMMUNITY LEADERSHIP

Type of leader	*System frame of reference*	*Range—specific or diffuse*	*Duration*
Key	two or more major systems	diffuse	indeterminate
Dominants	one major system	specific	indeterminate
Functionaries	one major system	specific	indeterminate
Organizational	one formal association	specific-diffuse	determinate
Issue	one community realignment	specific	determinate
Spokesman	a grouping or locality	diffuse	indeterminate

Such a paradigm becomes more useful if it is related to some illustrative studies of community power and examined in terms of the health system. Each study cited will provide information about some but not all of the types. Long views the key leaders—or "top leadership," as he calls them—as largely confined to ritual and ceremonial roles and usually identified with status position rather than with specifiable roles in social action. "The role of a top leader is ill-defined and to a large degree unstructured. It is in most cases a secondary role derived from a primary role as corporation executive, wealthy man, powerful ecclesiastic, holder of high social position, and the like" [47]. In terms of the paradigm and according to Long, key leadership is largely derivative of dominant leadership. By tying such leadership in with what he calls the "social game" he gives it cross-system character, for "the custodians of the symbols of top social standing provide goals that in a sense give all the individual games some common denominator of achievement. While the holders of top social prestige do not necessarily hold either top political or economic power, they do provide meaningful goals for the rest" [47]. Of course, Long does not in this statement exclude the dominants from movement into key leadership, but allows for other community variables, such as family background, to play their part. The conclusion to be drawn from such a statement is that key leadership is a strange mixture of prestige, as well as certain kinds of major system power (economic, religious, political). This proves disturbing again to those looking for neat operational definitions, but it is the way communities seem to allocate this type of power.

Miller views the community power structure as "composed of key influentials, top influentials, the community power complex, and those parts of the institutionalized power structure of the community that have come into play when activated by a community issue." In his comparison of a Pacific Northwest city and an English city, he deals only with the key influentials, who are the sociometric leaders among the top influentials, or those drawn from various systems of power relations according to the issue at stake [51]. If one thinks of the power grid as represented by the typology in Paradigm I, it can be observed that the key influentials compare with the key leaders and, as sociometric leaders, tend to have some permanence in that position, whereas the top influentials, or dominants in the typology, move into leadership as their relevance to issues increases. Contrary to Hunter's finding for a Southern city (that "crowds" of influentials exist, with top leaders of each crowd clearing with leaders of other "crowds"), Miller finds no repeated acting in concert by key influentials, although such leaders do bring various other influentials around them when they are responsible for carrying out a civic project. On the other hand, relatively stable groups of leaders (the dominants) are identified with certain institutional sectors of the community through which they express common interest—*i.e.*, business, labor, political party, education, and religion. (In the terminology used here these sectors are community systems; in Long's terminology, they are "games" [51].)

It is common for the key leaders and dominants to work through other types of leaders. The key leaders in finance or commerce may ask a functionary (the Secretary of the Chamber of Commerce) to make contact with political dominants about some matter of concern; or they may work through organizational leaders in hope of extending support through the associational network of the formal groups in a community. On certain questions, those issue leaders who have previously come out publicly for one side of the issue may be consulted and asked for help, while contact with the spokesmen (who know what is going on within a particular ethnic grouping, occupational segment, or local area) is usually considered essential at some point. But Freeman and Mayo [20] have shown that in a small North Carolina open-country community this use of intermediate leaders does not occur because (1) there are not enough intermediate leaders around, and (2) the local emphasis upon neighborliness and equalitarianism promotes direct contact between what they call "upper lay leaders" and people at other levels of the leadership structure. A few of the professional leaders (functionaries in the paradigm described here) did try to work through chosen upper lay leaders in the hope of getting ideas across to others indirectly through them.

Agger, unlike Mayo above, stresses the importance of all levels of the power grid in his report of a study of a small Oregon town:

> In this small community, it was expected that the informal face-to-face relationships of the top leadership and "constituents" would constitute a primary, if not the most important, channel for the exercise of influence. The data hint at the importance of formal organizations as influence channels in the community, as well as the possible importance of the roles played by people who resemble the top leadership and who are sought out for advice in the generation or maintenance of legitimacy relationships between the masses and the top leadership. The secondary leaders who are the most active politically probably have the most influence on others. The passive advisers are less likely to reinforce the influence relationships between their advisees and the top leadership because of their own unawareness of or antipathy to that leadership [1].

White, in studying the formal and informal roles of organizational leadership in a rural New York community, finds among other things that "the more independent from control by higher authorities these organizations are, the more likely they are to be staffed by informally influential formal leaders" [81].

The assumption is sometimes made, particularly by those looking for a quick way of dealing with power, that there is invariably a power hierarchy. The more we learn about the comparative study of communities, the more we find that their power structures vary widely from the rigidly hierarchical to the nearly amorphous, fleeting coalitions of people with some measure of power. This is illustrated in another study by Agger and Goldrich [2], who report that in the two Far West communities studied, one—Boomtown—had a polynucleated set of leadership groups at the top of the power structure, whereas the other—Valley City—had a hierarchical power structure, whose top leaders (or key leaders) frequently conferred with each other. Form and D'Antonio [19] investigated the degree of integration among the influentials in Juarez, Mexico, and El Paso, Texas. They found that in neither community was there a single power system, but that in El Paso conflicts arose between groups overlapping institutional boundaries (the major systems), whereas in Juarez conflicts arose between institutions.

Many of the points already mentioned about the power structure of a community give some insight into decision-making there. Janowitz, in his introduction to a series of essays by other writers on aspects of community political systems, reaffirms the importance of the community as the locus of power [38]. On the whole, however, as Polsby points out [60], most of our studies are concerned with the identification and description of the power-holders of the community; relatively few have actually described the behavior involved in specific issues. Perhaps Banfield's study of several major issues in Chicago comes closest to the dynamics of decision-making [5]. What we do know, however, indicates that there will be no easy formulation which will explain this complicated process. Schulze, in his study of economic dominants in a Midwestern industrial community of 20,000, finds that they are increasingly taking a "hands-off" position with regard to local political decision-making [69]; whereas Pellegrin and Coates [59]—in their study of a Southern industrial city—find a "power vacuum," for no one group there seemingly had the power.

It does seem clear that communities differ in their styles of decision-making. Merton has shown how some communities consist of local and cosmopolitan influentials, with the latter sensitive to issues and opinions outside the community [50]. Miller, in his study of 218 small hospital projects, found that the Southeast projects developed amidst arrangements made through constituted authority, while in the Northeast community organizational arrangements seemed related to the social psychological components of influence [53]. One aspect of decision-making is veto power, which means that a proposal can be stopped by a person with authority to say "no" at any point in the leadership structure. For some kinds of issues, the spokesman who can prove that the idea will not work with his "constituents" has veto power; for other issues involving the raising of much money from private contributions, organizational leaders may be in a position to give the "stop and go" sign. Or, if the proposal calls for significant modification of existing institutionalized arrangements, the functionaries and dominants swing into action to protect their own. This would imply that much clearance has to be gotten, at some stage in the proceedings, from several types of leaders. The key leaders, because their power is diffused across system lines, also have veto power. Their decisions, however, are not based on any absolute criteria of what is "good" or "bad" for the community, but upon their assessment of how the other types of leaders (dominants, for instance) and the general public are apt to react.

One might well ask how this excursion into community power structure and types of community leaders bears upon the system of health. It is necessary to derive propositions since little direct research on the health system has been undertaken. Several propositions may be advanced:

1. Communities differ widely in their power structure, so any health worker must be careful about automatically transferring the analysis of one community to another.
2. The health system has its own assortment of leaders, with varying degrees of power: dominants (usually nonprofessionals), functionaries (usually professionals), organizational officers, issue leaders, and spokesmen. Some of the key leaders include health within their province.
3. These health leaders are frequently in touch with their counterparts in other major systems and often work out technical or strategy details at this level, thus avoiding the necessity of involving key leaders in many routine or technical matters.

4. Power does not necessarily flow through the formal bureaucratic structure of any subsystem (health department, hospital complex, and so on) but may move through other parts of the power grid, depending upon the participants' definition of whose power is relevant to the decision to be made.
5. The leaders of one health subsystem may try to speak for the whole health system, but when their pronouncements are of broader compass than their power, their influence is limited. By the same token, health leaders who step outside their circumscribed spheres in an effort to wield power are apt to meet discouragement unless they have developed the attributes of key leaders, to whom is granted the right to speak on matters relating to more than one major system.
6. It can happen that certain leaders of the health system move into positions of key leadership in the community because of a number of qualities: high social status, competence outside the health system which has earned them the respect of dominants in other systems, personal prestige built up through an outstanding job as leader of several important local organizations, or such success as issue leaders that they have been catapulted into public notice and accepted as capable leaders on several matters. Therefore, the fact that one is a health leader need not rule out the possibility that he will attain a larger sphere of influence.
7. It is necessary to distinguish between economic, political, and social power and to decide which combination of these is most important for the promotion of the health subsystem in which one is interested. When the major concern is political, there is little point in enlisting the support of businessmen who may have no standing with those making the political decisions; when the major concern is fund raising, the help of political leaders—who may be prevented by law from using public funds for the cause—may be less important than one might at first imagine.
8. Should there be a well-recognized power clique in the community, getting the approval and tacit support of its members is not the full answer. Studies show that at the most they are willing to lend their name, make a few phone calls to intimates, or pass the word along to their following. This is all very helpful, but it in no way gets done the organizational job which any health program requires. Nor, does it inform and educate enough people at various levels to guarantee success. Key leaders can be of great help, but their contribution is limited by the time at their disposal, the competition for their sponsorship, and the extent to which they feel they can involve their followers in many disparate activities.

9. Decision-making relative to a health program should extend where appropriate to all levels of the power grid, with the reminder that the ordinary citizen more often than not has the veto power in support he renders to the program through making financial contributions, being a client, serving as a volunteer worker, re-electing officials responsible for aspects of the program, or shifting (or reinforcing) his opinion about the merits of those responsible for the program. Where there is public apathy, and this does exist in many communities, power does become more highly concentrated and less responsive to general community welfare.
10. Leaders of whatever rank have at best limited information about some major systems. They are not omniscient. Often, therefore, as much of an educational job needs to be done with them as with a much less influential person. Those promoting a health program, therefore, should have a clear-cut set of goals, a supporting rationale, and a description of expected gains worked out before contacting leaders who are not intimately involved with the broad spectrum of health. Even health personnel of one subsystem may be woefully ignorant of what goes on in other health subsystems. Health workers usually make a mistake in strategy when they contact key leaders prior to thinking through the implications of their program (its costs, effect on other programs, long-range benefits, allocation of responsibility, and the like).

Such considerations about community power and the health system give only one part of the picture of local health action and the kinds of controversies which arise. We need now to put matters in broader perspective.

Action programs and community issues

An increasing number of studies of the reasons for success and failure of community action programs are being made by sociologists [14, 64]. A few illustrative findings can be cited here, although they in no way constitute an exhaustive treatment of the literature.

Any action program must first be based on an awareness of need by someone. If this person is the health professional, then he needs facts to use in making others aware. Hoffer and Schuler have sought to describe a method of measuring medical needs and the extent to which they are or are not met [35]. Young and Mayo, in their study of the problem of participation in community action programs in a North Carolina rural community, reached the conclusion that although "a relatively small proportion of the community residents are participating at more than minimal level, the presence of favorable or neutral attitudes toward the organization on the part of the inactivity may provide adequate stimulus for the successful operation of such a program" [85]. Another line of inquiry lies in the delineation of stages through which action programs go [6, 8, 17, 25, 33, 36, 40, 73]. Some of these fail to take sufficiently into account the likelihood of community controversy or conflict. However, it is fair to make a distinction between an action program (or the inception, promotion, and effecting of a project or communitywide change) and a community issue, which by definition involves a cleavage, partisanship, and controversy. All issues involve programs of action but not all programs of action are controversial. Some types of health programs—such as raising money for a new hospital wing, though it calls for a big financial effort; adding a school health program, through the employment of a school nurse; pushing a large-scale program for chest X-rays—are not apt to become issues. Other types of health programs, such as fluoridation, can be predicted to emerge as community issues.

The Miller-Form theory of issue outcome [52] has been summarized and tested successfully in Denver, Colorado, by Hanson.

> The theory is based on the proposition that the combined social force of three factors brings about a community decision on a general issue. These factors are: (1) the critically activated parts of the institutional power structure, which are aligned for or against the issue proposition; (2) the power arrangement of the community power complex, which may be unstructured, semi-structured, or unified on either side of the issue; and (3) top influential solidarity and activity. If the top influentials are a single, exclusive, elite of autonomous power, the outcome may be forecast by an analysis of their stand on the issue. If the top influentials are not the exclusive elite type, their degree of activity on either side of the issue becomes a relevant variable [30].

Barth and Johnson have given leads for developing a typology of social issues [8]. They have sought to pick dimensions generic to all issues and to relate theoretically variations in each dimension to variations in patterns of influencing behavior. Their five dimensions are:

1. *Unique–recurrent,* with unique issues handled by emergent leadership and recurring leadership handled by constituted community agencies having access to regularly allocated resources.
2. *Salient-nonsalient to leadership,* with some issues being central to the interests of community leaders and the organizational structures in which they hold positions, and some being peripheral to their interests.
3. *Salient-nonsalient to community publics,* with issues thought to be highly salient to the public involving the potential decision makers in the "public relations" aspect of the decision.

4. *Effective action possible–effective action impossible,* a dimension indicating that issues thought highly salient may be perceived as necessitating impossible decisions or requiring inaccessible resources.
5. *Local–cosmopolitan,* with issues dealt with by other organizations in the state or nation thought to require guidance and direction from outside experts, which is not the case with local issues.

A third area of relevance to the study of social issues is some single health issue, such as fluoridation. In this connection, the present author has developed a typology of issue stages, which differ in part from the social action stages mentioned earlier [67]. A key to the application of this typology is the realization that these stages repeat themselves in a sequence as the issue is reopened and has to be dealt with by the community a second, third, or fourth time. Many useful leads for dealing with health issues can be gained from the growing body of literature dealing with fluoridation as a community issue [22].

This brief discussion of action programs and social issues has indicated the need for a systematic approach, whether in terms of the analysis of social power or type of issue, or the ability to view the program as an over-all sequence of interaction from its initiation to its resolution and aftermath. This stresses the primary importance of an over-all theoretical framework into which the details of technique and tactics can be appropriately fitted.

The problem of change

Health systems not only operate within a system of power but they also exist in a community constantly experiencing change. For one thing, the physical community is always changing. The built-up area expands, older residential areas deteriorate population shifts, new transportation routes are opened up, and the economic base expands or contracts as the physical city undergoes this change. Health personnel are constantly caught up in problems attendant upon these changes but much less frequently are called upon for advice with respect to measures for planned change.

The population of a community changes as well: not only in numbers, but in composition, in skills, in quality. New ethnic groupings make their appearance while older ethnic groupings "disappear" through absorption into the general population. Local attitudes and values toward health shift as cultural traditions associated with ethnic groupings change.

But even more important to those responsible for a community's health is what happens to the domain [44] of the health system *vis-à-vis* the other major systems in the community. Here one must be aware of the extra-community pressures which invade to exert changes of many kinds. Federal funds for health or schooling alter respective systemic domains; religious action on birth control, parochial schools, or perhaps fluoridation abets or hinders various health programs; economic trends, both in the organization of the economic system as well as in the contribution by corporations and labor unions to health and welfare, figure prominently in today's civic life. The whole health system has to be set into the social action field—the arena of interaction that is the community. Again, Long's analogy of the ecology of games is pertinent here. Every move that is made has some impact upon subsequent moves and there is seldom any reversal of the process. Thus change is built into community life, although much of it is greatly accelerated by the impact of outside forces.

Finally, there are changes going on within the health system itself. The subsystems themselves, which have been described, are in interaction with each other. As new statuses are created, old ones must give way or adjust; as new demands are made, the responses of some subsystems are quicker and more effective than others; as some subsystems become more institutionalized, the importance of the functionary rises and that of the layman declines—perhaps along with that of the general medical man whose training fails to prepare him for the complex of roles required of those administering and providing the specialties now called for in our health system. Geiger has indicated the degree to which the physician is faced with new medical problems and new concepts of health and illness and speaks of binding medicine to the rest of the changing social fabric [23]. Any health professional who fails to accept social change as a normal part of the dynamic society in which we live cannot relate himself or his work to the changing community. Furthermore, unless he tries to develop some theory of social change as it affects health [22], he misses much of the rich panorama of community life. If health personnel would spend only a fraction of the time that they devote to detailed laboratory-oriented, time-consuming but necessary medical and scientific techniques of their profession to studying their community, they and their communities would be much the richer.

References

1. Agger, Robert E., "Power Attributions in the Local Community: Theoretical and Research Considerations," *Social Forces,* 34 (May, 1956), 331.
2. ——— and Daniel Goodrich, "Community Power Structures and Partisanship," *American Sociological Review,* 23 (August, 1958), 383–92.
3. Arensberg, Conrad, "The Community as Object and as Sample," *American Sociological Review,* 63 (April, 1961), 241–64.
4. Back, Kurt W., Robert E. Coker, Jr., Thomas G. Donnelly, and Bernard S. Phillips, "Public Health as a Career of Medicine: Secondary Choice within a Profession," *American Sociological Review,* 23 (October, 1958), 533–41.
5. Banfield, Edward E., *Political Influence,* New York: The Free Press of Glencoe, Inc., 1961.

6. Beal, George and Harold Capener, "A Social Action Model" (unpublished, 1958).
7. Berry, Mildred C., "A Theoretical Framework for Community Organization," *Health Education Monographs*, 3 (1959), 8–17.
8. Berth, Ernest A. T. and Stuart D. Johnson, "Community Power and a Typology of Social Issues," *Social Forces*, 38 (October, 1959), 29–32.
9. Brower, George J., "Conceptions and Evaluations of Functions of Medical and Health Care Agencies by Present and Future Homemakers in Cortland County," *Rural Sociology*, 17 (March, 1952), 56–60.
10. Brunsman, Howard G., "Current Sources of Sociological Data in Housing," *American Sociological Review*, 12 (April, 1947), 150–55.
11. Chapin, F. Stuart, "New Methods of Sociological Research on Housing Problems," *American Sociological Review*, 12 (April, 1947), 143–49.
12. ———, Clarence A. Johanson, and Arthur L. Johnson, "Rental Rates and Crowding in Dwelling Units in Manhattan," *American Sociological Review*, 15 (February, 1950), 97.
13. Cohn, Werner, "Social Status and the Ambivalence Hypotheses: Some Critical Notes and A Suggestion," *American Sociological Review*, 25 (August, 1960), 508–13.
14. Coleman, James S., *Community Conflicts*. New York: The Free Press of Glencoe, Inc., 1957.
15. Croog, Sydney H., "Ethnic Origins, Educational Level, and Responses to a Health Questionnaire," *Human Organizations*, 20 (Summer, 1961), 65–69.
16. Dean, John P., "The Myths of Housing Reform," *American Sociological Review*, 14 (April, 1949), 281–88.
17. Eldridge, S., *The Dynamics of Social Action*. Washington, D.C.: Public Affairs Press, 1952.
18. Eller, C. Howe, Gordon M. Hatcher, and Bradley Buell, "Health and Welfare Issues in Community Planning for the Problem of Indigent Disability," Part II, *American Journal of Public Health*, 48 (1958), 49.
19. Form, William H. and William V. D'Antonio, "Integration and Cleavage and Community Influentials in Two Border Cities," *American Sociological Review*, 24 (December, 1959), 804–14.
20. Freeman, Charles and Selz C. Mayo, "Decision-Makers in Rural Community Action," *Social Forces*, 35 (May, 1957), 319–22.
21. Freeman, Howard E. and Ozzie G. Simmons, "Social Class and Posthospital Performance Levels," *American Sociological Review*, 24 (June, 1959), 345–51.
22. Gamson, William A. and Carolyn G. Lindberg, "An Annotated Bibliography of Social Science Aspects of Fluoridation," *Health Education Journal*, 19 (November, 1961), 209–30.
23. Geiger, H. Jack, "Social Responsibility of the Physician," *The Scientific American*, 85 (August, 1957), 89–94.
24. Ginzberg, Eli, James K. Anderson, Sol W. Ginsburg, and John L. Herma, *The Ineffective Soldier: Patterns of Performance*. New York: Columbia University Press, 1959.

25. Green, James W. and Selz C. Mayo, "A Framework for Research in the Actions of Community Groups," *Social Forces*, 31 (May, 1953), 320–27.
26. Haer, John L., "Social Stratification in Relation to Attitude toward Sources of Power in a Community," *Social Forces*, 35 (December, 1956), 137.
27. Hamilton, C. Horace, "Distribution and Characteristics of Physicians in Wisconsin: A Source Book of Tables." Madison, Wis.: University of Wisconsin, Department of Rural Sociology, September 1, 1960, p. 26. (Mimeo.)
28. ———, *Health and Health Services in the Southern Appalachians: A Source Book*. Progress Report RS-35, Southern Appalachian Studies and the N.C. Agricultural Experiment Station, September, 1959.
29. ———, *Hospitals and Hospital Service in Wisconsin*, Madison: University of Wisconsin, Department of Rural Sociology, September 1, 1960, p. 5. (Mimeo.)
30. Hanson, Robert C., "Predicting a Community Decision: A Test of the Miller-Form Theory," *American Sociological Review*, 24 (October, 1959), 662–63.
31. Harden, Warren R., "Social and Economic Effects of Community Size," *Rural Sociology*, 25 (June, 1960), 207.
32. Hassinger, Edward W. and Robert L. McNamara, "Relationships of the Public to Physicians in a Rural Setting," University of Missouri Agricultural Experiment Station, *Research Bulletin* 653 (January, 1958), p. 36.
33. Hoffer, Charles R., "Social Action in Community Development," *Rural Sociology*, 23 (March, 1958), 43–51.
34. ———, "Social Aspects of Health and Welfare in Rural Areas," *in* Alvin L. Bertrand, ed., *Rural Sociology*. New York: McGraw-Hill Book Company, Inc., 1958, p. 285.
35. ——— and Edgar A. Schuler, "Measurement of Health Needs and Health Care," *American Sociological Review*, 13 (December, 1948), 719–24.
36. Holland, John B., Kenneth E. Tiedke, and Paul A. Miller, "A Theoretical Model for Health Action," *Rural Sociology*, 22 (June, 1957), 149–55.
37. Jacobs, Jane, *The Death and Life of Great American Cities*. New York: Random House, 1961.
38. Janowitz, Morris, ed., *Community Political Systems*. Vol. I: *International Yearbook of Political Behavior Research*. New York: The Free Press of Glencoe, Inc., 1961.
39. Kanter, Mildred B. *et al.*, "Socio-Economic Level and Material Attitudes toward Parent-Child Relationships," *Human Organization*, 16 (Winter, 1958), 44–48.
40. Kaufman, Harold F., Willis A. Sutton, Jr., Frank D. Alexander, and Allen D. Edwards, *Toward A Delineation of Community Research*. Mississippi State College Bulletin (May, 1954).
41. Keyes, Fenton, "The Correlation of Social Phenomena with Community Size," *Social Forces*, 36 (May, 1958), 311–15.
42. Klaber, Eugene H. and Harold S. Buttenheim, "Housing," *The Encyclopedia Americana*, 14 (1947), p. 488.
43. Koos, E. L., *The Health of Regionville*. New York: Columbia University Press, 1954, pp. 32*ff*.

44. Larson, Olaf F. and Donald G. Hay, "Hypotheses for Sociological Research in the Field of Rural Health," *Rural Sociology*, 16 (September, 1951), 225–37.
45. Levine, Sol and Paul E. White, "Exchange as a Conceptual Framework for the Study of Interorganizational Relationships," *Administrative Science Quarterly*, 5 (March, 1961), 583–601.
46. Lieberson, Stanley, "Ethnic Groups and the Practice of Medicine," *American Sociological Review*, 23 (October, 1958), 542–49.
47. Long, Norton E., "The Local Community as an Ecology of Games," *American Journal of Sociology*, 64 (November, 1958), 251–61.
48. Loomis, Charles E., *The Social System: Essays on Their Persistence and Change*. New York: D. Van Nostrand Company, Inc., 1960.
49. Mercer, Blaine E., *The American Community*. New York: Random House, 1956.
50. Merton, Robert K., "Patterns of Influence: Local and Cosmopolitan Influentials," *Social Theory and Social Structures*. New York: The Free Press of Glencoe, Inc., 1957, pp. 387–420.
51. Miller, Delbert C., "Decision-Making Cliques in Community Power Structure: A Comparative Study of an American and an English City," *American Journal of Sociology*, 64 (November, 1958), 299–310.
52. ———, "The Prediction of Issue Outcome in Community Decision-Making," *Proceedings of the Pacific Sociological Society (Research Studies of the State College of Washington)* 25 (1957), 137–47.
53. Miller, Paul A., "The Process of Decision-Making within the Context of Community Organization," *Rural Sociology*, 17 (June, 1952), 153–61.
54. Nage, Saad Z., "Factors Related to Health Disease among Ohio Farmers," *Ohio Agricultural Experiment Station Research Bulletin* 842 (October, 1959), p. 27.
55. Nelson, Lowry, Charles E. Ramsey, and Coolie Verner, *Community Structure and Change*. New York: The Macmillan Company, 1960.
56. Parson, Talcott, *Essays in Sociological Theory*, rev. ed. New York: The Free Press of Glencoe, Inc., 1954.
57. ———, "Some Considerations on the Theory of Social Change," *Rural Sociology*, 26 (September, 1961), 220.
58. Paul, Benjamin D., "The Role of Beliefs and Customs in Sanitation Programs," *American Journal of Public Health*, 48 (November, 1958), 1502–1506.
59. Pellegrin, Roland J. and Charles H. Coates, "Absentee-Owned Corporation and Community Power Structure," *American Journal of Sociology*, 61 (March, 1956), 413–19.
60. Polsby, Nelson W., "The Sociology of Community Power: A Reassessment," *Social Forces*, 37 (March, 1959), 232–36.
61. Price, Paul H. and Homer L. Hitt, "The Availability of Medical Personnel in Rural Louisiana," *Louisiana Bulletin No.* 459 (June, 1951), p. 20.
62. Reeder, Leo G., "Social Factors in Heart Disease: A Preliminary Research Report on the Relationship of Certain Social Factors to Blood Pressure in Males," *Social Forces*, 34 (May, 1956), 367–71.

63. Reiss, Albert J., Jr., "The Sociological Study of Communities," *Rural Sociology*, 24 (June, 1959), 118–30.

64. Rossi, Peter H., "Community Decision-Making," *Administrative Science Quarterly*, 1 (March, 1957), 415–43.

65. Rumney, Jay, "The Social Costs of Slums," *Journal of Social Issues*, 7 (1951), 69–85.

66. Sanders, Irwin T., *The Community: An Introduction to a Social System*. New York: The Ronald Press Company, 1958.

67. ———, "The Stages of a Community Controversy: The Case of Fluoridation," *The Journal of Social Issues*, 17 (1961), 55–65.

68. Saunders, J. V. D. and H. Bruening, "Hospital-Community Relations in Mississippi," *Rural Sociology*, 24 (March, 1959), 48–51.

69. Schulze, Robert O., "The Role of Economic Dominants in Community Power Structure," *American Sociological Review*, 23 (February, 1958), 3–9.

70. Scotch, Norman A., "A Preliminary Report of the Relations of Sociocultural Factors to Hypertension among the Zulu," *Annals of the New York Academy of Science*, 84 (1960), 1000–1009.

71. Sills, David L., *The Volunteers: Means and Ends in a National Organization*. New York: The Free Press of Glencoe, Inc., 1958.

72. Smith, Harvey L., *Society and Health in a Mountain Community: A Working Paper*. Chapel Hill: University of North Carolina Institute for Research in Social Science, 1961, p. 25. (Multilith.) See the treatment of "stressor" and "stress."

73. Sower, Christopher, John Holland, Kenneth Tiedke, and Walter Freeman, *Community Involvement: The Webs of Formal and Informal Ties That Make for Action*. New York: The Free Press of Glencoe, Inc., 1957.

74. Straus, Robert, "Sociological Determinants of Health Beliefs and Behavior: A Generic Approach." Paper presented before American Public Health Association, October 19, 1959.

75. Sutton, Willis A., Jr., and Jiri Kolaja, "The Concept of Community," *Rural Sociology*, 25 (June, 1960), 197–203.

76. Twichell, Allan A., "An Appraisal Method for Measuring for Quality of Housing," *American Sociological Review*, 13 (June, 1948), 278–87.

77. U.S. Department of Health, Education and Welfare, Public Health Service, *Health and Demography*. Washington, D.C.: Government Printing Office, October, 1956.

78. U.S. Housing and Home Finance Agency, Urban Renewal Administration, *Cleveland's Neighborhood Improvement Program*, Urban Renewal Service Bulletin 3. Washington, D.C.: Government Printing Office, June, 1961.

79. Warren, Roland L., "Toward a Reformulation of Community Theory," *Human Organization*, 15 (Summer, 1956), 8–11.

80. Wellin, Edward, "Implications of Local Culture for Public Health," *Human Organization*, 16 (Winter, 1958), 16–18.

81. White, James E., "Theory and Method for Research in Community Leadership," *American Sociological Review*, 15 (February, 1950), 50–60.

82. Wilmer, Daniel M. *et al., The Housing Environment and Family Life.* Baltimore: Johns Hopkins Press, 1962.

83. Wilson, Robert N., "The Physician's Changing Hospital Role," *Human Organization*, 18 (Winter, 1959–60), 177–83.

84. Wirth, Louis, "Housing as a Field of Sociological Research," *American Sociological Review*, 12 (April, 1947), 137–43.

85. Young, James N. and Selz C. Mayo, "Manifest and Latent Participators in a Rural Community Action Program," *Social Forces*, 38 (December, 1959), 140–45.

16

HEALTH ACTION IN CROSS-CULTURAL PERSPECTIVE

Steven Polgar

Ill health affects all groups of mankind and every society has developed ways of coping with this condition. Anthropologists have discovered evidences of many different types of preventive safeguards and therapeutic practices; in most instances it is possible to show that these practices are closely interrelated with other aspects of the culture, from value orientations to daily activities.[1] Much has been written

[1] It would be impossible to provide references to the writings of Benjamin D. Paul, George Foster and Lyle Saunders at every point where they have influenced my thinking, so I would like to acknowledge my debt and gratitude to them here. Collaboration with Andie L. Knutson, Jack P. Kirscht, and other staff members at the Behavioral Science Unit of the School of Public Health, University of California has also given me a better perspective on the topics treated in this chapter. Thanks are due to Sylvia K. Polgar, Sherri Cavan and Marian E. Leach for their critique of the manuscript and to Edna J. Schade for editorial assistance.

about the thought processes involved in attributing death and illness to magical or naturalistic causes. Some ethnologists are indefatigable collectors of curious customs—they include lists of medicinal plants, charms and incantations in their monographs—leaving the task of analysis to those more interested in generalization. Disease causation and curing ceremonies also play a large part in discussions of social control. Within the last fifteen years anthropologists have become interested in collaborating with physicians. Such cooperation hopefully contributes both to a better understanding of human ecology and to improved disease prevention and health programs. In order to synthesize the wholistic and the structural views, we will emphasize the cultural matrix of health—as contrasted with sickness—and the social roles of individuals involved in health action systems. It is useful to begin with a delineation of a conceptual framework. The terminology used will represent a further development of the classificatory scheme set down in a previous article [69].

The term *health action* is used here to bring into a single analytical framework the procedures used by laymen and specialists to promote health, prevent sickness, and remedy sickness. It is important to note that "health" and "sickness" are by no means objective variables. To some degree they refer to measurements which can be obtained in the laboratory of a Western medical specialist. In most health action situations around the world, however, such clear-cut measures are not available. The great bulk of judgements that go into the identification of conditions which might call for health action are sociocultural, even in the office of a Western-trained physician. Health action, furthermore, can be seen as an interpersonal network involving *health actors* and *clients*. The difference between various health action systems is perhaps most apparent when we analyze the relationship between clients and health actors as a sequence of medical events or contingencies in a career [13, p. 183 and 31, pp. 134ff].

When an adult perceives some changes in the way he feels and starts to think about the possibility of sickness, he has begun a sequence of events that may or may not lead to an alteration in his social role. As long as he only takes a couple of aspirins and does not complain about his headache, his social position remains unaffected although physiological changes may have occurred in his body. We will call this part of the sequence the *self-addressed phase*. In this type of health action system the same person is performing both the client role and the health actor role. The term "self-medication" is commonly used in this context, but would hardly include such behaviors as going out to "take a breath of fresh air," getting some rest, or giving up the habit of drinking a cocktail after work—which often are very important in this phase. Many actions designed to promote health or prevent disease also occur within this self-addressed health action system, but we will set aside for the moment the problem of what "promoting health" actually means.

The next stage begins either when the person solicits help from another or when such help is offered without any request for it. He has entered what Erikson calls the "sick role," distinct from the "patient role" [21].[2] The manner in which this transition is made—the overt manifestation of symptoms—is a cultural pattern. An interesting description of the facial expressions and body postures used for conveying the message "I am sick" is given by Birdwhistell for two different subcultures in Kentucky [8]. In his examples the client is addressing a group of people; the *lay health actor* as we will call him, can be either a single person or a set of people. Similarly, when a housewife in Scotland gives a laxative to all her children as a matter of routine once a week [87], the client is made up of several individuals. In the lay health action phase, the first actors involved will ordinarily be members of the client's immediate social group. As Freidson has shown, the client may be given help successively by several people in a lay referral system [29].

The role of the sick person has been characterized as socially deviant [64, 65, 79]. Certain impairments in role performance, however, which can be defined both in terms of laboratory measurement and social disvaluation, are fully countenanced within the definition of particular roles—*e.g.*, those accompanying menstruation or senility. If these kinds of conditions are taken into account, if one does not accept Parsons' argument for the substantial part played by motivational factors in most illnesses [64, p. 430], or if one includes behavior aimed at health promotion, the usefulness of analyzing the client role in the health action system as social deviance is quite restricted.[3]

In many instances the lay health actors find themselves incapable of coping with the situation and have to call on outside help. Take the following case: a young Indian woman in a Guatemalan village after an acrimonious quarrel with her husband suffers an attack of *cólera* ("rage") and later lapses into unconsciousness [66]. In the sequence of events that follows, first the husband tries to help and later the husband's father, but without success. They then call successively on a non-Indian school mistress, on one of the village shamans, on a more specialized village shaman, and on a shaman from another town. Once the client sees a *professional health actor*—in the example cited, the first shaman—he assumes the position of being a patient and enters the *professional phase*. The time which elapses before a client becomes a patient is related to the severity of his

---

[2] See Chaps. 4 and 11 for other discussions of the sick role.
[3] See Chap. 4 for further discussion of this subject.

disease, the ability of lay health actors to treat his symptoms, and—last but not least—his social status and his position within the immediate social group. This last factor has been shown to influence not only the interval between the onset of disease and hospitalization of mentally disturbed people in New York City, but also the length of time they spent in the hospital [33]. Beyond the patient role, we can isolate a position for an invalid, who still may be a patient from time to time, but who is no longer expected to resume the privileges and obligations that were his before he entered the sick role. A slightly different situation obtains for a cripple who was disabled before becoming an adult. Even the role of the dead varies in the extent to which they remain as symbolic participants in the affairs of their social group; in some societies they can continue to be clients for health action for extended periods of time.

One more kind of structure should be mentioned—*indirect health action.* The training of health specialists, which belongs in this category, does not necessarily involve any concurrent behaviors *vis-à-vis* clients, but consists rather of one health actor drawing others into health actor positions. The teacher of medical subjects—unlike a hospital administrator, for example—is not part of a group of specialists carrying out coordinated tasks with respect to clients presently under treatment; his "audience" consists of potential health actors. Another example of an indirect health action situation would occur when a dentist urges a parent and teacher organization to work for a favorable vote on fluoridation.

What does "promoting health" mean? Parsons defines "health" in terms of an optimum capacity for task and role performance [65]. This is more meaningful than the negative view of health as the absence of disease, which has considerable currency in medical circles. The asymptotic view of health, like that of Parsons, is often used in conjunction with a spectrum from an optimum state to one approaching death [75]. Many nonindustrialized societies have conceptions related to an optimum state, such as the notion that the body must be completed in some way in the course of maturation [55]. The asymptotic view also appears in the World Health Organization's definition of health: "A state of complete physical, mental, and social well-being" [93]. The possibility does exist, however, of open-ended conceptions of health, and it is present among American Indians of the Great Lakes in connection with the *midewiwin* or medicine dance as the potential for acquiring more and more power, or in the Chinese breathing exercises for increased resistance to disease [37]. Taking into account this qualification, we can redefine individual health as the theoretically unlimited maximum capacity for performance of roles which are maximally valued and can be legitimized for the person. The health of a population, a group, or a species can also be defined, but suffice it to say here that the maximum potential for survival of future generations would be a central criterion [68].

Two further concepts remain to be discussed. *Popular health culture* will refer to value orientations, notions, and behaviors pertaining to self-addressed and lay action situations on the one hand, and to the client's part in the professional action situation on the other. *Professional health culture* incorporates the value orientations, notions, and behaviors of the health specialists in professional and indirect health action situations, the structure of organizations formed by sets of these specialists, and the social arrangements of the settings within which professional health actors perform their roles.

Popular Health Culture

Most social groups do not have a conceptually tight-knit and separate body of notions and practices coinciding with what we would call their "popular" health culture. Anthropologists have described part-cultures like "subsistence activities" or "kinship," however, when such categories fit into an analytical scheme of their own. "Popular health culture" is a similarly arbitrary unit which has become most important in the course of our collaboration with medical workers. It is always risky, therefore, to lift popular health culture out of the total cultural context entirely.

Value orientations

A recent publication by Kluckhohn and Strodtbeck incorporates the results of more than ten years of research on values at Harvard University [44]. Each of the five crucial problems of all human groups they single out can be connected to notions and behaviors in particular popular health cultures. Their first question is: what is the character of innate human nature? If human nature is perceived as evil, as in the more fundamentalist variations of Christian thought, disease will be seen as justly deserved by man even if he did nothing evil himself. Health action will then be merely palliative and major effort would be directed toward seeking release from the human condition. In a society where human nature is seen as neutral or as a mixture of good and evil, health action can be directed towards bringing in benevolent forces from outside or helping the better parts of man prevail. This type of struggle is often represented as a battle between spirits or between "black" and "white" magic. Kluckhohn and Strodtbeck doubt that any societies believe that man is all good, and few, if any, anthropologists would contradict this view.

The second question is: what is the relation of man to nature? If man is seen as subjugated to nature, he must petition the forces of nature to give him health or relieve him from illness, he must avoid giving offense and give ample thanks whenever he is allowed to recover. The dozens of little metal arms, legs, and other tokens pinned on the garments of the saints in Mexican churches are striking visual symbols of this relationship. The harmony-with-nature alternative is best exemplified among the Navajo who were probably the model from whom this classification was derived. In their summary of Navajo conception of health, Adair *et al.* [4] write that illness "bears evidence that one has fallen out of this delicate balance" with the environment. The attribution of disease to an imbalance between the "Yang" and the "Yin" in classical Chinese medicine is a similar conception [37]. Mastery over nature is one of the characteristic value orientations of modern middle-class Americans. In terms of health action this leads to a "big stick" approach, filth is attacked with detergents and laxatives, and mental disease can manifest itself in the compulsive emptying of ashtrays. This has spilled over into professional health culture as well and caused a more "harmony-with-nature" oriented scientist to wonder if the destruction of microbes constitutes the only possible or even the best approach to the problem of infectious disease [17].

The third value problem explored by Kluckhohn and Strodtbeck relates to the temporal focus—*i.e.*, whether the past, the present, or the future are most important. Societies which put great emphasis on ancestors, like the Ashanti of West Africa, are likely to attribute many types of disease to the wrath of these spirits. Preoccupation with the present is often found among lower-class groups in industrial societies. The problems of food, shelter, and job security are so immediate for such people that any long-range planning becomes totally unrealistic and irrelevant. Jefferys has commented on the relevance of this for health action in Britain: the poorest patients, it seems, are inevitably concerned with immediate symptom relief and little interested in long-term procedures [38]. Middle-class Americans are quite future-oriented, but they were easily outdone by the "big men" of the Manus in the Admiralty Islands [56]. These entrepreneurs contracted for the labor of young men, guaranteeing, in return, to provide their marriage feast. This arrangement necessitated ceaseless toil by almost all men, and the sanctions were fear of illness and death. We do not know what the incidence of ulcers or heart attacks were among the "big men"; perhaps the concrete presence of a skull, the "Sir Ghost" of each household, made their life less stressful in comparison with the internalized fear of failure which is supposed to haunt the Western executive. When the Manus decided to change their way of life, they dumped the skulls into the sea (perhaps an easier solution than trying to anesthetize one's fears with a constant intake of alcohol).

The fourth value dimension concerns the modality of human activity, whether it stresses *being* or *doing*. One way in which this contrast could be relevant parallels the distinction made earlier between health as an optimum state and as a limitless maximum. If health is an optimum state, activity must be directed toward maintaining it, to keep its qualities from flowing away or departing in some way. Strong fears about a general weakening of the body through the loss of blood or semen are present in many cultures. Another common type of danger to the individual's being is more abrupt: it is the loss of the "soul" during sleep or as a result of an emotional shock. The "becoming" orientation is reflected in the accumulation of more and more magical power or strength.

The last of the five dimensions is man's relationship to other men: *lineal, collateral* or *individualistic*. It is now commonplace to describe supernatural worlds as projections from the social organization of particular people—to say that man makes his gods in his own image. In considering the influence of the relational orientation on popular health culture we can safely include some examples from the supernatural as long as we do not overlap too much with the man-nature dominance problem. The Azande of the Sudan exemplify the lineal variant in their stratified social system; they also have a hierarchy of oracles who can diagnose trouble with a certitude increasing proportionately to their owners' social status [22, p. 345]. The collateral emphasis is often found among pastoral peoples and hunters; its further presence in the form of age grades among some more highly stratified settled agriculturalists illustrates the point made by Kluckhohn and Strodtbeck that the alternative answers to the value problems are not exclusive within any one culture but are merely differentially emphasized. The Nyakyusa of East Africa have a unique system where age-mates live in separate villages, apart from other generations [92]. The sanctions toward lateral solidarity are so strong in this society that the man who eats alone instead of sharing in the good fellowship of his age-mates runs the risk either of being accused of witchcraft or of thinking himself to be a victim of it. The individualistic principle was put into bold relief in the visionary quest of the Indians of the North American Plains [51, p. 111]. While many common threads ran through these experiences, the protection against illness—among other benefits—afforded by the spirit guardian, was entirely a personal matter between it and the individual whom it "adopted."

We might establish other dimensions of value orientation or rely entirely on the value pattern that would emerge from the orientations of particular groups, but the point would be the same: it is difficult to understand the popular health culture of any society unless we relate it to the most basic assumptions made in the culture, assumptions which we can codify in terms such as those used by Kluckhohn and Strodtbeck.

Notions and behaviors

Notions, unlike value orientations, are easily described in the terminology which people themselves use in ordinary conversations. In the three-step model of description we are relying on here, notions are in the middle, providing a conceptual bridge between value orientations on the one hand and observable behavior on the other. They would include ideas, cognitions, explanations, rationalizations, anticipations, sentiments, memories, and the like; they differ from motives and needs insofar as the investigator makes no assumptions about some autonomous power they might have to push people this way or that.

A central notion in popular health culture is the way in which the human body is regarded. Women in the village of Espinos in Peru, during the first three days of life of their new-born infants, offer oiled cotton to it, withhold the breast, discard the colostrum, and take a laxative [91]. All these behaviors are related to the "body image" which obtains in this culture, particularly the notions about the passage of waste products through various organs. In contrast to this idea of the body as a plumbing system requiring periodic flushing out, we often find the notion that when everything that was once attached or within the body remains a part of it and customs such as carefully hiding body exudates for fear that they fall into the hands of a sorcerer.

Anatomical knowledge is not randomly distributed among societies; certain peoples, particularly hunters and pastoralists, derive a great deal of information from dissecting animals. Laughlin refers to the custom of the Siberian Tungus to quiz each other on comparative anatomy and to bring home young animals for observation instead of killing them [47]. He also describes his own observations on the Aleuts of Alaska, detailing the way in which their extensive reliance on animal parts for manufacturing purposes made for a highly empirical attitude towards anatomy, medicine, and surgery. The pastoralist Masai of East Africa are another group famous for their knowledge of surgery [2]. Considerable evidence for prehistoric bone operations, as a matter of fact, is available from research in paleopathology [82].

Ideas about food and nutrition are often related to the body image. Prohibitions, applicable to entire societies, against eating the meat of certain animals have been documented [85]. In some societies, the consumption of symbolic animals and plants is frequently prohibited to certain sets of people, like members of a clan. An interesting theory about this type of food avoidance is presented by Fischer, Fischer, and Mahony who argue that some of these prohibitions might have arisen when an important person developed a reaction after eating some allergenic substance during a state of emotional arousal [24]. They further hypothesize that the continued observance of taboos against food which did have possible allergic potential (or, we might add, other risks like trichinosis, brucellosis and tapeworm) could have been reinforced by the reoccurrence of symptoms in transgressors of the taboo among descendants of the original patient. Another important set of food restrictions are those which apply to men or women, often connected to matters of prestige. Among the Zulu of South Africa, cattle are closely involved in the whole patrilineal kinship system and have many ritual functions. Women are dangerous to the cattle because of their evil influence during menstruation or pregnancy and are not allowed near the cattle—nor do they usually have access to the milk. When milk was distributed from a health center in powdered form, however, women were permitted to partake of it [12]. The most elaborate kinds of rules relating to food are tied up with certain special conditions or situations including pregnancy, lactation, infancy, puberty, and preparation for war. These occasions are almost invariably recognized as periods of high susceptibility to illness or death.

One system of ideas about the relationship of food to the body has a long history and a particularly wide distribution. The theory of the four elements together with the four seasons and the four body humors was highly elaborated in Greek philosophy and medicine [83]. Probably these ideas came to Greece from India [23, p. 194] and certainly were later passed on to the Arabic world and to Europe; from there, with the help of the Spanish and the Portuguese, they spread to Latin America [26], and the Philippines [63] and many other places. The persistence of these notions in modern India is also evident [39]. In the process of diffusion, the theory was often modified; the hot-cold distinction seems to be its most tenacious element. A conceptually simpler theory than the hot-cold classification, which makes use of the idea of duality, is the notion of a single elixir or royal principle. The supreme health-giving procedure can be anything from the eating of the heart of an enemy who is slain in battle to the drinking of apple cider vinegar.

We may justly ask why radical manipulations of the diet play such an important part in self-addressed health action, even in modern Western societies where scientific nutrition information has been widely circulated. First of all, a great proportion of human diseases affect the gastrointestinal tract—particularly among the inhabitants of densely settled agrarian villages—and some of their symptoms (such as diarrhea or constipation) readily respond to changes in the diet. Second, unlike the hunters and pastoralists whose interest in anatomy has already been noted, the task of butchering animals in agricultural and urban societies is relegated to low prestige specialists; as a consequence, the anatomical ideas of the majority of the people are likely to be most rudimentary. Regulating what goes into the alimentary canal (and checking up on what comes out of it) thus becomes a most important way in which a person can try to influence his health.

Many diverse notions and behaviors are involved in coping with sickness. The self-addressed health action phase begins when an individual perceives some changes in himself which he associates with notions about sickness. In some cultures, the client will try to remain in the self-addressed health action phase as long as possible.[4] Self-diagnosis often starts in the self-addressed phase and is usually the first step in lay health action. Ledley and Lusted [48], referring to diagnosis in scientific professional medicine, list three ingredients: medical knowledge, the signs and symptoms presented by the patient, and the final medical diagnosis itself.

A small girl in a Mexican-American community cries a great deal, sleeps very little and begins to have liquid stools; her mother discovers that her stomach is slightly distended; the mother takes the child to be examined by her *madrina,* the baptismal godmother: the *madrina* discovers that the child is cutting an upper tooth, attributes the condition to teething and gives it a rag dipped in whiskey to chew [13, p. 185]. In this case the *madrina,* the lay health actor, is a person who presumably has some sophistication in the popular health culture; this is her "medical knowledge." She examines the child and finds it is cutting a tooth. In her extensive experience with small children and through the opinions of others, she has come to know that teething is often connected with the symptoms observed. On the basis of these premises she makes her diagnosis and provides a remedy.

In the terms of Ledley and Lusted's analysis, she has performed the logical operations involved in a medical diagnosis. The incorrectness of her conclusion, as shown by the subsequent worsening in the child's condition, arose as Wallace puts it "from a lack of empirical knowledge rather than from a peculiarity of the logical forms" [88, p. 355]. Lay diagnosis then, like scientific medical diagnosis, consists of a cognitive process, taking place after the onset of symptoms, which reviews alternative relationships between pathogenic conditions and pathological states relevant to the given situation. If the remedies prescribed on the basis of the diagnosis are not effective, it may not be necessary to alter one's notions about causative relationships—be they "magical," "supernatural" or "scientific"—it is logically quite sufficient to hold that the reviewing or "scanning" process failed to bring up the causative relationship applicable to the present case.

The extent to which diagnostic belief systems can be elaborated among nonindustrialized groups is documented in an article by Frake [27]. The Subanun people in the Philippines, among whom he worked, clearly provide many positive sanctions for entering the sick state, since disease is one

[4] See Chap. 4 for further discussion of this phenomenon.

of their most frequent conversational topics. Frake's article presents data on 186 terms referring to skin diseases alone. He analyzes these according to the method which has recently come to be called "componential analysis." This involves the identification of cognitive dimensions and structure—in this instance, the various criteria by which disease entities are differentiated (*e.g.* prior diagnostic condition, depth of penetration in the skin, and so on)—and the conceptual "domains" in which each criterion is applicable. The disease notions of another group, the Maya Indians of Guatemala, have also been submitted to a similar kind of analysis [5].

The health actor making a diagnosis has to give answers to two questions which are often distinct: what is the course of this disease? and why did this person come down with this disease at this time? We will refer to answers to the first type of question as *etiological notions,* and answers to the second as *incidence notions.* Etiological notions relate to the agent of the disease or the mechanism by which it occurs, the characteristic symptoms it produces, and the prognosis of the client. Incidence notions are much more personal—they include ideas about who is susceptible, under what conditions, and why. Incidence notions current in all popular health cultures are apparently much more satisfying to the average patient than the ones our highly specialized scientific health actors can give. Ackerknecht [1, p. 491] holds that "primitives" emphasize causality too much and have no concept of accidents. The search for incidence notions nevertheless seems to be present in the popular health culture of all human groups. Sigerist has emphasized its importance in the relationship between the Western physician and his patient [82, p. 157]. The concept of a chance event, the coincidence of several factors which come together to allow for the disease to occur, is psychologically most difficult. It has already been noted that man makes his gods in his own image; we can now extend this to the total human environment: the idea of generalized volitional causation (or "anthropomorphic thinking") is a projection from the learned relationship between conscious cortical "decision" and subsequent motor "action." In other words, when you get an apple from the kitchen you have decided to do so beforehand (on a level that can be made conscious); by analogy, if you get sick, somebody must have decided to make you so, or you must have brought it upon yourself.

Detailed descriptions of the endless varieties of behavior used in curing are of greatest interest to the folklorist and the ethnohistorian. In any specific situation, however, it is necessary to find out what are the main patterns if one hopes to introduce new notions and behavior. Readers interested in general works on popular health culture outside the main Western traditions may refer to some general works on the subject [1, 14, 73, 82]; or to analyses of more limited geographical scope [3, 22, 26, 34, 46, 54, 60, 63, 80, 81, 86]. Reference should also be made to a recent bibliography on

"American Indian Medicine" [10] and to publications about the popular health culture of other groups in the United States such as those of Saunders [78], Clark [13] and Rubel [76] on Spanish speaking peoples, Eaton on the Hutterites [18], Kibbe and McCorkle on Czech-Americans [43], Koos on upstate New York [45], Macgregor on rural people in the Great Plains [53], Hassinger and McNamara on south Missouri Whites [35], Cornely and Bigman on Whites and Negroes in Washington, D.C. [15], and Miner on the "Nacirema" in general [58].

Professional Health Actors in Non-Western Societies

A health actor may be called a professional if he is recognized as a specialist by members of his community or group. He need not be a full-time specialist, but his concern with health and sickness should be the pivotal attribute of his role.[5] Let us consider, as an example, the "clever man" among the Australian aborigines [19]. Knowledge of secret ceremonies, psychic powers, and magical procedures among these tribes are to some degree the common property of all adult males. But if they get into more than usual difficulty they consult a specialist in these matters. The "clever man" does not usually attend to the treatment of ills and accidents which call for "ordinary" remedies—this is the province of old women. Being a "clever man" can be either an achieved role—as when the elders discover a child who has the requisite aptitudes—or an ascribed role—as when he is the son of another "clever man." Being an old woman, on the other hand, is strictly a recruitment role whose pivotal attribute is age and not the ability to handle the "ordinary" remedies.

The entry into the health specialist role (we will be using the terms "professional," "specialist," and "practitioner" interchangeably) varies from one society to the next. In addition to descent, ascribed attributes include sex, accidents of birth, and phenotype (*e.g.*, hairiness among some South American Indian shamans [57]) and mental status [89]. Long and arduous study is very commonly required in cases where the specialist role is an achieved one. In the biography of Gregorio, the Navajo hand trembler, it is shown that his choice of career and the reasons why he did not become a "singer" —the most prestigeful health practitioner role—were associated with the degree of ability and effort the latter profession requires [49]. Other achieved conditions necessary for becoming a professional include psychological experiences such as dreams or encounters with spiritual beings [42, p. 205; 72, p. 200; 86, p. 52] or the payment of fees [50]. The case of the Australian "clever man" is typical in requiring a combination of attributes,

[5] See Nadel [61, p. 32] for the definition of "pivotal attribute."

just as in the United States ethnic background, sex, personality, and academic standing may all be important for gaining admission to medical school.

Specialization has many parallels in non-Western cultures. The village of Guinhangdan in the Philippines has 1200 inhabitants who are served by midwives, masseurs, specialists on bites, and two different types of skin disease curers [63]. Referrals from one practitioner to a more specialized one occur in several such societies [22, 66].

The manner of recompensing the practitioner and the locale of health action differ both within and between cultures. These aspects of practice may also be intimately connected with the relative status of the professional, as in the Indian village studied by Mariott [54]. Dispensers of magic there sell their wares as commodities—an activity which does not affect their status. Religious exorcists are called "wise men," they are often called from a great distance, and their fees are negotiable (the benefits of treatment are expected to vary according to the price). Their status is higher than that of the dispensers of magic since they are devotees of particular deities. Domestic priests are often from high castes, their dispensing of religiously based prescriptions is regarded as more dignified than the exorcists' trade, but they must collect their payment personally. *Hakims* and *vaids* have offices where they practice their highly professionalized trade, they are often strangers in the village, have very high status, and do not set any fees, relying instead on the patient's gratitude—and they seem to make a good deal of money by this method. It is the snake-bite curers, however, who have the greatest merit in the eyes of the villagers, although they do not thereby gain social status in the secular sphere; their piety is manifested by the self-denial involved in their training and by the fact that they are not allowed to accept any payment at all, not even water, for performing their arduous task of casting spells at the patient's side. Mariott himself draws parallels between these practitioners and some of their Western counterparts: druggists, faith-healers, and doctors. The continuum from market hawking and collection plate to the medical office is present in both societies but, given the difference in value orientations, no Western specialist can parallel the structural position of the snake-bite curer.

In studying health culture it is important to distinguish between the great traditions and the little traditions [71]. The *hakims* and *vaids* referred to above obtain their learning in the context of the Unani and Ayurvedic traditions of India respectively, while the snake-bite curers and exorcists draw upon the unwritten traditions of villagers in the Uttar Pradesh. The interested reader may consult a number of sources about the theory of classical Indian medicine [23, 40, 83, 94]. The contemporary practice of *hakims, vaids,* and the practitioners who had received their training as pharmaceutical assistants to physicians (and who call themselves "doctors") tends to converge insofar as they all give injections of antibiotics (personal communication from J. J. Gumperz).

The Egyptian and Mesopotamian medical traditions have no direct descendant today; from the documentary evidence it is possible to learn a considerable amount about the notions they had about prevention and cure, but relatively little about the sociological aspects of the health action situation [82]. Chinese medicine represents an accumulation of knowledge at least equal to that of India in antiquity, continuity, and elaboration. In the twentieth century "acupuncture" seems to be gaining in popularity in the West and, at the same time, traditional practitioners of this art in China have been united with their scientific colleagues in a single medical society [37, p. 103]. The medical tradition of Arabic-speaking peoples formed an important link in the history of Western medicine during the Middle Ages [9]. A good description of its practice in Algeria fifty years ago is given by Hilton-Simpson [36]. Knowledge of the sociological aspects of contemporary medical practice in the non-Western great traditions is severely limited; anthropologists have mostly ignored them in favor of "primitive" medicine and the few Western physicians, like Weck [89], who were not content to peruse only the written texts nevertheless restricted their enquiry to notions and treatment procedures, passing over the structural factors involved in medicine as an institution.

All the medical systems belonging to the great traditions of the world—including the Western one until the eighteenth century—can be characterized by their dependence upon the various ontological notions current in the culture, and by an emphasis on compiling and systematizing prescriptions for specific conditions. With respect to the first of these traits, they differ little from the notions of sorcerers, shamans, mediums, and other specialists of little traditions. The presence of writing, of course, nearly limits the second trait to the great traditions. A few oral systems, like the one of the Subanun, are quite complex, but this is rare and can never equal the accumulation of recipes contained on papyri, tablets, sheepskin, and paper. The older a prescription in most great traditions, the more authority accrues to it—just as foreign charms are believed to have greater efficacy in the little traditions and the latest miracle drugs have the biggest sales potential in the United States today. Alongside the elite professionals, schooled in the writings of Huang Ti, Susruta, Hippocrates, Avicenna, or Pasteur, there usually emerges a large and varied group of marginal practitioners. These individuals often have great influence on popular health culture; they transmit some genuine notions from the high-prestige sources, bringing them closer to the majority of the population both by simplifying them conceptually and—due to their intermediate social position—by bridging the "status gap." [6]

Intercultural Health Programs

Sociology in medicine has developed in large part as a response to requests for collaboration from health professionals. In the early stages of collaboration, the social scientist is often confronted with questions about "Why don't 'they' (the clients, that is) do such and such?" The old answers to this type of question often contained words like "apathy" or "indifference"—concepts hardly productive of insight into the problem [67]. Our first task, therefore, is to show that different questions like "Why *do* they . . . *and* why do *you* . . . ?" are perhaps more useful.[7] In other words, it is important to inquire about the popular health culture of the client, about the professional health culture, and about the health action system. Since health workers have undergone a long process of medical education which entails socialization into new roles, it may be useful to think of the health action system as containing two separate subcultures, whether the clients are different from the health workers only in role or class position, or whether they live in an entirely foreign society. The following discussion will be divided into four sections, each labeled with a "fallacy" serving as a heuristic device to summarize several important sociocultural factors relevant to the interaction of the two subcultures in the health action system.

The fallacy of the empty vessels

Health workers who desire to pour out the "new wine" of information—to follow the Biblical parable—often see it spilled on the ground because they disregard the fact that clients already have established health customs. These customs are concordant with the value orientations prevalent in the culture and have been found to be logically consistent with the assumptions of the notion system. People have very definite ideas, for example, about the proper post-partum behavior for mothers and infants. To ignore these or to dismiss them scornfully as superstition will often result in fewer women coming to the hospital for deliveries. This is not inevitable, however, and did not take place in one charity hospital in Ecuador [20, p. 29]. The explanation for this particular case is given in terms of Reichenbach's "frequency interpretation theory": time after time mothers and infants

---

[6] See Chap. 9 for a discussion of marginal practitioners in the United States.

[7] This point is elaborated by Julius A. Roth in an excellent article, "Management Bias in the Study of Medical Treatment," in *Human Organization*, 21 (Spring, 1962), 47–50, which appeared after this chapter was written.

came home from the hospital alive despite the "improper" way in which they were treated there. If people can be induced to do something previously unknown or forbidden with visible advantages following, the same empiricism which reinforced the prohibition should now make for a change.

Popular health culture is not static, but to change it deliberately in a given way is difficult. Some customs may be so closely tied to the value system that deviating from them may itself be seen as pathogenic. Often a visible demonstration of results is impossible. Another way of gaining acceptance for new ideas is to phrase one's message in terms of existing notions—like introducing ascorbic acid into infants' diets by recommending the addition of a little "hot" honey to orange juice in order to compensate for the "coldness" of the latter [39]. Even if effective, such strategies may not affect notions except indirectly. Foster reports on an instance where latrines were dug in a Pakistani village in a burst of enthusiasm fueled by the eagerness of the men to try out the earth augers for boring holes [25, p. 38]. Later inspection showed that several latrines were in use—fascination with a new gadget must have been only one of several factors involved, but it may well have been the one that precipitated action. Changes in behavior often precede changes in notions, but if notions remain the same only strong sanctions can maintain the new behaviors [59].

The fallacy of the separate capsule

We have stated previously that "popular health culture" is an arbitrary unit of analysis. Professional health cultures, on the other hand, are more definite institutions tied to the roles of specialist actors. As a result of this contrast, health workers are apt to project into the cognitive-behavioral system of their clients a bounded area—a separate capsule if you will—related to health.

Spanish-Americans in San Jose regard matters of employment, residence, sex, child rearing, and recreation to be completely outside the curer's area of competence [13, p. 213]. Often a dichotomy develops between two types of conditions, one kind of illness falling within the realm of indigenous practitioners, while other kinds are seen as better treated by those trained in foreign ways, like *pakeha* diseases and Maori diseases in New Zealand [62]. Or else the doctor may be visited only as a last resort, as in Sonora, Mexico [20, p. 51]. Women in rural Greece go to the hospital, among other reasons, because it is prestigious to do so [30]. Housewives in Peru may not boil their drinking water because they simply don't have the time [90]. And many people the world over do not enter the professional health action system because they don't have the money—a factor which psychologists, sociologists, and anthropologists in search of causes falling within their own separate capsule have sometimes overlooked [74]. The people in San Jose, New Zealand, and Sonora draw the area within which medical advice is relevant more narrowly than a physician would; the women in Greece and Peru do or do not follow medical recommendations for reasons that have nothing to do with their popular health culture. But the professionals who would introduce change often reinterpret such factors in terms of ignorance or a lack of that elixir called "motivation." Health workers (and many social scientists too) could avoid such professional ethnocentrisms if they spent more time outside of their office, living near the people with whom they are concerned [11].

Some other correlates of encapsulation should be considered. One that is commonly mentioned is poor communication. This is apparently a serious problem in the United States: 42 per cent of the answers of White, Negro, and Spanish-American patients in a general hospital showed inadequate comprehension of words selected from physician-patient interviews and screened by a panel of doctors who eliminated those terms they "would not ordinarily use in talking to their patients" [77]. By no means were all of the less well understood terms highly "technical" (*e.g.*, "deficient," "intern," "nutrition," "orally," "secretions," "therapy," and "terminal"), but they did involve the specialized use of relatively current words. Another factor in intercultural programs is the extraneous "cultural baggage" the health worker brings with him, such as an insistence on having three meals a day [53, p. 309]. If the capsule of the health worker does not include experience with the extremely dry air of Iran, he may introduce flies along with latrines in a place where neither were present before [25, p. 15].

The fallacy of the single pyramid

This "fallacy" is derived from Freedman's discussion of health programs in Southeast Asia [28]. Administrative boundaries drawn on a map and officials appointed to posts associated with such units, he points out, may be quite irrelevant to real units of social organization. A related mistake can be made by health workers in metropolitan cities who think of low-income areas as inhabited by a homogeneous group of people [15, p. 167]. African villages, too, may be inhabited by members of different tribes, religions, castes, or other divisions which a foreigner may easily overlook [70, p. 34]. Sets of people, classed together by linguistic criteria—such as Spanish-Americans in the United States—can also belong to highly divergent subgroups [78]. Rural communities in the United States vary around three quite different organizational types [6]. Little wonder, then, that the county health department type of organization—which was largely developed in the South—does not fit the patterns for social action in Colorado, for example [53]. The health worker assuming the household to be the meaningful social unit can be told by a Puerto Rican tuberculosis patient in New York that she lives alone, and will thereby overlook the contacts in her extended family next door with whom the patient eats [7, p. 156].

Once the health worker has identified the significant social units in a particular setting, he still has to discover the patterns of communication within these units. The easy assumption is that this communication pattern is in the form of a pyramid, and influence can be poured in at the top and it will trickle down to the bulk of the population below. Health programs which rely on direct contact with each household, however, could be more successful among working-class Negro people in Washington, D.C. (15, p. 171) and Berkeley, California, for example [16], than programs relying on the trickle-down model. Agency workers will often consider persons to be "opinion leaders" not on the basis of actual inquiry, but by guessing at their over-all socio-economic status or because these individuals give them a sympathetic reception.

The fallacy of the interchangeable faces [8]

One of the most perceptive analyses of the physician-patient relationship in an intercultural setting is contained in an article written twenty years ago; the gradual development of callous superiority among White physicians on the Navajo reservation is shown to be related to the difficulty of understanding how a clinic patient from another culture regards the services given [41]. Clients and health workers are individuals first and last, but the exigencies of the situation often work to prevent the development of a relationship on a person-to-person basis. An American technician abroad may unwittingly block communication from his local colleague by constantly retreating beyond the distance at which the latter can talk comfortably [32, p. 160]. The cumulation of misunderstandings and frustrations are apt to put a great deal of strain on the health worker who may be deprived of "full nursing satisfaction" [52] or its equivalent, and also lead to hostility and doubt on the part of the clients.[9]

Interpersonal factors are also very important in the functioning of the health team. Many problems of collaboration are not related to cultural differences, but when an American doctor abroad fails to appreciate the relative status of his colleagues in their society, the tensions generated are no longer merely personal [84]. Status factors are also often intertwined with subcultural differences between health workers and social scientists. Hopefully these can be disentangled and resolved so that collaboration between them will become increasingly fruitful and rewarding.

---

[8] The term "fallacy" is perhaps least applicable to the interpersonal factors to be discussed here, but the pattern compulsion was too strong to resist.

[9] See Chap. 11 for more detailed treatment of this subject.

References

1. Ackerknecht, E. H., "Natural Diseases and Rational Treatment in Primitive Medicine," *Bulletin of Historical Medicine,* 19 (May, 1946), 467–97.

2. ———, "Primitive Surgery," *American Anthropologist,* 49 (January-March, 1947), 25–45.

3. ———, "Medical Practices," *in* J. H. Steward, ed., *Handbook of South American Indians.* Vol. 5. Washington, D.C.: Smithsonian Institution, Bureau of American Ethnology, 1949, 621–43.

4. Adair, J., K. Deuschle, and W. McDermott, "Patterns of Health and Disease among the Navahos," *Annals of the American Academy of Political and Social Science,* 311 (May, 1957), 80–94.

5. Adams, Richard N., "An Analysis of Medical Beliefs and Practices in a Guatamala Indian Town," Pan American Sanitary Bureau, Guatemala City, Guatemala, 1953. (Mimeo.)

6. Arensberg, Conrad M., "American Communities," *American Anthropologist,* 57 (December, 1955), 1143–62.

7. Berle, Beatrice, *Eighty Puerto Rican Families in New York City: Health and Disease Studied in Context.* New York: Columbia University Press, 1958.

8. Birdwhistell, R. C., "Body Movement and Kinesics," *in* N. McQuown, ed., *The Natural History of the Interview.* New York: Grune & Stratton, Inc., (on press).

9. Browne, Edward G., *Arabian Medicine.* London: Cambridge University Press, 1921.

10. Bureau of American Ethnology, *American Indian Medicine.* Smithsonian Institute Leaflet No. 99, 1957. (Mimeo.)

11. Burgess, Anne, "Nutrition Education in Public Health Programs—What Have We Learned," *American Journal of Public Health,* 51 (November, 1961), 1715–26.

12. Cassel, J., "A Comprehensive Health Program among South African Zulus," *in* Benjamin D. Paul, ed., *Health, Culture and Community.* New York: Russell Sage Foundation, 1955, pp. 15–42.

13. Clark, Margaret, *Health in the Mexican-American Culture: A Community Study.* Berkeley: University of California Press, 1959.

14. Clements, F. E., "Primitive Concepts of Disease," *University of California Publications in American Archeology and Ethnology,* 32 (1932), No. 2, 185–252.

15. Cornely, P. B. and S. K. Bigman, "Cultural Considerations in Changing Health Attitudes." Washington, D.C.: Howard University, College of Medicine, 1961. (Mimeo.)

16. Cowles, W. and S. Polgar, "Health and Communication in a Negro Census Tract," *Social Problems,* 10 (Winter 1963), 228–236.

17. Dubos, René, *The Mirage of Health: Utopias, Progress and Biological Change.* Garden City, N. Y.: Doubleday & Company, Inc., 1961.

18. Eaton, J. W., "Folk Obstetrics and Pediatrics Meet the M.D.: A Case Study of Social Anthropology and Medicine," *in* E. Gartly Jaco, ed.,

Patients, Physicians and Illness. New York: The Free Press of Glencoe, Inc., 1958, pp. 207–21.

19. Elkin, A. P., *Aboriginal Men of High Degree.* Sydney: Australasian Publishing Company, 1945.
20. Erasmus, C. J., *Man Takes Control: Cultural Development and American Aid.* Minneapolis: University of Minnesota Press, 1961.
21. Erikson, Kai T., "Patient Role and Social Uncertainty: A Dilemma of the Mentally Ill," *Psychiatry,* 20 (August, 1957), 263–74.
22. Evans-Pritchard, E. E., *Witchcraft, Oracles and Magic among the Azande.* Oxford: Clarendon Press, 1937.
23. Filliosat, J., *La Doctrine classique de la médicine indienne: ses origines et ces parallèles grecs.* Paris: Imprimerie Rationale, 1949.
24. Fischer, A., J. L. Fischer, and F. Mahony, "Totemism and Allergy," *International Journal of Social Psychiatry,* 5 (Summer, 1959), 33–40.
25. Foster, G. M., "Problems in Intercultural Health Programs," Social Science Research Council, Pamphlet No. 12, 1958.
26. ———, "Culture and Conquest: Americans Spanish Heritage," *Viking Fund Publications in Anthropology,* 27 (1960).
27. Frake, C. O., "The Diagnosis of Disease among the Subanun of Mindanao," *American Anthropologist,* 63 (February, 1961), 113–32.
28. Freedman, Maurice, "Health Education: How It Strikes an Anthropologist," *Health Education Journal,* 14 (March, 1956), 18–24.
29. Freidson, E., "Client Control and Medical Practice," *American Journal of Sociology,* 65 (January, 1960) 374–82.
30. Friedl, Ernestine, "Hospital Care in Provincial Greece," *Human Organization,* 16 (Winter, 1958), 24–27.
31. Goffman, Erving, "The Moral Career of the Mental Patient," *Asylums,* Garden City, N. Y.: Doubleday & Company, Inc., 1961, pp. 125–69.
32. Hall, Edward T., *The Silent Language.* New York: Fawcett World Library Premier Book, 1961.
33. Hammer, Muriel, *An Analysis of Social Networks as Factors Influencing the Hospitalization of Mental Patients.* Unpublished Ph.D. thesis, Columbia University, 1961.
34. Harley, George Way, *Native African Medicine: With Special Reference to Its Practice in the Mano Tribe of Liberia.* Cambridge, Mass.: Harvard University Press, 1951.
35. Hassinger, E. W. and R. McNamara, "Family Health Practices among Open-Country People in a South Missouri County," University of Missouri, College of Agriculture, Agric. Exp. Sta., Res. Bul. No. 699, 1959.
36. Hilton-Simpson, M. W., *Arab Medicine and Surgery: A Study of the Healing Arts in Algeria.* London: Oxford University Press, 1922.
37. Huard, Pierre and Ming Wong, *La Médicine chinoise au cours des siècles.* Paris: Roger Dacosta, 1959.
38. Jefferys, Margot, "Social Class and Health Promotion: Some Obstacles in Britain," *Health Education Journal,* 15 (May, 1957), 109–18.

39. Jelliffe, D. B., "Cultural Variation and the Practical Pediatrician," *Journal of Pediatrics*, 49 (December, 1956), 661–71.
40. Jolly, Julius, "Medizin," *in* George Bühler, ed., *Grundriss der Indo-Arischen Philologie und Altertumskunde*. Vol. 3, Part 10. Strassburg: Earl J. Trübner, 1901, 1–140.
41. Joseph, Alice, "Physician and Patient, Some Aspects of Interpersonal Relationships between Physicians and Patients, with Special Regard to the Relationships between White Physicians and Indian Patients," *Applied Anthropology*, 1 (July-August-September, 1942), 1–6.
42. Kemp, P., *Healing Ritual: Studies in the Technique and Tradition of the Southern Slavs*. London: Faber & Faber, Ltd., 1935.
43. Kibbe, E. and T. McCorkle, "Culture and Medical Behavior in a Bohemian Speech Community in Iowa," Institute of Agricultural Medicine, State University of Iowa, 1957. (Mimeo.)
44. Kluckhohn, F. R. and F. L. Strodtbeck, *Variations in Value Orientations*. New York: Harper & Row, Publishers, 1961.
45. Koos, Earl L., *The Health of Regionville*. New York: Columbia University Press, 1954.
46. Lantis, Margaret, "Folk Medicine and Hygiene: Lower Kuskokwim and Nunivak-Nelson Island Areas," *Anthropological Papers of the University of Alaska*, 8 (December, 1959), 1–75.
47. Laughlin, W. S., "Primitive Theory of Medicine: Empirical Knowledge," *in* Iago Galdston, ed., *Man's Image in Medicine and Anthropology*. New York: International Universities Press (on press).
48. Ledley, R. S. and L. B. Lusted, "Reasoning Foundations of Medical Diagnosis," *Science*, 130 (July, 1959), 9–21.
49. Leighton, A. H. and D. C. Leighton, "Gregorio, the Hand-trembler," *Papers of the Peabody Museum of American Archeology and Ethnology*. Vol. 40, No. 1. Cambridge: Harvard University, 1949.
50. Linton, Ralph, "The Tanala, A Hill Tribe of Madagascar," *Chicago, Field Museum of Natural History, Anthropological Series*, Vol. 22, Publication No. 317, 1933.
51. Lowie, R. H., *Indians of the Plains*. New York: McGraw-Hill Book Company, Inc., 1954.
52. McCabe, Gracia S., "Cultural Influences on Patient Behavior," *American Journal of Nursing*, 60 (August, 1960), 1101–1104.
53. Macgregor, G., "Social Determinants of Health Practices," *American Journal of Public Health*, 51 (November, 1961), 1709–14.
54. Marriott, McKim, "Western Medicine in a Village of Northern India," *in* Benjamin D. Paul, ed., *Health, Culture and Community*. New York: Russell Sage Foundation, 1955, pp. 239–68.
55. Mead, Margaret, ed., *Cultural Patterns and Technical Change*. Paris: UNESCO, 1953.
56. ———, *New Lives for Old*. New York: Mentor Books, 1961.
57. Métraux, Alfred, "Religion and Shamanism," *in* J. H. Steward, ed., *Handbook of South American Indians*. Vol. 5. Washington, D.C.: Smithsonian Institution, Bureau of American Ethnology, 1949, pp. 559–99.

58. Miner, Horace, "Body Ritual among the Nacirema," *American Anthropologist*, 58 (June, 1956), 503–507.

59. ———, "Culture Change under Pressure: A Hansa Case," *Human Organization*, 19 (Fall, 1960), 164–67.

60. Mischel, Frances, "Faith Healing and Medical Practice in the South Caribbean," *Southwestern Journal of Anthropology*, 15 (Winter, 1959), 409–17.

61. Nadel, S. F., *The Theory of Social Structure*. New York: The Free Press of Glencoe, Inc., 1957.

62. Newell, K. W., "Medical Development within a Maori Community," *Health Education Journal*, 15 (May, 1957), 83–90.

63. Nurge, Ethel, "Etiology of Illness in Guinhangdan," *American Anthropologist*, 60 (December, 1958), 1158–72.

64. Parsons, Talcott, *The Social System*. New York: The Free Press of Glencoe, Inc., 1951.

65. ———, "Definitions of Health and Illness in the Light of American Values and Social Structure," *in* E. Gartly Jaco, ed., *Patients, Physicians and Illness*. New York: The Free Press of Glencoe, Inc., 1958, pp. 165–187.

66. Paul, B. D., "Mental Disorder and Self-Regulating Processes in Culture: A Guatemalan Illustration," *Interrelations between the Social Environment and Psychiatric Disorders*. New York, Milbank Memorial Fund, 1953, pp. 51–67.

67. ———, "Respect for Cultural Differences," *Community Development Bulletin*, 4 (June, 1953), 43–47.

68. Polgar, Steven, "Evolution and the Thermodynamic Imperative," *Human Biology*, 33 (May, 1961), 99–109.

69. ———, "Health and Human Behavior: Areas of Interest Common to the Social and Medical Sciences," *Current Anthropology*, 3 (April, 1962), 159–205.

70. Read, Margaret, *Social and Cultural Backgrounds for Planning Public Health Programs in Africa*. Brazzaville: World Health Organization, 1957.

71. Redfield, Robert, *Peasant Society and Culture*. Chicago: University of Chicago Press, 1956.

72. Ritzenthaler, Robert, "Chippewa Preoccupation with Health: Change in Traditional Attitude Resulting from Modern Health Problems," *Milwaukee Public Museum Bulletin*, 19 (June, 1953), 175–258.

73. Rivers, W. H. R., *Medicine, Magic and Religion*. New York: Harcourt, Brace & World, Inc., 1924.

74. Roemer, M. I., "Health Service Organization as a Task in Applied Social Science," *Canadian Journal of Public Health*, 45 (April, 1954), 134–45.

75. Rogers, E. S., *Human Ecology and Health: An Introduction for Administrators*. New York: The Macmillan Company, 1960.

76. Rubel, A. J., "Concept of Disease in Mexican-American Culture," *American Anthropologist*, 62 (October, 1960), 795–814.

77. Samora, J., L. Saunders, and R. F. Larson, "Medical Vocabulary Knowledge among Hospital Patients," *Journal of Health and Human Behavior*, 2 (Summer, 1961), 83–92.

78. Saunders, L., *Cultural Difference and Medical Care.* New York: Russell Sage Foundation, 1954.

79. Schneider, D. M., "The Social Dynamics of Physician Disability in Army Basic Training," *in* C. Kluckhohn, H. A. Murray, and D. M. Schneider, eds., *Personality in Nature, Society and Culture.* New York: Alfred A. Knopf, Inc., 1953, pp. 386–97.

80. Shiloh, A., "Middle East Culture and Health," *Health Education Journal,* 16 (November, 1958), 232–44.

81. Shirokogoroff, S. M., *Psychomental Complex of the Tungus.* London: Routledge & Kegan Paul, Ltd., 1935.

82. Sigerist, H. E., *A History of Medicine, Vol. 1: Primitive and Archaic Medicine.* New York: Oxford University Press, 1951.

83. ———, *A History of Medicine, Vol. II: Early Greek, Hindu and Persian Medicine.* New York: Oxford University Press, 1961.

84. Simmons, Ozzie G., "Social Status and Public Health." Social Science Research Council, Pamphlet No. 13, 1958.

85. Simoons, F. J., *Eat Not This Flesh: Food Avoidances in the Old World.* Madison: University of Wisconsin Press, 1961.

86. Spencer, D. M., "Disease, Religion and Society in the Fiji Islands," *Monographs of the American Ethnological Society,* No. 2, 1941.

87. Stein, L. and S. A. Sklaroff, "The Health of an Urban Community," *British Journal of Social Medicine,* 6 (April, 1952), 118–51.

88. Wallace, A. F. C., "Culture and Cognition," *Science,* 135 (February 1, 1962), 351–57.

89. Weck, W., *Heilkunde und Volkstum auf Bali.* Stuttgart: Ferdinand Enke Verlag, 1937.

90. Wellin, E., "Water Boiling in a Peruvian Town," *in* Benjamin D. Paul, ed., *Health, Culture and Community.* New York: Russell Sage Foundation, pp. 71–103.

91. ———, "Maternal and Infant Feeding Practices in a Peruvian Village," *Journal of the American Dietetic Association,* 31 (September, 1955), 889–94.

92. Wilson, Monica, "Nyakyusa Age-Villages," *in* S. Ottenberg and P. Ottenberg, eds., *Cultures and Societies of Africa.* New York: Random House, 1960, pp. 227–36.

93. World Health Organization, *Constitution of the World Health Organization.* Geneva: World Health Organization, 1946.

94. Zimmer, H., *Hindu Medicine.* Baltimore: Johns Hopkins Press, 1948.

Part IV

STRATEGY, METHOD, AND STATUS OF MEDICAL SOCIOLOGY

17

THE STRATEGY OF SOCIOMEDICAL RESEARCH

Richard H. Williams

The strategy of sociomedical research could be understood in two distinctly different contexts. On the one hand, it might be concerned with sociomedical research as an emerging body of systematic science, with crucial gaps in the system, and hence with various strategies for furthering the systematics of this body of knowledge. On the other hand, it could be directed at identifying the institutional and other arrangements for getting sociomedical research done, and hence to the strategy for using present resources and developing new ones. This chapter is concerned primarily with the second perspective. Ideally, a large research operation would have preceded the writing of this chapter: one needs data from intensive interviews, participant observation, and operations research on the relative productivity of differing arrangements. No such research has been undertaken, and hence the data for this chapter are, of necessity, relatively meager. There are, however, several useful surveys of the field, including recent monographs by Suchman [18] and Wellin [19]. They both focus on the uses of sociology and related sciences in public health, but do not attempt to survey the entire range of sociomedical research. There are no comparable studies of the settings, requirements, problems, and sources of support for sociomedical research as a whole. The survey of the situation as it was in 1956 by Anderson and Seacat is useful [2]. Seacat and Wellin have reviewed research in this field for the period 1954–59, which is expected to appear in print shortly. Gerald Gordon is currently analyzing data collected for the Health Information Foundation concerning 250 projects in the area of the social epidemiology of disease. The study concerns itself with backgrounds of the researchers, their feelings about the research, whether or not the research was published, and other contextual aspects of sociomedical research.

An important conclusion of this chapter, which seems fitting to be drawn at the outset, is that there is need for research on the sociology of this obviously expanding and important field. Such research would contribute to the sociology of knowledge, as well as provide an empirical basis for evaluating alternative arrangements for developing the field of medical sociology.

Delineation of the Field

It is necessary to delineate the field under discussion, for it is a broad one with many facets. The categorization of the field by Kendall and Merton into the four areas of etiology and ecology, variations in response to illness and maintenance of health, organization of health facilities, and professional education and training is quite useful [8]. The distinction proposed by Straus, which cuts across these four areas, between the sociology *of* medicine and sociology *in* medicine is particularly useful for the present discussion [17]. The former is a facet of sociology qua sociology, which happens to take medicine and related medical activities as its subject matter. The latter is enmeshed in the medical field on a collaborative basis.

There is another distinction which is useful in order to avoid considerable confusion, especially in relation to the organization and funding of sociomedical research. It may best be illustrated by reference to the field of mental health.

There has been a tendency within the health field to view the behavioral sciences, including sociology, as coterminous with mental health. This tendency has been somewhat less pronounced within sociology, due in part to the work of such people as Merton, et al., on the student physician [10] and of several studies of hospitals and other health facilities unrelated to mental illness as such. By some lines of reasoning, they too can be presumed to be related to mental *health*. There are understandable historical reasons for this view. The subject matter of mental health is immediately and directly related to behavior. Whatever the etiology of mental disorders may be, their manifestations are primarily behavioral on levels of direct concern to psychology, sociology, and social or cultural anthropology. They involve deviant behavior which affects the general stance of the individual and has an impact on those around him. The program of the National Institute of Mental Health and other mental health programs have drawn heavily on the behavioral sciences and have recognized the urgent need for their further development and support. Indeed, some aspects of psychiatry itself have taken on many of the characteristics of a behavioral science.

More recently there has been a growing and proper recognition that the behavioral sciences are an integral and necessary part of the *armamentum* of research in public health and in health generally. On the basic side, the work of Dubos and others points to psychological, social, and cultural factors in the epidemiology of many communicable and chronic diseases. On the more applied side, the major question of relevance to service programs which behavioral scientists are especially qualified to provide an answer is: what are the conditions under which people will take action to control a health problem or improve a health situation? Knowledge of the nature of channels of communication in various types of organizations or of patterns of influence within segments of a community has relevance to the design of programs intended to affect behavior within such organizations or population segments. Knowledge of this type can be useful in deciding where the energies should go in a particular program.

The primary concern of research in mental health (hence in training for it) is with behavioral or "psychological" functioning as such; put in somewhat more sociological terms, it is concerned with the viability of the action systems of individual actors. This view is similar to one developed recently in psychology by Smith [15]. Such functioning is viewed on a broad continuum, from extreme behavioral incapacitation to optimal ability to act. Factors affecting status and movement on this continuum range from the physical environment through the biological to the social and cultural. Some of them are conditional to behavior; others, inherently a part of the behavioral system itself. Mental health is not directly concerned with the former but is with the latter. For example, the National Institute of Mental Health would not consider it a part of its mission to support research on paraplegia as such, but would certainly sponsor a good research project on the ways in which paraplegics cope with life, mentally and emotionally. To take a somewhat more subtle example, research on the behavioral factors producing or reducing dental disorders (*e.g.*, acceptance of fluoridation) would not fall within the province of the NIMH, but research on the impact of dental disorders on ego functioning would.

The conceptual difficulties arise from the fact that, in significant (although not precisely known) part, the "disease entity" in the field of mental health involves behavioral functioning as such in a direct sense. On these grounds, both the independent and the dependent variables can be conceptualized as variables within action systems (*e.g.*, impact of the action system of the mother on the action system of the child). There is a double incidence of social (and psychological) factors in much of the field of mental health. The independent variables may be sought for outside the action system as such; for example, the search for biochemical variables relating to schizophrenia. The population of schizophrenics under study has been defined by its behavioral manifestations and, in this sense, the dependent variables in research in mental health always are part of the action system. In other health and disease areas, one is looking for new independent variables of a social, social psychological, or sociocultural nature which might explain at least part of the variance of dependent variables that are not themselves part of the action system (in the Parsonian sense), although they may be conditional to it as, for example, in the studies of social factors in chronic illness (described by Saxon Graham; see Chap. 3). Or, one may be studying the structure and functioning of organizations or institutions (*e.g.*, hospitals, medical schools, medical profession, and so forth) as such, without particular concern with the viability (*i.e.*, mental health) of the individual actors.

Table 17-1 gives a few illustrations of these rather abstract distinctions. They are not meant to be rigid. There can be perfectly valid research efforts which cut across rows or down columns, or both. We believe, however, that they are analytically valid, and sociomedical research tends, in fact, to be organized in such a way as to fall primarily, if not exclusively, in one or another of these boxes. Furthermore, the predominant characteristic of a research project or program which would lead one to classify it one way or another according to this scheme will have considerable bearing on the types of setting and requirements appropriate to the research, the types of problems likely to arise in medical settings, and, quite clearly, the sources of support, to all of which we shall turn in subsequent sections.

TABLE 17-1

Studies of	*Focused on*	
	1. Behavioral or psychological function as such ("basic"), and viability of the action system of individual actors ("applied").	2. Social, social-psychological and socio-cultural factors in other aspects of health and disease ("basic") and their management ("applied").
Etiology and ecology of diseases *and* health.	3. Ecology of mental disorders; production and reproduction of successful or unsuccessful coping behavior in families; basic studies of motivation, learning, perception, etc.	4. Social factors in the epidemiology of cancer, rheumatoid arthritis, etc. (see esp. Chapter 3 by Saxon Graham).
Responses to health and disease.	5. Communication of mental health concepts; social and social-psychological careers of mental patients during and after hospitalization; emotional factors and coping behavior in relation to leukemia, death or other stressful situations.	6. Factors affecting acceptance of fluoridation or other public health programs; the impact of influenza on a community.
Organization of medical facilities and other groups affecting health.	7. Social structure and functioning of a mental hospital; mental health in schools and industry (i.e., impact of schools or industries as sociocultural systems on the viability of the action systems of their members).	8. Social structure and functioning of the general hospital, health departments, group practice of medicine, etc.
Education, career development and professionalization as a social process.	9. Career development in all the "mental health" professions (i.e., all those whose primary concern is with helping others achieve a more viable action system); development of new roles in the field of mental health (e.g., the mental health worker).	10. The development of student physicians; choice of public health as a career; social factors in revising education.

Settings for Sociomedical Research

The most relevant features of the settings for sociomedical research in relation to the problems of doing such research and to the problems of being a researcher in such settings relate to the characteristics of the social systems of these settings.

> Organized courses of action require cooperative action, the interaction of persons, a pattern of interpersonal relations, and, hence a social system. Social systems themselves have certain basic requirements which must be met, if they are to function adequately, at a minimum of social cost. Relatively less is known about the requirements of social systems, and it must be stressed that greater relative gains can be expected from research directed at that question than at questions pertaining to the economic and technological systems. The present discussion suggests some of the general types of requirements which social systems have. They may be summarized as follows:
>
> 1. The requirement of optimal structuring—too much structure blocks the entire action system, and inhibits the decision making process. Too much structure also involves too great an investment of action energy in maintaining the structure, at the expense of getting things done—too little structure leads to general confusion, faulty insulation, duplication of effort, and not enough meaningful pattern to provide adequate motivation.
>
> 2. The requirement of maximal institutionalization—the amount of institutionalization is not equivalent to the amount of structure. A social system only operates by virtue of being institutionalized and, in the sense in which that concept has been developed here, there cannot be too much of it. It should also be stressed that as the requirements of the situation of action change, institutional patterns must change. Otherwise, in the new situation, these patterns exist as ossified elements of structure rather than full-fledged institutions.
>
> 3. The requirement of minimal friction, but optimal tension—friction tends to develop when the density of interaction is too great, and when too many actions are originated for persons occupying certain positions. Friction can be reduced by proper insulation and by changes in the distribution of decisions and originations.
>
> 4. The requirement of optimal frustration and anxiety, but maximal motivation—frustration and anxiety tend to produce aggressive behavior up to a point, beyond which they may result in a blocked action system, *i.e.*, neurosis. Furthermore, the optimal amount of aggressive behavior is itself a variable, dependent in part on the requirements of the situation of action; the problem is a complex but highly important one. The ratios representing satisfaction and self-esteem should be neither too large nor too small.
>
> 5. The requirement of optimal distribution—of satisfactions, power, risks and responsibilities [20].

An hypothesis concerning social distance from medical settings

In the present stage of sociomedical research one can hypothesize with considerable assurance that the degree of difficulty in fulfilling the requirements of optimally functioning social systems varies inversely with the social distance between the research base and the medical setting itself, unless certain devices, such as institutionalized insulation, are evolved. Sociology as a science has grown and established traditional ways of procedure primarily, indeed almost exclusively, within the academic setting of the college or university department. As sociological researchers move out from these settings, the new settings are likely to appear to contain more structure than these researchers readily tolerate. In large measure this is due to the presence of elements of structure which are institutionalized in the view of medical practitioners and others accustomed to working in these settings, but which appear as roadblocks to the sociologist. Considerable friction can develop through interaction with persons whose roles, goals, and requirements are quite different and through origination of many actions by these persons, actions which do, in fact, affect the work of the sociologist. For example, the apparently simple matter of access to medical records or other sources of data burdened with the norm of confidentiality—a norm to which the sociologist is quite accustomed, but which he has institutionalized and internalized in ways different than those in the medical profession—can absorb a tremendous amount of time which to the sociologist may seem a waste of effort and a hindrance to his research. There is danger that the social researcher will become so frustrated and anxious that he will either behave in an overly aggressive way, or be blocked into apathy, either of which can do much to retard the accomplishments and potential usefulness of sociomedical research.

There is, simultaneously, another very important aspect to this problem. The presence of a sociologist, or even more of a behavioral science research team, in a medical setting based as part of its social system alters the system itself. The "native" inhabitants of the system may well view the newcomer as a "foreigner," the more so because he is there to perform tasks they may not understand. He is viewed as a new element of non-institutionalized structure, which easily gives the impression of excess baggage. New issues will arise concerning optimum distribution of satisfactions (*e.g.*, in relation to office space, salary levels, job satisfactions, and the like), power ("What *is* the relation of these researchers to the power hierarchy?"), risks (*e.g.*, tenure, or the consequences of failure or success in research), and responsibilities.

Types of settings

According to this hypothesis, then, the home-based social scientist, with a tenured position in a sociology department should have the least degree of difficulty in meeting social system requirements doing sociomedical research. Unless he is doing a survey of the literature or using readily accessible documentary sources, he will be faced with problems of social system requirements relating to access to data. He will have to obtain entree, establish rapport with subjects, and be mindful not to get himself thrown out once he has gotten in. But these problems are faced in *any* sociological research—in industry, school systems, community organization, or whatnot. Social researchers are generally trained to cope with such problems; and certainly they expect them to arise.

A social science team can be formally located in a medical setting, and yet be insulated from it in crucial ways. For example, a team with which the writer was closely familiar for several years was administratively housed in a school of public health. The school provided certain housekeeping and bookkeeping services to the research project. One of the more "inside" members of the school's faculty, himself a social scientist, provided liaison with the research team and acted in a consultative capacity to it. The research team was physically housed in donated space, in a building belonging to a local public health unit (not part of the school), physically at a perceptible but "convenient" distance from the school. Members of the research team informally, occasionally officially, could and did participate in regular activities of the school, taking part in a seminar or giving a lecture. But the insulation of the team was sufficiently great that the social system problems with which they were faced had almost exclusively to do with interdisciplinary research and very little, if at all, with their relations to the setting (the school).

The independent researcher based in a more or less permanent way in a medical setting—a situation which, to the knowledge of this author, is relatively rare—would more likely be faced with problems relating to the social system requirements of his setting than would a team. For him, insulation would be tantamount to social isolation. Unless he is of the type that flourishes in isolation, he would be in trouble if he took that course. On the other hand, his problems would be less than those of a noninsulated team, largely because his presence would constitute less of a change in the system, hence be less of a threat to it. He may, of course, be frustrated by the system, but the system is not likely to be much frustrated by him.

A very special case of a nonuniversity, medically oriented setting is the National Institute of Mental Health. In a crude sense, it could be said that all of the social scientists on its staff are in a medical setting, have no distance from it, and hence would be open to the full range of problems created by social system requirements as suggested by the general hypothesis formulated above. However, there are important variations within the Institute illustrative of the subtle complexities of such relationships. The Institute has the diversified functions of research, both intramural and through grants, training, and consultation for both hospital and community mental health programs. Social scientists are involved in all these functions.

Researchers in the intramural program are in an institutionalized setting which is virtually indistinguishable from that of scientists doing research in a university. The major boundary of their social system is the laboratory, and the bulk of their interactions are within it. Their research, in turn, may be done in a medical setting (for example, Saint Elizabeth's Hospital or the wards of the Clinical Center for the National Institutes of Health), or it may not (*e.g.*, studies of class difference in parent-child relationships, conducted on "normal" populations living in the community). If it is done in a medical setting, the researchers are defined and perceived as coming *from* the laboratory, their base being there. This situation is essentially no different, in point of institutional structure, from that of a sociologist based in a university department doing research in a hospital. In the grant program the function is research administration, a specialized function which is beginning to appear in some universities, and the main interactions are with actual or prospective grantees or study section members, the great majority of whom are university based.

An intermediate position is occupied by members of the Professional Services Branch, who develop research projects of a relatively applied sort, related to program development, and then participate to varying degrees in the conduct of the research on a collaborative basis with research teams in various universities. They consult occasionally with various medically oriented operating agencies, largely in terms of translating research results into program. Social scientists in the Training Branch are not directly engaged in research, although they are involved in the promotion of research training; their interactions are primarily with staffs of training institutions, mostly universities. Within their own Branch they face problems of interdisciplinary collaboration, although minimally because each training specialist concentrates pretty much on his own field.

Social scientists in the Community Services Branch and in the Regional Offices are in quite a different institutional setting. Within the group they are a small minority surrounded by psychiatrists, social workers, nurses, and clinical psychologists, yet all are concerned with the same types of programs. Their orientation must be of the sociology in medicine type, rather than the sociology of medicine. Outside the Institute, they act as consultants, sometimes to applied or evaluative research projects, sometimes directly to program. Their interactions in those situations are very largely but not exclusively with people responsible for operating mental health programs.

No systematic analysis of these variations within the National Institute of Mental Health has been made in relation to the hypothesis formulated above. Such an analysis would be difficult because the number of social scientists directly involved in consultation for service programs is very small. However, on the basis of the writer's general experience over several years, it seems clear that the problems of meeting social system requirements are least in the intramural laboratory, greatest in the extramural consultation, and middling (but closer to the intramural) in the other programs. No judgment is implied that the problems which do exist are insoluble or create insuperable barriers; indeed, it is the writer's impression that those who have faced the greatest problems in this respect have handled them particularly well.

The social scientist anchored in a school of public health, medical school, or school of nursing enjoys a setting which retains the general institutional characteristics of the university. The orientation is primarily toward learning rather than toward day-to-day responsibility for the operation of a health program. This is particularly true of schools of public health; medical schools and schools of nursing are intertwined with the operational exigencies of a hospital. The extreme end of this continuum of degree of social distance from a medical setting (conversely, from a liberal arts department) is employment in a health department, without ties to a university.

As indicated by Wellin,

> . . . a number of state and local health departments have employed, or now employ, social scientists on a full-time basis. Among the state health departments are those of California, Colorado, Connecticut, Florida, Kentucky, Maryland, New Mexico, New York, Pennsylvania, and Washington. In addition, social scientists are employed full-time in the health departments of the cities of New York, Philadelphia, and Cambridge, and in the St. Louis County Health Department. The Los Angeles City and County Health Departments make use of the part-time services of social scientists, mainly on a contractual basis [19].

None of these positions existed prior to 1952 and several of them are very recent.

These instances represent the case which, according to the general hypothesis, should present the most problems in relation to meeting the requirements of the social system of the setting. Unfortunately there is no systematic evidence to confirm or deny the theoretical expectations. Such a study would be particularly interesting at this stage of the development of sociomedical research, because of its recency and because, to date, the type of institutional arrangement and mode of participation of social scientists in health settings have been matters of opportunity and circumstance, not of planned development according to stated principles, as Suchman suggests [18]. It is the author's impression, however, based on talking with many people in the fields of mental and public health, that the hypothesis would hold.

The form of the hypothesis, hence the tenor of this section, might suggest the erroneous conclusion that sociomedical research should not be encouraged to decrease the social distance between the researchers and the medical settings. Both Suchman and Wellin have made a very good case for the functional value of social scientists engaging in research and other activities, especially consultation, within schools and state and local departments of public health. A similar case could probably be made for medical schools, schools of nursing, and other medical settings. Gouldner, among others, has indicated the potential value of applied research [5], and some kinds of applied medical research are very clearly better done based within a medical setting rather than conducted from outside. Thus, the question of strategy is one of facing problems created by the requirements of the social system, rather than retreating from them.

Solving the problems

The best approach to these problems is a direct one—clear recognition of the nature of the problems and open discussion of them. Occasionally, formal techniques of group dynamics, familiar to many social scientists, might be used, although a researcher based in a medical setting is in a somewhat awkward situation if he initiates formal procedures that are primarily and expressly intended to better his own position. If such techniques are used, it is probably best to focus them on fairly specific operating problems of the agency, and to develop clarifications and understandings of the social position of the social researcher indirectly as a byproduct.

There are various institutional devices which are potentially helpful. One of them is insulation, but that would be functional only under certain special circumstances. It would be damaging in others. Another is to make part-time use of university-based social scientists for research on a contractual basis. At least one major local public health program follows that practice. It would be a better arrangement, in the opinion of the author, to employ social scientists within health settings (health department or other) as their primary base, but at the same time permit them to hold appointments in a nearby university. This is done in the St. Louis County Health Department. As a corollary, such social scientists should not engage exclusively in research; their position in the system will be strengthened and be more functional for the system if they also participate in university teaching, inservice training, and consultation.

A particularly important question when sociomedical research (and other activities) is based in a health setting is the position given such research within the formal organization. Various arrangements have been used, but there are no hard data on which to evaluate the relative merits of each. In principle, however, a social scientist or the head of a social science unit should be placed in a staff position and report directly to the head of the health agency. The functions that social scientists perform, whether in research, training, or consultation, tend to relate to general matters affecting the entire setting, its operation, and the accomplishment of its general mission. If social scientists are identified with one segment of the total organization, and if they must relate to more than one link in the chain of command, their activities can readily become both distorted and frustrated. Other arrangements have been used and appear to work relatively well, but they might work even better if changed to conform with this principle.

Finally, the placement of sociomedical research in various settings should take cognizance of the distinction drawn in the introductory section of this chapter and illustrated in Table 17-1. If the research is predominantly of a character which would place it in any of the boxes in the left-hand column, it should either be based in an academic department in a university; or, if it is based in a medical setting, such a setting should be clearly identified as relating to mental health (*e.g.*, a department of psychiatry in a medical school, a mental health unit in a school of public health, a state or local department or division of mental health, a mental hospital, or whatever). If its predominant characteristic places it somewhere in the right-hand column, it should either be based in an academic department of a university, or in a health setting clearly *not* identified with mental health. The confusions arising from identification of the social and behavioral sciences in health with mental health are not likely to occur, in any event not to be of any particular consequence, in academic settings, but they do arise and are likely to be damaging in a service or teaching oriented medical setting.

Requirements for Adequate Professional Performance

Is standardization occurring and is it desirable?

It is clear that sociology *in* medicine is a very recent phenomenon, and it is also clear that it has grown relatively rapidly. The demand for qualified people currently exceeds the supply. As Wellin points out, "this, plus the fact that the health field is still nearer the margin than the center of employment acceptable to qualified people, increases the risk that marginal or poorly-trained social scientists will be recruited" [19].

Theoretically, one possible safeguard would be formal standardization of qualifications, through use of such devices as competitive examinations.

Wellin takes a cue from Sibley [13] who claims that the demand for formal criteria of qualifications is greater in applied fields where the employers are not themselves sociologists. Wellin takes the position that a trend toward standardization is inevitable, that those in the relevant behavioral sciences should take the leadership in this respect. He specifically recommends that "*standard examinations* be developed as part of the objective selection procedures for *social science personnel in official* (i.e., merit system) *agencies.* Inasmuch as such examinations would constitute concrete attempts to spell out the essential core(s) of knowledge required for social scientists, it is highly desirable that outstanding behavioral scientists be involved in the preparation of such materials" [19].

Such a development should be approached with considerable caution. There is as yet no consensus concerning what a sociologist should know to work in official health agencies, to say nothing of the various other fields of health or medicine, or what his particular skills should be. Standardized procedures could become uninstitutionalized and dysfunctional elements of structure, creating friction and noise in the system and impeding further, more imaginative development of the field.

The problem is much more complex for sociology *in* medicine than for sociology *of* medicine. In the latter field, the sociologist is most likely to be spending only some of his time on his research, the rest on his academic teaching. The fact that his research happens to be about something that utilizes data from the social fields of medicine or health does not in itself raise any special issues concerning his qualifications. The sociologist *in* medicine is likely to spend a great deal of his time on research, perhaps some in academic teaching, but he is also likely to put time into inservice training and consultation on program. Even if most of his time is devoted to research, he must be concerned with feedback and utilization, or his utility to the agency which employs him will appear to it minimal or nil. Standardized screening devices to assure possession of the skills necessary to meet requirements of these other functions would be extraordinarily difficult, if not impossible, to devise.

If standardized selection procedures are to be used at all, beyond the well-established ones of meeting certain formal requirements such as academic degrees and years of experience, they could only serve to determine minimal qualifications in research competence and substantive knowledge of the discipline. Possibly such procedures would help to establish a "solid floor," as Sibley suggests, but it seems more likely that they would be redundant with the more usual types of formal requirements for jobs. Would it really be worth the effort to devise standard examinations which might possibly screen out a very small number of people who met other formal requirements but couldn't pass the exams?

Another possible approach to formal standardization would be to follow the practice of the medical profession itself and have applied medical sociologists (or applied sociologists generally) be subject to licensing and, for higher level jobs, to board certification. To enter directly into the pros and cons of this issue, which has been debated for several years, would take us too far afield. Suffice it to say that there would be the serious danger, at this stage in the development of the field, of reinforcing a tendency to turn the medical sociologist into an unfortunate crossbreed, a matter which we will discuss further.

Alternatives to formal standardization

Since the problem of assuring that highly qualified people are involved in sociology in medicine, and since formal selection devices might be redundant or create more problems than they would solve, it seems important to consider the reinforcement of less formal, more fully institutionalized devices.

A relatively simple one, which could be reinforced through the usual channels of the American Sociological Association and the sociological journals, would be to emphasize the fact that the sociologist in medicine must be sufficiently qualified so that he could do sociological research and teaching in a college or university, and qualified also to meet the other demands of the setting into which he is going. The other demands require skills in interpersonal and group relations which may not be quite so crucial in all academic settings. Dissemination of this concept would also do much to raise the prestige of sociologists who choose to work in applied settings.

Another device is to preserve the professional identity of the applied sociologist as a sociologist, and to make sure that there are opportunities to maintain strong relations with his peers in sociology. This type of problem arises infrequently if at all in a setting such as the National Institute of Mental Health. There are sufficient numbers of sociologists and members of related disciplines to provide about as many peer relations as exist in most universities. In addition, there are seminars, consultant groups, study sections, and review committees which bring large numbers of peers in from the outside for varying periods of time. This type of problem is very apt to arise in the case of the lone social scientist in a medical school, school of public health, school of nursing, or health department. Various settings are intermediate between these two in this respect. But there are ways to offset this characteristic of the setting. The joint university appointment, for instance, has much to commend it from this point of view. The use of outside consultant groups can also be valuable and need not be on the scale used by the National Institute of Mental Health, which runs the risk of producing an overly rich diet. Certainly ample provision should be made for travel to professional meetings.

Characteristic Problems of Working in Medical Settings

There are no available data sufficiently exhaustive or systematic to say just what the range of problems facing sociological researchers based in medical settings is, or how "characteristic" they are. Many of these problems are probably found in varying degrees wherever research is based in an applied setting and done on a collaborative rather than independent basis. However, the well-known institutional characteristics of the medical profession and those in it, such as the role of the doctor and the sick role, and the high cultural value placed on the whole field generally undoubtedly heighten these problems in medical settings.

Interdisciplinary and team research

The inherently collaborative nature of research in the context of sociology in medicine gives rise to the full range of interdisciplinary problems, whether or not the research is organized as a formal interdisciplinary team. There is considerable literature discussing these problems, the most extensive of which is the volume edited by Luszki [9]; Wellin includes sixteen items on team and interdisciplinary relations in his bibliography [19].

These problems vary both with the type of medical setting and with the type of research. Probably the most inherently compatible medical setting for collaborative research in social science is public health, either in health departments or in schools of public health. Hanlon and others in public health maintain that public health is to a very significant extent an applied social science [6]. Within public health, the problems of ambiguity of roles and of communication are probably reduced to a minimum in research of a sort that would fall in Boxes 4 and 6 of Table 17-1—social factors in the epidemiology of various diseases, and social factors in the acceptance of public health programs. They become more sensitive issues in Box 8, for example, in studies of the social structure and function of a health department or a school of public health. Such studies might better be done, in the present stage of development, in a context of the sociology of medicine from an outside base. Straus may well be right when he alleges that "the sociologist in medicine risks a good relation if he tries to study his colleagues" [17].

Research teams which are relatively well insulated within their settings, as illustrated earlier in the chapter, serve to highlight the problems of interdisciplinary team research as such, relatively uncontaminated by the characteristics of the setting. Simmons and Davis, operating in such a relatively insulated setting, found that major problems and issues were methodological rather than conceptual [14]. There tends to be cleavage between those oriented to more qualitative, clinical methods and those oriented to more quantitative methods. The two approaches can, it has been found, be combined. A major effort to clarify these problems is the report on controls in psychiatric research of the Research Committee of the Group for the Advancement of Psychiatry [16]. This small volume is well worth studying by applied social scientists and members of other disciplines or professions who intend to engage in research. Simmons and Davis also indicate that they were not prepared for the amount of interaction in team research. There are "sustained and unremitting pressures" which can become quite wearing. This situation was probably heightened to some extent by the relative insulation, but is probably an experience common to team research generally.

The problems of interdisciplinary collaboration are greatest in relation to all of the types of research on the left-hand side of Table 17-1, for work done within a medical setting. The double incidence of social (or action system) factors, the subtle distinctions and considerable overlap between applied social science and mental health, the relative ignorance of the etiology of mental disorders, and the relatively high sensitivity to problems of differentiation of role within the mental health professions all serve to heighten and intensify the problems of interdisciplinary collaboration. It is in this area particularly that every effort must be made to maintain the professional identity of the sociologist as sociologist. If he tries to become a clinician, he is neither fish nor fowl, only a source of confusion.

At the present stage of development in medical sociology, it is probably wise to have the great bulk of sociomedical research proceed in areas falling within the odd-numbered boxes in Table 17-1, in a context of the sociology *of* medicine rather than of sociology *in* medicine. It should be emphasized, however, that this distinction, borrowed from Straus, does not imply (at least in this context) an equivalence to the distinction between "basic" and "applied" research. Research of all the types in the left-hand column can be done in such a way as to furnish the practitioner the basis for sounder judgments about alternatives in the organization and conduct of mental health programs.

Communication

Discussions of interdisciplinary research frequently point up problems of communication. The impression is sometimes given that they are essentially intellectual problems of conceptualization and vocabulary. The experience reported by Simmons and Davis does not substantiate this view; methodological posture rather than conceptual difficulties was the core of the problem. Back of either type of problem lie subtle cultural differences associated with the social process of professionalization in a given discipline. Jackson has indicated that what are frequently called problems of communication are only symptomatic of other difficulties found generically in organizations [7]. He indicates four problems which must be solved indirectly, but effectively, to overcome barriers to communication: "1. the problem of trust or lack of trust; 2. the problem of creating interdependence among persons: common goals and agreement about means for achieving them; 3. the problem of distributing rewards fairly, and 4. the exceedingly important problem of understanding and coming to common agreement about the social structure of the organization" [7].

Cross-disciplinary collaboration

Both Wellin and Suchman call attention to two particularly valuable analyses of problems of cross-disciplinary collaboration and of possible solutions to these problems, made by the Russell Sage Foundation [11, 12]. On the basis of these analyses the problems can be grouped essentially into cultural barriers, social position (role, status, and authority) within the social structure of the setting, and ambiguities in expectations. The solutions call for wider ranges of understanding. The analyses underline the importance of interpersonal skills important in addition to research skills. They make the very important point that caution should be exercised in attributing the difficulties which do arise to "personality clashes"; the probabilities are that they relate more fundamentally to "cultural, social-structural, and role specification problems" and could be dealt with more effectively in that context.

Relation to service functions

The sociologist in medicine will, of course, be surrounded by and must take cognizance of the requirements of training and service. In general, he is least well prepared to cope with demands of this kind. He has been trained to think, to raise issues, and to do research, but not necessarily to find answers to practical questions, and least of all to carry out service functions.

There is essentially only one type of medical setting where there could be any thought of a sociologist assuming treatment function in the sense of direct therapeutic intervention with individuals or with groups; namely, a setting where the primary responsibility is for mental health. The best approach to such a situation is to make it quite clear from the outset that sociologists are not therapists. They may, with proper experience and other qualifications, provide important consultation concerning programs of care, treatment and rehabilitation of the mentally ill, but they will merely add to such confusion as may already exist if they permit themselves to enter into treatment relations with patients.

The major contribution sociologists can make, apart from research, are through the indirect services of consultation in program development and inservice training to the staffs of their agency or other related agencies.

It is by no means always necessary to "do research" from scratch in relation to every sociologically relevant problem that may arise in service programs. There is already a considerable body of applicable knowledge plus useful perspectives and approaches. The sociologist can be quite helpful to others in the program, helping them to define their problems more sharply and systematically and bringing to their attention the documented experiences of other, similar programs. Inservice training may take the form of general sociological orientation, to sharpen awareness of a range of social factors influencing the service and program, or training in specific research techniques. If the sociologist has a dual appointment in a nearby university, he may be able to arrange a valuable combination of academic work with practical experience, thus to help prepare a better new generation of medical sociologists.

There are other, more direct, types of service functions which a sociologist may perform or in which he may share, in certain medical settings, notably in public health. To do them well requires additional training or some "secondary professionalization" in public health. Also, inservice training can work both ways—the sociologist can learn much from his colleagues in other professions. Perhaps the most promising field for direct sociological contribution in both public health and public mental health is community organization and development, including questions of the logistics in utilization of services. A second promising field, one in which somewhat more work has been done, is gaining acceptance of health programs.[1]

These service functions can be of strategic importance to research in an indirect way. If done well, they do much to validate the sociologist in the eyes of his colleagues from other disciplines in the medical setting. They help him "pay his freight" and legitimize the time he spends in the riskier ventures of research. Involvement in service functions can also have strategic importance for research in a somewhat more direct way. Such involvement helps to familiarize the sociologist with the laymen's hypotheses, which he can then test through research. As Gouldner indicates, "the latent function of such tests, however, is to document the inadequacy and breakdown of lay hypotheses, thus enlarging the area of intellectual discretion allowable to applied social scientists, and easing their introduction of independent variables that are novel to laymen" [5]. Finally, it can help to further in quite a direct way the detection and closure of those gaps between the basic and applied disciplines which, Gouldner points out, may "signalize, not only a handicap of the applied scientist, but also an unnecessary defect in pure theory itself" [5].

---

[1] For a detailed discussion of utilization of health services and acceptance of health programs, see Chaps. 14 and 15.

The major shift which is occurring within the health fields, notably within public health, from emphasis on communicable diseases to emphasis on chronic diseases and the "social diseases" or "social deviances" (alcoholism, drug addiction, juvenile delinquency, suicide) makes all of the problems of collaboration between social scientists and the health professions of crucial importance today.[2] The area of social deviances overlaps significantly with the field of mental health, hence with matters that appear to involve the actor and his action system primarily and the organism secondarily. There are very prominent sociobehavioral facets in the chronic diseases (Chapters 3 and 4). It seems important to emphasize again that it would be good strategy to put larger pieces of the present resources of sociomedical research into research relating to service programs in the health field.

Sources of Support

The general picture

Unfortunately, even in the relatively "simple" aspect of sources of financial support for sociomedical research, no systematic body of data has been collected for the entire field. In broad perspective, the Federal Government is the major single source of support by way of grants and occasionally through contracts; within it, the National Institute of Mental Health plays the major role. Other parts of the National Institute of Health are showing increasing interest in developing still broader support for the behavioral sciences in health. Also, the Bureau of State Services, in the Public Health Service, is making increasing use of social scientists, and has the beginnings of a grant program which may support sociomedical research in relation to the community health and environmental health areas. The Veterans Administration has a sizable program, especially in the psychiatric field, and the Office of Vocational Rehabilitation has a small but growing program of research and demonstration projects, some of which fall clearly within the sociomedical field. Some state governments are beginning to support sociomedical research, particularly in the field of mental health, as are a few city and county health programs.

Foundations support it in varying degrees and ways; some of them have played a major role in determining the course of the development of this field. The voluntary health agencies have supported research in the social sciences only to a limited extent.

Other sources of support which probably have assumed major proportions quite recently are the larger insurance companies and some labor unions, notably the United Mine Workers.

---

[2] See Chap. 5 for a discussion of the addictive diseases.

Federal support through
the National Institute of Mental Health

More specifically, the National Institute of Mental Health awarded 38 research grants for a total of $373,226, a mean size of $9,822 in 1948. In 1961 there were 1,286 active grants for a total of $30,492,087, a mean size of $23,711.[3] A marked increase in the program began in 1957 when it rose from $3,890,631 to $7,326,311, a trend that has continued since that time.

In fiscal 1961 there were 113 principal investigators sustained by NIMH grants from the social sciences (50 in anthropology and 63 in sociology), nine per cent of the total. However, there were 574 psychologists representing 45 per cent of the total, a significant number of whom are social psychologists. In terms of all investigators (actually listed, by discipline, in grant applications), there were 228 social scientists (84 in anthropology and 144 in sociology), for 10 per cent of the total, and 783 psychologists for 37 per cent of the total. Social scientists who are principal investigators are not evenly distributed on a regional basis. They represent only two per cent of the total in the South and Southwest, 15 per cent in the Middle Atlantic States, and 14 per cent on the West Coast. Psychologists, on the other hand, are fairly evenly distributed in terms of percentage of the total number of principal investigators. No cross-tabulations are available by sponsoring institution and discipline, but in 67 per cent of all grants (fiscal year 1961) the sponsoring institution was a college or university. It is safe to assume that this percentage is even higher for social scientists as they are less likely to be found in hospitals, clinics, or service organizations than are representatives of the other disciplines involved. Thus, it seems clear that as far as the NIMH grants represent a large share of the support of sociomedical research, it is very largely university based.

In the social science area, regardless of whether the principal investigator is listed as a social scientist or in some other discipline, there were 363 grants in fiscal year 1961, 28 per cent of all grants. Among these grants were 136 in group interaction, 53 in culture and personality, and 57 in social change, and a few others not categorized or tabulated.

The majority of all grants fall on the "basic" side. On a seven-point scale from the totally basic (11 per cent of the total) to the totally applied (16 per cent of the total), 61 per cent fall on the basic side of the midpoint, 35 per cent on the applied side and the remainder are equally basic

---

[3] All data concerning the National Institute of Mental Health is taken from two documents prepared by the Program Analysis Section of the Research Grants and Fellowships Branch, NIMH, under the direction of Dr. Julius Segal, "Summary Data NIMH Research Grants and Fellowships Fiscal Year 1961," and "Research in Social Psychology and the Social Sciences Supported by the National Institute of Mental Health—Fiscal Year 1960." Mimeo.

and applied. There is no cross-tabulation by discipline, but in view of the range of disciplines involved (including 21 per cent in psychiatry and a goodly number in clinical psychology) it may be assumed that social sciences would fall even more heavily on the basic side.

An analysis has been made to indicate the general scope of sociopsychological research in the grants program of the NIMH during fiscal year 1960. One hundred sixty grants were supported during that year, 15 per cent of the total. They are grouped by areas of research interest. There were large numbers in such areas as social roles, social perception, cross-cultural studies, and social behavior in animals, all of which tend to be fairly "basic." But there were perceptible numbers relating to schizophrenia (7), juvenile delinquency and the mental hospital (9), and a substantial number relating to community mental health (14, mostly in the mental health project grants rather than the regular research grant program). There were 21 grants in the area of marriage and the family, of which 12 were based in universities, and 9 in service organizations. They ranged from a project to restructure family theory to a family care demonstration project.

There are no hard data to show that the above patterns are typical or modal for all sociomedical research. However, the NIMH program is obviously a large one. Also, it follows a pattern of free competition for support, judged by peers of the grantees in their discipline, who, in turn, are drawn from a broad segment of these disciplines. NIMH staff exercise relatively little specific influence, through "programming," on the type of research or the direction it should take, although they do exercise leadership in certain special areas. It seems probable that the NIMH pattern is fairly typical of the general pattern of sociomedical research. If so, it is largely the sociology or related social science *of* medicine rather than *in* medicine, although a significantly perceptible segment is clearly in medicine. It is largely of a basic character at one or more removes from application to medical problems, yet, again, a significant segment is concerned rather directly with applications.

Private support

Brand made a study of private support of mental health, including support for research in this field [3]. One thousand one hundred eighty-two foundations and other granting agencies were surveyed by letter and questionnaire, and replies were received from 782, 66.1 per cent of the total. Only philanthropic or other tax-exempt agencies making grants on a national basis were included in the study. Of the 122 organizations that replied that they do support research, training, or service in mental health, 21 (17 per cent) said they supported "sociology and anthropology as related to mental health." This number ranks very close to the 27 (22 per cent) who said they support "psychology." Seven, one-third of the 21 organizations contributing to mental health at an annual average rate of 100,000 dollars or more support "sociology and anthropology as related to mental health," and an equal number support "psychology." Research is over-all the most richly supported category (56 per cent), both for the 122 organizations and for the 21 larger ones. It may be presumed that research is even more predominantly the type of support in sociology and anthropology.

Wellin calls attention to three groups that have made particularly strategic contributions to collaboration between the health field and the behavioral sciences: the Russell Sage Foundation, the Social Science Research Council, and the Health Information Foundation [19]. Russell Sage has emphasized relations between behavioral scientists and the practicing professions, including but not exclusively health. The Social Science Research Council, through its Committee on Preventive Medicine in Social Science Research, stimulated systematic development of the field. The Health Information Foundation has done much not only to sponsor research directly but to disseminate knowledge of the field through its annual *Inventory of Social and Economic Research in Health.*

Wellin makes the important suggestion that "the Russell Sage Foundation's residency and training program for social scientists in health sorely needs a counterpart program to enable selected medical and paramedical personnel to work in and deepen their understanding of the social sciences" [19].

Is the general pattern of support sound?

It is clear that sociomedical research is largely dependent on grants. A Congressional Committee of Consultants on Medical Research reported that 47 per cent of total national medical research was supported by the Federal Government in 1957, and estimated it would be 53 per cent in 1960 [4]. A large share of non-Federal support is given in the form of grants. This situation gives rise to two somewhat related problems. On the one hand, many people in this field are dependent on "soft" money with its real or fancied insecurities. On the other hand, granting agencies may, potentially, exercise extraneous influences on the development of the scientific fields related to medicine. There is a resulting danger that a special culture known as "grantsmanship" will develop, characterized by fads, fashions, and other qualities which are not only extraneous to the needs and requirements of scientific development as such, but may actually impede it.

We believe there are certain counterbalancing tendencies. By no means are all sociomedical researchers dependent on grants for their own salaries, although they generally are for supportive staff and equipment, at least if a perusal of NIMH grant applications is a fair indication. Also, there is a marked tendency to develop broad, long-term program support through grants. The grant-giving pattern of the National Institutes of Health and similar patterns, with varying modifications, followed by many other grant-giving agencies in the field of health, has certain very important built-in safeguards which, it is fair to say, have become quite well established and institutionalized, and which guard against whimsy in any form. A study section or review committee, composed of highly qualified experts in the relevant fields of research, and brought in from outside the granting agency, has the crucial role in determining the fate of the grant application. The major criteria relate to the qualifications of the investigator, the adequacy of his design in relation to his aims, and the realistic characteristics of the aims. They relate only secondarily, or occasionally, to judgments about the "importance of the field."

There is danger, of course, that institutionalization can lead to elements of ossified structures which cramp the development of research. However, there are constant proddings to approve high-risk or "maverick" applications and to encourage young investigators.

The review pattern has one especially important byproduct. Persons who participate in study sections and review committees have an opportunity for extensive interaction with key people in their fields in an intensely focused way not generally possible through professional meetings or otherwise, and they are exposed to a very large range of research ideas. It is the writer's opinion, based on discussions with many people who have been involved in the review pattern, that it has exercised a positive and equilibrating influence in the total development of sociomedical research.

The proper level of support

What is the proper range and scope of support? This question is extraordinarily difficult, if not impossible, to answer with any precision. The Congressional Committee of Consultants on Medical Research (in general) concluded, "the funds appropriated by the Congress for the support of medical research, although substantial, are still not sufficient to assure the full utilization of the Nation's potential for an attack on the dread diseases, and the present level of support is far from adequate to permit the great advances essential for the future." They recommended that "the Federal Government should supplement private, industrial, and State funds as may be necessary, to support medical research on the scale required to carry out a determined attack on major health problems. The magnitude of Federal support should be neither limited by nor paced by the rate of increase of non-Federal sources of support" [4]. Research in this field has expanded at rapid rates since 1957. From all appearances it has done so without undue growing pains.

Certain major social events in the fields of health suggest considerable expansion will be appropriate, and indeed necessary. The report of the Joint Commission on Mental Illness and Health [1] is receiving considerable attention, and there are indications that it will be implemented by greatly expanded mental health programs. The concept of "comprehensive medical care" is becoming widely disseminated and accepted. There are many unknowns, relevant to program development in both of these contexts, for which sociomedical research could provide important answers.

There are three areas, in particular, where increased research efforts are needed: 1. longitudinal studies; 2. studies of community organization, development and the logistics of health services; and 3. the development of population laboratories for a variety of studies in the field of health. All three areas require relatively large-scale and expensive research operations.

In the light of these considerations, it would seem safe to conclude that as a minimum the expansion should continue at the same rate for the next five years as it has in the past five years. Less rapid expansion would be inadequate, and more rapid expansion might be unfeasible in terms of manpower.

References

1. *Action for Mental Health,* Final Report of the Joint Commission on Mental Illness and Health. New York: Basic Books, Inc., 1961.
2. Anderson, Odin W. and Milvoy Seacat, *The Behavioral Scientists and Research in the Health Field.* Research Series No. 1. New York: Health Information Foundation, May, 1957.
3. Brand, Jeanne L., *Private Support for Mental Health.* Public Health Servive Publication No. 838. Washington: Government Printing Office, 1961.
4. Committee of Consultants on Medical Research, *Federal Support of Medical Research.* A Report to the Subcommittee on Departments of Labor and Health, Education, and Welfare of the Committee on Appropriations, United States Senate, 86th Congress, Second Session. Washington, May, 1960.
5. Gouldner, Alvin W., "Theoretical Requirements of the Applied Social Sciences," *American Sociological Review,* 22 (February, 1957), 92–102.
6. Hanlon, John J., *Principles of Public Health Administration.* St. Louis: The C. V. Mosby Company, 1960.
7. Jackson, J. M., "The Organization and Its Communications Problem," *Advanced Management,* February, 1959, 17–20.
8. Kendall, Patricia L. and Robert K. Merton, "Medical Education as a Social Process," *in* E. Gartley Jaco, ed., *Patients, Physicians and Illness.* New York: The Free Press of Glencoe, Inc., 1958, 321–50.
9. Luszki, Margaret B., *Interdisciplinary Team Research, Methods and Problems.* New York: New York University Press, 1958.
10. Merton, Robert K., George G. Reader, and Patricia L. Kendall, eds., *The Student-Physician.* Cambridge: Harvard University Press, 1957.

11. Russell Sage Foundation, "Direction to Solutions of Collaboration." New York: *Russell Sage Foundation Annual Report 1958–1959*, pp. 7–17.

12. ———, "An Appraisal of the Problems of Collaboration." New York: *Russell Sage Foundation Annual Report 1958–1959*, pp. 8–16.

13. Sibley, Elbridge, "The Objectives of Sociological Training," *American Sociological Review*, 25 (August, 1960), 571–75.

14. Simmons, Ozzie G. and James A. Davis, "Interdisciplinary Collaboration in Mental Illness Research," *American Journal of Sociology*, 63 (November, 1957), 297–303.

15. Smith, Brewster, " 'Mental Health' Reconsidered: A Special Case of the Problem of Values in Psychology," *American Psychologist*, 16 (June 1961), 299–306.

16. *Some Observations on Controls in Psychiatric Research*, Report No. 42. New York: Group for the Advancement of Psychiatry, May, 1959.

17. Straus, Robert, "The Nature and Status of Medical Sociology," *American Sociological Review*, 22 (April, 1957), 200–204.

18. Suchman, Edward A., "Sociology and the Field of Public Health." Manuscript prepared for the American Sociological Association under the sponsorship of the Russell Sage Foundation, September, 1960. (Mimeo.)

19. Wellin, Edward, "Uses of the Behavioral (Social) Sciences in Public Health." Prepared under contract and submitted to the National Institute of Mental Health, July, 1961. (Mimeo.)

20. Williams, Richard H., ed., *Human Factors in Military Operations: Some Applications of the Social Sciences to Operations Research*. Washington: Operations Research Office, September, 1954.

18

METHODS OF SOCIOMEDICAL RESEARCH

Jack Elinson

Exploration of problems of sociomedical concern, hitherto untouched by empirical investigation, has been made possible by the application of systematic social research methods largely forged in the twentieth century. Reproducible methods of observation and analysis have increased the likelihood of cumulation of knowledge and achievement of scientific consensus.

Clinical impressions of observers of varying acuity have lost none of their importance, but these are no longer the only source of understanding of social and psychological factors in illness and disease. Anecdotal accounts by both professional and unprofessional observers continue to provide pictorial accompaniment and promote dramatic interest, but they have become primarily supplemental or precursive to carefully developed quantitative studies in tracing changes in the attitude of the medical student as he proceeds through the medical school curriculum. The secret feelings and unexpressed sentiments of significant participants in patient-practitioner relationships and other medical settings are no longer entirely hidden and are beginning to become amenable to subtle techniques of observation of manifest behaviors which in turn can be made to yield information on latent relationships when analyzed by imaginative, yet rigorous, mathematical methods. Aggregate, routinely collected, economic statistics of medical care utilization and its cost have become background to household sample surveys which make possible—limited only by the creativity of the researcher, the computational facilities at his disposal, and the patience of patients—multivariate analyses of the intricate patterns of utilization of health services. Neatly-drawn organization charts carry grossly superficial and often mythical information about patterns of medical practice, while sophisticated analysis guided by sociological theory reveals underlying order in the apparent hodge-podge of bureaucratic structure and function.

Not all problems of proper medical concern are equally suitable subjects for social research. It is unlikely that studies of cell metabolism or electrolytic balance will directly benefit in the near future from social research methods. On the other hand, the health problems which easily engage the efforts of the social researcher are those with prominent or dominant social and behavioral components: alcoholism, addiction (to narcotics or food), venereal disease, accidents, mental disorders, and certain chronic diseases. Social disability and rehabilitation are broad areas in which social researchers have also been especially active. Patterns of participation (and nonparticipation) in public health programs are particularly intriguing. The organization of medical care in its social aspects can be fruitfully explored as a sociological question. The choice and pattern of medical care are significant areas of application for students of social psychology. In general, any health behavior—whether of a preventive or therapeutic nature—which demands the active cooperation of the patient is a fit subject for social research.

The specific social research methods which have been used to explore these health problem areas have been alluded to in the various content chapters and are elucidated in the references at the end of each chapter. There is no comprehensive text which deals with sociomedical research methods, as such. Perhaps some day a text will do for sociomedical research what such texts as Bradford Hill's *Medical Statistics* [32] and Donald Mainland's *Quantitative Medicine* [45] have done for biological medicine. There are, however, several well-known general codifications of social research methods: Goode and Hatt [23]; Selltiz, Jahoda, Deutsch, and Cook [58]; and Festinger and Katz [21]. In addition, some important specialized treatises have appeared which deal intensively with selected aspects of social research. Most notable among these are the two remarkable volumes by Hyman—one on *Survey Design and Analysis* [38] and the other on *Interviewing in Social Research* [37]. The latter is a compendium and carefully considered assessment of the empirical studies of the interviewing process up to a decade ago. It is interesting to note that although interviews to obtain medical histories have been carried out by physicians for a much longer time than interviews for social research, there exists no volume on medical history interviewing comparable to that of Hyman's on social research interviewing. Medical history interviewing has not been systematically studied, and thus has remained largely an art. Here indeed is a virginal area for sociomedical investigation. Another volume on interviewing by Kahn and Cannell [40] combines a theoretical and a how-to-do-it approach. Especially interesting in this volume is a transcript of a tape recording of a medical history interview conducted by a physician and criticized by social researchers. In the field of sampling there are a number of authoritative texts: Hansen, Hurwitz, and Madow [30]; Deming [18]; and Cochran [11]. But the one which deals most realistically and with a sophistication born of intimate acquaintance with problems faced by social researchers is *Sampling Opinions* by Stephan and McCarthy [66]. Stephan and McCarthy place sampling in the total context of the research process. They pay reasoned attention to the inescapable decision points where the investigator's judgment must enter along with theoretical considerations of mathematical probabilities. The pitfalls of question-wording have been handled in a clever and telling way by Payne's *Art of Asking Questions* [52], but sophistication in the design of sets of questions or scales for dimensionable variables is not to be found in this book. Two comprehensive theoretical treatises on scales of measurement are available; one by Torgersen [75] and the other edited by Gulliksen and Messick [26]. Since, except for demography, the fields of social research are unlikely to go beyond the need for ordinal scales of measurement, the work on measurement which is most applicable is perhaps the book on scale analysis by Riley, Riley, and Toby [55]. For many years the only available book on content analysis has been the one by Berelson [5], but a recent one edited by Pool [19] brings this aspect of the field up to date.

The field of social research is strongest in texts relating to data collection and classification and weakest in texts on how to analyze data statistically. Guilt feelings for this state of things have been recently expressed by Tukey [76], who holds that "the statistics of survey research today is much in the same position as the statistics of agricultural research was before R. A. Fisher." The logic of inference in data analysis made intelligible by Zeisel, using cross-tabulations and computation of percentages in *Say it With Figures* [84], has not substantially been improved upon by exercises in mathematical statistics. Zeisel's work eschews theoretical mathematical formulations and relies instead on the soundness of logical reasoning and simple arithmetic procedures as a basis for his analytical approaches to data. A more formal presentation and extension of data analysis for survey research is found in Kendall's chapter in Hyman's *Survey Design and Analysis* [38].

Almost all the methods referred to above have been employed in one or another study by sociomedical researchers. Essentially no new research methods have been devised by sociomedical researchers. Rather, the application of known social research methods to health problems to which they have not previously been applied has been the rule. New facts, insights, and understandings have been the results.

Of special interest is the conjoint application of social and medical research methods. It will help to clarify the ensuing discussion if a sharp, if arbitrary, distinction is made between social research carried out in a medical setting and the conjoint use of social and medical observations. Examples of the former are the sociological and social psychological studies of medical students: Cahalan, Collette, and Hilmar [6], Merton, Reader, and Kendall [48], Hammond and Kern [29], Becker and Hughes [4]; studies of the organization of medical practice: Hall [28], Freidson [22]; studies of the utilization of health services: Anderson and Feldman [2], Anderson and Collette [3], Shanas [59], Darsky [15], and J. J. Williams [78]. Examples of the latter are certain epidemiological studies of chronic disease: Graham, Levin, and Lilienfeld [24]; McMahon and Koller [44]; Stamler, Kjelsberg, Hall, and Scotch [64]; Trussell and Elinson [13]; Hinkle, *et al.* [34]; and community studies of mental disorder: Srole, *et al.* [63]; Leighton, *et al.* [43]; Gruenberg and Bellin [25]; and Hollingshead and Redlich [35]. The former has been called the sociology *of* medicine; the latter has been called sociology *in* medicine.

Theory

Both medicine and sociology are fields of research which are characterized by a low degree of articulation. "The degree of articulation of a field is the extent to which the phenomena with which the field is concerned are potentially capable of being explained and predicted in terms of a small number of fundamental concepts and constants" [14]. Unlike physics, both medicine and sociology require numerous concepts and theories to explain limited sets of phenomena. In the history of both medicine and sociology are the "grand theorists" who sought to explain everything with one idea they believed to be fundamental. Thus, in the eighteenth century, Dr. Benjamin Rush advanced a theory of convulsive action now regarded as a medical fad [71]. An example from psychology early in the twentieth century is John B. Watson's theory of behaviorism. In sociology the current efforts of Parsons with his theory of action exemplify more than others a struggle to "unify . . . scattered propositions" [51].

Much is made of the importance of the interplay between theory and research. Sometimes this is mainly an ideal and the paying of respects to the fruitfulness of such an attitude in the physical sciences. In social science, grand theorists and empiricists tend to remain psychologically far apart in practice, united principally in affirmations of the need for togetherness. It is interesting to note, for example, that in *Theories of Society* [51], a pair of impressive volumes totaling nearly 1500 pages, edited by Parsons, Shils, *et al.*, three outstanding latter-day sociological empiricists—Stouffer, Lazarsfeld, and Hughes—receive only single mention, and none for their contributions to theory. Stouffer is cited in a single footnote as the author of an empirical study, *Communism, Conformity and Civil Liberties* [68], which contains some data about the thought patterns of the lower class; Lazarsfeld is briefly mentioned in the epilogue to these volumes as one in a series of a half-dozen names who presented a "coherent sociological viewpoint in their work," and Hughes is referred to (in another footnote in this masterwork) only as the translater of an article by Simmel on sociability!

A hundred years ago, the physicist Helmholtz and some colleagues issued a scientific manifesto to the effect that all human activity—including consciousness—would be ultimately reducible to simple physical laws. Efforts along these lines persist even today in sociology where the prospect seems even dimmer than in medicine. It would be presumptuous to predict that the grand sociological theorists are doomed to the same fate that befell the early physicists. It is fitting, however, to observe that the terrain in sociology is qualitatively different and manifestly more variable than that in physics or chemistry. Is there not as much justification in the scientific exploration of a variable terrain as there is in the study of simpler concatenations of phenomena? Who will map this terrain?

A more hopeful approach is the development of limited theories, as in Merton's *Social Theory and Social Structure* [47], which are testable, as in Stouffer's *Social Research to Test Ideas* [69]. Examples of limited theories are so commonplace and have been so productive in medicine that they need no iteration here. It is sufficient to cite three currently argued examples—(1) relationships between nutrition and atherosclerosis, (2) relationships between cigarette smoking and lung cancer and cardiovascular disease, and (3) relationships between social isolation and schizophrenia—

to dramatize the stimulation to research afforded by viable but limited epidemiological theories of disease.

The linking of theories from both medicine and sociology is a relatively untouched area. Caudill [8] has suggested a chain of theoretical linkage between physiological and cultural phenomena. The testing of sociomedical theories by empirical research is even more virginal. Only rough efforts are beginning to be made in these areas in such settings as the "community health population laboratories." Such sociomedical laboratories are developing in several parts of the United States: Alameda-Contra Costa Counties in California; the Washington Heights Health District in New York City; the small town of Tecumseh in Michigan; and the island of Puerto Rico. All are facing the difficulty of explicitly formulating theories embodying both social and medical variables and of deciding which variables to emphasize as dependent or independent. All have the advantage of a community laboratory in which work is done by various combinations of medical and social scientists. A singular advantage of these community health population laboratories is that they provide unique opportunities for work in the interstices of academic disciplines, drawing on both medical and social sciences for hypotheses. It may well be that community laboratories will offer appropriate testing grounds for the linkage of theories from the various disciplines as suggested by Caudill.

Concepts

Organizing concepts are expressed in technical languages created because ordinary words have too many meanings in ordinary discourse and thus lack clarity and may be misleading. Confusion arises when sociologists use ordinary words and endow them with technical meanings. Although the use of polysyllabic words is less prevalent in sociology than in medicine (*e.g., atherosclerosis, carcinogenesis, bacteriology*), sociomedical scientists should not shrink from the thought that their technical language may some day approach that of medicine in novelty and polysyllabicity. In time, physicians will accept technical sociological terminology with the same equanimity now accorded medical terminology by sociologists.

It is paradoxical, but the initial use of ordinary terms and vague concepts, such as *illness* and *disease*, in research may stimulate research with clearer concepts precisely because the use of ordinary terms is controversial and leads to different interpretations by different researchers. Statements such as *illness is related to poverty* or *mental disorder is more prevalent among lower-class people* may be challenged by researchers because *illness* may be narrowly interpreted as and equated with *disease* and *mental disorder* may be narrowly interpreted as and equated with *psychosis*. Similarly, what is meant by *poverty* and *lower-class*? Challenges of this sort, when accepted positivistically, lead to refinement of concepts with increasing precision and subtlety of understanding.

The central phenomena of medical sociology are health, illness and disease, and the way society organizes to deal with these events. Empirical research and reflections thereon in the past decade have served to clarify the overly simple notions about the prevalence of illness and disease in the population. Technical distinctions have been made among the various methods of measuring morbid conditions. If we designate MM as a general symbol for measures of morbidity we can distinguish at least the following six types:

MM-1 tissue alterations, viewed as such and judged by pathologists to be causes of death—*e.g.*, "atherosclerosis," "carcinoma."

MM-2 records produced by physiologic measuring equipment—*e.g.*, the electrocardiogram; and the interpretations by specialists—*e.g.*, cardiologists—of such records as the "right bundle branch block."

MM-3 judgments rendered by clinicians in the form of a "diagnosis" after considering "all the evidence"—*e.g.*, "coronary artery disease." There is an analogy here to a judge rendering a decision in a court of law except that the clinician acts as prosecutor and defense attorney as well as judge. Sometimes he calls in other clinicians (*i.e.*, judges) to help him in rendering a decision.

MM-4 reports of people that they have a given "disease"—*e.g.*, "I have a bad heart." These reports have conventionally been put into two classes: (1) those in which the person reports that he has been so told by a physician (MM-4a); and (2) those in which he has not been so told (MM-4b).

MM-5 reports of symptoms objectively observable (*i.e.*, to other than the reporter)—*e.g.*, rash, sweating, swelling, lumps, sores, rapid breathing, and so on.

MM-6 reports of sensations, feelings or thoughts not directly or readily observable by others—*e.g.*, itch, headache, tiredness, anger, depression, guilt, fear, pain, discomfort, hallucinations, and so on. Again, although sensations, feelings, and thoughts are best known to the person who has them (MM-6a), useful inferences about them can often be made by objective observers (MM-6b)—*e.g.*, physicians, psychologists, social workers.

In the interests of conceptual clarity, each of the above morbidity measures and submeasures deserves a separate name. It is not our intention or task here to name them, but merely to call attention to their distinctions. Note must be taken that conceptual muddles arising from failure to make these distinctions in studies of illness and disease have resulted in misinterpretation and misunderstanding. These in turn can generate more fruitful research when properly perceived.

It is fair to say that social scientists dipping into epidemiology have tended to concentrate their observations on the last three (MM 4–6); medical scientists, on the first three (MM 1–3). In other words, each has been talking his own language under the general umbrella of "illness" or "disease" [12, 13, 20, 57, 79]. Recognition of these conceptual distinctions and their separation by distinct terms for which there can be consensus is a necessity for research progress in the sociomedical field. It should be noted that each of the "measures of morbidity" is subject to reliability studies. In addition to reliability studies, empirical correlations among the various measures should contribute to our understanding of each.

Measurement

Medical scientists, particularly epidemiologists, are fond of pointing out that it would be nice to be able to study the relationship between certain social variables—*e.g.*, stress and disease—if only it were possible to "measure" such variables. A report to the World Health Organization states that: "Despite the great importance of these factors [mental, emotional and socioeconomic], no adequate measuring techniques are available" [81]. The term *measure* in such comments undoubtedly refers to the higher order forms of measurement—*i.e.*, interval and ratio scales—and neglects the more rudimentary but useful forms such as nominal and ordinal scales. Social scientists, on the other hand, are so delighted to have even these more limited measures to work with that the possibilities of achieving more elegant measures rarely enter their research frame of reference. It will be shown here, however, that both medical and social scientists use all forms of measurement—the more rudimentary as well as the more elegant—to some extent.

The situation would be clarified if a general definition of *measurement* were accepted. According to Stevens, "measurement is the assignment of numerals to objects or events according to rules" [67]. The sets of rules that are commonly employed by scientists have been classified as various types of scales: nominal, ordinal, interval, and ratio. Several of these have been further divided into subtypes depending on whether or not they possess certain special properties. It will suffice for us here to review the four main types.

The nominal scale

A nominal scale is essentially no more than a nonoverlapping classification with numbers assigned to the various classes. Any numbers at all can be assigned to classes in a nominal scale providing that the same number is not assigned to two different classes. The numbers used in a nominal scale are then little more than names (hence, *nominal*) and have no advantage over names except as a kind of shorthand. A nominal scale is a primitive scale indeed and hardly deserves other than a formal place in a discussion of measurement.

Much of measurement in medical science has not passed beyond the primitive "nominal scale" stage—*i.e.*, the distinctive naming of sets of phenomena in order to distinguish among them. Nosology—the naming of diseases—constitutes no more than nominal measurement, yet the classification of disease entities is the bedrock of medical science and has fostered much epidemiologic research. The *International Classification of Diseases* [82] and the *Standard Nomenclature of Diseases and Operations* [1] are prime examples of nominal scales in medicine. The use of numbers to identify disease entities is not quantification in any real sense, but simply the substitution of small sets of numerals (codes) for larger sets of letters (disease names) to facilitate recording, data processing, and tabulating operations. That there is difficulty even in naming is exemplified by the work of an international committee attempting to arrive at consensus about criteria defining "coronary artery disease" [17, 81].

In social science, with few exceptions, variables of interest have not been classified, codified, and numbered in a way that makes them universally employable. The exceptions are the classifications of occupations and industries developed by the Census Bureau [9] and the *Dictionary of Occupational Titles* [77] developed by the U.S. Employment Service, both of which receive extensive use. Aside from such practically useful classifications, there is no universally accepted classification of either concept-terms or index-terms as used by social scientists. Sociologists are incurable conceptualizers and among them the naming of social categories is a great sport. Such terms as *innerdirected, reference groups,* and so on, have an important use, as Merton and Kitt have pointed out, "not because the term itself helps explain behavior, but because it does not easily allow us to overlook . . . components . . ." [46]. Perhaps most sociological measurement still takes place on a nominal level.

Most classifications and numbered codes in both medicine and social science have been *ad hoc*—*i.e.*, useful in a particular investigation—and have generally not survived the immediate use for which they have been constructed. Concept-naming in sociology is particularly ephemeral and few names survive their authors or the times. Distinctive names for social psychological variables, for example, have an uncertain stability and a high evanescent rate (*e.g., authoritarianism, permissiveness, apprehension, innerdirectedness*) and rarely survive a single study by the same investigator or a flurry of subsequent studies. There are notable exceptions of course; Freudian terms have been remarkably tenacious.

The ordinal scale

Ordinal scales are a step up the measurement ladder. In ordinal scales, numbers are assigned so that the order of the numbers corresponds to the order of magnitude of the instances of a property. The hardness scale of minerals and the pecking order of chickens in a barnyard are examples of ordinal scales. The concept of ranking as to more and less is a property of an ordinal scale, but nothing is implied as to the distances or intervals between ranks.

Ordinal scales are quite common in medicine. The patient is "cured," "improved," "unchanged," "worse." These adjectives constitute an ordered set of meaningful relationships in terms of better or worse, but say nothing quantitative about how much better "cured" is than "improved." Another example of an ordinal scale in medicine is the frequent classification of a condition along a dimension of severity—*e.g.*, "severe," "moderate," "mild." In the field of medical care an interesting ordinal scale is the one developed by Hassinger for characterizing the rank of a county within a state in terms of availability of medical care services [31].

A large number of obvious ordinal scales come to mind from the domain of the social sciences—*e.g.*, ratings of employee efficiency or conditions of housing. A large number also of less obvious ordinal scales have been demonstrated by Guttman's scalogram technique for sociological variables [72]. Among these, for example, is John Dollard's scale of a combat soldier's manifestations of fear in battle, and the various morale attitude scales developed by Stouffer and his associates in *Studies in Social Psychology in World War II* [71].

The interval scale

An interval scale has all the properties of nominal and ordinal scales (distinctiveness, order) but, in addition, has the property of operationally defined distance between ranks. Familiar examples of interval scales are the Centigrade and Fahrenheit temperature scales, in which the units between adjacent degrees are equal. In these scales the starting point is arbitrary (there is no absolute zero as in Kelvin), so that it is incorrect to say with these scales that 40° is "twice" as hot as 20°. Interval scales that are not also ratio scales are rare in medicine and practically nonexistent in the social sciences. Even standardized psychological tests—such as some aptitude and achievement tests, which provide numerical scores for right answers—are pseudointerval since the interval between scores is completely arbitrary, being dependent on the particular questions or items employed.

Attitude research has advanced to the use of ordinal measures (*i.e.*, cumulative noninterval scales), and efforts have been made to introduce equal-appearing intervals into attitude scales [74]. Attempts to do this have been seriously challenged on logical and empirical grounds. The so-called equal units were derived from averages of judges' ratings of attitudinal distances among items. The inadequacy of this approach derives from the empirical fact that the ratings vary with the judges used to do the judging [61].

The ratio scale

Ratio scales permit one to say that something exists in x times the amount of something else. This property of a scale is made possible by the existence of an absolute zero, as well as equal intervals, in the quantity being measured. Ratio scales are common in the physical sciences—*e.g.*, length and mass—and find practical application in measures of height and weight. The pulse and visual and auditory acuity are examples of measures that are ratio scales in medicine. In social science, ratio scales are to be found primarily in that most highly quantitative field of social science known as demography or population research. The counting—of babies born, of persons who migrate, of persons who die—makes possible the use of the most advanced measuring scales and the performance of the greatest variety of mathematical manipulations with the fewest assumptions.

The examples of different types of scales used in medicine and in social science set forth here illustrate the analogy between measurement in medicine and measurement in social science.

Reliability and Validity

Perhaps no words have been used more in connection with measurement than *reliability* and *validity*. Enough work has been done with these concepts that they no longer serve as useful scientific terms in an unqualified sense. They have become differentiated into several operationally definable "reliabilities" and "validities." In keeping within an operational frame of reference one can see that there are:

Alpha reliabilities *i.e.*, the correspondence between two observers or the same observer at different times, inter- and intraobserver reliability; and

Beta reliabilities *i.e.*, the correspondence between two measuring instruments or between briefer and lengthier versions of the same measuring instrument (*e.g.*, short and long intelligence tests).

The time dimension introduces an interesting paradox with respect to the concept of reliability. If what one observes is highly variable by nature (blood pressure, a mood, the position of an electron), how can one tell whether differences in repeated measurements are due to change in the observed phenomenon or to unreliability of the method of observation? This paradox has led to experiments with simultaneous observation of a given phenomenon by multiple observers—*e.g.*, multiple stethoscopy. In such instances the observer becomes an integral part of the measuring process; and the separation of unreliability of the measuring instrument—*e.g.*, the stethoscope—from that of the observer becomes difficult if not impossible. Very few reliability studies have been done in medicine. Many more have been done in behavioral and social science. It is as if to question the reliability of a medical measure is to interfere with the practice of medicine (have confidence in your doctor!). In one study it was shown that of two physicians with comparable training, one was able to find 50 per cent more diagnoses in equivalent random samples of patients [13].

The best-known reliability study of medical observations is Yerushalmy's study of X-ray readings [83]. Clark and his co-workers have shown how variable blood pressure readings are when taken under different conditions [10]. More recent studies deal with the reliability of electrocardiogram readings and of cardiovascular and psychiatric diagnoses [12, 41].

There is a danger in studies of reliability of permitting the perfect to become the enemy of the good or committing the error of errorlessness. Some investigators give up measurement of a phenomenon for scientific studies when they find any degree of unreliability. The important question is how much unreliability there is.

Validity is a more emotionally charged term than *reliability*. Clinicians usually regard validity as more important than reliability. "A dozen careless psychiatrists may all agree that a patient's marital adjustment is satisfactory solely because they have neglected to ask the important questions. In these instances reliability may be high, yet validity low . . ." [41]. On the other hand, statisticians and epidemiologists have a high regard for reliability, frequently leaving appraisals of validity to nonmethodologists, as in the definition of Validity A below. In a survey of current epidemiological research requirements reliability studies are listed first [80].

Just as for reliability, the time has come to regard a single definition of validity as no longer scientifically useful. Operationally there are at least four validities:

Validity A Construct validity is what the investigator says the measure is measuring: "Intelligence is what intelligence tests measure." What, with this concept of validity, is blood pressure [10]?

Validity B Consensual validity involves construct validity, but is assessed by the degree of consensus among investigators that a measure is measuring a certain quality. Should the investigators have a common background of training?

Validity C Criterion validity is the association between one measure and a measure of some other variable taken to be the criterion variable (*i.e.*, the "more valid" measure).

Validity D Predictive validity is the association between one measure and a measure of some other variable taken to be the criterion variable (*i.e.*, the "more valid" measure) over time—*i.e.*, predictive of some criterion.

Of the four definitions cited, Validity C is the most common. It is usually not expressed in such abstract terms as defined here. Nor is it usually understood that Validity C necessarily implies either Validity B or, in some instances, Validity A. To illustrate by a mean example:

Suppose there were a roomful of men and women behind a closed door. And suppose one wished to identify the sex of the occupants of the room by the sound of their voices from a position outside the room. The question is: Is the sound of the voice, so heard, a valid measure of sex? To answer this question one could, in an open-door situation, correlate judgments as to sex made on the basis of the sound of the voice with another measure of sex which ranks high on Validity B. The degree of association obtained would be considered an assessment of Validity C.

The closed-door situation frequently obtains both in medicine and in social science. An example from medicine is to be found in studies of diet and blood cholesterol. It has been shown that variations in diet are accompanied by variations in blood cholesterol [39]. Yerushalmy has dubbed this "the substitution game" [53a], since the interest in these studies is to learn what relationship there might be between diet and coronary heart disease. The question then is asked: Is blood cholesterol level a valid assessment of the likelihood of developing coronary heart disease? This question can be answered by prospective studies, and such investigations are actually currently underway [16, 33, 65]. Thus far, the reasoning is straightforward and practically self-evident. What is missing is the recognition of the necessity of assessing the validity of the diagnosis of coronary heart disease. We are now back to consensual validity: Validity B. Efforts at establishing criteria for diagnosing coronary heart disease are actually being made [81]. The establishment of such criteria is an example of Validity B. If one investigator should decide that he prefers another set of criteria, or modifications of these criteria, we should then have an example of Validity A.

Validity D enters the picture when predictions about dying from coronary heart disease are made from a knowledge of the presence or absence of this disease in living persons. It should be clear that the presence or absence of the disease in question may be consensually determined (Validity B) and that the prediction of death from the disease may be more or less successful (Validity D). Yet there are many who would argue that the validity of any method of measuring a variable is in question if successful predictions (Validity D) cannot be made. This argument is most commonly used by psychometricians and takes the following form: A mathematical aptitude test cannot be considered valid until it can be shown to predict success in a job involving mathematics—*e.g.*, actuary, computer, teacher, and so on.

Validity D (predictive validity) is clearly not equivalent to Validity C (criterion validity) or to Validities B and A (consensual and construct validities). Prediction is only one operational definition of validity.

Research in medicine and social science is often closed-door research. We cannot always measure directly what we wish to measure and have to content ourselves with some index. It is important, however, to distinguish between situations in which it is possible at times actually to get behind the closed door and situations in which we only imagine that if we could get behind the closed door there might be a reality there which could be directly measured and correlated with our more indirect measure.

The latter situation may be exemplified by reference to struggles by social scientists with measures of socioeconomic status or social position. Numerous ingenious combinations of the education-income-occupation complex have been proposed [35], as if there were some underlying variable which one really wants to measure but cannot because of a closed door. So far no one has come up with a real measure of socioeconomic status. The indices are all we have; and they are real enough.

Experiment

> The greatest difference between modern times and the Middle Ages, in medicine as well as in all sciences, is the objective, the experimental method [54]. . . . [T]he thing that differentiates the modern method from either the ancient or the medieval method is that it definitely abandons all attempts at a complete synthesis of knowledge, built up with any philosophic system, and starts by trying to get at definite facts and thus allows these facts themselves, with their inevitable consequences, to determine the direction in which conclusions are formed [49].

Experimentation with a capital *E* has won a properly revered place in scientific method. But too often the form is honored more than the substance. A carefully controlled experiment on a trivial variable which is manipulable makes a less significant contribution than a careful inferential analysis of the associations of nonmanipulable but nontrivial variables. The kind of evidence available for interpreting the association between smoking and lung cancer is a case in point.

The idea of experimentation is quite old and predates modern science. An example will be cited from the field of medical care. Petrarch, in a letter to Boccaccio, wrote that a famous physician once told him that

> . . . if 100 or 1000 individuals of the same age and the same constitution and mode of life at one and the same time were attacked by the same disease and half availed themselves of the physicians, the others acted without any medical advice, following their natural instincts and discretion, there could be no doubt whatsoever that the second half would happily recover [54].

A modern instance of this alleged phenomenon is contained in the results of an evaluation of rehabilitation in which an experimental group of patients in nursing homes receiving rehabilitative services had a slightly higher mortality than a control group of patients not receiving such services [50]!

The first point to be emphasized is that the variables studied are more important than the method available to study them. Second, a different logic is not involved in capital *E* experiments and other types of investigation. Third, there is a set of experimental designs—*i.e.*, E_1, E_2, E_3, and so on, and not one best way to design an experiment. And fourth, the classic experimental before–after design with control and experiment group is not always the design of choice—especially in sociomedical research—even where the choice is a feasible one.

It is a common philosophic gambit to contrast experiment with observation. The similarities between these two scientific approaches (if they are, indeed, two) are greater than their differences. In the first place, no experiment is of any value unless observation is an integral part of it. One has to observe change or lack of change in the experimental group and control, if any. Next, inferences are made after experimental observation as to the existence of a relationship; similarly with the observational "method." There is then no difference in kind between "experimental" and "observational" methods. To quote Cornfield:

> If important alternative hypotheses are compatible with available evidence, then the question is unsettled, even if the evidence is experimental. But if only one hypothesis can explain all the evidence, then the question is settled even if the evidence is observational. The proposition that some inherent logical incompetence attaches to an inference based on observational, as distinguished from experimental evidence seems to have little to commend it beyond the great positiveness with which it is sometimes asserted [14].

We turn now to the proposition that there is not one, but a set of experimental designs; that each design has its advantages and disadvantages; and that no one experimental design is superior to all other designs in all instances. Support for this proposition is contained in the writings of social scientists: Hovland [36], Payne [53], Solomon [62], and Stouffer [70]. The most comprehensive and insightful treatment of this subject has been presented by Donald T. Campbell [7]. The discussion here will be brief, but will follow Campbell's analysis closely.

Campbell lists the following types of designs:

Pre-experimental Designs

1. The One-Shot Case Study	X $\quad$ O
2. One Group Pre-test–Post-test Design	O_1 X O_2
3. The Static Group Comparison	X $\quad O_1$ (above line) / O_2 (below line)

True Experimental Designs

4. Pre-test–Post-test Control Group Design	O_1 X O_2
	$O_3 \quad O_4$

5. Solomon Four Group Design

$$\begin{array}{lll} O_1 & X & O_2 \\ O_3 & & O_4 \\ & X & O_5 \\ & & O_6 \end{array}$$

6. Post-test Only Control Group Design

$$\begin{array}{lll} A & X & O_1 \\ A & & O_2 \end{array}$$

In Campbell's notation, X is the exposure of a group to the experimental variable or event, the effects of which are to be assessed; and O refers to the process of observation or measurement. Further, the X's and O's in a given row are applied to the same specific persons. The left-to-right dimension indicates temporal order. Parallel rows represent equivalent samples of persons unless otherwise specified. A indicates assignment to groups at the same point in time.

1. The one-shot case study X O

A single individual or group is observed at one point and the observations are attributed to exposure to factors in a prior situation.

The lack of confidence to be placed in inferences from such a design is to be noted. At the same time the observation has been made [70] that much work in social science is of this nature.

2. The one-group pre-test–post-test design $O_1 \; X \; O_2$

This design provides for observations on the same group for two points in time, in between which the experimental variable has been introduced. Change can be noted in this design, but the attribution of change to the variable X is risky since change may have taken place because of any number of unobserved variables: Y, Z, and so on. One such class of variables Campbell calls "history"—*i.e.*, other events that took place at the same time as X. Another class of variables that can be confounded with the effect of X are "maturational" variables. Changes may take place systematically with the passage of time and are not specific to any period of time as historical variables are. Patients grow older, for example. In medical research, psychotherapy, and rehabilitation, some patients with some conditions get better (or worse) regardless of treatment.

A third class of confounding variables is the effect of making the observations itself (test-effect). Pregnant women who have been X-rayed have been found to produce a higher yield of congenital abnormalities. In an example from educational psychology, learning takes place when an achievement test is given so that when the test is repeated some of the change may be due to the test-taking itself.

An observational process which produces a change in the object being observed Campbell calls a "reactive measure." Any measurement procedure which is not part of the normal environment may be reactive, such as the taking of blood pressures. Weighing a fat person may stimulate dieting.

A fourth source of uncontrolled variance in this design is instrument decay. The examining physician gets tired at the end of the day. Spring scales fatigue. Raters or coders acquire different standards of rating or coding after the first batch of cases. A fifth extraneous factor is said to be statistical regression, whereby shifts toward the mean occur which are attributable to unreliability.

3. The Static Group Comparison

$$\begin{array}{cc} X & O_1 \\ \hline & O_2 \end{array}$$

This design, which is still labelled "pre-experimental" by Campbell, is commonly employed in epidemiology. There is a comparison of a group which has experienced X (*e.g.*, oophorectomy) with a group that has not, for the purpose of establishing the effect of X. There is in this design no way of ascertaining that the groups were equivalent at some prior time, although some correctives may be applied through a process of selective matching [56]. Two confounding variables are noticed in this design. One is that the groups are not really equivalent—*i.e.*, individuals in the groups are not randomly assigned at the beginning of the experiment. The other is that there may have been differential experimental mortality in the two groups, resulting in differences at the end of the experiment not attributable to the experimental variable.

4. Pre-test–Post-test Control Group Design

$$\begin{array}{ccc} O_1 & X & O_2 \\ O_3 & & O_4 \end{array}$$

Design 4 is recognizable as the classic experimental design using two equivalent groups, one of which is subjected to the experimental variable, and both groups observed before and after this event. (Note that Petrarch had suggested this approach to Boccaccio.) This design controls for the effects of history, maturation, testing, instrument fatigue, statistical regression, sampling selection, and differential mortality.

In many instances this is a completely adequate design. A source of variation remains if the process of measuring has an interactive effect with the experimental variable. For example, suppose an attitude survey in two equivalent groups were made with respect to fluoridation. Suppose, then, one group were shown a film on the effects of fluoridation. The prior attitude survey may have had a sensitizing effect so that the group seeing the film might be more affected by the film than it would have been had there been no prior attitude survey.

5. The Solomon Four-Group Design

$$\begin{array}{ccc} O_1 & X & O_2 \\ O_3 & & O_4 \\ & X & O_5 \\ & & O_6 \end{array}$$

This design was suggested to control and measure both main and interaction effects of the measuring process itself.

6. Post-test Only Control Group Design $\begin{matrix} A\ X\ O_1 \\ A\ \ \ \ O_2 \end{matrix}$

With this design it is possible to determine the group effect of the experimental variable using only two of the four groups in the Solomon design by making observations only after the application of the experimental variable. This truncated procedure, however, prevents any analyses of individual changes since there were no before measures. It should be noted that this apparently simple design, which uses two equivalent samples, controls for the effect of testing and interaction as well as for other effects controlled in the more elaborate classic design with pre-tests. It is therefore strongly recommended for sociomedical research using sensitizing observational measures.

A critical problem in experimentation is the extent to which the results of a given experiment, however neatly controlled, can be generalized beyond the experimental groups to other population groups. A way of thinking about this problem is provided by Cornfield's concept of articulation. In a field with a high degree of articulation, a single experimental physical law discovered on the earth's surface may be applied throughout the universe with confidence. A test-tube discovery in a chemical laboratory stands a good chance of being replicated in many other chemical laboratories. In medical and social science, because these are fields of low articulation, an experimental demonstration in one situation requires extensive replication before the findings can be accepted as generally applicable. It has been argued that relationships among variables found even in biased samples are stable [73], but convincing statistical reasoning has yet to be presented. For sociomedical research, the importance of defining the population in which an experiment has been conducted continues to require emphasis.

Conclusions

Both medical and social science research are concerned with problems inherent in studying man and his behavior. Virtually all problems of method in sociomedical research have their analogs in other areas of inquiry and the scientific issues that confront the medical sociologist are not endemic to his field. These problems are not solved simply, however; if anything, the methodological limitations in the two fields are often compounded in sociological investigations of health and illness. But a rigorous methodology is essential to the growth of systematic research in medical sociology. The available medical and behavioral science literature on method provides a basis for the development of appropriate designs, instruments, and analytical procedures. This literature reveals that the power of research methods in medical sociology is a function of the development of appropriate statistical theory, particularly in sampling, experimental design, and multivariate data analysis. The confrontation of the statistician with scientific problems conceptualized by the medical sociologist should continue to produce innovation in method, more efficient research, and greater certainty of inference toward a better quality of evidence for entertaining scientific propositions.

Sensitivity to the problems of method has resulted in improved and more sophisticated research techniques in both the medical and behavioral sciences. In the development of appropriate measures, in the assessment of their validity and reliability, and in the implementation of analysis procedures, creativity and conceptual skill, as well as technical knowledge, are essential. The logic of science and the craftsmanship of research transcend the disciplines of medicine and sociology.

References

1. American Medical Association, *Standard Nomenclature of Diseases and Operations.* 4th ed. New York: McGraw-Hill Book Company, Inc., 1952.
2. Anderson, O. W. and J. J. Feldman, *Family Medical Costs and Voluntary Insurance.* New York: McGraw-Hill Book Company, Inc., 1956.
3. Anderson, O. W., P. J. Collette, and J. J. Feldman, *Health Insurance Benefits for Health Insurance Services.* Health Information Foundation, Research Series No. 15, 1953–58. Nationwide Surveys.
4. Becker, H. S., E. C. Hughes, and B. Geer, *Boys in White.* Chicago: University of Chicago Press, 1961.
5. Berelson, B., *Content Analysis in Communication Research.* New York: The Free Press of Glencoe, Inc., 1952.
6. Cahalan, D., P. J. Collette, and N. Hilmar, "Career Expectations of Medical Students," *Journal of Medical Education,* 32:8 (August, 1957).
7. Campbell, D. T., "Factors Relevant to Validity of Experiments in Social Settings," *Psychological Bulletin* (1957), 297–311.
8. Caudill, W., *Effects of Social and Cultural Systems in Reactions to Stress.* New York: Social Science Research Council, Pamphlet 14 (June, 1958).
9. Census Bureau, *Alphabetical Index of Occupations and Industries.* Rev. ed. Washington, D.C.: United States Department of Commerce, 1960.
10. Clark, G. E., C. Y. Glock, and R. Vought, *Studies in Hypertension,* I–VI, *Journal of Chronic Diseases,* 4:3 (September, 1956), 4:4 (November, 1956), 5:2 (February, 1957).
11. Cochran, W. G., *Sampling Techniques.* New York: John Wiley & Sons, Inc., 1953.
12. Commission on Chronic Illness, *Chronic Illness in a Large City: The Baltimore Study.* Vol. 4. Cambridge: Harvard University Press, 1957.
13. Commission On Chronic Illness, *Chronic Illness in a Rural Area: The Hunterdon Study.* Vol. 3. R. E. Trussell and J. Elinson. Cambridge: Harvard University Press, 1959.

14. Cornfield, J., "Principles of Research," *American Journal of Mental Deficiency* (September, 1959), pp. 240–252.

15. Darsky, B. J., N. Sinai, and S. J. Axelrod, *Comprehensive Medical Services under Health Insurance: Study of Windsor Medical Services.* Cambridge: Harvard University Press, 1958.

16. Dawber, T. R. and F. E. Moore, "Longitudinal Study of Heart Disease in Framingham, Massachusetts: An Interim Report," *in Research in Public Health,* 1952, Milbank Memorial Fund, pp. 241–247.

17. Dawber, T. R., F. E. Moore, and G. V. Mann, "Coronary Heart Disease in the Framingham Study in Measuring Risk of Coronary Heart Disease in Adult Population Groups: A Symposium," *American Journal of Public Health,* 47 (April Supp., 1957), 4.

18. Deming, W. E., *Some Theory of Sampling.* New York: John Wiley & Sons, Inc., 1950.

19. deSola Pool, I., ed., *Trends in Content Analysis.* Urbana: University of Illinois Press, 1959.

20. Feldman, J. J., "The Household Interview Survey as a Technique for the Collection of Morbidity Data" *Journal of Chronic Diseases,* 11:5 (May, 1960), 535–57.

21. Festinger, L. and D. Katz, eds., *Research Methods in the Behavioral Sciences.* New York: Holt, Rinehart & Winston, Inc., 1953.

22. Freidson, E., *Patients' Views of Medical Practice.* New York: Russell Sage Foundation, 1961.

23. Goode, W. J. and P. K. Hatt, *Methods in Social Research.* New York: McGraw-Hill Book Company, Inc., 1952.

24. Graham, S., M. Levin, and A. M. Lilienfeld, "The Socio-Economic Distribution of Cancer at Various Sites in Buffalo, New York, 1948–52," *Cancer,* 13 (1960), 180.

25. Gruenberg, E. M. and S. S. Bellin, "The Impact of Mental Disease on Society," *Explorations in Social Psychiatry.* New York: Basic Books, Inc., 1957.

26. Gulliksen, H. and S. Messick, eds., *Psychological Scaling.* New York: John Wiley & Sons, Inc., 1960.

27. Gulliksen, H., *Theory of Mental Tests.* New York: John Wiley & Sons, Inc., 1950.

28. Hall, O., "The Informal Organization of the Medical Profession," *Canadian Journal of Economics and Political Science,* 12 (February, 1946), 30–41.

29. Hammond, K. and F. Kern, *Teaching Comprehensive Medical Care.* Cambridge: Harvard University Press, 1959.

30. Hansen, M. H., W. N. Hurwitz, and W. G. Madow, *Sample Survey Methods and Theory.* Vols. I and II. New York: John Wiley & Sons, Inc., 1953.

31. Hassinger, E. and R. L. McNamara, "The Pattern of Medical Services for Incorporated Places of 500-or-More Population in Missouri, 1950," *Rural Sociology,* 21:2 (June, 1956), 175–77.

32. Hill, A. B., *Principles of Medical Statistics.* 6th ed. London: The Lancet, Ltd., 1956.

33. Hilleboe, H. E., G. James, and J. T. Doyle, "Cardiovascular Health Center —Project Design for Public Health Research," *American Journal of Public Health*, 44:7 (July, 1954), 851–63.

34. Hinkle, L. E. and H. G. Wolff, "Ecologic Investigations of the Relationship between Illness, Life Experiences and the Social Environment," *Annals of Internal Medicine*, 49:6 (December, 1958), 1373–88.

35. Hollingshead, A. B. and F. C. Redlich, *Social Class and Mental Illness*. New York: John Wiley & Sons, Inc., 1958.

36. Hovland, C. I., A. A. Lumsdaine, and F. D. Sheffield, *Experiments in Mass Communication*. Princeton, N.J.: Princeton University Press, 1949.

37. Hyman, H. H., *et al.*, *Interviewing in Social Research*. Chicago: University of Chicago Press, 1954.

38. Hyman, H. H., *Survey Design and Analysis*. New York: The Free Press of Glencoe, Inc., 1955.

39. Jolliffe, N., S. H. Rinzler, and M. Archer, "The Anti-Coronary Club—Including a Discussion of the Effects of a Prudent Diet on the Serum Cholesterol Level of Middle-aged Men." The Diet and Coronary Heart Disease Study Project and the Bureau of Nutrition, Department of Health, City of New York, presented at meeting of National Vitamin Foundation, March, 1959.

40. Kahn, R. L. and C. F. Cannell, *The Dynamics of Interviewing*. New York: John Wiley & Sons, Inc., 1957.

41. Kreitman, N., "The Reliability of Psychiatric Diagnoses," *Journal of Mental Science*. 107:1450 (September, 1961).

42. Lasagna, L., "Clinical Analysis of Medical Fads." *The New York Times Magazine* (June 24, 1962), 22*ff*.

43. Leighton, A. H. *et al.*, *People of Cove and Woodlot: Communities from the Viewpoint of Social Psychiatry*, Stirling County Study, Vol. II. New York: Basic Books, Inc., 1960.

44. MacMahon, B. and E. K. Koller, "Ethnic Differences in the Incidence of Leukemia," *Blood*, 12 (January, 1957), 1–10.

45. Mainland, D., *Elementary Medical Statistics: The Principles of Quantitative Medicine*. Philadelphia: W. B. Saunders Co., 1952.

46. Merton, R. K. and A. S. Kitt, "Contributions to the Theory of Reference Group Behavior," *in* R. K. Merton and P .F. Lazarsfeld, eds., *Continuities in Social Research*. New York: The Free Press of Glencoe, Inc., 1950.

47. Merton, R. K., *Social Theory and Social Structure*. New York: The Free Press of Glencoe, Inc., 1957.

48. Merton, R. K., G. Reader, and P. L. Kendall, eds., *The Student-Physician*. Cambridge: Harvard University Press, 1957.

49. Millikan, R. A., "The Diffusion of Science." *The Scientific Monthly* (September, 1932), 203–208.

50. Muller, J. N., J. S. Tobis, and H. R. Kelman, "The Rehabilitation Potential of Nursing Home Residents." *American Journal of Public Health*, 53:2 (February, 1963), 243–247.

51. Parsons, T., E. Shils, K. D. Naegele and J. R. Pitts, eds., *Theories of Society*. Vols. I and II. New York: The Free Press of Glencoe, Inc., 1961.

52. Payne, S. L., *The Art of Asking Questions*. Princeton, N.J.: Princeton University Press, 1951.

53. ———, "The Ideal Model for Controlled Experiment," *Public Opinion Quarterly*, 15 (1951), 557–62.

53a. H. Pollack and D. E. Krueger, "Epidemiology of Cardiovascular Diseases Methodology—Hypertension and Arteriosclerosis," Supplement to *American Journal of Public Health*, 50:10 (October, 1960), 18.

54. Riesman, D., *Medicine in the Middle Ages*. New York: Paul B. Hoeber, Inc., 1935.

55. Riley, M. W., J. W. Riley, J. Toby, and M. Toby, *Sociological Studies in Scale Analysis; Applications, Theory, Procedures*. New Brunswick, N. J.: Rutgers University Press, 1954.

56. Ritterband, A. B., I. A. Jaffe, P. M. Densen, G. F. Magagna, and E. Reed, "Gonadal Function and the Development of Coronary Heart Disease," *Circulation*, 27:2 (February, 1963), 237–251.

57. Rosen, G., *Specialization of Medicine*. New York: Froben Press, 1944.

58. Selltiz, C., M. Jahoda, M. Deutsch, and S. W. Cook, *Research Methods in Social Relations*. New York: Holt, Rinehart & Winston, Inc., 1959.

59. Shanas, E., "Medical Care Among Those Age 65 and Over," *Health Information Foundation*, Research Series No. 16.

———, "Meeting Medical Care Costs Among the Aging," *Health Information Foundation*, Research Series No. 17.

60. Sheatsley, P., "Review of Chronic Illness in an Urban Area." *Journal of the American Statistical Association* (September, 1958).

61. Sherif, M. and C. I. Hovland, "Judgmental Phenomenon and Scales of Attitude Measurement." *Journal of Abnormal and Social Psychology* (1953), 135–41.

62. Solomon, R. W., "An Extension of Control Group Design," *Psychological Bulletin*, 46 (1949), 137–50.

63. Srole, L., T. Langner, *et al.*, *Mental Health in the Metropolis—the Midtown Manhattan Study*. New York: McGraw-Hill Book Company, Inc., 1962.

64. Stamler, J., M. Kjelsberg, Y. Hall, and N. Scotch, "Epidemiologic Studies on Cardiovascular-Renal Diseases: I–III," *Journal of Chronic Diseases*, 12:4 (October, 1960), 440–75.

65. Stamler, J., H. A. Lindberg, D. M. Berkson, *et al.*, "Prevalence and Incidence of Coronary Heart Disease in Strata of the Labor Force of a Chicago Industrial Corporation," *Journal of Chronic Diseases*, 11:405 (1960).

66. Stephan, F. F. and P. J. McCarthy, *Sampling Opinions*. New York: John Wiley & Sons, Inc., 1958.

67. Stevens, S. S., "Mathematics, Measurement and Psychophysics," *Handbook of Experimental Psychology*. New York: John Wiley & Sons, Inc., 1951.

68. Stouffer, S. A., *Communism, Conformity and Civil Liberties*. Garden City, N.Y.: Doubleday & Company, Inc., 1955.

69. ———, *Social Research to Test Ideas*. New York: The Free Press of Glencoe, Inc., 1962.

70. ———, "Some Observations on Study Design," *American Journal of Sociology*, 55 (1949–50), 355–61.

71. ——— *et al.*, *The American Soldier*. Vols. I and II of *Studies in Social Psychology in World War II*. Princeton, N.J.: Princeton University Press, 1949.

72. ———, *Measurement and Prediction*. Vol. IV of *Studies in Social Psychology in World War II*. Princeton, N.J.: Princeton University Press, 1950.

73. Suchman, E. A., "An Analysis of 'Bias' in Survey Research," *Public Opinion Quarterly*, 24:I (Spring, 1962), 102–11.

74. Thurstone, L. L. and E. J. Chave, *The Measurement of Attitude*. Chicago: University of Chicago Press, 1929.

75. Torgerson, W. S., *Theory and Methods of Scaling*. New York: John Wiley & Sons, Inc., 1958.

76. Tukey, J. W., "Statistical and Quantitative Methodology," *in* D. P. Ray, ed., *Trends in Social Science*. New York: Philosophical Library, Inc., 1961.

77. U. S. Employment Service, *Dictionary of Occupational Titles*. Washington, D.C.: Government Printing Office, 1944–49.

78. Williams, J. J. *et al.*, "Family Medical Care under Three Types of Health Insurance." Foundation on Employee Health, Medical Care, and Welfare. New York, 1962.

79. Woolsey, T. D. and H. Nisselson, "Some Problems in the Statistical Measurement of Chronic Disease," *in Improving the Quality of Statistical Surveys*. Washington, D.C.: American Statistical Association, 1956.

80. World Health Organization, *Epidemiology of Mental Disorders*. Series 185. Geneva: World Health Organization, 1960.

81. ———, *Scientific Group on Comparable Methodology for the Epidemiological Study of Hypertension and Ischaemic Heart Disease—Report to the Director General*. Geneva: World Health Organization, 1962.

82. ———, *International Lists of Diseases and Causes of Death*. 6th rev. Geneva: World Health Organization, 1948.

83. Yerushalmy, J., "Reliability of Chest X-Ray and Its Clinical Implications," *Diseases of the Chest* 24:2 (August, 1953), 133–147.

84. Zeisel, H., *Say it with Figures*. New York: Harper & Row, Publishers, 1957.

19

PRESENT STATUS OF MEDICAL SOCIOLOGY

Howard E. Freeman
Sol Levine
Leo G. Reeder

The magnitude of this volume is only one of the many indicators of the rapid growth of medical sociology. There have been a number of reviews of the literature of medical sociology; each review, including the most recent one by Polgar, remarks on the breadth of the field [2, 10, 14, 32, 33, 34]. The published studies of medical sociologists include some of the most theoretical as well as some of the most practical documents in the contemporary literature of the behavioral sciences. Hanlon, in commenting on Polgar's review, points to the very solid background of mutual interests and relationships on the parts of health personnel and social scientists [32].

The increase in the quantity of research in progress over the last few years is impressive, indeed. In the most recent survey of social and economic research undertaken by the Health Information Foundation, over 1000 different ongoing projects were reported and over 2000 research persons were involved in these studies [21]. While all of these projects cannot properly be classified as sociological, it is evident that a wealth of resources are being expended in sociomedical research. The annual reports of the Russell Sage Foundation are further testimony to the level of activity of social scientists in the health field [35].

Although the major "work role" of the sociologist in health is as a research investigator, a significant proportion of the 800 members of the medical sociology section of the American Sociological Association are engaged in other activities as well—teaching, administration, and consultation [37]. Particularly conspicuous has been the growth of opportunities for sociologists to participate in the education of physicians, dentists, nurses, and other health personnel. As Bloom has noted, the establishment of teaching roles for social scientists in medical settings is a concomitant of the persistent policy of innovation and change in the medical curricula. He notes that, as the scope of medicine has broadened and become more comprehensive in theory and practice, it increasingly has encountered the domain of the social sciences [8].

At present, a number of sociologists are regular members of departmental units in public health practice, preventive medicine, epidemiology, biostatistics, and psychiatry. They teach specialized courses and share the responsibilities for such courses as public health practice, epidemiology of chronic diseases, and hospital administration. At least one medical school, at the University of Kentucky, has established a department of behavioral science under the chairmanship of a sociologist and others, such as Stanford University Medical School, have social scientists attached to some of their major departments.

Medical sociologists have introduced their subject matter within traditional academic departments. Many graduate departments of sociology offer seminars in medical sociology and a number of institutions have developed pre- and post-doctoral training programs in medical sociology. Perhaps the most recent trend is the introduction of undergraduate courses in medical sociology, and virtually all major universities recognize the relevance of the field for persons heading toward careers in the health area.

Another development reflecting the growth of the field is the greater frequency of publications by sociologists in such medical journals as the *Journal of Chronic Disease*, *American Journal of Public Health*, *Journal of the American Medical Association*, *Gerontology*, and *Psychiatry*. A new quarterly, *The Journal of Health and Human Behavior*, provides a separate publication outlet for sociomedical research, and other sociological journals have devoted special issues to the field [39]. Further, special pamphlets and research series have been issued by such foundations as the Social Science Research Council and the Health Information Foundation, as well as by the National Institutes of Health.

The vital character of medical sociology is indicated further by a study of the composition of the members of the section on Medical Sociology of the American Sociological Association [5]. This survey by the Health Information Foundation shows that almost one-half of the sociologists who identify with the health field have been active in it for less than five years and only 12 per cent for more than ten. In addition, the survey indicates that, for the most part, medical sociologists are also young (almost half were under 40). Yet an increasing number of persons in the field occupy tenure positions in professional schools and academic departments, many are employed in permanent state and federal civil service positions, and several have actually moved up the administrative ladder to key policy and leadership positions. A dramatic illustration, and possibly auspicious development, is the recent appointment of a social psychologist as chairman of the department of public health administration in a leading school of public health.

The newness of the field and the youth of the participants in it is balanced by the active engagement in sociomedical problems of many of the leading and relatively more elder statesman in sociology. For example, Merton's studies of medical education, Parsons' analysis of the role of the patient, and Hughes' observations on the medical professions may properly be included within the scope of medical sociology [7, 23, 27, 30].

These salutory observations are not intended to becloud the frustrations, soul-searching, and attrition on the part of the physician and social scientist with a commitment to the field of medical sociology. In a number of the other chapters, points of controversy have been alluded to, such as Williams' discussion (see Chapter 17) of the organizational arrangements for sociologists in medical settings. As a subfield of sociology, and as perhaps its fastest growing one, medical sociology is beset by a number of problems which may hinder its further maturation and which will influence strongly its eventual fate. Not all of these problems are amenable to solution through the usual reportory of sociological research skills, for some represent conflicts in values and frames of reference.

The Field of Medical Sociology

Sociology, as a broad academic discipline, has a number of different roots [19, 24, 29]. The development of medical sociology mirrors the diverse orientations and parallels the genesis of other sociological specialities. Medical sociology is an applied field, and is distinctive only in its subject matter. Its boundaries are phenotypic, and there are no reasons for the development of unique or special theories in medical sociology. If medical sociology were to develop its own theoretical base, it would undoubtedly reflect that of general sociology: the activities of medical sociologists span such areas as social organization, deviant behavior, social control, socialization, and any number of other subjects of generic sociological interest.

Medical sociologists do vary, however, in their orientations toward their field. At one end of the spectrum are those whose interest in medicine is solely exploitative—they regard medical settings and health and illness as possible phenomena which can be subjected to study and which permit the elaboration, refinement, and testing of general propositions about social behavior. At the other end are sociologically trained persons who become enmeshed in the specific problems of the prevention and treatment of illness and the maximal allocation of health resources, and whose identification with medicine far overshadows their commitment to sociology. Most sociologists in the health field, we suspect, seek to maintain some balance between these two positions. They conceive of medical sociology as a field which permits one to add to the body of sociological knowledge and, simultaneously, to contribute to the solution of medical problems. This formulation is similar to the perspective of Straus [41]. He has suggested that medical sociology can be divided into the sociology *of* medicine and sociology *in* medicine.

As a consequence of trying to balance an interest in sociology and one in health, sociologists become concerned with the status of the field as an applied sociology, a topic which has been the subject of considerable discussion [17, 42]. Under what circumstances is the individual functioning as a sociologist when helping "men of action," such as medical practitioners, in the solution of *their* problems? One guideline, which most would agree with, is that his role performance must be based upon a reportory of skills and knowledge that are not possessed by just any intelligent person. The individual is not acting as a sociologist unless he utilizes available knowledge of social organization and social relationships in his work. The notion that applied sociology consists of the application of principles of social relations to the solution of action problems has been elaborated by Moore in considering the field of industrial relations [28].

It is clear that most of the sociology *of* medicine—the study of organizational structure, role relationships, value systems, rituals, and functions of medicine as systems of behavior—are legitimate activities for the applied sociologist; they contribute to the general body of sociological knowledge [41]. It is more questionable whether the work of sociologists *in* medicine typically contribute to general sociological knowledge. For this reason, the sociologist working in medicine is often quite defensive about his role. He is confronted by some of his sociological peers, like Hall, who insist that the applied sociologist must contribute to general sociology. As Hall states: "Medicine has no unique interest for sociology. The justification for its study lies in the light it throws on more general forms of social organization" [20].

In the eyes of most sociologists, however, such a stringent position is dismissed as puristic and unrealistic. Not only has a significant segment of the sociological profession traditionally had an interest in action fields, but the growth of all applied sociologies requires a commitment by some sociologists to the realization of some of the objectives of the action agents —in this case the health professions. It is unlikely that medical sociology would have flourished to the same extent without some attention to the goals of the medical community.

Under the most favorable circumstances, the sociologist is engaged at the same time in work which is regarded as useful to both his sociological peers and his medical colleagues. In the field of mental health, for example, the studies on social class by Hollingshead and Redlich and on hospital structure by Stanton and Schwartz are illustrations of such research [22, 40]. Most frequently, however, the activities of medical sociologists fail to accommodate the diverse expectations of both groups.[1] It is only realistic to recognize, however, that the medical sociologist is usually subject to diverse pressures and concomitant strain.

The sociologist in medicine often finds himself compelled to take on some of the trappings of his medical world—which range from wearing the proverbial white coat to actually holding an appointment which has medical overtones (*e.g.*, one of the editors of this Handbook is an Associate Professor of *Epidemiology*). Some of the trappings are undoubtedly useful in facilitating entree into medical settings, in fostering communication with medical colleagues, and in expediting the learning of the medical culture. But some of them have concomitant liabilities—physical isolation, social distance from colleagues, and diversion from sociological preoccupations. Most serious, however, are the potential loss of identification, relinquishment of a critical stance, and separation from the mainstream of sociological intercourse. He is often expected and tempted to play the "expert role" on matters beyond his sociological capacity, to assume consulting and administrative tasks in lieu of more scholarly roles, and to commit himself to a career course which impedes his re-entry into more traditional sociological jobs.

In these circumstances, a number of rationalizations come to the fore. One is that a minimal concession and involvement in medicine is a necessary precondition to the conduct of valid sociological work. Admittedly, in

[1] See the discussion by Richard H. Williams in Chap. 17, for a related treatment.

some cases, this is a fact. For example, Anderson, in describing his research program at the Health Information Foundation, claims that his early studies had to be directly relevant to the medical world before he could embark on more predominantly sociological research [3]. The problem however is that, in many cases, the "means" may indeed become "ends," and the earlier concessions may become irrevocable.

A second rationalization is that outside research support is more easily obtained if one is closer to and more accepted by the medical world. Here too there is some basis in fact. In general, grants by medical sociologists are reviewed by boards with heavy medical representation. There is a danger, however, that research integrity may be sacrificed by opportunism.

Another rationalization is that a "good" sociologist can convert every problem into one of sociological import. Again, there is some truth to this proposition; sensitive social scientists can often perceive the sociological dimensions of narrow medical problems. But it is necessary to recognize that a considerable waste of time and effort may be involved in conjuring useless conceptual frameworks around mundane problems.

A fourth rationalization is that closeness to medical personnel permits the acquisition of most penetrating insights and understanding. As in the other illustrations, there is some truth here too; many sociologists are sympathetic to the research potential of participant and field observation. Often, however, their very identification with settings and people makes objective date collection difficult and limits freedom of reporting.

The disadvantages accrue to the field as a whole, as well as to individual sociologists. Of current concern is the possibility that medical sociology, if not all of sociology, is likely to take on the structure of a guild-like occupation rather than a scholarly discipline [15]. While a trend toward a "guild-like" structure is not now evident among medical sociologists in their attitude toward certification, they do take a number of roles *vis-à-vis* medical personnel which have the earmarks of a narrow professionalism [4]. The more the medical sociologist becomes enmeshed in and subordinate to the "action system" he is serving, the more likely he is to assume a guild-like stance. His roles as administrator and consultant in medical settings especially make him most vulnerable to relinquishing his core identification as a sociologist. To the extent this pattern occurs, there is danger that the work of sociologists will feed back less and less to the dominant streams of sociology. It is highly problematic whether the quality of research by sociologists under these conditions would compare favorably with efforts in the main body of the field. On these grounds, Levine and Bennis warn against excessive involvement in the action system of the client: ". . . the sociologist may increasingly make contributions which stem from whatever unique virtues or skills he may possess as an individual rather than from the data, concepts and skills of his discipline. As the contribution he makes is less and less sociological, a point may be reached where the man of action may do the job just as well [25]."

A solution suggested by some sociologists, such as Gouldner, is the articulation, elaboration, and refinement of a "new brand" of sociology and a special breed of sociologists devoted to effecting social change in their own right and not as a byproduct of particular institutional affiliation. Rather than serve as a handmaiden to the medical practitioner, the sociologist in medicine could become a new action specialist and seek to develop a body of practice theory to supplement existing sociological knowledge [16, 17]. The need and potential acceptance of such a "clinical sociology" has been observed [25]. It is doubtful if most sociologists would concur with this projected development but it is probably a more desirable alternative than the subjugation of sociologists into action roles without such a systematic and explicit frame of reference.

In lieu of any marked departure from the present modes of conduct it is dangerous for the sociologist to proceed without safeguarding his professional identity. For the individual involved, this can be accomplished in part by effective organizational arrangements and open channels of communication with other sociologists. It is clear that well-developed structural mechanisms influence the effective conduct of the medical sociologist. It also means that he should limit his participation as a sociologist *in* medicine, both in time and in intensity of interest. Given the problem, it seems to us that all medical sociologists must be oriented at least in part toward the larger sociological field. As a report from the Russell Sage Foundation concludes: ". . . given a reasonable flexibility on the part of the host profession, a scientist who is competent and creative in his own discipline and can maintain his professional identity, can continue to contribute basic scientific knowledge and win appropriate recognition in his own discipline, and at the same time be responsive to the needs of the field of application in which he works [35]." We are not asking sociologists to relinquish their participation in a sociology of medicine but rather to regard health settings, at least in part, as field stations for research on a wide variety of problems, in much the same way as such disciplines as genetics and physiology participate in the work of agricultural experiment stations.

Values and the Role of the Sociologist

Our discussion of the field of medical sociology touches on part of the value framework of the sociologist, particularly the appropriateness of involvement by persons identified with science and scholarship in the action world. The place of values in science and in applied sociology cannot be treated here in depth. It would be presumptuous to attempt to resolve such problems in this brief analysis [6]. Current discussions for and against the notion of a value-free sociology reflects the extent of concern with the stance of sociology on matters of social policy [18]. Here, we wish only to indicate some of the specific types of problems of the sociologist in his relationship to the medical world.

Health, it would seem, is held in universal esteem and consequently the health world may appear to be a setting in which the sociologist is subjected to little strain or conflict over the appropriateness of his task. In fact, while health is an ultimate value, the means of realizing health objectives is pervaded by controversy within the health field itself. No one questions, for example, the desirability of reducing dental cavities but the technical expedient of fluoridating community water sources is not supported by all medically trained persons. Medical personnel clearly differ on the appropriateness of mechanical devices of birth control in order to limit population growth. Indeed some medical persons even argue about whether or not population control is consistent with the desired ultimate objective of health. Moreover, it is clear that the controversy over means to achieve maximal health in the medical world is overshadowed by the furor certain medical issues raise in the larger social scene. For example, few issues have touched off such deep feelings on the part of many Americans as deliberations on changing the methods of financing health services. The medical sociologist, as a community member, and as someone who is identified with the medical world or part of it—no matter what his own self-identification may be—is confronted by such value decisions. They occur particularly in connection with appropriate means for the realization of the ultimate goal, and with the selection of certain intermediate subgoals or facilitating objectives.

The general notions of democratic society and of consent of the governed may be counter to some of the most expeditious and effective means of realizing health objectives. The fluoridation controversy is a good illustration [31]. There is almost universal consensus that fluoridation is an effective technique for reducing dental caries but, in a number of communities, the public, when given an opportunity to vote on the issue, have rejected this public health practice. Fluoridation is most likely to be implemented when the decision can be made at an executive or expert level. If he is consulted, a recommendation by the social scientist that the decision be left in the hands of authorities may be congruent with health objectives but it is inimical with the democratic values which are typically harbored by him.

A related value conflict is the sociologist's choice in supporting and working for intermediate objectives which may have long-range negative consequences, or which may impede other types of desirable social change. For example, successful efforts at controlling epidemics have mitigated a major mechanism of population control; social scientists, particularly those engaged in disease control in underdeveloped areas, must face up to the potential consequences of their efforts on the long-term well being of the world community. Another example is the social science oriented aspects of public health programs with impoverished groups, whereby the amelioration of certain health problems may dissipate the intensity of and fever for radical changes in the over-all social and political structure. A specific illustration of the possibility of an inverse relationship between health action and political action can be drawn from reports of health care in South Africa, for it can be suggested that the provision of medical care acts as a brake on militant political activity [9].

Even the social scientist with "hard facts" often will find that his data are not regarded as neutral, and the way he casts his reports of findings must reflect to some extent his own value system, that of his sponsor, or his assessment of the community's climate (and often the three are not congruent). Even the unchallenged finding of a study undertaken by the National Opinion Research Center for the Health Information Foundation met with considerable derision from a portion of the medical community [1]. How does one, except in terms of some relative base of reference, report that 15 per cent of the costs of medical care are provided by health insurance—"only 15 per cent" or "as much as 15 per cent"? There are few facts on health and illness which can be communicated in a completely neutral and detached manner, and even if such were the case, the audience is unlikely to assess the data in neutral terms.

While anything but full and objective reporting is to be decried, there may be consequences for either the community or the medical world which are inconsistent with the value commitments of sociologists in the unrestricted issuance of research results. For example, a number of studies suggest the limited efficacy of mental health education efforts [36]. In view of the limited alternatives which are available, and the already existing programs to provide better approaches, do such studies serve any function but to undermine further the faith and confidence of the practitioner and consequently diminish his action role? While certain professional activities are ineffective, the social order may suffer more if community members are deprived of them.

One recourse available to the sociologist confronted with the uncertainty of possible inappropriate or undermining use of the results of his work is to confine his communication to his sociological peers, despite his avowed investment in his host setting. Certain studies, hidden in the more obscure sociological journals or confounded with the jargon of sociology have no impact on the practitioner. The sociologist is faced with weighing the gains and costs of limiting the communication of his research findings to his peers in comparison with directing the attention of medical personnel to them.

The sociologist often is discouraged from communicating with his medical colleagues because of tendencies, on their part, to accept his findings uncritically and to act on them even though he may plead that his results are incomplete and tentative. Moreover, the sociologist—particularly when placed in the role of a consultant—is pressured to make "best guesses," which are then treated as recommendations.

The different postures of medicine and sociology are related, to some extent at least, to the degree of acceptance of various research styles and orders of data. Although sociologists vary among themselves in styles of research, few question the utility of probability statements and quantitative analysis. This obtains to a lesser degree among medical persons, at least among clinically-oriented physicians. It is a paradox that many of those in the medical field most sympathetic and supportive of social science—*e.g.*, psychiatrists—are least enchanted with "hard" sociology. The sociologist is faced with the problem that the persons in medicine whom he is most likely to alienate by the implementation of certain research procedures are the ones most attuned to and appreciative of the social dimensions in health and illness.

Incompatibility in research styles is only one manifestation of the differences in orientation between sociology and medicine. Sometimes the sociologist's frame of reference and his body of knowledge challenge some of the basic assumptions of medicine. Physicians are prone to link the technology and the culture of their profession [26]. The American physician, for example, does not distinguish between diagnosing the patient's illness and examining him privately rather than in the presence of his relatives. As Freidson has pointed out (see Chapter 12), contrary to the views of some, there seems to be little relationship between the efficacy of medical practice and the mode of organizing services. The sociologist, seeking to separate the technology from the culture of medicine, may be accused of usurping the role of practitioner. Because the physician characteristically insists on mixing culture with technology, the sociologist may have no choice, at times, but to become involved in the study and evaluation of the technology of medicine, and the dilemma is that he usually knows how ill-equipped he is for this task.

There also are instances where some sociologists maintain that the technology involved in treatment of some illnesses is not the exclusive domain of the medical practitioner. This view is held particularly by certain sociologists involved in the mental health field. Here, where manifestations of illness are essentially behavioral and interpersonal, the sociologist may feel he is as appropriate a person as the physician to make judgment on the course of treatment. In dealing with drug addiction, alcoholism, and certain types of mental illness, sociologists do become involved in therapeutic relationships, which challenge the domain of the physician. There are sociologists who hold that their field offers more relevant training for group psychotherapy than does medicine. Obviously, the guild-like structure of medical practice presents barriers to involvement of nonmedical people in any therapeutic relationships. The social scientists who lay claim to these somewhat marginal therapeutic areas run the risk of being rejected in their research roles as well. It is interesting that certain aspects of the technology of medicine, again mainly in psychiatry, have been more enthusiastically supported by social scientists than by physicians. For example, psychodrama, as a method of therapy, probably has attracted proportionately more support from social scientists than from physicians.

The guild-like structure of the medical profession raises some other problems for the sociologist, particularly in studies which involve contact between the social researcher and patients. Physicians, legally (and perhaps morally) have the "ultimate" responsibility for the well-being of the patient. It is clear that sociologists do not question the ultimate responsibility of the physician in the treatment of patients, with the possible exception of those who suffer from certain behavior problems. In carrying out research projects, however, this authority may intrude on certain types of methodological decisions which are really the province of the methodologically astute person, often the sociologist. The sociologist, in arguing for research integrity, may sometimes appear to be assailing the physician's human concern for the patient.

It is certainly true that medical sociologists as well as physicians are often in conflict over the requirements of research design and the negative impact the research activity may have for the patient. The dilemma is typically most sharp in studies involving control groups which are deprived of potentially beneficial therapies. A dramatic study of this value conflict has been reported by Fox [13].

The medical sociologist also is beset with problems of a personal nature. For example, what is his line of action in those cases where he is not well received in the host setting, or even worse, where he finds that the objectives of his medical colleagues are unpalatable to his personal, social, and political outlooks? For example, can a sociologist who personally favors socialized medicine associate himself with a medical group active in opposition to government-financed medical care? There are times too, perhaps rare, when the sociologist may be nothing but window-dressing in a medical setting, simply because his presence may be advantageous in obtaining research funds.

These value problems are complex and pervasive and it is impossible to offer a set of instructions and prescriptions which will resolve them. One would suspect that the more mature sociologist anticipates many of the potential sources of strain and avoids them by explicitly structuring and clarifying his role to his medical colleagues at the outset and by actively assessing the needs and expectations of his medical hosts. The sociologist, by virtue of his training, has at his disposal an array of concepts and skills which are a potential source of strength in dealing with these problems.

The Development of a Body of Knowledge

Certain problems endemic to the development of the general body of sociological knowledge and to that of other sociological specialities also confront the field of medical sociology. Here, too, it is easier to characterize the dilemmas than to formulate ready solutions to them. Many of the limitations of current research efforts are solely technical, related to the present level of methodological sophistication in sociology, and the uneven training which sociologists are provided in graduate school, a point discussed in detail by Sibley [38]. A number of these technical problems have been alluded to by Elinson (see Chapter 18), and here we will concern ourselves with only a few of the broad issues, ones which really border more on the philosophy than the method of scientific inquiry.

In medical sociology, as in sociology in general, many worthwhile studies are solely descriptive, and one objective of research is to describe particular situations, settings, and social phenomena. But in all fields which embrace the traditions of science, part—most, many would say—of the research effort needs to be devoted to predictive and causal investigations. For example, measures of health, of quality of medical care, of rates of hospitalization are included in studies which utilize an independent-dependent variable frame of reference. One or more measures is looked upon as predictive or causative, and others as outcome or criteria variables. In more complex investigations, variables are assigned other statuses, *e.g.*, as intervening or control measures. There are, of course, clear-cut instances where studies adopt an explicit frame with respect to the ordering of variables. One well-known example is Hollingshead and Redlich's analysis of social class and mental illness, in which the former is clearly explicated as the independent variable and the latter as the dependent one [22]. Often, of course, the ordering of variables is purely arbitrary and "causal sequence" is not a relevant issue. Nevertheless, from the standpoint of the field of medicine, knowledge becomes relatively useless unless some ordering can be identified or at least assumed. Given the present status of knowledge, it is essential that careful explication of the actual or assumed ordering of variables be undertaken in all but solely descriptive studies. If it is not done, the practitioner does it anyway, and the medical sociologist finds himself in the position of contending with false inferences for which, through omission, he is at least in part responsible. The problem of "as if it were causal" has always plagued sociology but takes on particular importance in a field where findings may potentially, no matter how tentatively they are noted, be put to immediate use.

An illustration of concern with this issue is the comments of Feldman regarding the use of health survey data in demographic analysis [11]. He illustrates, using research on the relationship between social class measures and health status, that there is a tendency always to regard the former variable as the independent one and the latter as the dependent one. Admittedly, demographic variables are primarily governed by forces other than health. There is reasonably good evidence, by controlling for other influences in cross-sectional studies, and by tracing the time sequence in longitudinal ones, to regard the usual ordering as the correct one. But, this is not true in terms of other domains of variables, such as attitudinal measures. Consequently, it is poor science—and unfair to the practitioner—not to identify the time sequence or at least estimate the plausibility of sequence among variables.

Moreover, as Feldman notes, the tendency of social scientists working in the health field is to devote almost all their energies to trying to explain medical phenomena in terms of social processes, when in reality many of these processes have not been rigorously defined and so little is known about them. It is essential that the medical sociologist maximize his opportunities to investigate the bearing of physiological factors on the social environment—in other words, to view health measures as the independent variables. A provocative example of using health as an independent variable is the analysis of interpersonal competence by Foote and Cottrell, who specify a series of hypotheses in which health is regarded as a predictor of the competence of family members [12]. Admittedly, the interest of the medical professions is on health as the dependent variable, but the sociologist in the health field must recognize that his responsibility to his own field and his ultimate contribution to the medical field rests in being resistive to and circumspect about automatically accepting the ordering which is most meaningful to his medical colleagues.

A more specific issue, but of no less importance, is the development of realistic operational definitions, *i.e.*, those most appropriate and relevant to the needs of the action field. The medical sociologist is vulnerable to both barrels of a shotgun in this respect. The "medical variables" which often constitute part of his research are variously and differently defined by physicians and so are the variables from his own realm of competence.

The problem of operationalizing medical variables can be illustrated most readily by looking at studies of the quality of medical care—a phenomena defined variously as (1) the conduct of appropriate practices, (2) the fulfillment of certain obligations, (3) the attitudes of staff or patients, and (4) the actual illness or well-being of patients. Studies of medical efficacy may use, as measures of quality, such phenomena as how long an operation took, how the drug was dispensed, and how detailed was the medical record—all on the assumption that these and other such variables reflect real differences in patient outcome. The medical sociologist must be most aware of the hazards of assessing operational measures which are only believed to reflect the actual phenomenon being studied. Here the medical sociologist is compelled to challenge the "expert" knowledge of his medical colleagues, and either to carefully limit the generalization or conceptualization potential of his variables, or to demand the rigorous testing of the linkage between certain reflectors of major phenomena and the actual conditions. Another major problem lies in synthesizing the results of studies which make use of different operational measures of the same phenomenon.

The contrary is true, however, in the case of sociological variables. Sociologists working on medical problems not only fail to take advantage of sociomedical studies to refine measures more precisely, but often do not even utilize the sophistication developed in other areas of sociology. Accusations by sociologists about the naivete of some medical persons, such as epidemiologists, are often unfair. More often than not, medically trained epidemiologists will make use of a single measure of class status—usually occupation—in their analyses of disease causation. One reason is that they feel they thus have a reliable scale. But it also happens that the medical epidemiologist can understand what occupation is, while confounded by social class measures predicated on notions of "style of life" or "social prestige"—and perhaps rightly so because such concepts lie within the diffuse sociological realm of discourse. The joint sharing of concepts, and particularly of operational measures, represents an indispensable key to the development of a systematized body of sociomedical knowledge.

A wide range of methods is used within medical sociology, and it is clear that no one approach represents the most efficacious means for the development of the field. In a recent paper, Zelditch outlines the utility of various methods, such as field observation, surveys, and so on [43]. The choice of the appropriate method rarely is made on the basis of logic alone. It depends also upon which approach, at a given point, the particular investigator feels he is most competent in and to which he has the greatest commitment.

Persons concerned with the development of a body of knowledge need to realize, however, the relative impossibility of synthesizing findings obtained through vastly different methods. This is not to imply that one method is better than another or that several methods may not be appropriate for the study of the same problem, but that the probability of developing a body of knowledge without recurring use of similar methods in various areas is rather unlikely. For example, two volumes on medical education (see Chapter 7) report findings of studies of two medical schools [7, 27]. Different frames of reference may account for the rather diverse findings, but so may the use of a field approach in one case and a questionnaire approach in the other. While the justification for diverse approaches is apparent, the development of a systematic and codified body of knowledge requires sustained efforts and conscious attempts at replication. At the same time, the practitioner must develop a patient outlook toward the process of knowledge building.

Not only do methods differ, but so do the frames of reference of socio-medical research. A good illustration is the previously noted volumes on medical education. One study emphasizes an internal process of "becoming" and uses the approach of viewing a narrow scene as a "culture." But the other does not consider "boys in white" as a discrete entity but rather places them within the perspective of a larger medical system. It is not possible to determine whether the findings differ because of variations in the two medical schools studied, in the methodological approaches, or in the frames of reference. All fields grow and prosper by diversity and only continued research—particularly replicative investigations—can resolve differences in the findings of parallel efforts.

The problems discussed here are not unique to the field of medical sociology, but pervade the entire discipline. The sociological literature is replete with discussions and considerations of these and related issues in much more detailed and sophisticated ways. But as specialists within a discipline, medical sociologists have a responsibility to contribute to the unravelling of these problems.

Socialization of Medical Sociologists

If there *is* merit in our position that medical sociology is an applied specialty defined substantively and with theoretical and conceptual roots in general sociology, it follows that medical sociologists must be well trained and competent general sociologists. The diversity in the theoretical perspectives and emphases among sociologists are, of course, reflected in the orientations of various departments of sociology.

Virtually all departments, however, require certain minimal competencies today from their graduate students, such as a familiarity with the historical background of sociology, a grasp of contemporary theories, and a knowledge of research methods [38]. If medical sociology is to grow and prosper as part of general sociology, the training of the sociologist who turns to this field must be broad and comprehensive. But this does not mean that the sociologist can operate successfully in the medical field solely on the basis of his academic training. Sociologists vary in their opinions of the importance of "field training" to the educational process, but it is doubtful if any would contest that familiarity with the settings in which they are to work is not useful. A familiarity with the medical field, in one way or another, is essential to the development of the medical sociologist [8].

There are, however, a number of alternative points of entry into medical sociology. The most formal route consists, of course, of obtaining further graduate training in medicine. The number of sociologists who have attempted to complete medical school for the explicit purpose of becoming better medical sociologists is probably zero. A number of social scientists, however, have received training or degrees from schools of public health. A second formal route is through the various pre- and post-doctoral medical sociology programs in social science departments. Several of these programs recruit their students from medicine as well as sociology, and both the formal course work and field experiences are supplemented by informal contacts between physician and social scientist.

It is the informal contact system which has provided the immersion into medicine of most social scientists currently interested in health. Many of the sociologists who work in the medical field have held teaching or research appointments at medical schools or schools of public health or in programs of research in hospital and clinic settings. Most recently, public health departments have been adding sociologists to their staffs, and some medical practitioners concerned with social science advocate some sort of "internship" program.

The type of socialization process is perhaps not as important as whether there are safeguards to assure that the sociologist in training does not become a hybrid but maintains an identity with his field. Realistically, there are a number of stimuli which threaten the identification of the sociologist with his discipline. Medicine is both an intriguing scientific field and a creative art; moreover, it is pleasant to be identified with physicians—both as individuals and as a socioeconomic group. In many settings, such as schools of public health, there are other disciplines represented which also invite affiliation—biostatistics, medical epidemiology, and other "hard" health sciences. It is not a matter of faith in one's discipline which is important—although some of that is also useful to have—but a realization that orientations and tastes do differ and the guidelines appropriate in one field may not be as useful in another. Many of the choices in statistical procedure recommended by biostatisticians are not congruent with the necessary operations in social science research and many of the ways in which public health practitioners approach the study of social structure and social organization are incongruent with those of social scientists. The temptation exists, particularly for the sociological novice, to adapt to the modal patterns of the medical settings. The medical as well as the sociological professions have a responsibility for training and developing both the competence and autonomy of medical sociologists.

Conclusions

These are some of the problems in the rapidly growing field of medical sociology. Perhaps some of the recommendations are open to challenge. Certainly there is considerable need for systematic study of the development of the field, which will supplement already completed or ongoing research on the activities, roles, and views of medical sociologists.

Some of the dust raised by the swift development of medical sociology must be allowed to settle. Growth is rarely uniform and orderly, and perhaps a "homeostatic balance" is impossible to obtain at this point. The maturation of medical sociology depends on the development of mechanisms which yield a less precarious equilibrium. To be sure, there has been and will continue to be some disillusionment by impetuous and overenthusiastic physicians, as well as by overzealous and overpromising sociologists. The very fact that the issues elaborated in this chapter are a matter of explicit and continued concern reflect the investment and commitment of persons in medicine and social science to the field. Were medical sociology only a passing fad, it is not likely that these issues would have reached such a high degree of salience and intensity. The issues that we have raised are of secondary and minor importance when compared with the fruits of current efforts and the potential rewards of future endeavors.

References

1. Anderson, Odin W. and Jacob J. Feldman, *Family Medical Costs and Voluntary Health Insurance: A Nationwide Survey*. New York: McGraw-Hill Book Company, Inc., 1956.
2. Anderson, Odin W. and Milvoy S. Seacat, *The Behavioral Scientist and Research in the Health Field*. New York: Health Information Foundation, 1957.
3. Anderson, Odin W., "The Roads to Social Research," *American Behavioral Scientist*, 5 (March, 1962), 8–11.
4. ———, "Letter to Members of the Medical Sociology Section, American Sociological Association," 1962.
5. ——— and Milvoy S. Seacat, "An Analysis of Personnel in Medical Sociology," *Research Series, No. 21*. New York: Health Information Foundation, 1962.
6. Bain, Read, "Science, Values, and Sociology," *American Sociological Review*, 4 (August, 1939), 560–65.
7. Becker, Howard S., *et al.*, *Boys in White*. Chicago: University of Chicago Press, 1961.

8. Bloom, Samuel W., "The Sociologist as Medical Educator," *American Sociological Review*, 25 (February, 1960), 95–102.
9. Cassel, John, "A Comprehensive Health Program among South African Zulus," *in* Benjamin D. Paul ed., *Health, Culture, and Community*. New York: Russell Sage Foundation, 1955, pp. 15–41.
10. Caudill, William, "Applied Anthropology in Medicine," *in* A. L. Kroeber, ed., *Anthropology Today*. Chicago: University of Chicago Press, 1953, pp. 771–806.
11. Feldman, Jacob J., "Barriers to the Use of Health Survey Data in Demographic Analysis," *Milbank Memorial Fund Quarterly*, 36 (July, 1958), 203–219.
12. Foote, Nelson N. and Leonard S. Cotrell, *Identity and Interpersonal Competence*. Chicago: University of Chicago Press, 1955.
13. Fox, Renée C., *Experiment Perilous*. New York: The Free Press of Glencoe, Inc., 1959.
14. Freeman, Howard E. and Leo G. Reeder, "Medical Sociology: A Review of the Literature," *American Sociological Review*, 22 (February, 1957), 73–81.
15. Goode, William J., "Community Within a Community: The Professions," *American Sociological Review*, 22 (April, 1957), 194–99.
16. Gouldner, Alvin W., "Explorations in Applied Social Science," *Social Problems*, 3 (January, 1956), 169–81.
17. ———, "Theoretical Requirements of the Applied Social Sciences," *American Sociological Review*, 22 (February, 1957), 92–102.
18. ———, "The Myth of a Value-Free Sociology," *Social Problems*, 9 (Winter, 1962), 199–213.
19. Green, Arnold W., *Sociology: An Analysis of Life in Modern Society*. New York: McGraw-Hill Book Company, Inc., 1952.
20. Hall, Oswald, "Sociological Research in the Field of Medicine: Progress and Prospects," *American Sociological Review*, 16 (October, 1951), 639–49.
21. Health Information Foundation, *An Inventory of Social and Economic Research in Health*. 10th ed. New York: Health Information Foundation, 1961.
22. Hollingshead, August B. and Frederick C. Redlich, *Social Class and Mental Illness*. New York: John Wiley & Sons, Inc., 1958.
23. Hughes, Everett C., Helen M. Hughes, and Irwin Deutscher, *Twenty Thousand Nurses Tell Their Story*. Philadelphia: J. B. Lippincott Company, 1958.
24. Lee, Alfred M., "Sociologists in an Integrating Society," *Social Problems*, 2 (October, 1954), 57–66.
25. Levine, Sol and Warren G. Bennis, "The Action Role of the Sociologist." Paper read before American Sociological Association, New York, 1960.
26. McKin, Marriott, "Western Medicine in a Village of Northern India," *in* Benjamin D. Paul, ed., *Health, Culture, and Community*. New York: Russell Sage Foundation, 1955, pp. 239–68.
27. Merton, Robert K., George Reader, and Patricia L. Kendall, eds. *The Student-Physician*. Cambridge: Harvard University Press, 1957.

28. Moore, Wilbert E., *Industrial Relations and the Social Order*. New York: The Macmillan Company, 1947.
29. Odum, Howard W., *American Sociology*, New York: Longmans, Green, & Co., Inc., 1951.
30. Parsons, Talcott, *The Social System*. New York: The Free Press of Glencoe, Inc., 1951.
31. Paul, Benjamin D., William A. Gamson, and S. Stephen Kageles, eds., "Trigger for Community Conflict: The Case of Fluoridation," *Journal of Social Issues*, 17 (1961).
32. Polgar, Steven, "Health and Human Behavior: Areas of Interest Common to the Social and Medical Sciences," *Current Anthropology*, 3 (April, 1962), 159–205.
33. Reader, George G. and Mary E. W. Goss, "The Sociology of Medicine," *in* R. K. Merton, *et al.*, eds., *Sociology Today*. New York: Basic Books, Inc., 1959, pp. 229–46.
34. Rosen, George and Edward Wellin, "A Bookshelf on the Social Sciences and Public Health," *American Journal of Public Health*, 49 (April, 1959), 441–54.
35. Russell Sage Foundation, *Annual Report, 1960–1961*. New York: Russell Sage Foundation, 1961.
36. Scott, John F., "The Selective Influence of Social and Psychological Characteristics of Mothers or Information and Attitude Change in Mental Health Education Programs." Unpublished Ph.D. thesis, Brandeis University, 1961.
37. Section on Medical Sociology, American Sociological Association, "Newsletter," May, 1962.
38. Sibley, Elbridge, "The Objectives of Sociological Training," *American Sociological Review*, 25 (August, 1960), 571–75.
39. *Social Problems*, 4 (July, 1956).
40. Stanton, Alfred H. and Morris S. Schwartz, *The Mental Hospital*. New York: Basic Books, Inc., 1954.
41. Straus, Robert, "The Nature and Status of Medical Sociology," *American Sociological Review*, 22 (April, 1957), 200–204.
42. Williams, Robin M., "Application of Research to Practice and Intergroup Relations," *American Sociological Review*, 18 (February, 1953), 78–83.
43. Zelditch, Morris, "Methodological Problems of Field Studies," *American Journal of Sociology*, 67 (March, 1962), 566–76.

20

SOCIAL RESEARCH IN HEALTH AND MEDICINE: A BIBLIOGRAPHY

Ozzie G. Simmons

This bibliography is comprehensive of the literature on social research in health and medicine.[1] As many publications were included as could be found that report research in the fields of public health, mental health, and general medicine, but the coverage of research activity in sociology, social anthropology, and social psychology is more extensive than in experimental and clinical psychology and in psychiatry. In addition to the literature on

[1] The original version of this bibliography was prepared for my graduate seminar, "Social Research in Health and Medicine," at the University of Colorado, and has been somewhat expanded for this publication.

research, a substantial number of items have been included that constitute general statements about the past, present, and future status of the collaborative relationship between social science and medicine, or are concerned with the use of social science materials in medical education.

Some publications are relevant to more than one part of the bibliography, but no item is listed more than once. For example, many of the articles concerned with aspects of interpersonal relations in health programs and institutions are equally relevant to Parts III and IV of the bibliography, but have been allocated, sometimes arbitrarily, to only one or the other. Social scientists are doing research in a number of health-relevant areas that could not be considered in detail within the limits of this handbook. Nevertheless, the literature on these areas has been included in this bibliography, much of it in Part II.

The bibliography has been arranged in accordance with the organization of this book and has five parts entitled as follows:

I. General Statements, Historical Works, Source Books and Collections, Review Articles, and Bibliographies
II. The Sociology of Illness
III. Practitioners, Patients, and Medical Settings
IV. Sociology of Medical Care
V. Strategy, Method, and Status of Medical Sociology

Publications are listed alphabetically within each part. Only published materials have been included in this bibliography, and all foreign-language publications have been excluded.

I. General Statements, Historical Works, Source Books and Collections, Review Articles, and Bibliographies

ACKERKNECHT, Erwin H., "Hygiene in France, 1815–1848," *Bulletin of the History of Medicine,* 22 (March–April, 1948), 117–55.

ACKERKNECHT, Erwin H., *A Short History of Medicine,* New York: The Ronald Press Company, 1955.

ANDERSON, Odin W., "The Sociologist and Medicine," *Social Forces,* 31 (October, 1952), 38–42.

APPLE, Dorrian, ed., *Sociological Studies of Health and Sickness,* New York: McGraw-Hill Book Company, Inc., 1960.

AXELROD, S. J., *Public Assistance Medical Care: Areas of Research and an Annotated Bibliography,* Chicago: American Public Welfare Association, 1959.

BACON, Selden D., ed., "Understanding Alcoholism," *The Annals of the American Academy of Political and Social Science,* 315 (January, 1958), entire issue.

BADGLEY, R. F. and R. W. Hetherington, "Medical Sociology: A Selected Canadian Bibliography," *Canadian Medical Association Journal,* 85 (July, 1961), 88–89.

BEN-DAVID, Joseph, "Scientific Productivity and Academic Organization in Nineteenth Century Medicine," *American Sociological Review,* 25 (December, 1960), 828–43.

BLACKWELL, Elizabeth, *Essays in Medical Sociology*, London: Ernest Benn, 1902.

BLACKWELL, Gordon, "Behavioral Science and Health," *Social Forces*, 32 (December, 1953), 211–15.

BLUESTONE, E. M., "Social Psychiatry—A Critique," *International Journal of Social Psychiatry*, 4 (Spring, 1959), 291–95.

BOEK, Walter E. and Jean K. Boek, *Society and Health*, New York: G. P. Putnam's Sons, 1956.

BRIGGS, D. L., "Social Psychiatry in Great Britain," *American Journal of Nursing*, 59 (February, 1959), 215–20.

BULL, J. P., "The Historical Development of Clinical Therapeutic Trials," *Journal of Chronic Diseases*, 10 (September, 1959), 218–48.

CAUDILL, William, "Applied Anthropology in Medicine," *in* A. L. Kroeber, ed., *Anthropology Today*, Chicago: University of Chicago Press, 1953, 771–806.

CHEN, Edith and Sidney Cobb, "Family Structure in Relation to Health and Disease, A Review of the Literature," *Journal of Chronic Diseases*, 12 (November, 1960), 544–67.

CLAUSEN, John A., "Social Science Research in the National Mental Health Program," *American Sociological Review*, 15 (June, 1950), 402–09.

CLAUSEN, John A., "Sociology of Mental Health, 1945–1955," *in* H. L. Zetterberg, ed., *Sociology in the United States of America, A Trend Report*, Paris: UNESCO, 1956, 127–30.

CLAUSEN, John A., *Sociology and the Field of Mental Health*, New York: Russell Sage Foundation, 1956.

COMMITTEE ON MEDICAL CARE TEACHING OF THE ASSOCIATION OF TEACHERS OF PREVENTIVE MEDICINE, *Readings in Medical Care*, Chapel Hill: The University of North Carolina Press, 1958.

DAVIS, Michael M., "Wanted: Research in the Economic and Social Aspects of Medicine," *Milbank Memorial Fund Quarterly*, 13 (October, 1935), 339–46.

DAVIS, Michael M., "Social Medicine as a Field for Social Research," *American Journal of Sociology*, 44 (September, 1938), 274–79.

DUBOS, René J., *The Mirage of Health*, New York: Harper & Row, Publishers, 1959.

DUBOS, René J., "Health and Disease," *Journal of the American Medical Association*, 174 (October 1, 1960), 505–7.

DUNHAM, Francis Lee, *An Approach to Social Medicine*, Baltimore: The Williams & Wilkins Company, 1925.

DUNHAM, H. Warren, "The Field of Social Psychiatry," *American Sociological Review*, 13 (April, 1948), 183–97. Reprinted *in* A. M. Rose, ed., *Mental Health and Mental Disorder*, New York: W. W. Norton & Company, Inc., 1955.

FELIX, Robert H., "A Bookshelf on Mental Health," *American Journal of Public Health*, 46 (April, 1956), 397–407.

FRANK, Lawrence K., *Society as the Patient*, New Brunswick, N.J.: Rutgers University Press, 1948.

FREEMAN, Howard E. and Leo G. Reeder, "Medical Sociology: A Review of the Literature," *American Sociological Review*, 22 (February, 1957), 73–81.

FREIDSON, Eliot, *Classified and Annotated Bibliography*. To be published by UNESCO.

FRENCH, David G., "The Behavioral Sciences and the Professions," *Public Health Reports*, 71 (May, 1956), 504–10.

GALDSTON, Iago, *The Meaning of Social Medicine*, Cambridge: Harvard University Press, 1954.

GALDSTON, Iago, ed., *Medicine in a Changing Society*, New York: International Universities Press, 1956.

GALDSTON, Iago, ed., *Medicine and Anthropology*, New York: International Universities Press, 1959.

GAMSON, William A. and Carolyn G. Lindberg, "An Annotated Bibliography of Social Science Aspects of Fluoridation," *Health Education Journal*, 19 (November, 1961), 209–30.

GRANT, John B., "Social Medicine in the Curriculum," *British Medical Journal*, 1 (February 21, 1948), 333–36.

GREENBLATT, M., D. J. Levinson, and G. L. Klerman, *Mental Patients in Transition: Steps in Hospital-Community Rehabilitation*, Springfield, Ill.: Charles C Thomas, Publisher, 1961.

GREENBLATT, M., D. J. Levinson, and R. H. Williams, eds., *The Patient and the Mental Hospital*, New York: The Free Press of Glencoe, Inc., 1957.

GREENBLATT, M. and B. Simon, eds., *Rehabilitation of the Mentally Ill: Social and Economic Aspects: A Symposium*, Washington, D.C.: American Association for the Advancement of Science, Publication 58, 1959.

GREENHOW, Edward H., *Papers Relating to the Sanitary State of the People of England*, London: Eyre and Spottiswoode, 1858.

HALLIDAY, James L., *Psychosocial Medicine*, New York: W. W. Norton & Company, Inc., 1948.

HARVARD MEDICAL SCHOOL AND PSYCHIATRIC SERVICE, MASSACHUSETTS GENERAL HOSPITAL, *Community Mental Health and Social Psychiatry: A Reference Guide*, Cambridge: Harvard University Press, 1962.

HAWKINS, Norman G., *Medical Sociology, Theory, Scope and Methods*, Springfield, Ill.: Charles C Thomas, Publisher, 1958.

HAWKINS, Norman G., "A Research Program for a State Mental Hospital (Hollidaysburg) in Pennsylvania: Critical Review of the Pertinent Literature," *Journal of the American Geriatrics Society*, 9 (April, 1961), 253–76.

HEALTH EDUCATION JOURNAL, "Social Anthropology and Health Education," 15 (May, 1957), entire issue.

HEALTH INFORMATION FOUNDATION, *An Inventory of Social and Economic Research in Health*, New York: Health Information Foundation, published annually since 1952.

HUMAN ORGANIZATION, "Mental Health and Preventive Medicine," 16 (1958), entire issue.

HYDE, Henry Van Zile, "Public Health and the Social Sciences," *Public Health Reports*, 72 (May, 1957), 421–25.

JACO, E. Gartly, ed., *Patients, Physicians, and Illness*, New York: The Free Press of Glencoe, Inc., 1958.

JOINT COMMISSION ON MENTAL ILLNESS AND HEALTH, *Action for Mental Health: Final Report of the Joint Commission on Mental Illness and Health*, New York: Basic Books, Inc., 1961.

KING, Stanley H., "What We Can Learn from the Behavioral Sciences," *International Journal of Health Education*, 1 (October, 1958), 194–200.

KRAMER, Howard D., "The Beginnings of the Public Health Movement in the United States," *Bulletin of the History of Medicine*, 21 (1947), 352–76.

KROEGER, Gertrud, *The Concept of Social Medicine as Presented by Physicians and Other Writers in Germany, 1779–1932*, Chicago: Julius Rosenwald Fund, 1937.

KUTNER, B., H. B. Makover, and A. Oppenheim, "Delay in the Diagnosis and Treatment of Cancer: A Critical Analysis of the Literature," *Journal of Chronic Diseases*, 7 (February, 1958), 95–120.

LEAVELL, Hugh R., "Contributions of the Social Sciences to the Solution of Health Problems," *New England Journal of Medicine*, 247 (December, 1952), 885–97.

LEIGHTON, A. H., J. A. Clausen, and R. N. Wilson, eds., *Explorations in Social Psychiatry*, New York: Basic Books, Inc., 1957.

LEWIS, A., "Health as a Social Concept," *British Journal of Sociology*, 4 (June, 1953), 109–24.

LIDDLE, John, "On the Connection Between Medical Poor Relief and the Sanitary Condition of the People," *Journal of Public Health*, 1 (1948), 92–95.

MACKENZIE, James, *The Future of Medicine*, New York: Oxford University Press, 1919.

MANGUS, A. R., "Medical Sociology: Study of the Social Components of Illness and of Health," *Sociology and Social Research*, 39 (January–February, 1955), 158–64.

MARTI-IBANEZ, Felix, ed., *Henry E. Sigerist on the History of Medicine*, New York: M. D. Publications, Inc., 1960.

McCARTHY, Raymond G., ed., *Drinking and Intoxication*, New York: The Free Press of Glencoe, Inc., 1959.

McINTIRE, Charles, "The Importance of the Study of Medical Sociology," *Bulletin of the American Academy of Medicine*, 1 (February, 1894), 425–34.

MERRILL, B. R., "Some Psychosomatic Aspects of Pulmonary Tuberculosis: A Review of the English Language Literature," *Journal of Nervous and Mental Disease*, 117 (1953), 9–28.

MEYER, A. S., *Social and Psychological Factors in Opiate Addiction: A Review of Research Findings Together With an Annotated Bibliography*, New York: Bureau of Applied Social Research, Columbia University, 1952.

MILBANK MEMORIAL FUND, *Epidemiology of Mental Disorder*, New York: Milbank Memorial Fund, 1950.

MILBANK MEMORIAL FUND, *Research in Public Health*, New York: Milbank Memorial Fund, 1952.

MILBANK MEMORIAL FUND, *Interrelations Between the Social Environment and Psychiatric Disorders*, New York: Milbank Memorial Fund, 1953.

MILBANK MEMORIAL FUND, *Thirty Years of Research in Human Fertility—Retrospect and Prospect*, New York: Milbank Memorial Fund, 1959.

MILBANK MEMORIAL FUND, *Causes of Mental Disorders: A Review of Epidemiological Knowledge*, New York: Milbank Memorial Fund, 1961.

NEWMAN, George, *Health and Social Evolution*, London: Allen & Unwin, Ltd., 1931.

NEWSHOLME, Arthur, *Story of Modern Preventive Medicine*, New York: The Williams & Wilkins Company, 1929.

OPLER, Marvin K., "Cultural Anthropology and Social Psychiatry," *The American Journal of Psychiatry*, 113 (October, 1956), 302–11.

OPLER, Marvin K., ed., *Culture and Mental Health*, New York: The Macmillan Company, 1959.

PASAMANICK, Benjamin, *Epidemiology of Mental Disorder*, Washington, D.C.: American Association for the Advancement of Science, Publication 60, 1959.

PAUL, Benjamin D., ed., *Health, Culture, and Community*, New York: Russell Sage Foundation, 1955.

PAUL, Benjamin D., "Anthropology and Public Health," *in* Joseph B. Casagrande and Thomas Gladwin, eds., *Some Uses of Anthropology: Theoretical and Applied*, Washington, D.C.: The Anthropological Society of Washington, 1956.

PAUL, Benjamin D., "Medicine's Third Dimension," *Journal of the National Medical Association*, 48 (September, 1956), 323–25.

PAUL, Benjamin D., "Social Science in Public Health," *American Journal of Public Health*, 46 (November, 1956), 1390–96.

PEARSE, I. H. and Lucy H. Crocker, *The Peckham Experiment: A Study in the Living Structure of Society*, London: George Allen & Unwin, Ltd., 1943.

PEQUIGNOT, H., "Scientific and Social Aspects of Modern Medicine," *Impact of Science on Society*, 5 (December, 1954), 203–59.

PITTMAN, David J., ed., *Alcoholism: An Interdisciplinary Approach*, Springfield, Ill.: Charles C Thomas, Publisher, 1959.

PITTMAN, David J. and Charles R. Snyder, *Society, Culture, and Drinking Patterns*, New York: John Wiley & Sons, Inc., 1962.

POLGAR, Steven, "Health and Human Behavior: Areas of Interest Common to the Social and Medical Sciences," *Current Anthropology*, 3 (April, 1962), 159–206.

READER, George C. and Mary E. W. Goss, "The Sociology of Medicine," *in* R. K. Merton *et al.*, eds., *Sociology Today*, New York: Basic Books, Inc., 1959, 229–46.

RIESE, W., *The Conception of Disease: Its History, Its Versions and Its Nature*, New York: Philosophical Library, Inc., 1953.

RIESMAN, David, *Medicine in Modern Society*, Princeton, N.J.: Princeton University Press, 1939.

ROEMER, Milton I., "Relationship of Social Medicine to the Social Sciences," *Journal of the Association of American Medical Colleges*, 23 (September, 1948), 324–29.

ROEMER, Milton I. and James M. Mackintosh, eds., *Henry E. Sigerist on the Sociology of Medicine*, New York: M.D. Publications, Inc., 1960.

RONEY, James G., "Medical Anthropology, A Synthetic Discipline," *The New Physician*, 8 (March, 1959).

RONEY, James G., "Medicine and the Behavioral Sciences," *The New Physician*, 9 (February, 1960), 13–14.

RONEY, James G., "An Anthropologist Looks at Medicine," *The Pennsylvania Medical Journal*, 63 (July, 1960), 1000–04.

ROSE, Arnold M., ed., *Mental Health and Mental Disorder: A Sociological Approach*, New York: W. W. Norton & Company, Inc., 1955.

ROSEN, George, *The History of Miners' Diseases, A Medical and Social Interpretation*, New York: Abelard-Schuman, Inc., Publishers, 1943.

ROSEN, George, "An Eighteenth Century Plan for a National Health Service," *Bulletin of the History of Medicine*, 16 (December, 1944), 429–36.

ROSEN, George, "What is Social Medicine? A Genetic Analysis of the Concept," *Bulletin of the History of Medicine*, 21 (July–August, 1947), 674–733.

ROSEN, George, "Approaches to a Concept of Social Medicine: A Historical Survey," *in Backgrounds of Social Medicine*, New York: Milbank Memorial Fund, 1949, 9–23.

ROSEN, George, "The Idea of Social Medicine in America," *Canadian Medical Association Journal*, 61 (September, 1949), 316–23.

ROSEN, George, "Political Order and Human Health in Jeffersonian Thought," *Bulletin of the History of Medicine*, 26 (January–February, 1952), 32–44.

ROSEN, George, "Cameralism and Concept of Medical Police," *Bulletin of the History of Medicine*, 27 (January–February, 1953), 21–42.

ROSEN, George, "Medical Care and Social Policy in Seventeenth Century England," *Bulletin of the New York Academy of Medicine*, 29 (April, 1953), 420–37.

ROSEN, George, "Economic and Social Policy in the Development of Public Health," *Journal of Historical Medicine*, 8 (October, 1953), 407–30.

ROSEN, George, "Problems in the Application of Statistical Analysis to Questions of Health, 1700–1880," *Bulletin of the History of Medicine*, 29 (January–February, 1955), 27–45.

ROSEN, George, "Hospitals, Medical Care and Social Policy in the French Revolution," *Bulletin of the History of Medicine*, 30 (January–February, 1956), 124–49.

ROSEN, George, "The Fate of the Concept of Medical Police," *Centaurus*, 5 (1957), 97–113.

ROSEN, George, *A History of Public Health,* New York: M.D. Publications, Inc., 1958.

ROSEN, George, "Social Stress and Mental Disease from the Eighteenth Century to the Present: Some Origins of Social Psychiatry," *Milbank Memorial Fund Quarterly,* 37 (January, 1959), 5–32.

ROSEN, George, "Mercantilism and Health Policy in Eighteenth Century French Thought," *Medical History,* 3 (October, 1959), 259–77.

ROSEN, George and Edward Wellin, "A Bookshelf on the Social Sciences and Public Health," *American Journal of Public Health,* 49 (April, 1959), 441–55.

RUBIN, Vera, ed., "Culture, Society, and Health," *Annals of the New York Academy of Sciences,* 84 (December, 1960), 783–1060.

RUMSEY, Henry W., *Essays on State Medicine,* London: John Churchill, 1856.

RYLE, John A., "Social Medicine: Its Meaning and Its Scope," *British Medical Journal,* 2 (November 20, 1943), 633–36.

SAND, René, *The Advance to Social Medicine,* London: Staples Press, Ltd., 1952.

SANUA, Victor D., "Sociocultural Factors in Families of Schizophrenics: A Review of the Literature," *Psychiatry,* 24 (August, 1961), 246–65.

SARASON, Seymour B. and Thomas Gladwin, "Psychological and Cultural Problems in Mental Subnormality: A Review of Research," *Genetic Psychology Monographs,* 57 (1958), 3–290.

SARBIN, Theodore R., *Studies in Behavior Pathology,* New York: Holt, Rinehart & Winston, Inc., 1961.

SCHERMERHORN, R. A., "Social Psychiatry," *The Antioch Review,* 13 (Spring, 1953), 67–85. Reprinted *in* A. M. Rose, ed., *Mental Health and Mental Disorder,* New York: W. W. Norton & Company, Inc., 1955.

SCHWARTZ, Charlotte G., *Rehabilitation of Mental Hospital Patients,* Washington, D.C.: Government Printing Office, Public Health Monograph 17, 1953.

SHOCK, Nathan W., *A Classified Bibliography of Gerontology and Geriatrics,* Stanford, Calif.: Stanford University Press, 1951.

SHRYOCK, Richard H., *American Medical Research: Past and Present,* New York: The Commonwealth Fund, 1947.

SHRYOCK, Richard H., *The Development of Modern Medicine: An Interpretation of the Social and Scientific Factors Involved,* New York: Alfred A. Knopf, Inc., 1947.

SHRYOCK, Richard H., "Medicine and Social Science," *Johns Hopkins Magazine,* 2 (March, 1951), 14–15, 25–26.

SHRYOCK, Richard H., "The Interplay of Social and Internal Factors in the History of Modern Medicine," *Scientific Monthly,* 76 (1953), 221–30.

SHRYOCK, Richard H., *Medicine and Society in America, 1660–1860,* New York: New York University Press, 1960.

SIGERIST, Henry E., "Historical Background of Industrial and Occupational Diseases," *Bulletin of the New York Academy of Medicine,* 12 (November, 1936), 597–609.

SIGERIST, Henry E., *Civilization and Disease,* New York: Cornell University Press, 1943.

SIGERIST, Henry E., *A History of Medicine, Vol. I: Primitive and Archaic Medicine,* New York: Oxford University Press, 1951.

SIGERIST, Henry E., *A History of Medicine, Vol. II: Early Greek, Hindu and Persian Medicine,* New York: Oxford University Press, 1961.

SIMMONS, Leo W. and Harold G. Wolff, *Social Science and Medicine,* New York: Russell Sage Foundation, 1954.

SIMMONS, Ozzie G., *Social Status and Public Health,* New York: Social Science Research Council, Pamphlet 13, 1958.

SOCIAL PROBLEMS, "Medical Sociology," 4 (July, 1956), entire issue.

STEARNS, A. Warren, "Integration of Medical Science and Sociology," *Journal of Nervous and Mental Disease*, 103 (June, 1946), 612–25.

SUCHMAN, E. A. and A. L. Scherzer, *Current Research in Childhood Accidents*, New York: Association for the Aid of Crippled Children, 1960.

SYDENSTRICKER, Edgar, *Health and Environment*, New York: McGraw-Hill Book Company, Inc., 1933.

TERRIS, Milton, "Social Medicine as an Academic Discipline," *Journal of Medical Education*, 33 (August, 1958), 565–73.

TIBBITS, Clark, ed., *Handbook of Social Gerontology: Societal Aspects of Aging*, Chicago: University of Chicago Press, 1960.

WALTER REED ARMY INSTITUTE OF RESEARCH, *Symposium on Preventive and Social Psychiatry*, Washington, D.C.: Government Printing Office, 1957.

WEBB, Sidney and Beatrice Webb, *The State and the Doctor*, London: Longmans, Green & Company, Ltd., 1910.

WHEELER, W., ed., *Social Change and Mental Health*, Parkville, Mo.: Park College Press, 1960.

WINSLOW, Charles Edward A., *The Evolution and Significance of the Modern Public Health Campaign*, New Haven, Conn.: Yale University Press, 1923.

WINSLOW, Charles Edward A., *The Conquest of Epidemic Disease*, Princeton, N.J.: Princeton University Press, 1943.

WINSLOW, Charles Edward A., *Man and Epidemics*, Princeton, N.J.: Princeton University Press, 1952.

WOOTTON, B., *Social Science and Social Pathology*, London: George Allen & Unwin, Ltd., 1959.

WORLD HEALTH ORGANIZATION, *Health Education, A Selected Bibliography*, Paris: UNESCO, 1956.

YOUNG, D., "Sociology and the Practicing Professions," *American Sociological Review*, 20 (1955), 641–48.

ZINSSER, Hans, *Rats, Lice, and History*, New York: Bantam Books, Inc., 1960.

II. The Sociology of Illness

ABDELLAH, F. G. and E. Levine, "Developing a Measure of Patient and Personnel Satisfaction with Nursing Care," *Nursing Research*, 5 (February, 1957).

ABRAHAMS, J. and E. Varon, *Maternal Dependency and Schizophrenia*, New York: International Universities Press, 1953.

ABRAMSON, J. H., B. Gampel, N. Scotch, and C. Slome, "Diet and Serum Protein Levels of Urban Zulu Adults," *British Journal of Preventive and Social Medicine*, 14 (October, 1960), 190–95.

ACKERMAN, Nathan W., *Psychodynamics of Family Life: Diagnosis and Treatment of Family Relationships*, New York: Basic Books, Inc., 1958.

ACKERMAN, Nathan W., "The Schizophrenic Patient and His Family Relationships," *in* M. Greenblatt, D. J. Levinson, and G. L. Klerman, eds., *Mental Patients in Transition*, Springfield, Ill.: Charles C Thomas, Publisher, 1961, 273–84.

ADAMS, Richard N., "Nutrition, Anthropology, and the Study of Man," *Nutrition Reviews*, 17 (April, 1959), 97–99.

ADAMS, W. A., "The Negro Patient in Psychiatric Treatment," *American Journal of Orthopsychiatry*, 20 (1950), 305–10.

ADLER, Leta McKinney, "The Relationship of Marital Status to Incidence and Recovery from Mental Disease," *Social Forces*, 32 (December, 1953).

ADLER, Leta McKinney, "Patients of a State Mental Hospital: The Outcome of Their Hospitalization," *in* A. M. Rose, ed., *Mental Health and Mental Disorders*, New York: W. W. Norton & Company, Inc., 1955, 501–23.

ADLER, Leta McKinney, J. W. Coddington, and Donald D. Stewart, *Mental Illness in Washington County, Arkansas: Incidence, Recovery, and Posthospital Adjustment*, Fayetteville, Ark.: University of Arkansas, Research Series 23, July, 1952.

AITKEN-SWAN and R. Paterson, "The Cancer Patient: Delay in Seeking Advice," *British Medical Journal*, 1 (March 12, 1955), 623ff.

ALCOHOL, SCIENCE AND SOCIETY, New Haven, Conn.: Quarterly Journal of Studies on Alcohol, 1945.

ALEXANDER, Franz, *Psychosomatic Medicine*, New York: W. W. Norton & Company, Inc., 1950.

ALLINSMITH, W. and G. W. Goethals, "Cultural Factors in Mental Health: An Anthropological Perspective," *Review of Educational Research*, 26 (1956), 429–50.

ALMY, T. P. *et al.*, "Constipation and Diarrhea as Reactions to Life Stress," *Proceedings of the Association for Research in Nervous and Mental Disease*, 29 (1950), 724–31.

ANDERSON, Odin W., "Infant Mortality and Social and Cultural Factors: Historical Trends and Current Patterns," *in* E. Gartly Jaco, ed., *Patients, Physicians and Illness*, New York: The Free Press of Glencoe, Inc., 1958, 10–24.

ANDERSON, Odin W. and G. Gordon, "Social Research in Respiratory Disease," *Bulletin of the National Tuberculosis Association*, 47 (February, 1961), 11–12.

ANDERSON, Odin W. and Monroe Lerner, *Measuring Health Levels in the United States*, New York: Health Information Foundation, Research Series 11, 1960.

ANSLINGER, Harry J., "Drug Addicts," *Journal of the American Medical Association*, 144 (1950), 333.

ARBOUS, A. G., "Accident Statistics and the Concept of Accident Proneness: Part I, A Critical Evaluation," *Biometrics*, 7 (1951), 340–90.

ARMSTRONG, John D., "The Search for the Alcoholic Personality," *The Annals of the American Academy of Political and Social Science*, 315 (January, 1958), 40–47.

ARNOLD, Arthur, "The Implications of Two-Person and Three-Person Relationships for Family Psychotherapy," *Journal of Health and Human Behavior*, 3 (Summer, 1962), 94–96.

AULD, Frank, Jr. and J. K. Myers, "Contributions to a Theory for Selecting Psychotherapy Patients," *Journal of Clinical Psychology*, 10 (January, 1954), 56–60.

AUSUBEL, David P., *Drug Addiction: Physiological, Psychological and Sociological Aspects*, New York: Random House, 1958.

BACK, Kurt W. and J. Mayone Stycos, *The Survey under Unusual Conditions: The Jamaica Human Fertility Investigation*, New York: Society for Applied Anthropology, Monograph 1, 1959.

BACON, Selden D., "Inebriety, Social Integration, and Marriage," *Memoirs of the Section on Alcohol Studies*, No. 2, New Haven, Conn.: Hillhouse Press, 1945.

BACON, Selden D., "Sociology and the Problems of Alcohol," *Memoirs of the Section on Alcohol Studies*, No. 1, New Haven, Conn.: Hillhouse Press, 1946.

BACON, Selden D., "Alcoholism: Nature of the Problem," *Federal Probation*, 11 (1947), 3–7.

BACON, Selden D., "Studies of Drinking in Jewish Culture: I. Introduction," *Quarterly Journal of Studies on Alcohol*, 12 (1951), 444–50.

BACON, Selden D., "Social Settings Conducive to Alcoholism," *Journal of the American Medical Association*, 164 (May 11, 1957), 177–81.

BACON, Selden D., "Alcoholics Do Not Drink," *The Annals of the American Academy of Political and Social Science*, 315 (January, 1958), 55–64.

BACON, Selden D., "Alcohol and Complex Society," *in* D. J. Pittman and C. R. Snyder, eds., *Society, Culture, and Drinking Patterns,* New York: John Wiley & Sons, Inc., 1962, 78–94.

BAIRD, Dugald, "Social and Economic Factors Affecting the Mother and Child," *American Journal of Public Health,* 42 (May, 1952), 516–20.

BAKER, A. A. *et al.,* "Social Status After Five Years in a Mental Hospital," *British Journal of Medical Psychology,* 30 (1957), 113–18.

BALES, Robert Freed, "Types of Social Structure as Factors in 'Cures' for Alcohol Addiction," *Applied Anthropology,* 1 (1942), 1–13.

BALES, Robert Freed, "Social Therapy for a Social Disorder—Compulsive Drinking," *Journal of Social Issues,* 1 (December, 1945), 1–9.

BALES, Robert Freed, "Cultural Differences in Rates of Alcoholism," *Quarterly Journal of Studies on Alcohol,* 6 (1946), 480–99. Reprinted *in* D. Apple, ed., *Sociological Studies of Health and Sickness,* New York: McGraw-Hill Book Company, Inc., 1960.

BALES, Robert Freed, "The Therapeutic Role of Alcoholics Anonymous as Seen by a Sociologist," *Quarterly Journal of Studies on Alcohol,* 5 (1944), 267–78. Reprinted *in* D. J. Pittman and C. R. Snyder, eds., *Society, Culture, and Drinking Patterns,* New York: John Wiley & Sons, Inc., 1962.

BALES, Robert Freed, "Attitudes Toward Drinking in the Irish Culture," *in* D. J. Pittman and C. R. Snyder, eds., *Society, Culture, and Drinking Patterns,* New York: John Wiley & Sons, Inc., 1962, 157–87.

BARD, Morton, "Perspectives in Medicopsychological Research with Regard to Grave Physical Illness," *in* Vera Rubin, ed., "Culture, Society, and Health," *Annals of the New York Academy of Sciences,* 84 (December, 1960), 1010–13.

BARKER, R. G., "The Social Psychology of Physical Disability," *Journal of Social Issues,* 4 (1958), 28–38.

BARKER, R. G. *et al., Adjustment to Physical Handicap and Illness: A Survey of the Social Psychology of Physique and Disability,* New York: Social Science Research Council, Bulletin 55, 1953.

BARNETT, Milton L., "Alcoholism in the Cantonese of New York City: An Anthropological Study," *in* Oskar Diethelm, ed., *Etiology of Chronic Alcoholism,* Springfield, Ill.: Charles C Thomas, Publisher, 1955.

BARRABEE, Paul and Otto Von Mering, "Ethnic Variations in Mental Stress in Families with Psychotic Children," *Social Problems,* 1 (October, 1953), 48–53. Reprinted *in* A. M. Rose, ed., *Mental Health and Mental Disorders,* New York: W. W. Norton & Company, Inc., 1955.

BARRON, Milton J., "The Dynamics of Occupational Roles and Health in Old Age," *in* John E. Anderson, ed., *Psychological Aspects of Aging,* Washington, D.C.: American Psychological Association, 1956.

BATESON, Gregory, "Minimal Requirements for a Theory of Schizophrenia," *A.M.A. Archives of General Psychiatry,* 2 (May, 1960), 477–91.

BATESON, Gregory, D. D. Jackson, Jay Haley, and John Weakland, "Toward a Theory of Schizophrenia," *Behavioral Science,* 1 (October, 1956), 251–64.

BEADENKOPF, William G. *et al.,* "An Epidemiological Approach to Traffic Accidents," *Public Health Reports,* 71 (January, 1956), 15–24.

BECK, Aaron T. and Marvin S. Hurvich, "Psychological Correlates of Depression," *Psychosomatic Medicine,* 21 (1959). Reprinted *in* T. R. Sarbin, ed., *Studies in Behavior Pathology,* New York: Holt, Rinehart & Winston, Inc., 1961.

BECK, S. J., "Families of Schizophrenic and of Well Children: Methods, Concepts and Some Results," *American Journal of Orthopsychiatry,* 30 (April, 1960), 247–75.

BECKER, Ernest, "Socialization, Command of Performance, and Mental Illness," *American Journal of Sociology,* 67 (March, 1962), 494–501.

BECKER, Howard S., "Becoming a Marihuana User," *American Journal of Sociology*, 59 (November, 1953), 235–42. Reprinted *in* A. M. Rose, ed., *Mental Health and Mental Disorders*, New York: W. W. Norton & Company, Inc., 1955.

BECKER, Howard S., "Marihuana Use and Social Control," *Social Problems*, (July, 1955), 35–44.

BEHRENS, M. L. and William Goldfarb, "A Study of Patterns of Interaction of Families of Schizophrenic Children in Residential Treatment," *American Journal of Orthopsychiatry*, 28 (April, 1958), 300–12.

BELKNAP, Ivan and H. J. Friedsam, "Age and Sex Categories as Sociological Variables in the Mental Disorders of Later Maturity," *American Sociological Review*, 14 (1950), 367–76.

BELLAK, L. and B. J. Black, "The Rehabilitation of Psychotics in the Community," *American Journal of Orthopsychiatry*, 30 (1960), 346–55.

BELLIN, Seymour and Robert H. Hardt, "Mental Status and Mental Disorders Among the Aged," *American Sociological Review*, 23 (April, 1958), 155–62.

BENEDICT, Paul K., "Socio-Cultural Factors in Schizophrenia," *in* L. Bellak, ed., *Schizophrenia*, New York: Logas Press, 1958, 694–727.

BENEDICT, Paul K. and Irving Jacks, "Mental Illness in Primitive Societies," *Psychiatry*, 17 (1954), 377–90.

BERKSON, D. M., J. Stamler, H. A. Lindberg, W. Miller, H. Mathies, H. Lasky, and Y. Hall, "Socioeconomic Correlates of Atherosclerotic and Hypertensive Heart Diseases," *in* Vera Rubin, ed., "Culture, Society, and Health," *Annals of the New York Academy of Sciences*, 84 (December, 1960), 835–50.

BERNE, E., "The Cultural Problem, Psychopathology in Tahiti," *American Journal of Psychiatry*, 116 (1960), 1076–81.

BERREMAN, Gerald D., "Drinking Patterns of the Aleuts," *Quarterly Journal of Studies on Alcohol*, 17 (September, 1956), 503–15.

BLEULER, Manfred, "A Comparative Study of the Constitutions of Swiss and American Alcoholic Patients," *in* O. Diethelm, ed., *Etiology of Chronic Alcoholism*, Springfield, Ill.: Charles C Thomas, Publisher, 1955, 167–78.

BOCKOVEN, J. S. *et al.*, "Social Adjustment of the Patients in the Community 3 Years After Commitment to the Boston Psychiatric Hospital," *Mental Hygiene*, 40 (1956), 353–74.

BOEK, W. E., E. D. Lawson, A. Yankauer and M. B. Sussman, *Social Class, Maternal Health and Child Care*, Albany: New York State Department of Health, 1957.

BOEK, Walter E., Marvin B. Sussman, and Alfred Yankauer, "Social Class and Child Care Practices," *Marriage and Family Living*, 20 (November, 1958), 326–33.

BONNER, H., "Sociological Aspects of Paranoia," *American Journal of Sociology*, 56 (1950), 255–62.

BOTHWELL, P. W., "The Epidemiology of Cigarette Smoking in Rural School Children," *Medical Officer* (London), 102 (1959), 125–32.

BOWEN, M., R. H. Dysinger, and B. Basamania, "The Role of the Father in Families with a Schizophrenic Patient," *American Journal of Psychiatry*, 115 (May, 1959), 1017–20.

BOWLBY, John, *Maternal Care and Mental Health*, Geneva, Switzerland: World Health Organization, Monograph 2, 1951.

BRITTEN, R. H., "Accidents in the Urban Home as Recorded in the National Health Survey," *Public Health Reports*, 55 (1940), 2067–86.

BRITTEN, R. H. and I. Altman, "Illness and Accidents among Persons Living under Different Housing Conditions," *Public Health Reports*, 56 (1941), 609–40.

BRITTON, Joseph H., "Assessment of Services for the Aged in Rural Communities," *Journal of Gerontology*, 13 (July, 1958), Supplement 2, 67–69.

BROOKS, George W., William Deane, and Donald Eldred, "Through the Eyes of the Schizophrenic," *Journal of Rehabilitation*, (November–December, 1959).

BROWN, George W., "Experiences of Discharged Chronic Schizophrenic Patients in Various Types of Living Groups," *Milbank Memorial Fund Quarterly*, 37 (April, 1959), 105–31.

BROWN, G. W., G. M. Carstairs, and Gillian Topping, "Post-Hospital Adjustment of Chronic Mental Patients," *Lancet* (September 27, 1958), 685–89.

BROWN, G. W., E. M. Monck, G. M. Carstairs, and J. K. Wing, "Influence of Family Life on the Course of Schizophrenic Illness," *British Journal of Preventive and Social Medicine*, 16 (April, 1962), 55–68.

BRUNN, Kettil, ed., *Drinking Behavior in Small Groups: An Experimental Study*, (tr. by Fred A. Fewster), Stockholm: Almqvist and Wiksell, 1959.

BRUNN, Kettil, "The Significance of Roles and Norms in the Small Group for Individual Behavioral Changes While Drinking," *Quarterly Journal of Studies on Alcohol*, 20 (1959), 53–64. Reprinted *in* D. J. Pittman and C. R. Snyder, eds., *Society, Culture, and Drinking Patterns*, New York: John Wiley & Sons, Inc., 1962.

BUNZEL, Ruth, "The Role of Alcoholism in Two Central American Cultures," *Psychiatry*, 3 (August, 1940), 361–87.

BURGESS, Ernest W., "Social Factors in the Etiology and Prevention of Mental Disorders," *Social Problems*, 1 (October, 1953), 53.

BURGESS, Ernest W., "Mental Health in Modern Society," *in* A. M. Rose, ed., *Mental Health and Mental Disorder*, New York: W. W. Norton & Company, Inc., 1955, 3–17.

BURGESS, Ernest W., ed., *Aging in Western Societies*, Chicago: University of Chicago Press, 1960.

BUSTAMANTE, J. A., "Cultural Factors in Some Schizophrenic Patterns," *International Journal of Social Psychiatry*, 5 (Summer, 1959), 50–55.

CAIN, L. D. Jr., "The Sociology of Aging: A Trend Report and Bibliography," *Current Sociology*, 8 (1959), 55–133.

CAMERON, Norman, "The Paranoid Pseudo-Community," *American Journal of Sociology*, 49 (July, 1943), 32–38. Reprinted *in* A. M. Rose, ed., *Mental Health and Mental Disorders*, New York: W. W. Norton & Company, Inc., 1955.

CAMERON, Norman, "Role Concepts in Behavior Pathology," *American Journal of Sociology*, 55 (March, 1950), 464–67.

CANNON, Walter B., *The Wisdom of the Body*, New York: W. W. Norton & Company, Inc., 1932.

CAROTHERS, J. C., *The African Mind in Health and Disease: A Study of Ethnopsychiatry*, Geneva, Switzerland: World Health Organization, Monograph Series 17, 1953.

CARSTAIRS, G. M., "Social Factors in the Outcome of Mental Illness," *Proceedings of the Royal Society of Medicine*, 52 (April, 1959), 279.

CARSTAIRS, G. M. and G. W. Brown, "A Census of Psychiatric Cases in Two Contrasting Communities," *The Journal of Mental Science*, 104 (January, 1956), 72–81.

CARTWRIGHT, Ann, Frederick M. Martin, and J. G. Thomson, "Distribution and Development of Smoking Habits," *Lancet* (October 31, 1959), 725–27.

CASSEL, John, Ralph Patrick, and David Jenkins, "Epidemiological Analysis of the Health Implications of Culture Change: A Conceptual Model," *in* Vera Rubin, ed., "Culture, Society, and Health," *Annals of the New York Academy of Sciences*, 84 (December, 1960), 938–49.

CASSEL, John and Herman A. Tyroler, "Epidemiological Studies of Culture Change," *The Archives of Environmental Health*, 3 (July, 1961), 25–33.

CAUDILL, William, *Effects of Social and Cultural Systems in Reactions to Stress*, New York: Social Science Research Council, Pamphlet 14, 1958.

CAVAN, R. S. *et al.*, *Personal Adjustment in Old Age,* Chicago: Science Research Association, 1949.

CHAPMAN, Loring F. *et al.*, "Human Ecology, Disease, and Schizophrenia," *American Journal of Psychiatry,* 117 (September, 1960), 193–204.

CHASSEL, I., "Family Constellation in the Etiology of Essential Alcoholism," *Psychiatry,* 1 (1938), 473–503.

CHEIN, Isidor and Eva Rosenfeld, "Juvenile Narcotics Use," *Law and Contemporary Problems,* 22 (Winter, 1957).

CHEN, William Y., L. B. Crittenden, Nathan Mantel, and W. R. Cameron, "Site Distribution of Cancer Deaths in Husband-Wife and Sibling Pairs," *Journal of the National Cancer Institute,* 27 (1961), 875–92.

CHESS, S., K. B. Clark and A. Thomas, "The Importance of Cultural Evaluation in Psychiatric Diagnosis and Treatment," *Psychiatry,* 27 (1953), 102–14.

CIOCCO, Anthony, "Chronic Sickness in Relation to Survivorship Twenty Years Later," *Human Biology,* 18 (1946), 33–48.

CLARDY, E. R., "A Study of the Development and Course of Schizophrenia in Children," *Psychiatric Quarterly,* 25 (1951), 81–90.

CLARK, G. E., C. Y. Glock, and R. Vought, "Studies in Hypertension," *Journal of Chronic Diseases,* 4 (September, 1956), 4 (November, 1956), 5 (February, 1957).

CLARK, Robert E., "Psychoses, Income, and Occupational Prestige," *American Journal of Sociology,* 54 (1949), 433–40.

CLAUSEN, John A., "Social Patterns, Personality, and Adolescent Drug Use," *in* A. H. Leighton, J. A. Clausen, and R. N. Wilson, eds., *Explorations in Social Psychiatry,* New York: Basic Books, Inc., 1957, 230–77.

CLAUSEN, John A, "The Ecology of Mental Disorders," *in* Walter Reed Army Institute of Research, *Symposium on Preventive and Social Psychiatry,* Washington, D.C.: Government Printing Office, 1957, 97–110.

CLAUSEN, John A., "The Sociology of Mental Illness," *in* R. K. Merton *et al.*, eds., *Sociology Today,* New York: Basic Books, Inc., 1959, 485–508.

CLAUSEN, John A., "Mental Disorders," *in* R. K. Merton and R. A. Nisbet, *Contemporary Social Problems,* New York: Harcourt, Brace & World, Inc., 1961, 127–80.

CLAUSEN, John A., "Drug Addiction," *in* R. K. Merton and R. A. Nisbet, *Contemporary Social Problems,* New York: Harcourt, Brace & World, Inc., 1961, 181–221.

CLAUSEN, John A. and Melvin L. Kohn, "The Ecological Approach in Social Psychiatry," *American Journal of Sociology,* 60 (1954), 140–49.

CLAUSEN, John A. and Melvin L. Kohn, "Parental Authority Behavior and Schizophrenia," *The American Journal of Orthopsychiatry,* 26 (April, 1956), 297–313.

CLAUSEN, John A. and Melvin L. Kohn, "Relation of Schizophrenia to the Social Structure of a Small City," *in* B. Pasamanick, ed., *Epidemiology of Mental Disorder,* Washington: American Association for the Advancement of Science, 1959, 69–94.

CLAUSEN, John A. and Marian Radke Yarrow, eds., "The Impact of Mental Illness on the Family," *Journal of Social Issues,* 11 (1955), entire issue.

CLEMMESEN, J. and A. Nielson, "Social Distribution of Cancer in Copenhagen, 1943–1947," *British Journal of Cancer,* 5 (1951), 159–71.

CLEVELAND, E. J. and W. D. Longaker, "Neurotic Patterns in the Family," *in* A. H. Leighton, J. A. Clausen, and R. N. Wilson, eds., *Explorations in Social Psychiatry,* New York: Basic Books, Inc., 1957, 167–200.

CLINARD, Marshall B., "The Public Drinking House and Society," *in* D. J. Pittman and C. R. Snyder, eds., *Society, Culture, and Drinking Patterns,* New York: John Wiley & Sons, Inc., 1962, 270–92.

COBB, B. *et al.*, "Patient-Responsible Delay of Treatment in Cancer: Social Psychological Study," *Cancer,* 7 (September, 1954), 920–26.

COBB, Sidney, Stanley H. King, and Edith Chen, "Differences Between Respondents and Non-respondents in a Morbidity Survey Involving Clinical Examination," *Journal of Chronic Diseases,* 6 (August, 1957), 95–108.

COBB, Sidney, Martha Miller, and Martha Wieland, "On the Relationship Between Divorce and Rheumatoid Arthritis," *Arthritis and Rheumatism,* 2 (October, 1959), 414–18.

COHART, Edward M., "Socioeconomic Distribution of Stomach Cancer in New Haven," *Cancer,* 7 (May, 1954), 455–61.

COHART, Edward M., "Socioeconomic Distribution of Cancer of the Female Sex Organs in New Haven," *Cancer,* 8 (January–February, 1955), 34–41.

COHART, Edward M., "Socioeconomic Distribution of Cancer of the Lung in New Haven," *Cancer,* 8 (November–December, 1955), 1126–29.

COHART, Edward M. and Charlotte Muller, "Socioeconomic Distribution of Cancer of the Gastrointestinal Tract in New Haven," *Cancer,* 8 (March–April, 1955), 379–88.

COHEN, S. I. and A. J. Silverman, "Psycho-physiological Investigations of Vascular Response Variability," *Journal of Psychosomatic Research,* 3 (1959), 185–210.

COHEN, Yehudi A., *Social Structure and Personality,* New York: Holt, Rinehart & Winston, Inc., 1961.

COMMISSION ON CHRONIC ILLNESS, *Chronic Illness in the United States,* Cambridge: Harvard University Press, Vols. 1–4 (1956–1959).

CONGER, John J., "Perception, Learning, and Emotion: The Role of Alcohol," *The Annals of the American Academy of Political and Social Science,* 315 (January, 1958), 31–39.

CONGER, John J. *et al.,* "Psychological and Psychophysiological Factors in Motor Vehicle Accidents," *Journal of the American Medical Association,* 169 (April, 1959), 1581–87.

CONNOR, Ralph G., "The Self-Concepts of Alcoholics," *in* D. J. Pittman and C. R. Snyder, eds., *Society, Culture, and Drinking Patterns,* New York: John Wiley & Sons, Inc., 1962, 455–67.

CROCETTI, G. M., "Suicide and Public Health: An Attempt at Reconceptualization," *American Journal of Public Health,* 49 (1959), 881–87.

CROOG, Sydney H., "Ethnic Origins, Educational Level, and Response to a Health Questionnaire," *Human Organization,* 20 (Summer, 1961), 65–69.

CUMMING, Elaine, Lois R. Dean, David S. Newell, and Isabel McCaffrey, "Disengagement—A Tentative Theory of Aging," *Sociometry,* 23 (March, 1960), 23–35.

CUMMING, Elaine and William E. Henry, *Growing Old: The Process of Disengagement,* New York: Basic Books, Inc., 1961.

CUMMING, John M., "The Family and Mental Disorder: An Incomplete Essay," *Milbank Memorial Fund Quarterly,* 39 (April, 1961), 185–228.

DAI, Bingham, *Opium Addiction in Chicago,* Shanghai: The Commercial Press, 1937.

DAI, Bingham, "A Socio-Psychiatric Approach to Personality Organizaton," *American Sociological Review,* 17 (February, 1952), 44–49. Reprinted *in* A. M. Rose, ed., *Mental Health and Mental Disorders,* New York: W. W. Norton & Company, Inc., 1955.

DAI, Bingham, "Obsessive-Compulsive Disorders in Chinese Culture," *Social Problems,* 4 (April, 1957). Reprinted *in* M. K. Opler, ed., *Culture and Mental Health,* New York: The Macmillan Company, 1959.

DAVIS, Fred, "Definitions of Time and Recovery in Paralytic Polio Convalescence," *American Journal of Sociology,* 61 (May, 1956), 582–88.

DAVIS, James A., Howard E. Freeman, and Ozzie G. Simmons, "Rehospitalization and Performance Level among Former Mental Patients," *Social Problems,* 5 (July, 1957), 37–44.

DAVIS, Kingsley, "Mental Hygiene and the Class Structure," *Psychiatry*, 1 (February, 1938), 55–65. Reprinted *in* A. M. Rose, ed., *Mental Health and Mental Disorders*, New York: W. W. Norton & Company, Inc., 1955.

DAWBER, Thomas R., F. Meadors Gilcin, and Felix E. Moore, "Epidemiological Approaches to Heart Disease: the Framingham Study," *American Journal of Public Health*, 41 (March, 1951), 279–86.

DAWBER, T. R., F. E. Moore, and G. V. Mann, "Coronary Heart Disease in the Framingham Study in Measuring Risk of Coronary Heart Disease in Adult Population Groups: A Symposium," *American Journal of Public Health*, 47 (April Supp., 1957).

DAWBER, Thomas R. *et al.*, "Some Factors Associated with the Development of Coronary Heart Disease," *American Journal of Public Health*, 49 (October, 1959), 1349–56.

DAY, M. and I. Rosen, "The Group Behavior of Mothers of Schizophrenics," *Journal of Nervous and Mental Disorders*, 119 (1954), 336.

DEMERATH, N. J., "Schizophrenia among Primitives," *American Journal of Psychiatry*, 98 (March, 1942), 703–7. Reprinted *in* A. M. Rose, ed., *Mental Health and Mental Disorders*, New York: W. W. Norton & Company, Inc., 1955.

DEMERATH, Nicholas J. and Anthony F. C. Wallace, "Human Adaptation to Disaster," *Human Organization*, 16 (1957), 1–2.

DEUSCHLE, Kurt W., "Tuberculosis Among the Navajo," *The American Review of Respiratory Diseases*, 80 (August, 1959), 200–06.

DEVEREUX, G., *A Study of Abortion in Primitive Societies*, New York: The Julian Press, 1955.

DE VOS, George and Horace Miner, "Oasis and Casbah—A Study in Acculturative Stress," *in* M. K. Opler, ed., *Culture and Mental Health*, New York: The Macmillan Company, 1959, 333–50.

DEXTER, Louis Anthony, "Towards a Sociology of the Mentally Defective," *American Journal of Mental Deficiency*, 61 (July, 1956), 10–16.

DIETHELM, Oskar, ed., *Etiology of Chronic Alcoholism*, Springfield, Ill.: Charles C Thomas, Publisher, 1955.

DINITZ, S., M. Lefton, S. Angrist, and B. Pasamanick, "Psychiatric and Social Attributes as Predictors of Case Outcome in Mental Hospitalization," *Social Problems*, 8 (Spring, 1961), 322–28.

DINKEL, Robert M., "Occupation and Fertility in the United States," *American Sociological Review*, 17 (April, 1952), 178–83.

DOBSON, H. L. et al., "Socioeconomic Status and Diabetes Mellitus," *Journal of Chronic Diseases*, 7 (May, 1958), 413–21.

DOLL, Richard and A. B. Hill, "Lung Cancer and Other Causes of Death in Relation to Smoking: Second Report on Mortality of British Doctors," *British Medical Journal*, 2 (1956), 1071ff.

DONAHUE, W. and C. Tibbits, *The New Frontiers of Aging*, Ann Arbor: University of Michigan Press, 1957.

DORN, Harold F., "The Incidence and Future Expectancy of Mental Disease," *Public Health Reports*, 53 (1938).

DORN, Harold F. and S. J. Cutler, *Morbidity From Cancer in the United States*, Washington, D.C.: Government Printing Office, Public Health Monograph, 46, 1959.

DOVENMUEHLE, Robert H., "Health and Aging," *Journal of Health and Human Behavior*, 1 (Winter, 1960), 273–78.

DOWNES, Jean, "Social and Environmental Factors in Illness," *Milbank Memorial Fund Quarterly*, 26 (October, 1948), 366–81.

DOWNES, J. and K. Simon, "Characteristics of Psychoneurotic Patients and Their Families as Revealed in a General Morbidity Study," *Milbank Memorial Fund Quarterly*, 32 (1954), 42–64.

DOWNING, Joseph, Isabel McCaffrey, and Eugene Rogot, "An Investigation of Seasonal Variations of Mental Hospitalization for Old Age Psychoses," *in* B. Pasamanick, ed., *Epidemiology of Mental Disorder*, Washington, D.C.: American Association for the Advancement of Science, 1959, 273–90.

DUHL, L. J., "Alcoholism: The Public Health Approach. A New Look from the Viewpoint of Human Ecology," *Quarterly Journal of Studies on Alcohol*, 20 (1959), 112–25.

DUNHAM, H. W., "Some Persistent Problems in the Epidemiology of Mental Disorders," *American Journal of Psychiatry*, 109 (1953), 567–75.

DUNHAM, H. Warren, *Sociological Theory and Mental Disorder*, Detroit: Wayne State University Press, 1959.

DUNHAM, H. Warren, "Social Structures and Mental Disorders: Competing Hypotheses of Explanation," *Milbank Memorial Fund Quarterly*, 39 (April, 1961), 259–311.

DUNN, John E., Jr., "Public Health Research in Chronic Disease," *Public Health Reports*, 71 (January, 1956), 481–87.

DYK, Ruth B. and Arthur M. Sutherland, "Adaptation of the Spouse and Other Members to the Colostomy Patient," *Cancer*, 8 (January–February, 1956), 123–38.

EARLE, Anne and B. V. Earle, "Mental Illness in British Guiana," *International Journal of Social Psychiatry*, 1 (1956), 53.

EATON, Joseph W., "The Assessment of Mental Health," *American Journal of Psychiatry*, 108 (1951), 81–90.

EATON, Joseph W. and Robert J. Weil, "The Mental Health of the Hutterites," *Scientific American*, 189 (December, 1953), 31–37. Reprinted *in* A. M. Rose, ed., *Mental Health and Mental Disorders*, New York: W. W. Norton & Company, Inc., 1955.

EHRLICH, Shelley S., "The Family Structure of Hospitalized Adolescents," *Journal of Health and Human Behavior*, 3 (Summer, 1962), 121–24.

EITINGER, Leo, "The Incidence of Mental Disease Among Refugees in Norway," *Journal of Mental Science*, 105 (1959), 326–38.

ELIOT, Thomas D., "The Adjustive Behavior of Bereaved Families: A New Field for Research," *Social Forces*, 8 (June, 1930), 543–49.

ELIOT, Thomas D., "Interactions of Psychiatric and Social Theory Prior to 1940," *in* A. M. Rose, ed., *Mental Health and Mental Disorder*, New York: W. W. Norton & Company, Inc., 1955, 18–41.

ELLIS, John M., "Socio-Economic Differentials in Mortality from Chronic Diseases," *Social Problems*, 5 (July, 1957), 30–36. Reprinted *in* E. G. Jaco, ed., *Patients, Physicians, and Illness*, New York: The Free Press of Glencoe, Inc., 1958.

ELLSWORTH, R. B., Beverley T. Mead, and W. H. Clayton, "The Rehabilitation and Disposition of Chronically Hospitalized Schizophrenic Patients," *Mental Hygiene*, 42 (July, 1958), 343–48.

EPSTEIN, Frederick H., E. P. Boas, and Rita Simpson, "The Epidemiology of Atherosclerosis Among a Random Sample of Clothing Workers of Different Ethnic Origins in New York City," *Journal of Chronic Diseases*, 5 (1957), 300–28.

EPSTEIN, N. B., "Concepts of Normality in Evaluation of Emotional Health," *Behavioral Science*, 3 (October, 1958), 335–43.

ERIKSON, Erik H., *Childhood and Society*, New York: W. W. Norton & Company, Inc., 1950.

ERIKSON, Erik H., "Identity and the Life Cycle: Selected Papers," *Psychological Issues*, New York: International Universities Press, Monograph 1, 1959.

EVANS, John W., "Stratification, Alienation, and the Hospital Setting: A Study in the Social Psychology of Chronic Illness," *Engineering Experiment Station Bulletin*, Ohio State University, 29 (November, 1960).

FARBER, B., *Family Organization and Crisis: Maintenance of Integration in Families with a Severely Mentally Retarded Child*, Lafayette, Ind.: Child Development Publications, 1960.

FARBER, B., "Perception of Crisis and Related Variables in the Impact of a Retarded Child on the Mother," *Journal of Health and Human Behavior*, 1 (Summer, 1960), 108–18.

FARBER, B., W. C. Jenne, and R. Toigo, "Family Crisis and the Decision to Institutionalize the Retarded Child," *Council for Exceptional Children Research Monograph Series*, No. 1, 1960.

FARINA, Amerigo, "Patterns of Role Dominance and Conflict in Parents of Schizophrenic Patients," *Journal of Abnormal and Social Psychology*, 61 (July, 1960), 31–38.

FARIS, Robert E. L., "Reflections of Social Disorganization in the Behavior of a Schizophrenic Patient," *American Journal of Sociology*, 50 (September, 1944), 134–41. Reprinted *in* A. M. Rose, ed., *Mental Health and Mental Disorders*, New York: W. W. Norton & Company, Inc., 1955.

FARIS, Robert E. L. and H. Warren Dunham, *Mental Disorders in Urban Areas*, Chicago: University of Chicago Press, 1939.

FAUNCE, William A. *et al.*, "The Sociology of Death: A Neglected Area of Research," *Social Forces*, 36 (March, 1958), 205–9.

FELIX, R. H. and H. V. Bowers, "Mental Hygiene and Socio-Environmental Factors," *Milbank Memorial Fund Quarterly*, 26 (April, 1948), 125–47.

FELIX, R. H. and Morton Kramer, "Research in Epidemiology of Mental Illness," *Public Health Reports*, 67 (February, 1952), 152–60.

FERNANDEZ-MARINA, Ramon and Ursula M. von Eckardt, "Cultural Stresses and Schizophrenogenesis in the Mothering-one in Puerto Rico," *in* Vera Rubin, ed., "Culture, Society, and Health," *Annals of the New York Academy of Sciences*, 84 (December, 1960), 864–77.

FIELD, L. W., R. T. Ewing, and D. W. Mayne, "Observations on the Relation of Psychosocial Factors to Psychiatric Illness Among Coal-Miners," *International Journal of Social Psychiatry*, 3 (1957), 133–44.

FIELD, M. G., "Approaches to Mental Illness in Soviet Society: Some Comparisons and Conjectures," *Social Problems*, 7 (Spring, 1960), 277–97.

FIELD, Minna, *Patients are People: A Medico-Social Approach to Prolonged Illness*, New York: Columbia University Press, 1953.

FIELD, M. J., "Mental Disorder in Rural Ghana," *Journal of Mental Science*, 104 (1958), 1043–51.

FIELD, Peter B., "A New Cross-Cultural Study of Drunkenness," *in* D. J. Pittman and C. R. Snyder, eds., *Society, Culture, and Drinking Patterns*, New York: John Wiley & Sons, Inc., 1962, 48–74.

FINESTONE, Harold, "Cats, Kicks and Color," *Social Problems*, 5 (July, 1957), 3–13.

FISCHER, A. and J. L. Fischer, "Culture and Epidemiology: A Theoretical Investigation of Kuru," *Journal of Health and Human Behavior*, 2 (Spring, 1961), 16–25.

FISCHER, J. L., A. Fischer, and F. Mahony, "Totemism and Allergy," *International Journal of Social Psychiatry*, 5 (Summer, 1959), 33–40.

FISHER, S., T. Boyd, E. Walker, and D. Sheer, "Parents of Schizophrenics, Neurotics, and Normals," A.M.A. *Archives of General Psychiatry*, 1 (August, 1959), 149–66.

FLECK, Stephen, "Family Dynamics and Origin of Schizophrenia," *Psychosomatic Medicine*, 22 (September–October, 1960), 333–44.

FORM, William H. *et al.*, "The Persistence and Emergence of Social and Cultural Systems in Disaster," *American Sociological Review*, 21 (1956), 180–85.

FORT, Twila and Austin L. Porterfield, "Some Backgrounds and Types of Alcoholism Among Women," *Journal of Health and Human Behavior*, 2 (Winter, 1961), 283–92.

FOX, R. C., "Symposium on the Study of Drugs in Man: Part IV. Some Social and Cultural Factors in American Society Conducive to Medical Research on Human Subjects," *Clinical Pharmacology and Therapeutics*, 1 (July–August, 1960), 423–43.

FREEDMAN, Lawrence Z. and August B. Hollingshead, "Neurosis and Social Class I: Social Interaction," *American Journal of Psychiatry*, 113 (March, 1957), 769–75.

FREEMAN, Howard E. and Ozzie G. Simmons, "Wives, Mothers, and the Posthospital Performance of Mental Patients," *Social Forces*, 37 (December, 1958), 153–59.

FREEMAN, Howard E. and Ozzie G. Simmons, "Mental Patients in the Community: Family Settings and Performance Levels," *American Sociological Review*, 23 (April, 1958), 147–54. Reprinted *in* D. D. Apple, ed., *Sociological Studies of Health and Sickness*, New York: McGraw-Hill Book Company, Inc., 1960. Reprinted *in* T. R. Sarbin, ed., *Studies in Behavior Pathology*, New York: Holt, Rinehart & Winston, Inc., 1961.

FREEMAN, Howard E. and Ozzie G. Simmons, "Social Integration of Former Mental Patients," *International Journal of Social Psychiatry*, 4 (Spring, 1959), 264–71.

FREEMAN, Howard E. and Ozzie G. Simmons, "Social Class and Posthospital Performance Levels," *American Sociological Review*, 24 (June, 1959), 345–51.

FREEMAN, Howard E., Ozzie G. Simmons, and Bernard J. Bergen, "Possessiveness as a Characteristic of Mothers of Schizophrenics," *Journal of Abnormal and Social Psychology*, 58 (March, 1959), 271–73.

FREEMAN, Howard E., Ozzie G. Simmons, and Bernard J. Bergen, "Residential Mobility Inclinations among Families of Mental Patients," *Social Forces*, 38 (May, 1960), 320–24.

FREEMAN, Howard E. and Ozzie G. Simmons, *The Mental Patient Comes Home*, New York: John Wiley & Sons, 1963.

FRIED, Edrita G. and Karl Stern, "The Situation of the Aged Within the Family," *American Journal of Orthopsychiatry*, 18 (January, 1948), 31–54.

FRIED, Jacob, "Acculturation and Mental Health among Indian Migrants in Peru," *in* M. K. Opler, ed., *Culture and Mental Health*, New York: The Macmillan Company, 1959, 119–40.

FRIED, Jacob, "Social Organization and Personal Security in a Peruvian Hacienda Indian Community: Vicos," *American Anthropologist*, 64 (August, 1962), 771–80.

FRIEDMAN, M. and R. H. Rosenman, "Association of Specific Overt Behavior Pattern with Blood and Cardiovascular Findings," *Journal of the American Medical Association*, 169 (March 21, 1959), 1286–96.

FRIEDMAN, M., R. H. Rosenman, and V. Carroll, "Changes in the Serum Cholesterol and Blood Clotting Time in Men Subjected to Cyclic Variation of Occupational Stress," *Circulation*, 17 (May, 1958), 852–61.

FROMM, Erich, "Individual and Social Origins of Neurosis," *American Sociological Review*, 9 (August, 1944), 380–84. Reprinted *in* A. M. Rose, ed., *Mental Health and Mental Disorders*, New York: W. W. Norton & Company, Inc., 1955.

FRUMKIN, Robert M., "Comparative Rates of Mental Illnesses for Urban and Rural Populations in Ohio," *Rural Sociology*, 19 (March, 1954), 70–72.

FRUMKIN, Robert M., "Social Factors in Schizophrenia," *Sociology and Social Research*, 38 (July–August, 1954), 383–86.

FRUMKIN, Robert M., "Race and Major Mental Disorders: A Research Note," *Journal of Negro Education*, 23 (1954), 98–99.

FRUMKIN, Robert M., "Occupation and Major Mental Disorders," *in* A. M. Rose, ed., *Mental Health and Mental Disorders,* New York: W. W. Norton & Company, Inc., 1955, 136–60.

FUNKENSTEIN, Daniel H., Stanley H. King, and Margaret Drolette, *Mastery of Stress,* Cambridge: Harvard University Press, 1957.

GAITONDE, M. R., "Cross-Cultural Study of the Psychiatric Syndromes in Out-Patient Clinics in Bombay, India and Topeka, Kansas," *International Journal of Social Psychiatry,* 4 (1958), 98–104.

GALDSTON, Iago, *The Epidemiology of Health,* New York: Health Education Council, 1953.

GALVIN, James, "Mothers of Schizophrenics," *Journal of Nervous and Mental Disease,* 123 (1956), 568–70.

GARDNER, Margaret S., "Changing Patterns of Retirement," *Journal of Gerontology,* 15 (1960), 300–04.

GARMEZY, Norman and Eliot H. Rodnick, "Premorbid Adjustment and Performance in Schizophrenia: Implications for Interpreting Heterogeneity in Schizophrenia," *Journal of Nervous and Mental Disease,* 129 (1959), 450–66.

GARNER, A. M. and C. Wenar, *The Mother-Child Interaction in Psychosomatic Disorders,* Urbana: University of Illinois Press, 1959.

GELBER, Ida, *Alcoholism in New York City,* New York: New York City Department of Health, 1960.

GERARD, Donald L. and Joseph Siegel, "The Family Background of Schizophrenia," *Psychiatric Quarterly,* 24 (1950), 47–73.

GERTMAN, Samuel, "The Physician Views the Psychosocial Health of the American," *Journal of Health and Human Behavior,* 1 (Fall, 1960), 237–41.

GIBBS, Jack P., "Suicide," *in* R. K. Merton and R. A. Nisbet, eds., *Contemporary Social Problems,* New York: Harcourt, Brace & World, Inc., 1961, 222–61.

GIBSON, Robert W., "The Family Background and Early Life Experience of the Manic-Depressive Patient: A Comparison with the Schizophrenic Patient," *Psychiatry,* 21 (February, 1958), 71–90. Reprinted *in* T. R. Sarbin, ed., *Studies in Behavior Pathology,* New York: Holt, Rinehart & Winston, Inc., 1961.

GITELSON, M., "A Critique of Current Concepts in Psychosomatic Medicine," *Bulletin of the Menninger Clinic,* 23 (1959), 165ff.

GLAD, D. D., "Attitudes and Experiences of American-Jewish and American-Irish Male Youth as Related to Differences in Adult Rates of Inebriety," *Quarterly Journal of Studies on Alcohol,* 8 (1947), 406–72.

GLADWIN, Thomas and Seymour B. Sarason, "Culture and Individual Personality Integration on Truk," *in* M. K. Opler, ed., *Culture and Mental Health,* New York: The Macmillan Company, 1959, 173–212.

GLIDEWELL, J. C., ed., "Mental Health in the Classroom," *Social Issues,* 15 (1959), 1–62.

GLOCK, C. Y. and H. L. Lennard, "Studies in Hypertension. V. Psychologic Factors in Hypertension: An Interpretive Review," *Journal of Chronic Diseases,* 5 (February, 1957), 174–85.

GOLDHAMER, Herbert and Andrew Marshall, *Psychosis and Civilization,* New York: The Free Press of Glencoe, Inc., 1953.

GOLDSTEIN, George S. and Paul F. Wehrle, "The Influence of Socioeconomic Factors on the Distribution of Hepatitis in Syracuse, N. Y.," *American Journal of Public Health,* 49 (April, 1959), 473–80.

GORDON, John, "Treatment of Alcoholism," *New York State Journal of Medicine,* 58 (June, 1958), 1011–18.

GORDON, John E., "Epidemiology of Accidents," *American Journal of Public Health,* 39 (April, 1949), 504–15.

GORDON, John E., "Medical Ecology and the Public Health," *American Journal of the Medical Sciences*, 235 (March, 1958), 337–59.

GORDON, John E. *et al.*, "The Biological and Social Sciences in an Epidemiology of Mental Disorder," *American Journal of the Medical Sciences*, 223 (March, 1952), 316–43.

GOTTLEIB, David, "The Neighborhood Tavern and Cocktail Lounge: A Study of Class Differences," *American Journal of Sociology*, 62 (May, 1957), 559–62.

GOUCH, Harrison G., "A Sociological Theory of Psychopathy," *American Journal of Sociology*, 53 (March, 1948), 359–66. Reprinted *in* A. M. Rose, ed., *Mental Health and Mental Disorders*, New York: W. W. Norton & Company, Inc., 1955.

GOWMAN, A. G., *The War Blind in American Social Structure*, New York: American Foundation for the Blind, 1957.

GRACE, W. J., "Life Situations, Emotions, and Chronic Ulcerative Colitis," *Proceedings of the Association for Research in Nervous and Mental Disease*, 29 (1950), 679–91.

GRAHAM, Saxon, "Ethnic Background and Illness in a Pennsylvania County," *Social Forces*, 4 (July, 1956), 76–82.

GRAHAM, Saxon, "Disability in Butler County," *Public Health Reports*, 71 (November, 1956), 115–18.

GRAHAM, Saxon, "Social Factors in the Epidemiology of Cancer at Various Sites," *in* Vera Rubin, ed., "Culture, Society, and Health," *Annals of the New York Academy of Sciences*, 84 (December, 1960), 807–15.

GRAHAM, Saxon, Morton Levin, and Abraham M. Lilienfeld, "The Socioeconomic Distribution of Cancer of Various Sites in Buffalo, N.Y., 1948–1952," *Cancer*, 13 (January–February, 1960), 180–91.

GRAHAM, Saxon and Abraham M. Lilienfeld, "Genetic Studies of Gastric Cancer in Humans: An Appraisal," *Cancer*, 11 (September, 1958).

GRAYSON, Morris *et al.*, *Psychiatric Aspects of Rehabilitation*, New York: Institute of Physical Medicine and Rehabilitation, Monograph 2, 1952.

GREEN, Arnold W., "The Middle-Class Male Child and Neurosis," *American Sociological Review*, 11 (February, 1946), 31–41. Reprinted *in* A. M. Rose, ed., *Mental Health and Mental Disorders*, New York: W. W. Norton & Company, Inc., 1955.

GREENBERG, Leon A., "Intoxication and Alcoholism: Physiological Factors," *The Annals of the American Academy of Political and Social Science*, 315 (January, 1958), 22–30.

GREENFIELD, Norman S., "The Relationship between Recalled Forms of Childhood Discipline and Psychopathology," *The Journal of Consulting Psychology*, 23 (1959). Reprinted *in* T. R. Sarbin, ed., *Studies in Behavior Pathology*, New York: Holt, Rinehart & Winston, Inc., 1961.

GREGORY, I., "An Analysis of Familial Data on Psychiatric Patients: Parental Age, Family Size, Birth Order, and Ordinal Position," *British Journal of Preventive and Social Medicine*, 12 (1958), 42–59.

GRIPE, Richard P. *et al.*, "Returning the Farmer with Cardiac Disease to Work," *American Journal of Cardiology*, 7 (March, 1961), 354–64.

GRUENBERG, Ernest M., "The Epidemiology of Mental Disease," *Scientific American*, 190 (March, 1954), 38–42.

GRUENBERG, Ernest M., "Socially Shared Psychopathology," *in* A. H. Leighton, J. A. Clausen, and R. N. Wilson, eds., *Explorations in Social Psychiatry*, New York: Basic Books, Inc., 1957, 201–29.

GURSSLIN, O. R., R. G. Hunt, and J. L. Roach, "Social Class and the Mental Health Movement," *Social Problems*, 8 (1959–1960), 210–18.

GUSFIELD, Joseph R., "Status Conflicts and the Changing Ideologies of the American Temperance Movement," *in* D. J. Pittman and C. R. Snyder, eds., *Society, Culture, and Drinking Patterns*, New York: John Wiley & Sons, Inc., 1962, 101–20.

HAENSZEL, William, "Cancer Mortality Among the Foreign Born in the United States," *Journal of the National Cancer Institute*, 26 (January, 1961), 37–132.

HAER, John L., "Drinking Patterns and the Influence of Friends and Family," *Quarterly Journal of Studies on Alcohol*, 16 (March, 1955), 178–85.

HAGGARD, H. W. and E. M. Jellinek, *Alcohol Explored*, New York: Doubleday & Company, Inc., 1942.

HALEY, Jay, "The Family of the Schizophrenic: A Model System," *The Journal of Nervous and Mental Disease*, 129 (October, 1959), 357–74.

HALEY, Jay, "An Interactional Description of Schizophrenia," *Psychiatry: Journal for the Study of Interpersonal Processes*, 22 (November, 1959), 321–32.

HALEY, Jay, "Observation of the Family of the Schizophrenic," *American Journal of Orthopsychiatry*, 30 (July, 1960), 460–67.

HALLOWELL, A. Irving, "Culture and Mental Disorder," *Journal of Abnormal and Social Psychology*, 29 (April–June, 1934), 1–9.

HALLOWELL, A. Irving, "Psychic Stresses and Culture Patterns," *American Journal of Psychiatry*, 92 (1936), 1291–1310. Reprinted *in* M. K. Opler, ed., *Culture and Mental Health*, New York: The Macmillan Company, 1959.

HALLOWELL, A. Irving, "Fear and Anxiety as Cultural and Individual Variables in a Primitive Society," *The Journal of Social Psychology*, 9 (1938), 25–47. Reprinted *in* M. K. Opler, ed., *Culture and Mental Health*, New York: The Macmillan Company, 1959.

HALLOWELL, A. Irving, "Some Psychological Characteristics of the Northeastern Indians," *in* F. Johnson, ed., *Man in Northeastern America*, Andover, Mass.: Papers of the Peabody Foundation for Archeology, 1946, 195–225.

HALLOWELL, A. Irving, "Values, Acculturation, and Mental Health," *American Journal of Orthopsychiatry*, 20 (October, 1950), 732–43.

HAMMOND, E. Cuyler and D. Horn, "Smoking and Death Rates—Report on Forty-four Months of Follow-up, 187,783 Men," *Journal of the American Medical Association*, 166 (1958), 1159–1308.

HANFMANN, Eugenia, "The Life History of an Ex-Alcoholic," *Quarterly Journal of Studies on Alcohol*, 12 (September, 1951), 405–43.

HARDT, Robert H. and Sherwin J. Feinhandler, "Social Class and Mental Hospitalization Prognosis," *American Sociological Review*, 24 (December, 1959), 815–21. Reprinted *in* T. R. Sarbin, ed., *Studies in Behavior Pathology*, New York: Holt, Rinehart & Winston, Inc., 1961.

HARE, E. H., "Mental Illness and Social Class in Bristol," *British Journal of Preventive and Social Medicine*, 9 (1955), 191–95.

HARE, E. H., "Mental Illness and Social Conditions in Bristol," *Journal of Mental Science*, 102 (1956), 349–57.

HARE, E. H., "Family Setting and the Urban Distribution of Schizophrenia," *Journal of Mental Science*, 102 (1956), 753–60.

HATT, Paul K., *Backgrounds of Human Fertility in Puerto Rico*, Princeton, N.J.: Princeton University Press, 1952.

HAWKINS, N. G., "Sociology and Tuberculosis: A Brief Review," *International Journal of Social Psychiatry*, 3 (Autumn, 1957), 114–22.

HAWKINS, N. G. and T. H. Holmes, "Environmental Considerations in Tuberculosis: Ecologic Factors in Tuberculosis Morbidity," *Transactions of the Fiftieth Anniversary Meeting of the National Tuberculosis Association*, 1954, 233–38.

HEASMAN, M. A. and D. D. Reid, "Theory and Observation in Family Epidemics of the Common Cold," *British Journal of Preventive and Social Medicine*, 15 (January, 1961), 12–17.

HEATH, Dwight B., "Drinking Patterns of the Bolivian Camba," *Quarterly Journal of Studies on Alcohol*, 19 (September, 1958), 491–508. Reprinted *in* D. J. Pittman and C. R. Snyder, eds., *Society, Culture, and Drinking Patterns,* New York: John Wiley & Sons, Inc., 1962.

HEINZELMAN, Fred, "Factors in Prophylaxis Behavior in Treating Rheumatic Fever: An Exploratory Study," *Journal of Health and Human Behavior,* 3 (Summer, 1962), 67–72.

HELFAND, Isidore, "Role Taking in Schizophrenia," *Journal of Consulting Psychology,* 20 (1956). Reprinted *in* T. R. Sarbin, ed., *Studies in Behavior Pathology,* New York: Holt, Rinehart & Winston, Inc., 1961.

HENRY, Jules, "Family Structure and the Transmission of Neurotic Behavior," *American Journal of Orthopsychiatry,* 21 (1951), 800–18.

HENRY, Jules, "Cultural Change and Mental Health," *Mental Hygiene,* 41 (July, 1957), 323–26.

HENRY, Jules and Henry Warson, "Family Structure and Psychic Development," *American Journal of Orthopsychiatry,* 21 (January, 1951), 59–73.

HESTERLY, S. O. and Irwin A. Berg, "Deviant Responses as Indicators of Immaturity and Schizophrenia," *Journal of Consulting Psychology,* 22 (1958). Reprinted *in* T. R. Sarbin, ed., *Studies in Behavior Pathology,* New York: Holt, Rinehart & Winston, Inc., 1961.

HEYMAN, Dorothy, "Manifestations of Psychoneurosis in Negroes," *Mental Hygiene,* 29 (1945), 231–35.

HILL, Reuben L., ed., *Families Under Stress: Adjustment to the Crisis of War Separation and Reunions,* New York: Harper & Row, Publishers, 1949.

HILL, Reuben, J. Mayone Stycos, and Kurt W. Back, *The Family and Population Control: A Puerto Rican Experiment in Social Change,* Chapel Hill: The University of North Carolina Press, 1959.

HINKLE, Lawrence E., "Ecological Observations on the Relation of Physical Illness, Mental Illness, and the Social Environment," *Psychosomatic Medicine,* 23 (July–August, 1961), 289–97.

HINKLE, Lawrence E. and Harold G. Wolff, "Health and the Social Environment: Experimental Investigations," *in* A. H. Leighton, J. A. Clausen, and R. N. Wilson, eds., *Explorations in Social Psychiatry,* New York: Basic Books, Inc., 1957, 105–37.

HINKLE, Lawrence E. and Harold G. Wolff, "Ecologic Investigations of the Relationship between Illness, Life Experiences and the Social Environment," *Annals of Internal Medicine,* 49 (December, 1958), 1373–88.

HINKLE, Lawrence E. *et al.,* "An Investigation of the Relation Between Life Experience, Personality Characteristics, and General Susceptibility to Illness," *Psychosomatic Medicine,* 20 (July–August, 1958), 278–95.

HIRSH, J., "Suicide: I. Demography of Suicide," *Mental Hygiene,* 43 (1959), 516–25.

HITSON, Hazel M. and Daniel H. Funkenstein, "Family Patterns and Paranoidal Personality Structure in Boston and Burma," *International Journal of Social Psychiatry,* 5 (1960), 182–90.

HOCH, Paul H., "The Etiology and Epidemiology of Schizophrenia," *American Journal of Public Health,* 47 (September, 1957), 1071–76.

HOCH, Paul H. and Joseph Zubin, eds., *Comparative Epidemiology of the Mental Disorders,* New York: Grune & Stratton, Inc., 1961.

HOLLINGSHEAD, August B., "Views on the Etiology of Alcoholism," *in* H. D. Kruse, ed., *Alcoholism as a Medical Problem,* New York: New York Academy of Medicine, Committee on Public Health Relations, 1956.

HOLLINGSHEAD, August B., "Some Issues in the Epidemiology of Schizophrenia," *American Sociological Review,* 26 (February, 1961), 5–13.

HOLLINGSHEAD, A. B., R. Ellis, and E. Kirby, "Social Mobility and Mental Illness," *American Sociological Review,* 19 (October, 1954), 577–84.

HOLLINGSHEAD, August B. and Lawrence Z. Freedman, "Social Class and the Treatment of Neurotics," *in The Social Welfare Forum,* New York: Columbia University Press, 1955, 194–205.

HOLLINGSHEAD, August B. and Frederick C. Redlich, "Social Class and Psychiatric Disorders," *Interrelations Between the Social Environment and Psychiatric Disorders,* Milbank Memorial Fund, New York, 1953, 195–208.

HOLLINGSHEAD, August B. and Frederick C. Redlich, "Social Stratification and Psychiatric Disorders," *American Sociological Review,* 18 (April, 1953), 163–69. Reprinted *in* A. M. Rose, ed., *Mental Health and Mental Disorder,* New York: W. W. Norton & Company, Inc., 1955.

HOLLINGSHEAD, August B. and Frederick C. Redlich, "Schizophrenia and Social Structure," *American Journal of Psychiatry,* 110 (March, 1954), 695–701.

HOLLINGSHEAD, August B. and Frederick C. Redlich, "Social Stratification and Schizophrenia," *American Sociological Review,* 19 (June, 1954), 302–6.

HOLLINGSHEAD, August B. and Frederick C. Redlich, "Social Mobility and Mental Illness," *American Journal of Psychiatry,* 112 (September, 1955), 179–85.

HOLLINGSHEAD, August B. and Frederick C. Redlich, *Social Class and Mental Illness: A Community Study,* New York: John Wiley & Sons, Inc., 1958.

HOLMES, T. H. *et al.,* "Psychosocial and Psychophysiologic Studies of Tuberculosis," *Psychosomatic Medicine,* 19 (March–April, 1957), 134–43.

HONIGMANN, J. J. and I. Honigmann, "Drinking in an Indian-White Community," *Quarterly Journal of Studies on Alcohol,* 5 (1945), 575–619.

HORN, Daniel, Frederick A. Courts, Robert M. Taylor, and Erwin Solomon, "Cigarette Smoking Among High School Students," *American Journal of Public Health,* 49 (November, 1959), 1497–1511.

HORTON, Donald, "The Functions of Alcohol in Primitive Societies: A Cross-Cultural Study," *Quarterly Journal of Studies on Alcohol,* 4 (September, 1943), 199–320.

HUNT, Raymond G., "Socio-Cultural Factors in Mental Disorder," *Behavioral Science,* 4 (1959), 96–106.

HUNT, W. A., "The Relative Incidence of Psychoneurosis Among Negroes," *Journal of Consulting Psychology,* 45 (1947), 133–36.

HUNTER, D., *The Diseases of Occupations,* Boston: Little, Brown & Company, 1957.

IKEDA, Kiyoshi, Harry V. Ball, and Douglas S. Yamamura, "Ethnocultural Factors in Schizophrenia: The Japanese in Hawaii," *The American Journal of Sociology,* 68 (September, 1962), 242–48.

JACKSON, Don D., ed., *The Etiology of Schizophrenia,* New York: Basic Books, Inc., 1960.

JACKSON, Don D. and John H. Weakland, "Schizophrenic Symptoms and Family Interaction," *A.M.A. Archives of General Psychiatry,* 1 (December, 1959), 618–21.

JACKSON, Joan K., "Alcoholism and the Family," *The Annals of the American Academy of Political and Social Science,* 315 (January, 1958), 90–98. Reprinted *in* D. J. Pittman and C. R. Snyder, eds., *Society, Culture, and Drinking Patterns,* New York: John Wiley & Sons, Inc., 1962.

JACKSON, Joan K. and Thomas H. Holmes, "Alcoholism and Tuberculosis," *Human Organization,* 16 (1958), 41–43. Reprinted *in* D. Apple, ed., *Sociological Studies of Health and Sickness,* New York: McGraw-Hill Book Company, Inc., 1960.

JACO, E. Gartly, "The Social Isolation Hypothesis and Schizophrenia," *American Sociological Review,* 19 (October, 1954), 567–77.

JACO, E. Gartly, "Incidence of Psychoses in Texas, 1951–52," *Texas State Journal of Medicine,* 53 (February, 1957), 86–91.

JACO, E. Gartly, "Social Factors in Mental Disorders in Texas," *Social Problems,* 4 (April, 1957), 322–28.

JACO, E. Gartly, "Attitudes Toward, and Incidence of, Mental Disorder: A Research Note," *Southwestern Social Science Quarterly,* (June, 1957), 27–38.

JACO, E. Gartly, "Mental Health of the Spanish-American in Texas," *in* M. K. Opler, ed., *Culture and Mental Health,* New York: The Macmillan Company, 1959, 467–88.

JACO, E. Gartly, *The Social Epidemiology of Mental Disorders,* New York: Russell Sage Foundation, 1960.

JACOBS, Herbert H., Edward A. Suchman, *et al., Behavioral Approaches to Accident Research,* New York: Association for the Aid of Crippled Children, 1961.

JAHODA, Marie, "Toward a Social Psychology of Mental Health," *in* M. J. E. Senn, ed., *Problems of Infancy and Childhood,* New York: Josiah Macy, Jr., Foundation, 1950. Reprinted *in* A. M. Rose, ed., *Mental Health and Mental Disorders,* New York: W. W. Norton & Company, Inc., 1955.

JAHODA, Marie, *Current Concepts of Positive Mental Health,* New York: Basic Books, Inc., 1958.

JAHODA, Marie, *Race Relations and Mental Health,* Paris: UNESCO, 1960.

JANIS, Irving L., *Psychological Stress: Psychoanalytic and Behavioral Studies of Surgical Patients,* New York: John Wiley & Sons, Inc., 1958.

JELLINEK, E. M., ed., *Alcohol Addiction and Chronic Alcoholism,* Vol. 1, New Haven, Conn.: Yale University Press, 1942.

JELLINEK, E. M., "Phases of Alcohol Addiction," *Quarterly Journal of Studies on Alcohol,* 13 (1952), 673–87. Reprinted *in* D. J. Pittman and C. R. Snyder, eds., *Society, Culture, and Drinking Patterns,* New York: John Wiley & Sons, Inc., 1962.

JELLINEK, E. M., *The Disease Concept of Alcoholism,* New Haven, Conn.: Hillhouse Press, 1960.

JELLINEK, E. M., "Cultural Differences in the Meaning of Alcoholism," *in* D. J. Pittman and C. R. Snyder, eds., *Society, Culture, and Drinking Patterns,* New York: John Wiley & Sons, Inc., 1962, 382–88.

JENSEN, Howard E., "Sociological Aspects of Aging," *Public Health Reports,* 73 (1958), 569–76.

JEWELL, Donald P., "A Case of a 'Psychotic' Navaho Indian Male," *Human Organization,* 11 (1952), 32–36. Reprinted *in* D. Apple, ed., *Sociological Studies of Health and Sickness,* New York: McGraw-Hill Book Company, Inc., 1960.

JOINT COMMITTEE OF THE AMERICAN BAR ASSOCIATION AND THE AMERICAN MEDICAL ASSOCIATION, *Drug Addiction: Crime or Disease?* Bloomington: Indiana University Press, 1961.

JOINT COMMITTEE OF THE ROYAL COLLEGE OF OBSTETRICIANS AND GYNECOLOGISTS AND THE POPULATION INVESTIGATION COMMITTEE, *Maternity in Great Britain: A Survey of Social and Economic Aspects of Pregnancy and Childbirth,* London: Oxford University Press, 1948.

JONES, Edward G., Ian MacDonald, and Lester Breslow, "A Study of Epidemiologic Factors in Carcinoma of the Uterine Cervix," *American Journal of Obstetrics and Gynecology,* 76 (July, 1958), 1–10.

KAPLAN, Arthur and Lois Wolf, "The Role of the Family in Relation to the Institutionalized Mental Patient," *Mental Hygiene,* 38 (October, 1954), 634–39.

KAPLAN, Bert, Robert B. Reed, and Wyman Richardson, "A Comparison of the Incidence of Hospitalized and Non-Hospitalized Cases of Psychosis in Two Communities," *American Sociological Review,* 21 (August, 1956), 472–79.

KAPLAN, H. B. and S. W. Bloom, "The Use of Sociological and Social-Psychological Concepts in Physiological Research: A Review of Selected Experimental Studies," *Journal of Nervous and Mental Disease,* 130 (August, 1960), 128–34.

KAPLAN, H. I. and H. S. Kaplan, "Current Theoretical Concepts in Psychosomatic Medicine," *American Journal of Psychiatry,* 115 (June, 1959), 1091–96.

KARVONEN, M. J. *et al.*, "Cardiovascular Studies on Lumberjacks," *Journal of Occupational Medicine*, 3 (February, 1961), 49–54.

KASANIN, J., E. Knight, and P. Sage, "The Parent-Child Relationship in Schizophrenia," *Journal of Nervous and Mental Disease*, 79 (1934), 249–63.

KELLER, Mark, "Alcoholism: Nature and Extent of the Problem," *The Annals of the American Academy of Political and Social Science*, 315 (January, 1958), 1–11.

KELLER, Mark, "The Definition of Alcoholism and the Estimation of Its Prevalence," *in* D. J. Pittman and C. R. Snyder, eds., *Society, Culture, and Drinking Patterns*, New York: John Wiley & Sons, Inc., 1962, 310–29.

KELLER, Mark and Vera Efron, "The Prevalence of Alcoholism," *Quarterly Journal of Studies on Alcohol*, 16 (December, 1955), 619–44.

KENNARD, Edward A., "Native Endowment and Mental Health and Illness: A Cross-cultural Perspective," *in* Vera Rubin, ed., "Culture, Society, and Health," *Annals of the New York Academy of Sciences*, 84 (December, 1960), 906–10.

KENNAWAY, E. L., "Racial and Social Incidence of Cancer of the Uterus," *British Journal of Cancer*, 2 (September, 1948), 177ff.

KEPHART, William M., "Status After Death," *American Sociological Review*, 15 (October, 1950), 635–43.

KEYES, Ancel, "The Diet and the Development of Coronary Heart Disease," *Journal of Chronic Diseases*, 4 (October, 1956), 364–80.

KING, Stanley H., "Psychosocial Factors Associated with Rheumatoid Arthritis," *Journal of Chronic Diseases*, 2 (September, 1955), 287–302. Reprinted *in* E. G. Jaco, ed., *Patients, Physicians, and Illness*, New York: The Free Press of Glencoe, Inc., 1958.

KING, Stanley H. and Sidney Cobb, "Psychosocial Factors in the Epidemiology of Rheumatoid Arthritis," *Journal of Chronic Diseases*, 7 (June, 1958), 466–75.

KING, Stanley H. and Sidney Cobb, "Psychosocial Studies of Rheumatoid Arthritis: Parental Factors Compared in Cases and Controls," *Arthritis and Rheumatism*, 2 (August, 1959), 322–31.

KING, Stanley H. and Daniel Funkenstein, "Religious Practice and Cardiovascular Reactions During Stress," *The Journal of Abnormal and Social Psychology*, 55 (1957), 135–37. Reprinted *in* E. G. Jaco, ed., *Patients, Physicians, and Illness*, New York: The Free Press of Glencoe, Inc., 1958.

KING, Stanley H. and Andrew F. Henry, "Aggression and Cardiovascular Reactions Related to Parental Control over Behavior," *The Journal of Abnormal and Social Psychology*, 50 (1955). Reprinted *in* T. R. Sarbin, ed., *Studies in Behavior Pathology*, New York: Holt, Rinehart & Winston, Inc., 1961.

KING, Stanley H., *Perceptions of Illness and Medical Practice*, New York: Russell Sage Foundation, 1962.

KISER, Clyde V., "Changes in Fertility by Socio-Economic Status During 1940–1950," *Milbank Memorial Fund Quarterly*, 33 (October, 1955), 393–429.

KLEINER, Robert J. and Seymour Parker, "Migration and Mental Illness: A New Look," *American Sociological Review*, 24 (October, 1959), 687–90.

KOHN, Melvin S. and John A. Clausen, "Social Isolation and Schizophrenia," *American Sociological Review*, 20 (June, 1955), 265–73. Reprinted *in* T. R. Sarbin, ed., *Studies in Behavior Pathology*, New York: Holt, Rinehart & Winston, Inc., 1961.

KOLB, Lawrence, "Narcotic Addiction—An Interview," *Spectrum*, 5 (March, 1957), 136.

KORNER, I. N., "Of Values, Value Lag, and Mental Health," *American Psychologist*, 11 (1956), 543–46.

KRAMER, M., "A Discussion of the Concepts of Incidence and Prevalence as Related to Epidemiologic Studies of Mental Disorders," *American Journal of Public Health*, 47 (1957), 826–40.

KUBIE, Lawrence S., "Social Forces and the Neurotic Process," *Journal of Nervous and Mental Disorders,* 128 (1959), 65–80. Reprinted *in* A. H. Leighton, J. A. Clausen, and R. N. Wilson, eds., *Explorations in Social Psychiatry,* New York: Basic Books, Inc., 1957.

KUTNER, B. and W. G. Smillie, "The Problem of Mental Health Among the Aged," *American Journal of Public Health,* 46 (1956), 204–8.

LA BARRE, M. B., L. Jessner, and L. Ussery, "The Significance of Grandmothers in the Psychopathology of Children," *American Journal of Orthopsychiatry,* 30 (January, 1960), 175–84.

LA BARRE, Weston, "A Cultist Drug-Addiction in an Indian Alcoholic," *Bulletin of Menninger Clinic,* 5 (1941), 40–46.

LANDMAN, R. H., "Studies of Drinking in Jewish Culture: III. Drinking Patterns of Children and Adolescents Attending Religious Schools," *Quarterly Journal of Studies on Alcohol,* 13 (1952), 87–94.

LANDY, David, "Cultural Antecedents of Mental Illness in the United States," *Social Service Review,* 32 (December, 1958), 350–61.

LANDY, David and Robert S. Albert, "Waiting for Hospitalization," *A.M.A. Archives of General Psychiatry,* 1 (November, 1959), 519–29.

LANE, R. C. and J. L. Singer, "Familial Attitudes in Paranoid Schizophrenics and Normals from Two Socioeconomic Classes," *Journal of Abnormal and Social Psychology,* 59 (November, 1959), 328–39.

LANTZ, E. L. and P. Wood, "Nutrition of New Mexican Spanish-American and Anglo Adolescents," *Journal of the American Dietetic Association,* 34 (1958), 138–53.

LAPOUSE, Rema and Mary A. Monk, "An Epidemiologic Study of Behavior Characteristics in Children," *American Journal of Public Health,* 48 (1958), 1134–44.

LAPOUSE, Rema, Mary A. Monk, and Milton Terris, "The Drift Hypothesis and Socioeconomic Differentials in Schizophrenia," *American Journal of Public Health,* 46 (1956), 978–86.

LAUGHTON, Katherine B., Carol W. Buck, and G. E. Hobbs, "Socio-Economic Status and Illness," *Milbank Memorial Fund Quarterly,* 36 (January, 1958), 46–57.

LAWRENCE, Joseph J. and Milton A. Maxwell, "Drinking and Socio-Economic Status," *in* D. J. Pittman and C. R. Snyder, eds., *Society, Culture, and Drinking Patterns,* New York: John Wiley & Sons, Inc., 1962, 141–45.

LAWRENCE, P. S., "Chronic Illness and Socio-Economic Status," *Public Health Reports,* 63 (November 19, 1948), 1507–21. Reprinted *in* E. G. Jaco, ed., *Patients, Physicians, and Illness,* New York: The Free Press of Glencoe, Inc., 1958.

LEACOCK, Eleanor, "Three Social Variables and the Occurrence of Mental Disorder," *in* A. H. Leighton, J. A. Clausen, and R. N. Wilson, eds., *Explorations in Social Psychiatry,* New York: Basic Books, Inc., 1957, 308–40.

LEAVELL, Hugh R., "Chronic Disease and the Behavioral Sciences," *Journal of Chronic Diseases,* 2 (July, 1955), 113.

LEE, Dorothy, "Cultural Factors in Dietary Choice," *The American Journal of Clinical Nutrition,* 5 (1957), 166–70.

LEFTON, Mark, Shirley Angrist, Simon Dinitz, and Benjamin Pasamanick, "Social Class, Expectations, and Performance of Mental Patients," *American Journal of Sociology,* 158 (July, 1962), 79–87.

LEIGHTON, Alexander H., "Psychiatric Disorder and Social Environment: An Outline for a Frame of Reference," *Psychiatry,* 18 (1955), 367–83.

LEIGHTON, Alexander H., *An Introduction to Social Psychiatry,* Springfield, Ill.: Charles C Thomas, Publisher, 1960.

LEIGHTON, Alexander H. and Jane H. Hughes, "Cultures as Causative of Mental Disorder," *in Causes of Mental Disorders: A Review of Epidemiological Knowledge,* New York: Milbank Memorial Fund, 1961, 341–65.

LEIGHTON, D. C., "The Distribution of Psychiatric Symptoms in a Small Town," *American Journal of Psychiatry*, 112 (1956), 716–23.

LEMERT, Edwin M., "An Exploratory Study of Mental Disorders in a Rural Problem Area," *Rural Sociology*, 13 (March, 1948), 47–64.

LEMERT, Edwin M., *Social Pathology*, New York: McGraw-Hill Book Company, Inc., 1951.

LEMERT, Edwin M., "Alcohol and the Northwest Coast Indians," *University of California Publications in Culture and Society*, 2 (1954), 303–406.

LEMERT, Edwin M., "The Use of Alcohol in Three Salish Indian Tribes," *Quarterly Journal of Studies on Alcohol*, 19 (March, 1958), 90–107.

LEMERT, Edwin M., "Stuttering and Social Structure in Two Pacific Societies," *Journal of Speech and Hearing Disorders*, 27 (February, 1962), 3–10.

LEMERT, Edwin M., "Paranoia and the Dynamics of Exclusion," *Sociometry*, 25 (March, 1962), 2–20.

LEMERT, Edwin M., "Alcohol, Values, and Social Control," *in* D. J. Pittman and C. R. Snyder, eds., *Society, Culture, and Drinking Patterns*, New York: John Wiley & Sons, Inc., 1962, 553–71.

LEMKAU, Paul V., "The Epidemiological Study of Mental Illness and Mental Health," *American Journal of Psychiatry*, 111 (May, 1955), 801–9.

LEMKAU, Paul V., C. Tietze, and M. Cooper, "A Survey of Statistical Studies on the Prevalence and Incidence of Mental Disorder in Sample Populations," *Public Health Reports*, 58 (December, 1943), 1090–1927.

LENNARD, Henry L. and Arnold Bernstein, *The Anatomy of Psychotherapy*, New York: Columbia University Press, 1960.

LEVIN, Morton L., L. C. Kress, and H. Goldstein, "Syphilis and Cancer: Reported Syphilis Prevalence Among 7,760 Cancer Patients," *New York State Journal of Medicine*, 42 (1942), 1737ff.

LEVINE, D. and L. Delman, "Community Adjustment of Schizophrenics," *Journal of Clinical Psychology*, 17 (1961), 138–39.

LEVINE, Gene N., "Anxiety About Illness: Psychological and Social Bases," *Journal of Health and Human Behavior*, 3 (Spring, 1962), 30–34.

LIDZ, Ruth W. and Theodore Lidz, "The Family Environment of Schizophrenic Patients," *American Journal of Psychiatry*, 106 (1949), 332–45.

LIDZ, Theodore, "Schizophrenia and the Family," *Psychiatry*, 21 (February, 1958), 21–27.

LIDZ, T., A. R. Cornelison, S. Fleck, and D. Terry, "The Intrafamilial Environment of the Schizophrenic Patient: I. The Father," *Psychiatry*, 20 (1957), 329–42.

LIDZ, T., A. R. Cornelison, S. Fleck, and D. Terry, "The Intrafamilial Environment of Schizophrenic Patients: II. Marital Schism and Marital Skew," *American Journal of Psychiatry*, 114 (1957), 241–48.

LIDZ, T., A. R. Cornelison, S. Fleck, and D. Terry, "Intrafamilial Environment of the Schizophrenic Patient: VI. The Tranmission of Irrationality," *A.M.A. Archives of Neurology & Psychiatry*, 79 (March, 1958), 305–16.

LIDZ, Theodore and Stephen Fleck, "Schizophrenia, Human Integration, and the Role of the Family," *in* Don Jackson, ed., *The Etiology of Schizophrenia*, New York: Basic Books, Inc., 1959, 323–44.

LIDZ, T., B. Parker, and A. Cornelison, "The Role of the Father in the Family Environment of the Schizophrenic Patient," *American Journal of Psychiatry*, 113 (1956), 126–32.

LILIENFELD, Abraham, "Diagnostic and Therapeutic X-Radiation in an Urban Population," *Public Health Reports* (January 4, 1959), 29–36.

LILIENFELD, Abraham and Saxon Graham, "Validity of Determining Circumcision Status by Questionnaire as Related to Epidemiological Studies of Cancer of the Cervix," *Journal of the National Cancer Institute*, 21 (1958), 713–20.

LIN, T., "Study of Incidence of Mental Disorder in Chinese and Other Cultures," *Psychiatry*, 16 (November, 1953), 313–36.

LINDEMANN, Erich, "Symptomatology and Management of Acute Grief," *American Journal of Psychiatry*, 101 (September, 1944), 141–48.

LINDEMANN, Erich, "Modification in the Course of Ulcerative Colitis in Relationship to Changes in Life Situations and Reaction Patterns," *Proceedings of the Association for Research in Nervous and Mental Disease*, 29 (1950), 706–23.

LINDEMANN, Erich and Ina May Greer, "A Study of Grief: Emotional Responses to Suicide," *Pastoral Psychology* (December, 1953), 9–13.

LINDEMANN, James E., George W. Fairweather, Gideon B. Stone, Robert S. Smith, and Ira T. London, "The Use of Demographic Characteristics in Predicting Length of Neuropsychiatric Hospital Stay," *Journal of Consulting Psychology*, 23 (1959). Reprinted *in* T. R. Sarbin, ed., *Studies in Behavior Pathology*, New York: Holt, Rinehart & Winston, Inc., 1961.

LINDEN, Maurice E. and Douglas Courtney, "The Human Life Cycle and Its Interruptions—A Psychologic Hypothesis," *American Journal of Psychiatry*, 109 (June, 1953), 906–15. Reprinted *in* A. M. Rose, ed., *Mental Health and Mental Disorders*, New York: W. W. Norton & Company, Inc., 1955.

LINDER, Marjorie P. and David Landy, "Post-Discharge Experience and Vocational Rehabilitation Needs of Psychiatric Patients," *Mental Hygiene*, 42 (January, 1958), 29–44.

LINDESMITH, Alfred R., *Opiate Addiction*, Bloomington, Ind.: Principia Press, 1947.

LINDESMITH, Alfred, "The British System of Narcotics Control," *Law and Contemporary Problems*, 22 (Winter, 1957), 138–54.

LINTON, Ralph, *Culture and Mental Disorders*, Springfield, Ill.: Charles C Thomas, Publisher, 1956.

LISANSKY, Edith S., "The Woman Alcoholic," *The Annals of the American Academy of Political and Social Science*, 315 (January, 1958), 73–81.

LLEWELLYN-THOMAS, Edward, "The Prevalence of Psychiatric Symptoms within an Island Fishing Village," *Canadian Medical Association Journal*, 83 (July, 1960), 197–204.

LOLLI, G., E. Serianni, G. M. Golder, and P. Luzzatto-Fegiz, *Alcohol in Italian Culture*, New York: The Free Press of Glencoe, Inc., 1958.

LOMHOLT, E., *Home Conditions: A Socio-Medical Study of 1066 Hospitalized Patients with Skin and Venereal Diseases*, Copenhagen: Rosenkilde and Bagger, 1958.

LONGAKER, William D. and John O. Godden, "A Comparison of Organic and Psychiatric Symptoms in a Small Town," *Acta Psychiatrica et Neurologica Scandinavica*, 35 (Fasc. 1, 1960), 91–100.

LOUDON, J. B., "Psychogenic Disorder and Social Conflict among the Zulu," *in* M. K. Opler, ed., *Culture and Mental Health*, New York: The Macmillan Company, 1959, 351–72.

LU, Yi-Chuang, "Contradictory Parental Expectations in Schizophrenia," *The Archives of General Psychiatry*, 6 (March, 1962), 219–34.

LYSTAD, M. H., "Social Mobility Among Selected Groups of Schizophrenic Patients," *American Sociological Review*, 22 (June, 1957), 288–92.

MABRY, John H., "Some Ecological Contributions to Epidemiology," *in* E. G. Jaco, ed., *Patients, Physicians, and Illness*, New York: The Free Press of Glencoe, Inc., 1958, 49–54.

MacGREGOR, Frances Cooke, "Some Psycho-Social Problems Associated with Facial Deformities," *American Sociological Review*, 16 (October, 1951), 629–38. Reprinted *in* E. G. Jaco, ed., *Patients, Physicians, and Illness*, New York: The Free Press of Glencoe, Inc., 1958.

MacGREGOR, Frances Cooke, "Some Psychological Hazards of Plastic Surgery of the Face," *Plastic and Reconstructive Surgery,* 12 (1953), 123–30. Reprinted *in* D. Apple, ed., *Sociological Studies of Health and Sickness,* New York: McGraw-Hill Book Company, Inc., 1960.

MacGREGOR, Frances Cooke, *Facial Deformities and Plastic Surgery,* Springfield, Ill.: Charles C Thomas, Publisher, 1956.

MacLACHLAN, John M., "Cultural Factors in Health and Disease," *in* E. G. Jaco, ed., *Patients, Physicians and Illness,* New York: The Free Press of Glencoe, Inc., 1958, 95–105.

MacMAHON, Brian and Ernest K. Koller, "Ethnic Differences in the Incidence of Leukemia," *Blood,* 12 (January, 1957), 1–10.

MacMAHON, Brian, Thomas F. Pugh, and Johannes Ipsen, *Epidemiologic Methods,* Boston: Little, Brown & Company, 1960.

MADDOX, George L., "Teenage Drinking in the United States," *in* D. J. Pittman and C. R. Snyder, eds., *Society, Culture, and Drinking Patterns,* New York: John Wiley & Sons, Inc., 1962, 230–45.

MAIN, T. F., "Rehabilitation and the Individual," *in* N. G. Harris, ed., *Modern Trends in Psychological Medicine,* New York: Paul B. Hoeber, Inc., 1948, 386–441.

MALIPHANT, R. G., "The Incidence of Cancer of the Uterine-Cervix," *British Medical Journal,* 1 (June 4, 1949), 978ff.

MALMO, Robert B., Charles Shagass, David J. Belanger, and A. Arthur Smith, "Motor Control in Psychiatric Patients under Experimental Stress," *The Journal of Abnormal and Social Psychology,* 46 (1951). Reprinted *in* T. R. Sarbin, ed., *Studies in Behavior Pathology,* New York: Holt, Rinehart & Winston, Inc., 1961.

MALZBERG, Benjamin, "A Comparison of First Admissions to the New York Civil State Hospitals During 1919–1921 and 1949–1951," *Psychiatric Quarterly,* 28 (April, 1954), 312–19.

MALZBERG, Benjamin, "Mental Disease Among the Native and Foreign-Born Populations of New York State, 1939–41," *Mental Hygiene,* 39 (October, 1955), 545–63.

MALZBERG, Benjamin, "Distribution of Mental Diseases in New York State, 1949–1951," *Psychiatric Quarterly Supplement,* 29 (1955), 209–38.

MALZBERG, Benjamin, "Mental Disease Among Native and Foreign-Born Negroes in New York State," *Journal of Negro Education,* 25 (1956), 175–81.

MALZBERG, Benjamin, "Mental Disease in Relation to Economic Status," *Journal of Nervous and Mental Disease,* 123 (1956), 257–61.

MALZBERG, Benjamin, "Marital Status and Mental Disease Among Negroes in New York State," *Journal of Nervous and Mental Disease,* 123 (1956), 457–65.

MALZBERG, Benjamin, "Mental Disease Among Puerto Ricans in New York State," *Mental Hygiene,* 40 (1956), 127–29.

MALZBERG, Benjamin, "Education and Mental Disease in New York State," *Mental Hygiene,* 40 (April, 1956), 177–95.

MALZBERG, Benjamin, "Mental Disease Among Negroes: An Analysis of First Admissions in New York State, 1949–51," *Mental Hygiene,* 43 (July, 1959), 422–59.

MALZBERG, Benjamin, *Mental Disease Among Jews in New York State,* New York: Intercontinental Medical Book Corporation, 1960.

MALZBERG, Benjamin, *The Alcoholic Psychoses: Demographic Aspects at Midcentury in New York State,* New Haven: Yale Center of Alcohol Studies, 1960.

MALZBERG, Benjamin and Everett S. Lee, *Migration and Mental Disease: A Study of First Admissions to Hospitals for Mental Disease, New York 1939–1941,* New York: Social Science Research Council, 1956.

MANGIN, William, "Drinking Among Andean Indians," *Quarterly Journal of Studies on Alcohol,* 18 (March, 1957), 55–66.

MANGIN, William, "Mental Health and Migration to Cities: A Peruvian Case," *in* Vera Rubin, ed., "Culture, Society, and Health," *Annals of the New York Academy of Sciences,* 84 (December, 1960), 911–17.

MANGUS, A. R., "Family Impacts on Mental Health," *Marriage and Family Living,* 19 (August, 1957), 256–62.

MARCIAL, Victor A., "Socioeconomic Aspects of the Incidence of Cancer in Puerto Rico," *in* Vera Rubin, ed., "Culture, Society, and Health," *Annals of the New York Academy of Sciences,* 84 (December, 1960), 981–88.

MARGOLIN, S. G., "Genetic and Dynamic Psycho-physiological Determinants of Pathophysiological Processes," *in* F. Deutsch, ed., *The Psychosomatic Concept in Psychoanalysis,* New York: International Universities Press, 1953.

MARKHAM, Jean E., "The Case of Mary Doe," *The Annals of the American Academy of Political and Social Science,* 315 (January, 1958), 82–89.

MASLAND, R. L., S. B. Sarason, and T. Gladwin, *Mental Subnormality: Biological, Psychological and Cultural Factors,* New York: Basic Books, Inc., 1958.

MAXWELL, Milton A., "Alcoholics Anonymous: An Interpretation," *in* D. J. Pittman and C. R. Snyder, eds., *Society, Culture, and Drinking Patterns,* New York: John Wiley & Sons, Inc., 1962, 577–85.

MAY, Jacques M., "Cultural Aspects of Tropical Medicine," *American Journal of Tropical Medicine,* 3 (May, 1954), 420–30.

MAY, Jacques M., *The Ecology of Human Disease,* New York: M.D. Publications, Inc., 1958.

MAY, Jacques M., "Sociocultural Factors in Chronic Organic Disease: The Ecology of Human Disease," *in* Vera Rubin, ed., "Culture, Society, and Health," *Annals of the New York Academy of Sciences,* 84 (December, 1960), 789–94.

MAY, Jacques M., *Studies in Disease Ecology,* New York: Hafner Publishing Co., Inc., 1961.

MAY, J. M. and I. S. Jarcho, *The Ecology of Malnutrition in the Far and Near East,* New York: Hafner Publishing Co., Inc., 1961.

MAYER, Albert J. and Philip Hauser, "Class Differentials in Expectation of Life at Birth," *in* R. Bendix and S. M. Lipset, eds., *Class, Status, and Power,* New York: The Free Press of Glencoe, Inc., 1953, 281–84.

MAYER, Albert J. and Sue Marx, "Social Change, Religion, and Birth Rates," *American Journal of Sociology,* 62 (January, 1957), 383–90.

MAYER-GROSS, W., "The Chronic Mental Patient in India and England," *Lancet,* 1 (1958), 1265–67.

McCAFFREY, I. and J. Downing, "The Usefulness of Ecological Analyses in Mental Disease Epidemiology," *American Journal of Psychiatry,* 113 (1957), 1063–68.

McCORD, William and Joan McCord, *Origins of Alcoholism,* Stanford, Calif.: Stanford University Press, 1960.

McCORD, William and Joan McCord, "A Longitudinal Study of the Personality of Alcoholics," *in* D. J. Pittman and C. R. Snyder, eds., *Society, Culture, and Drinking Patterns,* New York: John Wiley & Sons, Inc., 1962, 413–30.

McCORD, William, Joan McCord, and P. Verden, "Familial Correlates of 'Psychosomatic' Symptoms in Children," *Journal of Health and Human Behavior,* 1 (Fall, 1960), 192–99.

McFARLAND, Ross A., "Epidemiologic Principles Applicable to the Study and Prevention of Child Accidents," *American Journal of Public Health,* 45 (October, 1955), 1302–08.

McKEOWN, J. E., "The Behavior of Parents of Schizophrenic, Neurotic, and Normal Children," *American Journal of Sociology,* 56 (1950), 175–79.

McPARTLAND, Thomas S. and John H. Cumming, "Self-Conception, Social Class and Mental Health," *Human Organization,* 17 (Fall, 1958), 24–29.

MEAD, Margaret, "Some Theoretical Considerations on the Problem of Mother-Child Separation," *American Journal of Orthopsychiatry*, 24 (July, 1954), 471–83.

MEAD, Margaret, "Mental Health in World Perspective," *in* M. K. Opler, ed., *Culture and Mental Health*, New York: The Macmillan Company, 1959, 501–16.

MECHANIC, David, "Relevance of Group Atmosphere and Attitudes for the Rehabilitation of Alcoholics: A Pilot Study," *Quarterly Journal of Studies on Alcohol*, 22 (December, 1961), 634–45.

MECHANIC, David, "Some Factors in Identifying and Defining Mental Illness," *Mental Hygiene*, 46 (January, 1962), 66–74.

MENDELSON, M., S. Hirsch, and C. S. Webber, "A Critical Examination of Some Recent Theoretical Models in Psychosomatic Medicine," *Psychosomatic Medicine*, 18 (October, 1956), 363–73.

MESSING, Simon D., "Group Therapy and Social Status in the Zar Cult of Ethiopia," *American Anthropologist*, 60 (December, 1958), 1120–26. Reprinted *in* M. K. Opler, ed., *Culture and Mental Health*, New York: The Macmillan Company, 1959.

MESZAROS, A. F. and E. S. Meszaros, "Integration of the Discharged Schizophrenic Patient Within the Family," *in* M. Greenblatt, D. J. Levinson, and Gerald L. Klerman, eds., *Mental Patients in Transition*, Springfield, Ill.: Charles C Thomas, Publisher, 1961, 218–28.

MEZEY, A. G., "Personal Background, Emigration, and Mental Disorder in Hungarian Refugees," *Journal of Mental Science*, 106 (April, 1960), 618–27.

MEZEY, A. G., "Psychiatric Illness in Hungarian Refugees," *Journal of Mental Science*, 106 (April, 1960), 628–37.

MICHAELS, J. J., "A Psychiatric Adventure in Comparative Pathophysiology of the Infant and Adult," *Journal of Nervous and Mental Disease*, 100 (1944), 49ff.

MILGRAM, Norman A., "Cognitive and Emphatic Factors in Role-Taking by Schizophrenic and Brain Damaged Patients," *The Journal of Abnormal and Social Psychology*, 60 (1960). Reprinted *in* T. R. Sarbin, ed., *Studies in Behavior Pathology*, New York: Holt, Rinehart & Winston, Inc., 1961.

MILLER, F. J. W. *et al.*, *Growing Up in Newcastle Upon Tyne: A Continuing Study of Health and Illness in Young Children Within Their Families*, London: Oxford University Press, 1960.

MILLER, J. G., "Mental Health Implications of a General Behavior Theory," *American Journal of Psychiatry*, 113 (1957), 776–82.

MILLER, S. M. and E. G. Mishler, "Social Class, Mental Illness, and American Psychiatry," *Milbank Memorial Fund Quarterly*, 37 (April, 1959), 174–99.

MILLS, Enid, *Living with Mental Illness*, London: Routledge & Kegan Paul, 1962.

MONIQUE, S. J., "The Alcoholic," *Alcohol Hygiene*, 3 (March, 1957), 5–10.

MONTAGU, Ashley, "Culture and Mental Illness," *American Journal of Psychiatry*, 117 (July, 1961), 15–23.

MORRIS, J. N. and J. A. Heady, "Social and Biological Factors in Infant Mortality," *Lancet* (February, 1955), 343–49.

MORRIS, J. N. and Richard N. Titmuss, "Health and Social Change: I. The Recent History of Rheumatic Heart Disease," *Medical Officer* (London), 72 (1944), 69–71, 77–79, 85–87.

MORRIS, P., "Some Disturbances of Family Functioning Associated with Psychiatric Illness," *British Journal of Medical Psychology*, 31 (1958), 104–16.

MOSER, Marvin, "Epidemiology of Hypertension with Particular Reference to Racial Susceptibility," *in* Vera Rubin, ed., "Culture, Society, and Health," *Annals of the New York Academy of Sciences*, 84 (December, 1960), 989–1000.

MOYER, J. H., ed., *Symposium on Hypertension*, Philadelphia: W. B. Saunders Co., 1959.

MULFORD, Harold A. and Donald E. Miller, "Drinking Behavior Related to Definitions of Alcohol: A Report of Research in Progress," *American Sociological Review,* 24 (June, 1959), 385–89.

MULFORD, Harold A. and Donald E. Miller, "Drinking in Iowa: I. Sociocultural Distribution of Drinkers, II. The Extent of Drinking and Selected Sociocultural Categories," *Quarterly Journal of Studies on Alcohol,* 20 (December, 1959), 704–26.

MULFORD, Harold A. and Donald E. Miller, "Drinking in Iowa: III. A Scale of Definitions of Alcohol Related to Drinking Behavior," *Quarterly Journal of Studies on Alcohol,* 21 (June, 1960), 267–78.

MULFORD, Harold A. and Donald E. Miller, "Drinking in Iowa: IV. Preoccupation with Alcohol and Definitions of Alcohol, Heavy Drinking and Trouble Due to Drinking," *Quarterly Journal of Studies on Alcohol,* 21 (June, 1960), 279–91.

MULFORD, Harold A. and Donald E. Miller, "Drinking in Iowa: V. Drinking and Alcoholic Drinking," *Quarterly Journal of Studies on Alcohol,* 21 (September, 1960), 483–99.

MULFORD, Harold A. and Donald E. Miller, "An Index of Alcoholic Drinking Behavior Related to the Meanings of Alcohol," *Journal of Health and Human Behavior,* 2 (Spring, 1961), 26–31.

MUNTENDAN, P., "The Influence of the Social Milieu on the Manifestation and Course of Tuberculosis," *Acta Tuberculosa Scandinavica,* 37 (1959), 63–87.

MURPHY, H. B. M., "Culture and Mental Disorder in Singapore," *in* M. K. Opler, ed., *Culture and Mental Health,* New York: The Macmillan Company, 1959, 291–318.

MYERS, J. K., "An Empirical Approach to the Study of Schizophrenia," *Psychiatric Research Report 5,* American Psychiatric Association (June, 1956), 29–48.

MYERS, Jerome K. and F. Auld, Jr., "Some Variables Related to Outcome of Psychotherapy," *Journal of Clinical Psychology,* 11 (January, 1955), 51–54.

MYERS, Jerome K. and Bertram H. Roberts, "A Sociological-Psychiatric Case Study of Schizophrenia," *Sociology and Social Research,* 39 (September–October, 1954), 11–17.

MYERS, Jerome K. and Bertram H. Roberts, *Family and Class Dynamics in Mental Illness,* New York: John Wiley & Sons, Inc., 1959.

MYERSON, A., "Social Psychology of Alcoholism," *Diseases of the Nervous System,* 1 (1940), 43–50.

MYERSON, A., "Alcohol: A Study of Social Ambivalence," *Quarterly Journal of Studies on Alcohol,* 1 (1940), 13–20.

MYERSON, L., "Physical Disability as a Social Psychological Problem," *Journal of Social Issues,* 4 (1948), 2–10.

NAGE, Saad Z., *Factors Related to Heart Disease Among Ohio Farmers,* Wooster: Ohio Agricultural Experiment Station, Research Bulletin 842, October, 1959.

NORRIS, V., *Mental Illness in London,* London: Chapman & Hall, Ltd., 1959.

NOTESTEIN, Frank W., "Class Differences in Fertility," *Annals of the American Academy of Political and Social Science,* 188 (November, 1936), 26–36.

ODEGAARD, O., "Emigration and Mental Health," *Mental Hygiene,* 20 (October, 1936), 546–53.

ODEGAARD, O., "The Incidence of Psychoses in Various Occupations," *The International Journal of Social Psychiatry,* 2 (Autumn, 1956), 85–104.

ODEGAARD, O., "Incidence of Mental Disease in Norway During World War II," *Acta Psychiatrica et Neurologica Scadinavica,* 29 (1959), 333–55.

OLSHANSKY, S., S. Grob, and M. Ekdahl, "Survey of Employment Experiences of Patients Discharged from Three State Mental Hospitals during Period 1951–1953," *Mental Hygiene,* 44 (October, 1960), 510–21.

OPLER, Marvin K., "Cultural Perspectives in Mental Health Research," *The American Journal of Orthopsychiatry*, 25 (January, 1955).

OPLER, Marvin K., "The Influence of Ethnic and Class Subcultures on Child Care," *Social Problems*, 3 (July, 1955), 14–21.

OPLER, Marvin K., *Culture, Psychiatry, and Human Values*, Springfield, Ill.: Charles C Thomas, Publisher, 1956.

OPLER, Marvin K., "Epidemiological Studies of Mental Illness," *in* Walter Reed Army Institute of Research, *Symposium on Preventive and Social Psychiatry*, Washington, D.C.: Government Printing Office, 1957, 111–48.

OPLER, Marvin K., "Cultural Differences in Mental Disorders: An Italian and Irish Contrast in the Schizophrenias—U. S. A.," *The Psychiatric Quarterly* (July, 1959). Reprinted *in* M. K. Opler, ed., *Culture and Mental Health*, New York: The Macmillan Company, 1959.

OPLER, Marvin K., "Social Psychiatry—Evolutionary, Existentialist and Transcultural Findings," *Psychosomatics*, 2 (November–December, 1961), 430–35.

OPLER, Marvin K. and Jerome L. Singer, "Ethnic Differences in Behavior and Psychopathology," *International Journal of Social Psychiatry*, 2 (Summer, 1956), 11–22.

OSGOOD, Charles E. and Evelyn G. Walker, "Motivation and Language Behavior: A Content Analysis of Suicide Notes," *The Journal of Abnormal and Social Psychology*, 59 (1959). Reprinted *in* T. R. Sarbin, ed., *Studies in Behavior Pathology*, New York: Holt, Rinehart & Winston, Inc., 1961.

PALOLA, Ernest G., Theodore L. Dorpat, and William R. Larson, "Alcoholism and Suicidal Behavior," *in* D. J. Pittman and C. R. Snyder, eds., *Society, Culture, and Drinking Patterns*, New York: John Wiley & Sons, Inc., 1962, 511–34.

PALOLA, Ernest G., Joan K. Jackson, and Daniel Kelleher, "Defensiveness in Alcoholics: Measures Based on the Minnesota Multiphasic Personality Inventory," *Journal of Health and Human Behavior*, 2 (Fall, 1961), 185–89.

PALOUCEK, Frank P. and J. B. Graham, "Precipitating Factors in Cancer of the Cervix," *Surgical Forum of the American College of Surgeons*, 10 (1959).

PARK, Peter, "Problem Drinking and Role Deviation: A Study in Incipient Alcoholism," *in* D. J. Pittman and C. R. Snyder, eds., *Society, Culture, and Drinking Patterns*, New York: John Wiley & Sons, Inc., 1962, 431–54.

PARKER, Seymour, Robert J. Kleiner, and Hayward G. Taylor, "Level of Aspiration and Mental Disorder: A Research Proposal," *in* Vera Rubin, ed., "Culture, Society, and Health," *Annals of the New York Academy of Sciences*, 84 (December, 1960), 878–86.

PARSONS, Talcott, "Toward a Healthy Maturity," *Journal of Health and Human Behavior*, 1 (Fall, 1960), 163–73.

PARSONS, Talcott and Renée Fox, "Illness, Therapy, and the Modern Urban American Family," *The Journal of Social Issues*, 8 (1952), 2–3, 31–44. Reprinted *in* E. G. Jaco, ed., *Patients, Physicians, and Illness*, New York: The Free Press of Glencoe, Inc., 1958.

PASAMANICK, Benjamin *et al.*, "Socioeconomic Status and Some Precursors of Neuropsychiatric Disorder," *American Journal of Orthopsychiatry*, 26 (1956), 594–601.

PASAMANICK, Benjamin *et al.*, "A Survey of Mental Disease in an Urban Population," *American Journal of Public Health*, 47 (August, 1957), 923–29.

PASAMANICK, Benjamin and Hilda Knobloch, "Race, Complications of Pregnancy, and Neuropsychiatric Disorder," *Social Problems*, 5 (Winter, 1957–58), 264–78.

PASAMANICK, Benjamin, Dean W. Roberts, Paul W. Lemkau, and Dean B. Krueger, "A Survey of Mental Disease in an Urban Population: Prevalence by Race and Income," *in* B. Pasamanick, ed., *Epidemiology of Mental Disorder*, Washington, D.C.: American Association for the Advancement of Science, 1959, 183–202.

PATERSON, R., "Why Do Cancer Patients Delay?" *The Canadian Medical Association Journal,* 73 (December 15, 1955), 931–40.

PAUL, Benjamin D., "Mental Disorder and Self-Regulating Processes in Culture: A Guatemalan Illustration," *in* Milbank Memorial Fund, *Interrelations between the Social Environment and Psychiatric Disorders,* New York: Milbank Memorial Fund, 1953, 51–68.

PEARL, Arthur, Robert Buechley, and Wendell R. Lipscomb, "Cirrhosis Mortality in Three Large Cities: Implications for Alcoholism and Intercity Comparisons," *in* D. J. Pittman and C. R. Snyder, eds., *Society, Culture, and Drinking Patterns,* New York: John Wiley & Sons, Inc., 1962, 345–52.

PEMBERTON, J. and H. Willard, eds., *Recent Studies in Epidemiology,* Oxford: Blackwell Scientific Publications, 1958.

PERROTT, George, "The Problem of Chronic Disease," *Psychosomatic Medicine,* 7 (1945), 21–27.

PESCOR, Michael J., "Follow-Up Study of Treated Narcotic Drug Addicts," *Public Health Reports,* Supplement 170, 1943, 1–18.

PESCOR, Michael J., "A Statistical Analysis of the Clinical Records of Hospitalized Drug Addicts," *Public Health Reports,* Supplement 143, 1943.

PHILLIPS, Bernard S., "A Role Theory Approach to Adjustment in Old Age," *American Sociological Review,* 22 (April, 1957), 212–17.

PHILLIPS, Harry T., "An Inter-Racial Study in Social Conditions and Infant Mortality in Cape Town," *Milbank Memorial Fund Quarterly,* 35 (January, 1957), 7–28.

PHILLIPS, Leslie and Bernard Cowitz, "Social Attainment and Reactions to Stress," *Journal of Personality,* 22 (December, 1953), 270–83.

PHILLIPS, Leslie and M. Sam Rabinovitch, "Social Role and Patterns of Symptomatic Behaviors," *The Journal of Abnormal and Social Psychology,* 57 (September, 1958). Reprinted *in* T. R. Sarbin, ed., *Studies in Behavior Pathology,* New York: Holt, Rinehart & Winston, Inc., 1961.

PITTMAN, David J. and C. Wayne Gordon, *Revolving Door: A Study of the Chronic Police Case Inebriate,* New York: The Free Press of Glencoe, Inc., 1958.

PITTMAN, David J. and C. Wayne Gordon, "Criminal Careers of the Chronic Drunkenness Offender," *Quarterly Journal of Studies on Alcohol,* 19 (1958), 255–68. Reprinted *in* D. J. Pittman and C. R. Snyder, eds., *Society, Culture, and Drinking Patterns,* New York: John Wiley & Sons, Inc., 1962.

PLANK, Robert, "The Family Constellation of a Group of Schizophrenic Patients," *American Journal of Orthopsychiatry,* 23 (1953), 817–25.

PLUNKETT, Richard J. and John E. Gordon, *Epidemiology and Mental Illness,* New York: Basic Books, Inc., 1960.

POLLAK, Otto, *Social Adjustment in Old Age,* New York: Social Science Research Council, Bulletin 59, 1948.

POND, M. Allen, "The Influence of Housing on Family Health," *Marriage and Family Living,* 19 (1957), 154–59.

POST, F., "Social Factors in Old Age Psychiatry," *Geriatrics,* 13 (September, 1958), 576–80.

PROUT, Curtis T. and Mary Alice White, "A Controlled Study of Personality Relationships in Mothers of Schizophrenic Male Patients," *American Journal of Psychiatry,* 107 (1950), 251–56.

PULLMAN, Douglas R., "Some Social Correlates of Attitudes Toward the Use of Alcoholic Beverages," *Quarterly Journal of Studies on Alcohol,* 19 (December, 1958), 623–35.

PURCELL, Kenneth, Lewis Bernstein, and Samuel C. Bukantz, "A Preliminary Comparison of Rapidly Remitting and Persistently Steroid-Dependent Asthmatic Children," *Psychosomatic Medicine,* 23 (July–August, 1961), 305–10.

QUEEN, S. A., "The Ecological Study of Mental Disorders," *American Sociological Review*, 5 (1940), 201–9.

QUISENBERRY, Walter B., "Sociocultural Factors in Cancer in Hawaii," *in* Vera Rubin, ed., "Culture, Society, and Health," *Annals of the New York Academy of Sciences*, 84 (December, 1960), 795–806.

QUISENBERRY, Walter B., I. L. Tilden, and J. L. Rosengard, "Racial Incidence of Cancer in Hawaii: A Study of 3,257 Cases of Malignant Neoplastic Diseases," *Hawaiian Medical Journal*, 13 (1954), 449ff.

RAINER, John D. and Franz J. Kallmann, "Genetic and Demographic Aspects of Disordered Behavior Patterns in a Deaf Population," *in* B. Pasamanick, ed., *Epidemiology of Mental Disorder*, Washington, D.C.: American Association for the Advancement of Science, 1959, 229–48.

RAJOTTE, Paul and Herman C. B. Denber, "Intensive Follow-Up Study of Fifty Chronic Relapsing Psychotic Female Patients," *in* M. Greenblatt, D. J. Levinson, and Gerald L. Klerman, eds., *Mental Patients in Transition*, Springfield, Ill.: Charles C Thomas, Publisher, 1961, 139–50.

RAPOPORT, Rhona V. and Robert N. Rapoport, "Patients' Families: Assets and Liabilities," *in* M. Greenblatt, D. J. Levinson, and Gerald L. Klerman, eds., *Mental Patients in Transition*, Springfield, Ill.: Charles C Thomas, Publisher, 1961, 208–17.

RAY, Marsh B., "The Cycle of Abstinence and Relapse Among Heroin Addicts," *Social Problems*, 9 (Fall, 1961), 132–40.

REDLICH, Frederick C., "The Concept of Normality," *American Journal of Psychotherapy*, 6 (1952), 551–76.

REDLICH, Frederick C., "The Influence of Environment on Mental Health," *Bulletin of the New York Academy of Medicine*, 30 (August, 1954), 608–21.

REDLICH, Frederick C., "The Concept of Health in Psychiatry," *in* A. H. Leighton, J. A. Clausen, and R. N. Wilson, eds., *Explorations in Social Psychiatry*, New York: Basic Books, Inc., 1957, 138–64.

REDLICH, Frederick C., A. B. Hollingshead, and Elizabeth Bellis, "Social Class Differences in Attitudes toward Psychiatry," *American Journal of Orthopsychiatry*, 25 (1955), 60–70. Reprinted *in* D. Apple, ed., *Sociological Studies of Health and Sickness*, New York: McGraw-Hill Book Company, Inc., 1960.

REDLICH, Frederick C., A. B. Hollingshead, B. H. Roberts, H. A. Robinson, L. Z. Freedman, and J. K. Myers, "Social Structure and Psychiatric Disorder," *American Journal of Psychiatry*, 109 (April, 1953), 729–34.

REEDER, Leo G., "The Socio-Economic Effects of Heart Disease," *Social Problems*, 4 (1956), 51–55.

REEDER, Leo G., "Social Factors in Heart Disease: A Preliminary Research Report on the Relationship of Certain Social Factors to Blood Pressure in Males," *Social Forces*, 34 (1956), 367–71.

REEDER, Leo G., "Occupation and Socioeconomic Status as Variables in Heart Disease Research: A Critique," *American Journal of the Medical Sciences*, 238 (September, 1959), 297–307.

REICHARD, Suzanne and Carl Tillman, "Patterns of Parent-Child Relationships in Schizophrenia," *Psychiatry*, 13 (1950), 247–57.

RENNIE, T. A. C. and L. Srole, "Social Class Prevalence and Distribution of Psychosomatic Conditions in an Urban Population," *Psychosomatic Medicine*, 18 (1956), 449–56.

RENNIE, T. A. C. *et al.*, "Urban Life and Mental Health: Socio-economic Status and Mental Disorder in the Metropolis," *American Journal of Psychiatry*, 13 (1957), 831–37.

REZNIKOFF, Marvin, "Psychological Factors in Breast Cancer," *Psychosomatic Medicine*, 17 (March–April, 1955), 96–108.

RICHARDSON, Stephen A. *et al.*, "Cultural Uniformity in Reaction to Physical Disabilities," *American Sociological Review*, 26 (April, 1961), 241–47.

RILEY, John W. and C. S. Marden, "The Social Patterns of Alcohol Drinking," *Quarterly Journal of Studies on Alcohol*, 8 (September, 1947), 265–73.

ROBERTS, B. H. and J. K. Myers, "Religion, National Origin, Immigration, and Mental Illness," *The American Journal of Psychiatry*, 110 (April, 1954), 759–64.

ROBERTS, B. H. and J. K. Myers, "Schizophrenia in the Youngest Male Child of the Lower Middle Class," *American Journal of Psychiatry*, 112 (September, 1955), 179–85.

ROBERTS, G. W., and Lloyd Braithwaite, "Fertility Differentials by Family Type in Trinidad," *in* Vera Rubin, ed., "Culture, Society, and Health," *Annals of the New York Academy of Sciences*, 84 (December, 1960), 963–80.

ROBINS, Eli and Patricia O'Neal, "Culture and Mental Disorder: A Study of Attempted Suicide," *Human Organization*, 16 (Winter, 1958), 7–11.

ROBINS, Lee N., William M. Bates, and Patricia O'Neal, "Adult Drinking Patterns of Former Problem Children," *in* D. J. Pittman and C. R. Snyder, eds., *Society, Culture, and Drinking Patterns*, New York: John Wiley & Sons, Inc., 1962, 395–412.

ROBINSON, G. Canby, "Proper Attention to the Role of Emotional and Social Factors in Illness as a New Step in Public Health," *Milbank Memorial Fund Quarterly*, 23 (January, 1945), 20–27.

ROBINSON, H. A., F. C. Redlich, and A. B. Hollingshead, "An Investigation of Social Structure and Psychiatric Disorder," *The Psychologist*, 7 (1952), 348.

ROEMER, Ruth, "Mental Health Legislation Affecting Patient Care," *American Journal of Public Health*, 52 (April, 1962), 592–99.

ROGERS, E. S., *Human Ecology and Health: An Introduction for Administrators*, New York: The Macmillan Company, 1960.

ROGLER, Lloyd H. and August B. Hollingshead, "Class and Disordered Speech in the Mentally Ill," *Journal of Health and Human Behavior*, 2 (Fall, 1961), 178–85.

ROSE, Arnold M., "Factors in Mental Breakdown in Combat," *in* A. M. Rose, ed., *Mental Health and Mental Disorders*, New York: W. W. Norton & Company, Inc., 1955, 291–313.

ROSE, Arnold M., "Social Psychological Effects of Physical Deprivation," *Journal of Health and Human Behavior*, 1 (Winter, 1960), 285–90.

ROSE, Arnold M. and Holger B. Stub, "Summary of Studies on the Incidence of Mental Disorders," *in* A. M. Rose, ed., *Mental Health and Mental Disorders*, New York: W. W. Norton & Company, Inc., 1955, 87–116.

ROSENGREN, W. R., "Social Sources of Pregnancy as Illness or Normality," *Social Forces*, 39 (February, 1961), 260–67.

RUBINGTON, Earl, "The Chronic Drunkenness Offender," *The Annals of the American Academy of Political and Social Science*, 315 (January, 1958), 65–72.

RUBINGTON, Earl, " 'Failure' as a Heavy Drinker: The Case of the Chronic-Drunkenness Offender on Skid Row," *in* D. J. Pittman and C. R. Snyder, eds., *Society, Culture, and Drinking Patterns*, New York: John Wiley & Sons, Inc., 1962, 146–53.

RUESCH, Jurgen, "Social Technique, Social Status, and Social Change in Illness," *in* Clyde Kluckhohn and Henry A. Murray, eds., *Personality in Nature, Society, and Culture*, New York: Alfred A. Knopf, Inc., 1949, 117–30.

RUESCH, Jurgen *et al.*, *Chronic Disease and Psychological Invalidism: A Psychosomatic Study*, Berkeley: University of California Press, 1951.

RUSK, H. A. and J. Novey, "The Impact of Chronic Illness on Families," *Marriage and Family Living*, 19 (1957), 193–97.

RUSSEK, H. I., "Role of Heredity, Diet, and Emotional Stress in Coronary Heart Disease," *Journal of the American Medical Association*, 171 (October, 1959), 503–8.

RUST, R. M., "Epidemiology of Mental Health in College," *Journal of Psychology*, 49 (1960), 235–48.

RYCKOFF, Irving, Juliana Day, and Lyman C. Wynne, "Maintenance of Stereotyped Roles in the Families of Schizophrenics," A.M.A. *Archives of Psychiatry*, 1 (July, 1959), 93–98.

SABIN, A. B., "Paralytic Consequences of Poliomyelitis Infection in Different Parts of the World and in Different Population Groups," *American Journal of Public Health*, 41 (October, 1951), 1215–30.

SAMPSON, Harold, Sheldon L. Messinger, and Robert D. Towne, "Two Types of Schizophrenic Crises in Women," *Bulletin of the Menninger Clinic*, 25 (November, 1961), 298–306.

SAMPSON, Harold, Sheldon L. Messinger, and Robert D. Towne, "Family Processes and Becoming a Mental Patient," *American Journal of Sociology*, 68 (July, 1962), 88–96.

SANGREE, Walter H., "The Social Functions of Beer Drinking in Bantu Tiriki," *in* D. J. Pittman and C. R. Snyder, eds., *Society, Culture, and Drinking Patterns*, New York: John Wiley & Sons, Inc., 1962, 6–21.

SANUA, Victor D., "Sociocultural Factors in Response to Stressful Life Situations: The Behavior of Aged Amputees as an Example," *Journal of Health and Human Behavior*, 1 (Spring, 1960), 17–24.

SARASON, S. B. and T. Gladwin, *Psychological Problems in Mental Deficiency*, New York: Harper & Row, Publishers, 1959.

SAUER, Herbert I., "Epidemiology of a Cardiovascular Mortality—Geographic and Ethnic," *American Journal of Public Health*, 52 (January, 1962), 94–105.

SAYRES, William C., "Ritual Drinking, Ethnic Status and Inebriety in Rural Colombia," *Quarterly Journal of Studies on Alcohol*, 17 (March, 1956), 53–62.

SCHERMERHORN, R. A., "Psychiatric Disorders among Negroes: A Sociological Note," *American Journal of Psychiatry*, 112 (1956), 878–82.

SCHMIDT, W. S. and R. G. Smart, "Alcoholics, Drinking and Traffic Accidents," *Quarterly Journal of Studies on Alcohol*, 20 (September, 1959), 631–44.

SCHNEIDER, David M., "The Social Dynamics of Physical Disability in Army Basic Training," *Psychiatry*, 10 (1947), 323–33.

SCHNORE, L. F. and J. D. Cowhig, "Some Correlates of Reported Health in Metropolitan Centers," *Social Problems*, 7 (Winter, 1959–60), 218–26.

SCHOFIELD, William and Lucy Balian, "A Comparative Study of the Personal Histories of Schizophrenic and Nonpsychiatric Patients," *The Journal of Abnormal and Social Psychology*, 59 (September, 1959). Reprinted *in* T. R. Sarbin, ed., *Studies in Behavior Pathology*, New York: Holt, Rinehart & Winston, Inc., 1961.

SCHROEDER, W. Widick and J. Allan Beegle, "Suicide: An Instance of High Rural Rates," *Rural Sociology*, 18 (March, 1953), 45–52. Reprinted *in* A. M. Rose, ed., *Mental Health and Mental Disorders*, New York: W. W. Norton & Company, Inc., 1955.

SCHULZINGER, M. D., *The Accident Syndrome*, Springfield, Ill.: Charles C Thomas, Publisher, 1956.

SCHUR, Edwin M., "Drug Addiction Under British Policy," *Social Problems*, 9 (Fall, 1961), 156–66.

SCHWARTZ, Charlotte Green, "Perspectives on Deviance—Wives' Definitions of their Husbands' Mental Illness," *Psychiatry*, 20 (August, 1957), 275–91.

SCOTCH, Norman A., "A Preliminary Report on the Relation of Sociocultural Factors to Hypertension Among the Zulu," *in* Vera Rubin, ed., "Culture, Society, and

Health," *Annals of the New York Academy of Sciences,* 84 (December, 1960), 1000–1009.

SCOTT, Frances G., "Factors in the Personal Adjustment of Institutionalized and Non-Institutionalized Aged," *American Sociological Review,* 20 (October, 1955), 538–46.

SCOTT, William A., "Social Psychological Correlates of Mental Illness and Mental Health," *Psychological Bulletin,* 55 (March, 1958), 65–87.

SEELEY, John R., "Social Values, the Mental Health Movement, and Mental Health," *The Annals of the American Academy of Political and Social Sciences,* 286 (March, 1953), 15–24. Reprinted *in* A. M. Rose, ed., *Mental Health and Mental Disorders,* New York: W. W. Norton & Company, Inc., 1955.

SEELEY, J. R., "Estimating the Prevalence of Alcoholism: A Critical Analysis of the Jellinek Formula," *Quarterly Journal of Studies on Alcohol,* 20 (1959), 245–55.

SEELEY, John R., "Alcoholism Is a Disease: Implications for Social Policy," *in* D. J. Pittman and C. R. Snyder, eds., *Society, Culture, and Drinking Patterns,* New York: John Wiley & Sons, Inc., 1962, 586–93.

SEELEY, John R., "The Ecology of Alcoholism: A Beginning," *in* D. J. Pittman and C. R. Snyder, eds., *Society, Culture, and Drinking Patterns,* New York: John Wiley & Sons, Inc., 1962, 330–44.

SEIDENFELD, Morton A., ed., "The Evaluation of Rehabilitation in the Individual," *American Journal of Orthopsychiatry,* 27 (January, 1957), 9–37.

SELYE, Hans, *The Stress of Life,* New York: McGraw-Hill Book Company, Inc., 1956.

SEWELL, William H., "Infant Training and the Personality of the Child," *American Journal of Sociology,* 58 (September, 1952), 150–59. Reprinted *in* A. M. Rose, ed., *Mental Health and Mental Disorders,* New York: W. W. Norton & Company, Inc., 1955.

SHEPHERD, Michael, *A Study of the Major Psychoses in an English County,* London: Chapman & Hall, Ltd., Maudsley Monograph 3, 1957.

SHERFEY, Mary Jane, "Psychopathology and Character Structure in Chronic Alcoholism," *in* O. Diethelm, ed., *Etiology of Chronic Alcoholism,* Springfield, Ill.: Charles C Thomas, Publisher, 1955, 16–42.

SIFNEOS, P. E., C. Gore, and A. C. Sifneos, "A Preliminary Psychiatric Study of Attempted Suicide as Seen in a General Hospital," *American Journal of Psychiatry,* 112 (1956), 883–88.

SILVERMAN, Maurice, "Psychological and Social Aspects of Psychiatric Disorders in the Aged," *Journal of Mental Science,* 99 (1953), 257–64.

SILVERMAN, Maurice, "Further Studies on Psychological and Social Aspects of Psychiatric Disorders in the Aged," *Social Review,* 6 (December, 1958), 181–89.

SIMMONS, J. S., T. F. Whayne, G. W. Anderson, H. M. Horack, *et al., Global Epidemiology: A Geography of Disease and Sanitation,* Philadelphia: J. B. Lippincott Company, 3 Vols., 1944–54.

SIMMONS, Leo, "Cultural Patterns in Childbirth," *American Journal of Nursing,* 52 (August, 1952), 989–91.

SIMMONS, Ozzie G., "Drinking Patterns and Interpersonal Performance in a Peruvian Mestizo Community," *Quarterly Journal of Studies on Alcohol,* 20 (March, 1959), 103–11.

SIMMONS, Ozzie G., "Ambivalence and the Learning of Drinking Behavior in a Peruvian Community," *American Anthropologist,* 62 (December, 1960), 1018–27. Reprinted *in* D. J. Pittman and C. R. Snyder, eds., *Society, Culture, and Drinking Patterns,* New York: John Wiley & Sons, Inc., 1962.

SIMMONS, Ozzie G., *After Hospitalization: The Mental Patient and His Family,* Austin, Tex.: The Hogg Foundation for Mental Health, 1960.

SIMMONS, Ozzie G. and Howard E. Freeman, "Familial Expectations and Posthospital Performance of Mental Patients," *Human Relations,* 12 (August, 1959), 233–42.

SINGER, Jerome L. and Marvin K. Opler, "Contrasting Patterns of Fantasy and Motility in Irish and Italian Schizophrenics," *The Journal of Abnormal and Social Psychology,* 53 (July, 1956). Reprinted *in* T. R. Sarbin, ed., *Studies in Behavior Pathology,* New York: Holt, Rinehart & Winston, Inc., 1961.

SLOTKIN, J. S., "The Nature and Effects of Social Interaction in Schizophrenia," *Journal of Abnormal and Social Psychology,* 37 (July, 1942), 345–68.

SLOTKIN, J. S., "Culture and Psychopathology," *Journal of Abnormal and Social Psychology,* 51 (September, 1955), 269–75.

SMITH, M., "Occupational Differentials in Physical Status," *American Sociological Review,* 13 (February, 1948), 72–82.

SMITH, M. Brewster, " 'Mental Health' Reconsidered: A Special Case of the Problem of Values in Psychology," *American Psychologist,* 16 (1961), 299–306.

SNYDER, Charles R., *Alcohol and the Jews: A Cultural Study of Drinking and Sobriety,* New York: The Free Press of Glencoe, Inc., 1958.

SNYDER, Charles R., "Culture and Jewish Sobriety: The Ingroup-Outgroup Factor," *in* D. J. Pittman and C. R. Snyder, eds., *Society, Culture, and Drinking Patterns,* New York: John Wiley & Sons, Inc., 1962, 188–225.

SNYDER, Charles R. and Ruth H. Landman, "Studies of Drinking in Jewish Culture: II. Prospectus for Sociological Research on Jewish Drinking Patterns," *Quarterly Journal of Studies on Alcohol,* 12 (1951), 451–74.

SOMMER, Robert and Robert Hall, "Alienation and Mental Illness," *American Sociological Review,* 23 (August, 1958), 418–20.

SOUTHARD, Samuel, *The Family and Mental Illness,* Philadelphia: The Westminster Press, 1957.

SPAIN, David M., "Problems in the Study of Coronary Atherosclerosis in Population Groups," *in* Vera Rubin, ed., "Culture, Society, and Health," *Annals of the New York Academy of Sciences,* 84 (December, 1960), 816–34.

SPARER, P. J., ed., *Personality, Stress, and Tuberculosis,* New York: International Universities Press, 1956.

SPENCE, James C. *et al., A Thousand Families in Newcastle Upon Tyne: An Approach to the Study of Health and Illness in Children,* New York: Oxford University Press, 1954.

SPIEGEL, John P., "Mental Health and the Family," *New England Journal of Medicine,* 251 (November, 1954), 843–46.

SPIEGEL, John P., "The Resolution of Role Conflict Within the Family," *Psychiatry,* 20 (1957), 1–16.

SPIEGEL, John P. and Norman W. Bell, "The Family of the Psychiatric Patient," *American Handbook of Psychiatry,* New York: Basic Books, Inc., 1959, 114–49.

SPIRO, Melford E., "Cultural Heritage, Personal Tensions, and Mental Illness in a South Sea Culture," *in* M. K. Opler, ed., *Culture and Mental Health,* New York: The Macmillan Company, 1959, 141–72.

SROLE, Leo and Thomas Langner, "Treated and Untreated Mental Disorder in the Metropolis," *in* B. Pasamanick, ed., *Epidemiology of Mental Disorder,* Washington, D.C.: American Association for the Advancement of Science, 1959, 175–82.

SROLE, Leo *et al., Mental Health in the Metropolis: The Midtown Manhattan Study,* New York: McGraw-Hill Book Company, Inc., 1962.

THE STAFF OF THE BENJAMIN ROSE HOSPITAL, "Multidisciplinary Study of Illness of Aged Persons. I. Methods and Preliminary Results," *Journal of Chronic Diseases,* 7 (1958).

THE STAFF OF THE BENJAMIN ROSE HOSPITAL, "Multidisciplinary Studies of Illness in Aged Persons," *Journal of Chronic Diseases,* 13 (May, 1961), 453–64.

STAINBROOK, Edward, "Some Characteristics of the Psychopathology of Schizophrenic Behavior in Bahian Society," *American Journal of Psychiatry,* 109 (November, 1952), 330–35.

STAMLER, J., M. Kjelsberg, Y. Hall, and N. Scotch, "Epidemiologic Studies of Cardiovascular-Renal Diseases: I–III," *Journal of Chronic Diseases,* 12 (October, 1960), 440–75.

STAMLER, J., H. A. Lindberg, D. M. Berkson, *et al.,* "Prevalence and Incidence of Coronary Heart Disease in Strata of the Labor Force of a Chicago Industrial Corporation," *Journal of Chronic Diseases,* 11 (1960).

STEARNS, S., "Some Emotional Aspects of Treatment of Diabetes Mellitus and the Role of the Physician," *New England Journal of Medicine,* 249 (September, 1953), 471–76.

STEIN, L., " 'Social Class' Gradient in Schizophrenia," *British Journal of Preventive and Social Medicine,* 11 (1957), 181–95.

STEINER, P. O. and R. Dorfman, *The Economic Status of the Aged,* Berkeley: University of California Press, 1957.

STENDLER, Celia B., "Sixty Years of Child-Training Practices," *Journal of Pediatrics,* 36 (1950), 122–34. Reprinted *in* D. D. Apple, ed., *Sociological Studies of Health and Sickness,* New York: McGraw-Hill Book Company, Inc., 1960.

STENGEL, Erwin and N. G. Cook, *Attempted Suicide: Its Social Significance and Effects,* London: Chapman & Hall, Ltd., Maudsley Monograph 4, 1958.

STERN, Bernhard J., "Socio-Economic Aspects of Heart Disease," *The Journal of Educational Sociology,* 24 (April, 1951), 450–62. Reprinted *in* E. G. Jaco, ed., *Patients, Physicians and Illness,* New York: The Free Press of Glencoe, Inc., 1958.

STEWART, Donald D., "A Note on Mental Illness in Rural Arkansas," *Social Problems,* 1 (October, 1953), 57–60.

STEWART, Donald D., "Posthospital Social Adjustment of Former Mental Patients from Two Arkansas Counties," *South Western Social Science Quarterly,* 35 (March, 1955), 317–23.

STONE, Gregory P., "Drinking Styles and Status Arrangements," *in* D. J. Pittman and C. R. Snyder, eds., *Society, Culture, and Drinking Patterns,* New York: John Wiley & Sons, Inc., 1962, 121–40.

STRAIGHT, E. M., "Evaluation of Group Psychotherapy by Follow-Up Study of Formerly Hospitalized Patients," *Group Psychotherapy,* 13 (1960), 110–18.

STRAUS, Robert, "Alcoholism," *in* A. M. Rose, ed., *Mental Health and Mental Disorders,* New York: W. W. Norton & Company, Inc., 1955, 434–47.

STRAUS, Robert, "Sociological Determinants of Health Beliefs and Behavior," *American Journal of Public Health,* 51 (October, 1961), 1547–1551.

STRAUS, R. and S. D. Bacon, *Drinking in College,* New Haven, Conn.: Yale University Press, 1953.

STRAUS, Robert and Selden D. Bacon, "The Problems of Drinking in College," *in* D. J. Pittman and C. R. Snyder, eds., *Society, Culture, and Drinking Patterns,* New York: John Wiley & Sons, Inc., 1962, 246–58.

STRAUS, Robert and R. G. McCarthy, "Nonaddictive Pathological Drinking Patterns of Homeless Men," *Quarterly Journal of Studies on Alcohol,* 12 (1951), 601–11.

STYCOS, J. Mayone, "Family and Fertility in Puerto Rico," *American Sociological Review,* 17 (October, 1952), 572–80.

SUCHMAN, E. A., "A Conceptual Analysis of the Accident Phenomenon," *Social Problems,* 8 (Winter, 1960–61), 241–53.

SUTHERLAND, I., *Stillbirths: Their Epidemiology and Social Significance,* New York: Oxford University Press, 1949.

TALBERT, Robert H., "Ecological Variations in Dental Health in a Metropolitan Community," *Journal of Health and Human Behavior,* 3 (Summer, 1962), 128–32.

TAYBACK, Matthew, "Social Barriers to Optimal Health," *Milbank Memorial Fund Quarterly,* 35 (July, 1957), 245–57.

TERRIS, Milton, "Relation of Economic Status to Tuberculosis Mortality by Age and Sex," *American Journal of Public Health,* 38 (August, 1948), 1061–70.

TERRIS, Milton and Margaret C. Oalmann, "Carcinoma of the Cervix," *Journal of the American Medical Association,* 174 (December 3, 1960), 1847–51.

THOMPSON, Wayne E. and Gordon F. Streib, "Situational Determinants: Health and Economic Deprivation in Retirement," *Journal of Social Issues,* 14 (1958), 18–34.

THORNER, Isidor, "Ascetic Protestantism and Alcoholism," *Psychiatry,* 16 (1953), 167–76.

TIBBITTS, Clark, "The Impact of Aging on Social Institutions," *Journal of Gerontology,* 13 (July, 1958), Supplement 2, 48–52.

TIBBITTS, Helen G., Nicholas J. Demerath, and Albert F. Wessen, "Sociology and Staphylococcus," *American Journal of Sociology,* 54 (November, 1959), 298–300.

TIETZE, Christopher, Paul Lemkau, and Marcia Cooper, "Schizophrenia, Manic-Depressive Psychosis and Social-Economic Status," *American Journal of Sociology,* 47 (1941), 167–75.

TIETZE, Christopher, Paul Lemkau, and Marcia Cooper, "Personality Disorder and Spatial Mobility," *American Journal of Sociology,* 48 (July, 1942), 29–39.

TIETZE, Trude, "A Study of Mothers of Schizophrenic Patients," *Psychiatry,* 12 (1949), 55–65.

TOKUHATA, George K. and Vernon A. Stehman, "Sociological Implications, and Epidemiology, of Mental Disorders in Recent Japan," *American Journal of Public Health,* 51 (May, 1961), 697–705.

TONGUE, Archer, "What the State Does about Alcohol and Alcoholism: An International Survey," *in* D. J. Pittman and C. R. Snyder, ed., *Society, Culture, and Drinking Patterns,* New York: John Wiley & Sons, Inc., 1962, 594–600.

TOOR, Mordecai, A. Katchalsky, J. Agmon, and D. Allalouf, "Atherosclerosis and Related Factors in Immigrants to Israel," *Circulation,* 12 (August, 1960), 265–79.

TOOTH, Geoffrey, *Studies in Mental Illness in the Gold Coast,* London: Her Majesty's Stationery Office, Colonial Research Publications 6, 1950.

TOWNE, Robert D., Harold Sampson, and Sheldon L. Messinger, "Schizophrenia and the Marital Family: Identification Crises," *The Journal of Nervous and Mental Disease,* 133 (November, 1961), 423–29.

TRICE, Harrison M., "Alcoholics Anonymous," *The Annals of the American Academy of Political and Social Science,* 315 (January, 1958), 108–16.

TRICE, Harrison M., "The Job Behavior of Problem Drinkers," *in* D. J. Pittman and C. R. Snyder, eds., *Society, Culture, and Drinking Patterns,* New York: John Wiley & Sons, Inc., 1962, 493–510.

TRICE, Harrison M. and J. Richard Wahl, "A Rank Order Analysis of the Symptoms of Alcoholism," *Quarterly Journal of Studies on Alcohol,* 19 (1958), 636–48. Reprinted *in* D. J. Pittman and C. R. Snyder, eds., *Society, Culture, and Drinking Patterns,* New York: John Wiley & Sons, Inc., 1962.

TUNBRIDGE, R. E., "Sociomedical Aspects of Diabetes Mellitus," *Lancet* (October, 1953), 893–99.

TYHURST, James S., "Paranoid Patterns," *in* A. H. Leighton, J. A. Clausen and R. N. Wilson, eds., *Explorations in Social Psychiatry,* New York: Basic Books, Inc., 1957, 31–76.

ULLMAN, Albert D., "The Psychological Mechanism of Alcohol Addiction," *Quarterly Journal of Studies on Alcohol,* 13 (1952), 602–8.

ULLMAN, Albert D., "The First Drinking Experience of Addictive and of 'Normal' Drinkers," *Quarterly Journal of Studies on Alcohol,* 14 (1953), 181–91.

ULLMAN, Albert D., "Sociocultural Backgrounds of Alcoholism," *Annals of the American Academy of Political and Social Science,* 315 (January, 1958), 48–54.

ULLMAN, Albert D., "Ethnic Differences in the First Drinking Experience," *Social Problems,* 8 (Summer, 1960), No. 1, 45–56.

ULLMAN, Albert D., "First Drinking Experience as Related to Age and Sex," *in* D. J. Pittman and C. R. Snyder, eds., *Society, Culture, and Drinking Patterns,* New York: John Wiley & Sons, Inc., 1962, 259–66.

UNTERBERGER, Hilma and Simon S. Olshansky, "Vocational Rehabilitation and the Psychotic Patient," *Journal of Rehabilitation,* 3 (January–February, 1955).

USEEM, John and Ruth Useem, "Social Stresses and Resources Among Middle Management Men," *in* E. G. Jaco, ed., *Patients, Physicians, and Illness,* New York: The Free Press of Glencoe, Inc., 1958, 74–90.

VOGEL, E. F., "The Marital Relationship of Parents of Emotionally Disturbed Children: Polarization and Isolation," *Psychiatry,* 23 (February, 1960), 1–12.

VOGEL, Sidney, "Psychiatric Treatment of Alcoholism," *The Annals of the American Academy of Political and Social Science,* 315 (January, 1958), 99–107.

VOLKART, Edmund H., "Man, Disease, and the Social Environment," *Stanford Medical Bulletin,* 18 (1960), 29–33.

VOLKART, Edmund H. and S. T. Michael, "Bereavement and Mental Health," *in* A. H. Leighton, J. A. Clausen, and R. N. Wilson, eds., *Exploration in Social Psychiatry,* New York: Basic Books, Inc., 1957, 281–304.

WALKER, R., R. Williams, and F. Kelley, "An Evaluation of Maintenance Medication in the Post-Hospital Adjustment of 66 Schizophrenic Patients," *Journal of Clinical and Experimental Psychopathology,* 21 (1960), 304–8.

WANKLIN, J. M. *et al.,* "The Distribution of Mental Disease," *Mental Hygiene,* 40 (1956), 85–89.

WEAKLAND, John H., "The 'Double-bind' Hypothesis of Schizophrenia and Three-Party Interaction," *in* D. D. Jackson, ed., *The Etiology of Schizophrenia,* New York: Basic Books, Inc., 1960, 373–88.

WEINBERG, Kirson S., "A Sociological Analysis of a Schizophrenic Type," *American Sociological Review,* 15 (October, 1950), 600–10. Reprinted *in* A. M. Rose, ed., *Mental Health and Mental Disorders,* New York: W. W. Norton & Company, Inc., 1955.

WEINBERG, Kirson S., *Society and Personality Disorders,* Englewood Cliffs, N. J.: Prentice-Hall, Inc., 1952.

WEINER, Herbert, Margaret Thaler, Morton F. Reiser, and I. Arthur Mirsky, "Etiology of Duodenal Ulcer," *Psychosomatic Medicine,* 19 (January–February, 1957), 1–10. Reprinted *in* T. R. Sarbin, ed., *Studies in Behavior Pathology,* New York: Holt, Rinehart & Winston, Inc., 1961.

WEINERMAN, E. Richard, "Accident-Proneness: A Critique," *American Journal of Public Health,* 39 (December, 1949), 1527–30.

WELFORD, A. T., "The Assessment of Mental and Social Health in Relation to Age," *Journal of Gerontology,* 13 (July, 1958), Supplement 2, 32–35.

WELLIN, Edward, "Cultural Factors in Nutrition," *Nutrition Reviews,* 13 (May, 1955, 129–31.

WERTHEIMER, Nancy, "The Differential Incidence of Rheumatic Fever in the Histories of Paranoid and Non-Paranoid Schizophrenics," *The Journal of Nervous and Mental Disease,* 125 (October–December, 1957), 637–41.

WERTHEIMER, Nancy, " 'Rheumatic' Schizophrenia," *Archives of General Psychiatry,* 4 (June, 1961), 579–96.

WESTOFF, Charles F., "Differential Fertility in the United States: 1900 to 1952," *American Sociological Review,* 19 (October, 1954), 549–61.

WHITING, J. W. M. and I. C. Child, *Child Training and Personality: A Cross-Cultural Study,* New Haven, Conn.: Yale University Press, 1953.

WILLIAMS, Richard H., *The Prevention of Disability in Mental Disorders,* Washington, D.C.: Government Printing Office, Public Health Service Publication 924, Mental Health Monograph 1, 1962.

WILLIAMS, Warren S., "Class Differences in the Attitudes of Psychiatric Patients," *Social Problems,* 4 (January, 1957), 240–44.

WILLIE, Charles V., "A Research Note on the Changing Association between Infant Mortality and Socio-Economic Status," *Social Forces,* 37 (March, 1959), 221–27.

WILLIE, Charles V., "Sociology in Medicine," *New York State Journal of Medicine,* 61 (May, 1961), 1715–20.

WILNER, Daniel M. and Rosabelle Price Walkley, "Housing Environment and Mental Health," *in* B. Pasamanick, ed., *Epidemiology of Mental Disorder,* Washington, D.C.: American Association for the Advancement of Science, 1959, 143–74.

WILNER, Daniel M., Rosabelle P. Walkley, Marvin N. Glasser, and Matthew Tayback, "The Effects of Housing Quality on Morbidity," *American Journal of Public Health,* 48 (December, 1958), 1607–15.

WILNER, Daniel M., R. P. Walkley, and M. Tayback, "How Does the Quality of Housing Affect Health and Family Adjustment?" *American Journal of Public Health,* 46 (1956), 736–44.

WILNER, Daniel M. *et al.,* "The Baltimore Study on the Effects of Housing on Health," *Baltimore Health News* (Baltimore City Health Department), 37 (June, 1960), 45–52.

WINICK, Charles, "Narcotics Addiction and Its Treatment," *Law and Contemporary Problems,* 22 (Winter, 1957), 31.

WITTENBORN, J. R. and Clark Bailey, "The Symptoms of Involutional Psychosis," *Journal of Consulting Psychiatry,* 17 (1952). Reprinted *in* T. R. Sarbin, ed., *Studies in Behavior Pathology,* New York: Holt, Rinehart & Winston, Inc., 1961.

WITTKOWER, Eric D. and Jacob Fried, "Some Problems of Transcultural Psychiatry," *The International Journal of Social Psychiatry,* 3 (1958), 245–52. Reprinted *in* M. K. Opler, ed., *Culture and Mental Health,* New York: The Macmillan Company, 1959.

WITTKOWER, Eric D., H. B. Murphy, J. Fried, and H. Ellenberger, "Crosscultural Inquiry into the Symptomatology of Schizophrenia," *in* Vera Rubin, ed., "Culture, Society, and Health," *Annals of the New York Academy of Sciences,* 84 (December, 1960), 854–63.

WOLF, Stewart *et al., Life Stress and Essential Hypertension,* Baltimore: The Williams & Wilkins Co., 1955.

WOLFF, Harold G., "Life Stress and Cardiovascular Disorders," *Circulation,* 1 (February, 1950), 187–203.

WOLFF, Harold G., *Stress and Disease,* Springfield, Ill.: Charles C Thomas, Publisher, 1953.

WOLFF, Harold G., "Changes in the Vulnerability of Tissue: An Aspect of Man's Response to Threat," in National Institutes of Health, *Annual Lectures,* Washington, D.C.: United States Department of Health, Education, and Welfare, 1953, 38–71.

WOLFF, Harold G., "Disease and the Patterns of Behavior," *in* E. G. Jaco, ed., *Patients, Physicians, and Illness,* New York: The Free Press of Glencoe, Inc., 1958, 54–60.

WORLD HEALTH ORGANIZATION, *Mental Health Problems of Aging and the Aged,* Geneva: World Health Organization, Expert Committee on Mental Health, Technical Report Series 171, 1959.

WORLD HEALTH ORGANIZATION, *Epidemiology of Mental Disorders,* Geneva: World Health Organization, Expert Committee on Mental Health, Technical Report Series 185, 1960.

WYNDER, Ernest L., Jerome Cornfield, P. D. Schroff, and K. R. Doraiswaml, "Study of Environmental Factors and Carcinoma of the Cervix," *American Journal of Obstetrics and Gynecology* (October, 1954), 1016–52.

WYNNE, Lyman C., Juliana Day, Stanley Hirsch, and I. Ryckoff, "The Family Relations of a Set of Monozygotic Quadruplet Schizophrenics," *Congress Report of the IInd International Congress for Psychiatry*, 2 (September, 1957), Zurich, Switzerland, 43–49.

WYNNE, Lyman C., Irving M. Ryckoff, Juliana Day, and Stanley I. Hirsch, "Pseudo-Mutuality in the Family Relations of Schizophrenics," *Psychiatry*, 2 (May, 1958), 205–20.

YANKAUER, Alfred *et al.*, "Social Stratification and Health Practices in Child-Bearing and Child-Rearing," *American Journal of Public Health*, 48 (June, 1958), 732–41.

YANKAUER, Alfred and Norman C. Allaway, "The Relation of Indices of Fetal and Infant Loss to Residential Segregation: A Follow-Up Report," *American Sociological Review*, 23 (October, 1958), 573–78.

YAP, P. M., "Mental Diseases Peculiar to Certain Cultures: A Survey of Comparative Psychiatry," *Journal of Mental Science*, 97 (April, 1951), 313–27.

YAP, P. M., *Suicide in Hong Kong with Special Reference to Attempted Suicide*, New York: Oxford University Press, 1958.

YOST, O. R., *The Bane of Drug Addiction*, New York: The Macmillan Company, 1954.

YOUNG, M., "The Variation in the Mortality from Cancer of Different Parts of the Body in Groups of Men of Different Social Status," *Journal of Hygiene*, 25 (1926), 209–17.

ZBOROWSKI, Mark, "Cultural Components in Responses to Pain," *Journal of Social Issues*, 8 (1952), 16–30. Reprinted *in* E. G. Jaco, ed., *Patients, Physicians, and Illness*, New York: The Free Press of Glencoe, Inc., 1958. Reprinted *in* D. Apple, ed., *Sociological Studies of Health and Sickness*, New York: McGraw-Hill Book Company, Inc., 1960.

ZIMMERING, Paul, J. Toolan, R. Safrin, and S. Wortis, "Heroin Addiction in Adolescent Boys," *Journal of Nervous and Mental Disease*, 114 (1951), 19–34.

ZUBIN, Joseph, ed., *Field Studies in the Mental Disorders*, New York: Grune & Stratton, Inc., 1961.

ZUBIN, Joseph, E. I. Burdock, Samuel Sutton, and Frances Cheek, "Epidemiological Aspects of Prognosis in Mental Illness," *in* B. Pasamanick, ed., *Epidemiology of Mental Disorder*, Washington, D.C.: American Association for the Advancement of Science, 1959, 119–42.

ZUCKERMAN, M., M. Oltean, and I. Monashkin, "The Parental Attitudes of Mothers of Schizophrenics," *Journal of Consulting Psychology*, 22 (1958), 307–10.

III. Practitioners, Patients, and Medical Settings

ABEL-SMITH, B., *A History of the Nursing Profession*, London: William Heinemann, Ltd., 1960.

ADAMS, Stuart, "Trends in Occupational Origins of Physicians," *American Sociological Reveiw*, 18 (August, 1953), 404–9.

ALBEE, George W., *Mental Health Manpower Trends*, New York: Basic Books, Inc., 1959.

ALBRIGHT, Robert, "Economics of Doctor-Patient Relations," *in* E. G. Jaco, ed., *Patients, Physicians, and Illness*, New York: The Free Press of Glencoe, Inc., 1958, 506–16.

ANDERSON, B. E., "Some Paradoxes in Nursing," *Teachers College Record,* 54 (December, 1953), 211.

BACK, Kurt W., Robert E. Coker, Jr., Thomas G. Donnelly, and Bernard S. Phillips, "Public Health as a Career in Medicine: Secondary Choice Within a Profession," *American Sociological Review,* 23 (October, 1958), 533–41.

BALINT, Michael, *The Doctor, His Patient, and the Illness,* New York: International Universities Press, Inc., 1957.

BALOGH, Joseph K., Herbert Gerjuoy, Robert McDevitt, and James Bond, "Patterns of Interaction Among Chronic Female Schizophrenics," *Journal of Health and Human Behavior,* 3 (Summer, 1962), 157–60.

BARBEAU, Marius, "Medicine-Men on the North Pacific Coast," *National Museum of Canada Bulletin 152, Anthropological Series No. 42,* 1958.

BARNARD, C. I., "Social Factors in the Medical Career," *General Magazine and Historical Chronicle,* 50 (November, 1948), 114–20.

BARTLETT, Harriet, *Social Health Practices in the Health Field,* New York: National Association of Social Workers, 1961.

BEALE, Lathrop V. and Louis Kriesberg, "Career-Relevant Values of Medical Students —A Research Note," *Journal of the American Medical Association,* 171 (November, 1959), 1447–48.

BECKER, Howard and Blanche Geer, "Student Culture in Medical School," *Harvard Education Review,* 28 (Winter, 1958), 70–80.

BECKER, Howard S. and Blanche Geer, "The Fate of Idealism in Medical School," *American Sociological Review,* 23 (February, 1958), 50–56. Reprinted *in* E. G. Jaco, ed., *Patients, Physicians, and Illness,* New York: The Free Press of Glencoe, Inc., 1958.

BECKER, Howard S., Blanche Geer, Everett C. Hughes, and Anselm L. Strauss, *Boys in White: Student Culture in Medical School,* Chicago: University of Chicago Press, 1961.

BELL, Robert, "The Medicine Man, or Indian and Eskimo Notions of Medicine," *Canadian Medical and Surgical Journal,* 14 (1886), 456–62.

BEN-DAVID, Joseph, "The Professonal Role of the Physician in Bureaucratized Medicine: A Study in Role-Conflict," *Human Relations,* 11 (1958), 255–74.

BEN-DAVID, Joseph, "Roles and Innovations in Medicine," *American Journal of Sociology,* 65 (1960), 557–68.

BERKOWITZ, Joanne E. and Norman M. Berkowitz, "Nursing Education and Role Conception," *Nursing Research,* 9 (Fall, 1960), 218–19.

BEVINGTON, S., *Nursing Life and Discipline: A Study Based on Over 500 Interviews,* London: H. K. Lewis & Co., Ltd., 1943.

BIXLER, Genevieve Knight and Roy White Bixler, "The Professional Status of Nursing," *American Journal of Nursing,* 45 (September, 1945), 730–35.

BLOOM, Samuel W., "Some Implications of Studies in the Professionalization of the Physician," *in* E. G. Jaco, ed., *Patients, Physicians, and Illness,* New York: The Free Press of Glencoe, Inc., 1958, 313–21.

BLUM, R. H., *The Management of the Doctor-Patient Relationship,* New York: McGraw-Hill Book Company, Inc., 1960.

BOEHM, Werner W., "The Role of Psychiatric Social Work in Mental Health," *in* A. M. Rose, ed., *Mental Health and Mental Disorders,* New York: W. W. Norton & Company, Inc., 1955, 536–55.

BRIGANTE, T. R., "Some Defensive and Offensive Patterns of the Psychologically Sophisticated," *Journal of Health and Human Behavior,* 1 (Summer, 1960), 101–7.

BRODY, E. G., "Interprofessional Relations of Psychologists and Psychiatrists Are Human Too, Only More So," *American Psychologist,* 11 (February, 1956), 105–11.

BRODY, I., "The Decision to Study Medicine," *New England Journal of Medicine*, 252 (1955), 130–34.

BROTHERSTON, J. H. F. *et al.*, "General Practice on a New Housing Estate," *British Journal of Preventive and Social Medicine*, 10 (October, 1956), 200–7.

BROWN, Esther Lucile, *Nursing for the Future*, New York: Russell Sage Foundation, 1948.

BROWN, Esther Lucile, *Newer Dimensions of Patient Care*, New York: Russell Sage Foundation, 1961.

BUCK, Rodger L., "Sociocultural Stresses and the Physician-Patient Relationship," *Journal of the American Medical Association*, 170 (1959), 1648–51.

BULLOCK, Robert P., "What Do Nurses Think of Their Profession?" Columbus: *The Ohio State University Research Foundation*, 1954, 27–62.

BULLOUGH, Vern L., "Status and Medieval Medicine," *Journal of Health and Human Behavior*, 2 (Fall, 1961), 204–10.

BUTLER, J. J. and E. M. O'Hern, "Medical Education and Research in Catholic Medical Schools and Hospitals," *American Catholic Sociological Review*, 19 (October, 1958), 224–37.

CADZOW, Donald A., "The Vanishing American Indian Medicine-Man," *Scientific American*, 140 (1929), 418–20.

CAHALAN, Don, Patricia Collette, and Norman A. Hilmar, "Career Interests and Expectations of U. S. Medical Students," *Journal of Medical Education*, 32 (August, 1957), 557–63.

CAPLAN, Gerald, "The Mental Hygiene Role of the Nurse in Maternal and Child Care," *Nursing Outlook*, 2 (January, 1954), 14–19.

CARTWRIGHT, A., "The Career Ambitions and Expectations of Medical Students," *Journal of Medical Education*, 35 (March, 1960), 251–57.

CHANCE, E., *Families in Treatment: From the Viewpoint of the Patient, the Clinician, and the Researcher*, New York: Basic Books, Inc., 1959.

CHRIST, Edwin A., *Nurses at Work*, Columbia: University of Missouri, 1956.

CHRISTIE, Richard and Robert K. Merton, "Procedures for the Sociological Study of the Values Climate of Medical Schools," *Journal of Medical Education*, 33 (October, 1958), 125–53.

CLEVELAND, S. E., "Personality Patterns Associated with the Professions of Dietitian and Nurse," *Journal of Health and Human Behavior*, 2 (Summer, 1961), 113–24.

COBB, Beatrix, "Why Do People Detour to Quacks?" *The Psychiatric Bulletin*, 3 (Summer, 1954), 66–69. Reprinted *in* E. G. Jaco, ed., *Patients, Physicians, and Illness*, New York: The Free Press of Glencoe, Inc., 1958.

COKER, Robert E., Jr., K. W. Back, T. G. Donnelly, Norman Miller, and B. S. Phillips, "Public Health as Viewed by the Medical Student," *American Journal of Public Health*, 49 (May, 1959), 601–9.

COKER, Robert E., Jr., K. W. Back, T. G. Donnelly, Norman Miller, and L. H. Strickland, "Patterns of Influence: Medical School Faculty Members and the Values and Specialty Interests of Medical Students," *Journal of Medical Education*, 35 (1960), 518–27.

COKER, Robert E., Jr., Norman Miller, K. W. Back, and T. G. Donnelly, "The Medical Student: Specialization and General Practice," *North Carolina Medical Journal*, 21 (March, 1960), 96–101.

CORTLETT, T., *The Medicine-Man of the American Indian and His Cultural Background*, Springfield, Ill.: Charles C Thomas, Publisher, 1935.

CORWIN, Ronald G., "Role Conception and Career Aspiration: A Study of Identity in Nursing," *The Sociological Quarterly*, 2 (April, 1961), 69–86.

CORWIN, Ronald G., "The Professional Employee: A Study of Conflict in Nursing Roles," *American Journal of Sociology*, 66 (May, 1961), 604–15.

CREIGHTON, B., Sr., "Socio-Economic Status and the Nursing Candidate," *American Catholic Sociological Review*, 15 (March, 1954), 19–29.

CROATMAN, W. and P. B. Sheatsley, "The Prescription Pharmacist Today," New York: Health Information Foundation, Research Series 3, 1958.

DANIELS, Morris J., "Affect and its Control in the Medical Intern," *American Journal of Sociology*, 66 (November, 1960), 259–67.

DAVIS, Fred, "Uncertainty in Medical Prognosis, Clinical and Functional," *American Journal of Sociology*, 66 (1960), 41–47.

DEMBO, Tamara and E. Hanfmann, "The Patient's Psychological Situation Upon Admission to a Mental Hospital," *American Journal of Psychology*, 67 (1935), 381–408.

DEMBO, Tamara, G. L. Leviton, and Beatrice A. Wright, "Adjustment to Misfortune—A Problem of Social Psychological Rehabilitation," *Artificial Limbs*, 3 (1956), 4–62.

DEUTSCHER, Irwin and Ann Montague, "Professional Education and Conflicting Value Systems: The Role of Religious Schools in the Educational Aspirations of Nursing Students," *Social Forces*, 32 (December, 1956), 126–31.

DEVEREUX, George and Florence R. Weiner, "The Occupational Status of Nurses," *American Sociological Review*, 15 (October, 1950), 628–34.

DIAMOND, Lorraine and David J. Fox, "Turnover Among Hospital Staff Nurses," *Nursing Outlook*, 6 (July, 1958), 388–91.

DICHTER, E., "The Hospital-Patient Relationship," *Modern Hospital*, 83, 84 (September, October, November, December, 1954, and January, February, 1955).

DODGE, Joan S., "Why Nurses Leave—and What to do About It," *Modern Hospital*, 94 (May, 1960), 116ff.

DODGE, Joan S., "Nurse-Doctor Relations and Attitudes Toward the Patient," *Nursing Research*, 9 (Winter, 1960), 32–38.

DODGE, Joan S., "Nurses' Sense of Adequacy and Attitudes Toward Keeping Patients Informed," *Journal of Health and Human Behavior*, 2 (Fall, 1961), 213–16.

DORFFELD, Mildred E., Thomas S. Ray, and Theodore S. Baumberger, "A Study of Selection Criteria for Nursing School Applicants," *Nursing Research*, 7 (Spring, 1958), 67–70.

DUNBAR, Flanders, *Psychiatry in the Medical Specialties*, New York: McGraw-Hill Book Company, Inc., 1959.

DYKMAN, R. A. and J. M. Stalnaker, "Survey of Women Physicians Graduating From Medical School 1925–1940," *Journal of Medical Education*, 32 (March, 1957), 1–38.

EATON, Joseph F., "The Client-Practitioner Relationship as a Variable in the Evaluation of Treatment Outcome," *Psychiatry*, 22 (May, 1959), 189–95.

ELINSON, Jack, "The Physician's Dilemma in Puerto Rico," *Journal of Health and Human Behavior*, 3 (Spring, 1962), 14–20.

ERIKSON, Kai T., "Patient Role and Social Uncertainty: A Dilemma of the Mentally Ill," *Psychiatry*, 20 (1957), 263–74.

ERON, Leonard D., "Effects of Medical Education on Medical Students' Attitudes," *Journal of Medical Education*, 30 (October, 1955), 559–66.

FABRICANT, N. D., *Why We Became Doctors*, New York: Grune & Stratton, Inc., 1954.

FANSHEL, D., "A Study of Case Workers' Perceptions of Their Clients," *Social Case Work*, 39 (December, 1958), 543–51.

FERGUSON, R. S., "The Doctor-Patient Relationship and 'Functional' Illness," *The Practitioner*, 176 (June, 1956), 656–62. Reprinted *in* E. G. Jaco, ed., *Patients, Physicians, and Illness*, New York: The Free Press of Glencoe, Inc., 1958.

FIELD, Mark G., "Structured Strain in the Role of the Soviet Physician," *American Journal of Sociology*, 58 (March, 1953), 493–502.

FIELD, Mark G., "The Doctor-Patient Relationship in the Perspective of 'Fee-for-Service' and 'Third-Party Medicine,'" *Journal of Health and Human Behavior*, 2 (Winter, 1961), 252–62.

FLECK, Stephen, Alice R. Cornelison, Bea Norton, and Theodore Lidz, "II. Interaction Between Hospital Staff and Families," *Psychiatry*, 20 (November, 1957), 343–50.

FLEXNER, Abraham, *Medical Education in the United States and Canada. A Report to the Carnegie Foundation for the Advancement of Teaching*, New York: The Carnegie Foundation for the Advancement of Teaching, 1910.

FLEXNER, Abraham, *Medical Education in Europe. A Report to the Carnegie Foundation for the Advancement of Teaching*, New York: The Carnegie Foundation, 1912.

FLEXNER, Abraham, "A Layman's View of Osteopathy," *Journal of the American Medical Association*, 42 (June, 1914), 1831–33.

FORD, Thomas T. and Diane D. Stephenson, *Institutional Nurses: Role Relationships and Attitudes in Three Alabama Hospitals*, University: University of Alabama Press, 1954.

FOX, Renée C., "Training for Uncertainty," *in* R. K. Merton, G. Reader, and P. Kendall, eds., *The Student-Physician*, Cambridge: Harvard University Press, 1957, 207–43.

FRANK, Jerome D., "Group Methods in Psychotherapy," *Journal of Social Issues*, 8 No. 2 (1952), 35–44. Reprinted *in* A. M. Rose, ed., *Mental Health and Mental Disorders*, New York: W. W. Norton & Company, Inc., 1955.

FRANK, Jerome D., *Persuasion and Healing: A Comparative Study of Psychotherapy*, Baltimore, Md.: Johns Hopkins Press, 1961.

FREEMAN, Howard E. and Ozzie G. Simmons, "Consensus and Coalition in the Release of Mental Patients: A Research Note," *Human Organization*, 20 (Summer, 1961), 89–91.

FRUMKIN, Robert M., *Hospital Nursing: A Sociological Interpretation*, Buffalo, N.Y.: University of Buffalo, 1956.

GEE, H. H. and C. G. Child, III, eds., *Report of the Second Institute on Clinical Teaching*, Evanston, Ill.: Association of American Medical Colleges, 1961.

GEE, H. H. and J. T. Cowles, eds., *The Appraisal of Applicants to Medical Schools*, Evanston, Ill.: Association of American Medical Colleges, 1957.

GEE, H. H. and R. J. Glaser, eds., *The Ecology of the Medical Student*, Evanston, Ill.: Association of American Medical Colleges, 1958.

GEIGER, H. Jack, "Social Responsibility of the Physician," *Scientific American*, 85 (August, 1957), 89–94.

GELFAND, S. and L. P. Ullmann, "Change in Attitudes About Mental Illness Associated with Psychiatric Clerkship Training," *International Journal of Social Psychiatry*, 7 (1961), 292–98.

GELFAND, S. and L. P. Ullmann, "Attitude Change Associated with Psychiatric Affiliation," *Nursing Research*, 10 (1961), 200–04.

GILLIN, John, "The Making of a Witch Doctor," *Psychiatry*, 19 (May, 1956), 131–36.

GLASER, William A., "Internship Appointments of Medical Students," *Administrative Science Quarterly*, 4 (December, 1959), 337–56.

GOLDSTEIN, B. and P. Dommermuth, "The Sick Role Cycle: An Approach to Medical Sociology," *Sociology and Social Research*, 47 (October, 1961), 1–12.

GOODE, William J., "Encroachment, Charlatanism, and the Emerging Profession: Psychology, Sociology, and Medicine," *American Sociological Review*, 25 (December, 1960), 902–14.

GOSS, Mary E. W., "Change in the Cornell Comprehensive Care and Teaching Program," *in* R. K. Merton, G. Reader, and P. Kendall, eds., *The Student-Physician*, Cambridge: Harvard University Press, 1957, 249–70.

GOSS, Mary E. W., "Administration and the Physician," *American Journal of Public Health*, 52 (February, 1962), 183–91.

GRAHAM, Thomas F., "Stereotypes of Nationalities by Student Nurses," *Journal of Clinical Psychology*, 14 (July, 1958), 324–26.

GRALNICK, Alexander and Robert S. Duncan, "Problems of the Patient in Transit from Hospital to Community," *in* M. Greenblatt, D. J. Levinson, and Gerald L. Klerman, eds., *Mental Patients in Transition*, Springfield, Ill.: Charles C Thomas, Publisher, 1961, 26–33.

GRAY, P. G. and A. Cartwright, "Choosing and Changing Doctors," *Lancet*, 2 (December 19, 1953), 1308–9.

GRAY, Robert M. and W. R. Elton Newman, "The Relationship of Medical Students' Attitudes of Cynicism and Humanitarianism to Performance in Medical School," *Journal of Health and Human Behavior*, 3 (Summer, 1962), 147–51.

GRIFFITHS, W., "A Study of the Overlap of Job Functions: The Community Health Worker on the Navajo Indian Reservation," *Journal of Psychology*, 48 (1959), 147–65.

GRIFFITHS, W., "A Study of Work Role Perceptions: The Community Health Worker on the Navajo Indian Reservation," *Journal of Psychology*, 48 (1959), 167–80.

GURSSLIN, Orville, Raymond G. Hunt, and Jack L. Roach, "Social Class, Mental Hygiene, and Psychiatric Practice," *Social Service Review*, 33 (September, 1959), 237–44.

HABENSTEIN, Robert A. and Edwin A. Christ, *Professionalizer, Traditionalizer, and Utilizer*, Columbia: University of Missouri, 1955.

HALL, Oswald, "The Informal Organization of the Medical Profession," *Canadian Journal of Economic and Political Science*, 12 (1946), 30–44.

HALL, Oswald, "The Stages of a Medical Career," *The American Journal of Sociology*, 53 (March, 1948), 327–36. Reprinted *in* E. G. Jaco, ed., *Patients, Physicians, and Illness*, New York: The Free Press of Glencoe, Inc., 1958.

HALL, Oswald, "Types of Medical Careers," *American Journal of Sociology*, 55 (November, 1949), 243–53.

HALL, Oswald, "Half Medical Man, Half Administrator: A Medical Dilemma," *Canadian Public Administration*, 2 (December, 1959), 185–94.

HAMMOND, Kenneth R. and F. Kern, Jr., *Teaching Comprehensive Medical Care*, Cambridge: Harvard University Press, 1959.

HARTMANN, George W., "The Relative Social Prestige of Representative Medical Specialties," *Journal of Applied Psychology*, 20 (December, 1936), 659–63.

HASSINGER, E. W. and R. L. McNamara, *Relationships of the Public to Physicians in a Rural Setting*, Missouri Agricultural Experiment Station Research Bulletin 653, January, 1958.

HEELEY, I. and W. R. Borg, "Personality Characteristics of Nursing School Students and Graduate Nurses," *Journal of Applied Psychology*, 35 (1951), 275–80.

HEINE, R. W., "The Negro Patient in Psychotherapy," *Journal of Clinical Psychology*, 6 (1950), 373–76.

HENDERSON, L. J., "Physician and Patient as a Social System," *New England Journal of Medicine*, 212 (May, 1935), 819–23.

HENRY, Jules, "The Culture of Interpersonal Relations in a Therapeutic Institution for Emotionally Disturbed Children," *American Journal of Orthopsychiatry*, 27 (October, 1957), 725–34.

HOFFMAN, Lois, "Problem Patient: The Christian Scientist," *Medical Economics*, 33 (December, 1956), 265–83. Reprinted *in* E. G. Jaco, ed., *Patients, Physicians, and Illness*, New York: The Free Press of Glencoe, Inc., 1958.

HOFFMAN, Lois, "How Do Good Doctors Get That Way?" *Medical Economics*, 34 (May, 1957), 164–73; 34 (June, 1957), 124–9; 34 (July, 1957), 222–34; 34 (August, 1957), 144–53. Reprinted *in* E. G. Jaco, ed., *Patients, Physicians, and Illness*, New York: The Free Press of Glencoe, Inc., 1958.

HOLLANDER, I. Fred, "The Specific Nature of the Clergy's Role in Mental Health," *Pastoral Psychology*, 10 (November, 1959), 11–21.

HOLT, R. R., L. Luborsky, *et al.*, *Personality Patterns of Psychiatrists: A Study of Methods for Selecting Residents*, New York: Basic Books, Inc., 1958.

HUGHES, Everett C., "The Making of a Physician—A General Statement of Ideas and Problems," *Human Organization*, 14 (Winter, 1956), 21–25.

HUGHES, Everett C., "Stress and Strain in Professional Education," *Harvard Educational Review*, 29 (Fall, 1959), 319–29.

HUGHES, Everett C., H. M. Hughes, and Irwin Deutscher, *Twenty Thousand Nurses Tell Their Story*, Philadelphia: J. B. Lippincott Company, 1958.

HUNTINGTON, Mary Jean, "The Development of a Professional Self-Image," *in* R. K. Merton, G. Reader, and P. Kendall, eds., *The Student-Physician*, Cambridge: Harvard University Press, 1957, 179–88.

HUTCHINS, Edwin B. and Helen Hofer Gee, "The Study of Applicants, 1959–60," *Journal of Medical Education*, 36 (April, 1961), 289–304.

HYDE, Robert W. and Richard H. York, "A Technique for Investigating Interpersonal Relationships in a Mental Hospital," *Journal of Abnormal and Social Psychology*, 43 (July, 1948), 287–99.

INGAIRE, Alice E., "Attitudes of Student Nurses at the University of California," *Nursing Research*, 1 (October, 1952), 36–39.

JACKSON, D. D., J. Block, and V. Patterson, "Psychiatrist's Conceptions of the Schizophrenogenic Parent," *A.M.A. Archives of Neurology & Psychiatry*, 79 (1958), 448–59.

JELLIFFE, D. B., "Cultural Variation and the Practical Pediatrician," *The Journal of Pediatrics*, 49 (December, 1956), 661–71. Reprinted *in* E. G. Jaco, ed., *Patients, Physicians, and Illness*, New York: The Free Press of Glencoe, Inc., 1958.

JESSOR, Richard, "Social Values and Psychotherapy," *Journal of Consulting Psychology*, 20 (1956), 264–66.

JOHN, A. L., *A Study of the Psychiatric Nurse*, Edinburgh: E. & S. Livingstone, Ltd., 1961.

JOHNSON, Miriam M. and Harry W. Martin, "A Sociological Analysis of the Nurse Role," *American Journal of Nursing*, 58 (1958), 373–77.

JONES, Louis C., "Practitioners of Folk Medicine," *Bulletin of the History of Medicine*, 23 (September–October, 1949), 480–93.

JOSEPH, Alice, "Physician and Patient: Some Aspects of Inter-Personal Relations Between Physicians and Patients, with Special Regard to the Relationship Between White Physicians and Indian Patients," *Applied Anthropology*, 1 (July–September, 1942), 1–6.

JOY, R. J. T., "The Natural Bonesetters With Special Reference to the Sweet Family of Rhode Island. A Study of an Early Phase of Orthopedics," *Bulletin of the History of Medicine*, 28 (July–August, 1954), 416–41.

KADUSHIN, Charles, "Social Distance Between Client and Professional," *American Journal of Sociology*, 67 (March, 1962), 517–31.

KAPLAN, Stanley M. and George C. Curtis, "Discharge From a Psychosomatic Unit of a General Hospital," *in* M. Greenblatt, D. J. Levinson, and Gerald L. Klerman, eds., *Mental Patients in Transition*, Springfield, Ill.: Charles C Thomas, Publisher, 1961, 7–15.

KELLY, Isabel, "An Anthropological Approach to Midwifery Training in Mexico," *Journal of Tropical Pediatrics*, 1 (1956), 200–5.

KENDALL, Patricia L., "Clinical Teachers' Use of the Basic Science Curriculum," *Journal of Medical Education*, 35 (February, 1960), 148–57.

KENDALL, Patricia L., "Impact of Training Programs on the Young Physician's Attitudes and Experiences," *The Journal of the American Medical Association*, 176 (June 24, 1961), 992–97.

KENDALL, Patricia L. and Robert K. Merton, "Medical Education as a Social Process," *in* E. Gartly Jaco, ed., *Patients, Physicians, and Illness*, New York: The Free Press of Glencoe, Inc., 1958, 321–50.

KENDALL, Patricia L. and Hanan C. Selvin, "Tendencies Toward Specialization in Medical Training," *in* R. K. Merton, G. Reader, and P. Kendall, eds., *The Student-Physician*, Cambridge: Harvard University Press, 1957, 153–76.

KENDLER, Harriet *et al.*, "A Study of Nurse-Patient Interaction in a Mental Hospital," *American Journal of Nursing*, 52 (September, 1952), 1100–3.

KOESECKER, Raymond P., *The Osteopathic Movement in Medicine*, Chicago: American Osteopathic Association, 1957.

KOOS, Earl L., *The Sociology of the Patient*, New York: McGraw-Hill Book Company, Inc., 1959.

KOUNIN, J., N. Polansky, B. Biddle, H. Coburn, and A. Fenn, "Experimental Studies of Clients' Reactions to Initial Interviews," *Human Relations*, 9 (1956), 265–93.

KREITMAN, N., "The Reliability of Psychiatric Diagnoses," *Journal of Mental Science*, 107 (September, 1961).

KUTNER, Bernard, "Surgeons and Their Patients: A Study in Social Perceptions," *in* E. G. Jaco, ed., *Patients, Physicians, and Illness*, New York: The Free Press of Glencoe, Inc., 1958, 384–96.

LA BARRE, Weston, "Primitive Psychotherapy in Native American Cultures," *Journal of Abnormal and Social Psychology*, 42 (July, 1947), 294–309.

LEDERER, Henry D., "How the Sick View Their World," *The Journal of Social Issues*, 8 (1952), 4–15. Reprinted *in* E. G. Jaco, ed., *Patients, Physicians, and Illness*, New York: The Free Press of Glencoe, Inc., 1958.

LEE, Alfred McClung, "The Social Dynamics of the Physician's Status," *Psychiatry*, 7 (November, 1944), 371–77.

LESSER, M. S. and V. R. Keane, *Nurse-Patient Relationships in a Hospital Maternity Service*, St. Louis: The C. V. Mosby Company, 1956.

LEVIN, Eugene, "Turnover Among Nursing Personnel in General Hospitals," *Hospitals*, 31 (September, 1957).

LEWIN, G. W., "Some Characteristics of the Socio-Psychological Life Space of the Epileptic Patient," *Human Relations*, 10 (1957), 249–56.

LIPSITT, Don R., "Institutional Dependency: A Rehabilitation Problem," *in* M. Greenblatt, D. J. Levinson, and Gerald L. Klerman, eds., *Mental Patients in Transition*, Springfield, Ill.: Charles C Thomas, Publisher, 1961, 34–45.

LORTIE, Dan, "Anesthesia: From Nurse's Work to Medical Specialty," *in* E. G. Jaco, ed., *Patients, Physicians, and Illness*, New York: The Free Press of Glencoe, Inc. 1958, 405–12.

MacGREGOR, Frances C., *Social Science in Nursing*, New York: Russell Sage Foundation, 1960.

MARTIN, Harry W. and Fred E. Katz, "The Professional School as a Molder of Motivation," *Journal of Health and Human Behavior*, 2 (Summer, 1961), 106–12.

MARTIN, H. W. and I. H. Simpson, *Patterns of Psychiatric Nursing: A Survey of Psychiatric Nursing in North Carolina*, Chapel Hill, N.C.: American Nurses' Foundation, Inc., 1956.

MARTIN, William, "Preferences for Types of Patients," *in* R. K. Merton, G. Reader, and P. Kendall, eds., *The Student-Physician*, Cambridge: Harvard University Press, 1957, 189–206.

MARYO, Joann S. and Julian J. Lasky, "A Work Satisfaction Survey Among Nurses," *American Journal of Nursing*, 59 (April, 1959), 501–3.

MATARAZZO, Joseph D., "The Role of the Psychologist in Medical Education and Practice," *Human Organization*, 14 (1955), 9–14.

McCORKLE, Thomas, "Chiropractic: A Deviant Theory of Disease and Treatment in Contemporary Western Culture," *Human Organization*, 20 (Spring, 1961), 20–23.

McCORMACK, Thelma H., "The Druggists' Dilemma: Problems of a Marginal Occupation," *American Journal of Sociology*, 61 (January, 1956), 308–15.

MECHANIC, David, "Role Expectations and Communication in the Therapist-Patient Relationship," *Journal of Health and Human Behavior*, 2 (Fall, 1961), 190–97.

MECHANIC, David and Edmund H. Volkart, "Illness Behavior and Medical Diagnoses," *Journal of Health and Human Behavior*, 1 (Summer, 1960), 86–94.

MECHANIC, David and Edmund H. Volkart, "Stress, Illness Behavior, and the Sick Role," *American Sociological Review*, 26 (February, 1961), 51–58.

MERTON, Robert K., "Some Preliminaries to a Sociology of Medical Education," *in* R. K. Merton, G. Reader, and P. Kendall, eds., *The Student-Physician*, Cambridge: Harvard University Press, 1957, 3–80.

MERTON, Robert K., Samuel Bloom, and Natalie Rogoff, "Studies in the Sociology of Medical Education," *Journal of Medical Education*, 31 (1956), 552–64.

MERTON, Robert K., George G. Reader, and Patricia L. Kendall, eds., *The Student-Physician: Introductory Studies in the Sociology of Medical Education*, Cambridge: Harvard University Press, 1957.

MEYER, Genevieve Rogge, "Conflict and Harmony in Nursing Values," *Nursing Outlook*, 7 (July, 1959), 298–99.

MEYER, Genevieve Rogge, *Tenderness and Technique: Nursing Values in Transition*, Los Angeles: Industrial Relations Monographs of the Institute of Industrial Relations, 6, 1960.

MIDDLEWOOD, Esther L., "Why Do Students Drop Out?" *American Journal of Nursing*, 46 (December, 1946), 838–40.

MILLER, Walter B., "Implications of Urban Lower Class Culture for Social Work," *Social Service Review*, 33 (1959), 219–36.

MONGEAU, Beatrice B., Harvey L. Smith, and Ann C. Maney, "The 'Granny' Midwife: Changing Roles and Functions of a Folk Practitioner," *American Journal of Sociology*, 64 (March, 1961), 497–505.

MORE, Douglas M., "A Note on Occupational Origins of Health Service Professions," *American Sociological Review*, 25 (June, 1960), 403–4.

MORE, D. M., "The Dental Student," *Journal of the American College of Dentists*, 28 (March, 1961), 1–93.

MORE, D. M. and Nathan Kohn, Jr., "Some Motives for Entering Dentistry," *American Journal of Sociology*, 66 (July, 1960), 48–53.

MORGAN, William, "Navaho Treatment of Sickness: Diagnosticians," *American Anthropologist*, 33 (July–September, 1931), 390–402.

MYERS, R. C., "Influence of Age on Physicians' Views Concerning Mental Health Matters," *Public Opinion Quarterly*, 19 (Fall, 1955), 252–58.

NABOISEK, Herbert, Ozzie G. Simmons, Dorothy M. Mathews, and Stanley H. Cath, "Hospital Image and Post-Hospital Experience," *in* M. Greenblatt, D. J. Levinson, and R. H. Williams, eds., *The Patient and the Mental Hospital*, New York: The Free Press of Glencoe, Inc., 1957, 565–76.

NEW, Peter K., "The Osteopathic Student: A Study in Dilemma," *in* E. G. Jaco, ed., *Patients, Physicians, and Illness*, New York: The Free Press of Glencoe, Inc., 1958, 413–20.

NEW, Peter K., Gladys Nite, and Josephine M. Callahan, *Nursing Service and Patient Care: A Staffing Experiment*, Kansas City: Community Studies, Inc., Publication 119, November, 1959.

NEWMAN, C., *The Evolution of Medical Education in the Nineteenth Century*, London: Oxford University Press, 1957.

NUNNALLY, J. C., "Opinions of Psychologists and Psychiatrists About Mental Health Problems," *Journal of Consulting Psychology*, 22 (1958), 178–82.

OLENCKI, Margaret, "Range of Patient Contacts in the Comprehensive Care and Teaching Program," *in* R. K. Merton, G. Reader, and P. Kendall, eds., *The Student-Physician*, Cambridge: Harvard University Press, 1957, 271–86.

OPLER, Marvin K., "Dream Analysis in Ute Indian Therapy," *in* M. K. Opler, ed., *Culture and Mental Health*, New York: The Macmillan Company, 1959, 97–118.

OPLER, Marvin K., "Industrial Societies and the Changing Role of Doctors," *Journal of Occupational Medicine*, 4 (May, 1962), 237–41.

OPLER, Morris E., "Some Points of Comparison and Contrast Between the Treatment of Functional Disorders by Apache Shamans and Modern Psychiatric Practice," *American Journal of Psychiatry*, 92 (1936), 1371–87.

ORZACK, Louis M. and John R. Uglum, "Sociological Perspectives of the Profession of Optometry," *American Journal of Optometry and Archives of American Academy of Optometry*, (August, 1958).

PARKES, C. Murray and G. W. Brown, "The General Practitioner and the Schizophrenic Patient," *British Medical Journal*, 1 (April, 1962), 972–76.

PARSONS, Talcott, "Illness and the Role of the Physician: A Sociological Perspective," *American Journal of Orthopsychiatry*, 21 (1951), 452–60.

PAULSEN, Alice E., "Religious Healing," *Journal of the American Medical Association*, 86 (May, 15, 22, and 29, 1926), 1519–24, 1617–23, 1692–97.

PEARLIN, L. I., "Alienation from Work: A Study of Nursing Personnel," *American Sociological Review*, 27 (June, 1962), 314–26.

PFAUTZ, Harold W., "Christian Science: A Case Study of the Social Psychological Aspect of Secularization," *Social Forces*, 34 (March, 1956), 246–51.

PINE, Fred and Daniel J. Levinson, "Two Patterns of Ideology, Role Conception, and Personality Among Hospital Aides," *in* M. Greenblatt, D. J. Levinson, and R. H. Williams, eds., *The Patient and the Mental Hospital*, New York: The Free Press of Glencoe, Inc., 1957, 209–18.

POLANSKY, N. and J. Kounin, "Client's Reaction to Initial Interviews," *Human Relations*, 9 (1956), 237–64.

POLLAK, Otto, Charles Westoff, and Marvin Dressler, "Pilot Study of Nursing Functions," *Nursing Research*, 2 (June, 1953), 15–22.

POWELSON, Harvey and Reinhard Bendix, "Psychiatry in Prison," *Psychiatry*, 14 (February, 1951), 73–86. Reprinted *in* A. M. Rose, ed., *Mental Health and Mental Disorders*, New York: W. W. Norton & Company, Inc., 1955.

PRATT, Lois, Arthur Seligmann, and George Reader, "Physicians' Views on the Level of Medical Information Among Patients," *American Journal of Public Health*, 47 (October, 1957), 1277–83. Reprinted *in* E. G. Jaco, ed., *Patients, Physicians, and Illness*, New York: The Free Press of Glencoe, Inc., 1958.

PUSCHMANN, T., *A History of Medical Education from the Most Remote to the Most Recent Times* (tr. and ed., by E. H. Hare), London: Lewis, 1891.

QUARANTELLI, Enrico L., "Attitudes of Dental Students Toward Specialization and Research," *Journal of the American College of Dentists*, 27 (1960), 101–7.

QUARANTELLI, Enrico L., "The Career Choice Patterns of Dental Students," *Journal of Health and Human Behavior*, 2 (Summer, 1961), 124–32.

QUARANTELLI, Enrico L., "The Dental Student Image of the Dentist-Patient Relationship," *American Journal of Public Health*, 51 (September, 1961), 1312–19.

RAPOPORT, R., "The Family and Psychiatric Treatment," *Psychiatry*, 23 (February, 1960), 53–62.

RAVITZ, Mel J., "Occupational Values and Occupational Selection," *Nursing Research*, 6 (June, 1957), 35–40.

READER, George G., "The Cornell Comprehensive Care and Teaching Program," *in* R. K. Merton, G. Reader, and P. Kendall, eds., *The Student-Physician*, Cambridge: Harvard University Press, 1957, 81–104.

READER, George G., Lois Pratt, and Margaret C. Mudd, "What Patients Expect from Their Doctors," *Modern Hospital*, 89 (1957), 88–94.

REED, Louis, *Midwives, Chiropodists, and Optometrists*, Chicago: University of Chicago Press, Publication 15 of the Committee on the Costs of Medical Care, 1932.

REED, Louis, *The Healing Cults*, Chicago: University of Chicago Press, Publication 16 of the Committee on the Costs of Medical Care, 1932.

REINHARDT, James M. and Paul Meadows, *Society and the Nursing Profession: An Introductory Sociology*, Philadelphia: W. B. Saunders Co., 1953.

REISSMAN, Leonard and John H. Rohrer, eds., *Change and Dilemma in the Nursing Profession*, New York: G. P. Putnam's Sons 1957..

REISSMAN, Leonard, Ralph V. Platou, *et al.*, "The Motivation and Socialization of Medical Students," *Journal of Health and Human Behavior*, 1 (Fall, 1960), 174–82.

REITZES, D. C., *Negroes and Medicine*, Cambridge: Harvard University Press, 1958.

RETTIG, S., F. N. Jacobson, and B. Pasamanick, "Status Overestimation, Objective Status, and Job Satisfaction Among Professions," *American Sociological Review*, 23 (February, 1958), 75–81.

ROBINSON, G. C., *The Patient as a Person*, New York: The Commonwealth Fund, 1939.

ROBINSON, H. A., F. C. Redlich, and J. K. Myers, "Social Structure and Psychiatric Treatment," *American Journal of Orthopsychiatry*, 24 (April, 1954), 307–16.

ROGLER, Lloyd H. and August B. Hollingshead, "The Puerto Rican Spiritualist as a Psychiatrist," *American Journal of Sociology*, 67 (July, 1961), 17–21.

ROGOFF, Natalie, "The Decision to Study Medicine," *in* R. K. Merton, G. Reader, and P. Kendall, eds., *The Student-Physician*, Cambridge: Harvard University Press, 1957, 109–30.

ROSEN, George, *The Specialization of Medicine With Particular Reference to Ophthalmology*, New York: Froben Press, 1944.

ROSEN, George, "Some Substantive Limiting Conditions in Communication Between Health Officers and Medical Practitioners," *American Journal of Public Health*, 51 (December, 1961), 1805–16.

ROSENGREN, W. R., "Social Instability and Attitudes Toward Pregnancy as a Social Role," *Social Programs*, 9 (Spring, 1962), 371–78.

ROUECHE, Berton, *Eleven Blue Men*, New York: Little, Brown & Company, 1953. Also, New York: Berkeley Publishing Company, 1955.

SAPIR, Jean V., "Social Work and Alcoholism," *The Annals of the American Academy of Political and Social Science*, 315 (January, 1958), 125–32.

SAUNDERS, Lyle, "The Changing Role of Nurses," *American Journal of Nursing*, 54 (September, 1954), 1094–98.

SAUNDERS, Lyle, "Culture and Nursing Care," *in* E. G. Jaco, ed., *Patients, Physicians, and Illness*, New York: The Free Press of Glencoe, Inc., 1958, 538–48.

SCHULMAN, Sam, "Basic Functional Roles in Nursing: Mother Surrogate and Healer," *in* E. G. Jaco, ed., *Patients, Physicians, and Illness*, New York: The Free Press of Glencoe, Inc., 1958, 528–37.

SCHUMACHER, Charles F., "The 1960 Medical School Graduate: His Biographical History," *Journal of Medical Education*, 36 (May, 1961), 398–406.

SCHWARTZ, Morris S. and Emmy Lanning Shockley, *The Nurse and the Mental Patient: A Study in Interpersonal Relations*, New York: Russell Sage Foundation, 1956.

SCHWARTZ, Morris S. and Alfred H. Stanton, "A Social Psychological Study of Incontinence," *Psychiatry*, 13 (1950), 399–416.

SEEMAN, M. and J. W. Evans, "Apprenticeship and Attitude Change," *American Journal of Sociology*, 67 (January, 1962), 365–78.

SEGAL, B. E., "Nurses and Patients: Time, Place and Distance," *Social Problems*, 9 (Winter, 1962), 257–64.

SENTER, Donovan, "Witches and Psychiatrists," *Psychiatry*, 10 (February, 1947), 49–56.

SHRYOCK, R. H., *The History of Nursing, An Interpretation of the Social and Medical Factors Involved*, Philadelphia: W. B. Saunders Co., 1959.

SHUVAL, Judith, "Social Factors Conditioning Recruitment of Nurses in Israel," *Journal of Health and Human Behavior*, 3 (Summer, 1962), 73–81.

SIMMONS, Ozzie G., "The Clinical Team in a Chilean Health Center," *in* B. D. Paul, ed., *Health, Culture, and Community*, New York: Russell Sage Foundation, 1955, 325–48.

SIMMONS, Ozzie G., James A. Davis, and Katherine Spencer, "Interpersonal Strains in Release from a Mental Hospital," *Social Problems*, 4 (July, 1956), 21–28.

SIMPSON, Richard L., "The Psychiatric Attendant: Development of an Occupational Self-Image in a Low-Status Occupation," *American Sociological Review*, 24 (June, 1959), 389–92.

SKIPPER, James K., " 'Functional Significance' of the Nurse Role: An Evaluation," *Journal of Health and Human Behavior*, 3 (Spring, 1962), 41–45.

SMITH, Harvey L., "Psychiatry: A Social Institution in Process," *Social Forces*, 33 (May, 1955), 310–16.

SMITH, Harvey L., "Psychiatry in Medicine: Intra- or Inter-Professional Relationships?" *American Journal of Sociology*, 63 (November, 1957), 285–89.

SMITH, Harvey L., "Contingencies of Professional Differentiation," *American Journal of Sociology*, 63 (January, 1958), 410–14.

SOLOMON, David N., "Ethnic and Class Differences among Hospitals as Contingencies in Medical Careers," *American Journal of Sociology*, 66 (March, 1961), 463–71.

SOLON, Jerry A. *et al.*, "Staff Perceptions of Patients' Use of a Hospital Outpatient Department," *Journal of Medical Education*, 33 (January, 1958), 10–21.

STANFORD RESEARCH INSTITUTE, *Chiropractic in California*, Los Angeles: Haynes Foundation, 1960.

STERN, Bernhard J., "The Specialist and the General Practitioner," *in* E. G. Jaco, ed., *Patients, Physicians and Illness*, New York: The Free Press of Glencoe, Inc., 1958, 352–60.

STEWART, Donald D. and Christine E. Needham, *The General Duty Nurse*, Fayetteville: University of Arkansas Press, 1955.

TANTUM, Julien Rundell, "Changing Roles of Professional Personnel in the Field of Medical Care," *Nursing Outlook*, 1 (January, 1953), 694–96.

TERRIS, Milton and Mary Monk, "Changes in Physicians' Careers: Relation of Time After Graduation to Specialization," *The Journal of the American Medical Association*, 160 (1956), 653–55. Reprinted *in* E. G. Jaco, ed., *Patients, Physicians, and Illness*, New York: The Free Press of Glencoe, Inc., 1958.

THIELENS, Wagner, Jr., "Some Comparisons of Entrants to Medical and Law School," *in* R. K. Merton, G. Reader, and P. Kendall, eds., *The Student-Physician*, Cambridge: Harvard University Press, 1957, 131–52.

THOMPSON, J. D. and F. L. Bates, "Technology, Organization and Administration," *in* J. D. Thompson, *et al.*, eds., *Comparative Studies in Administration*, Pittsburgh: University of Pittsburgh Press, 1959.

THOMAS, E., N. Polansky, and J. Kounin, "The Expected Behavior of a Potentially Helpful Person," *Human Relations*, 8 (1955), 165–74.

THORNER, Isidor, "Pharmacy: The Functional Significance of an Institutional Pattern," *Social Forces*, 20 (March, 1942), 321–28.

THORNER, Isidor, "Nursing: The Functional Significance of an Institutional Pattern," *American Sociological Review*, 20 (October, 1955), 531–38.

TURNER, Helen, "The Patient as a Person in the Treatment Relationship," *Journal of Health and Human Behavior*, 1 (Winter, 1960), 278–85.

WARDWELL, Walter I., "A Marginal Professional Role: The Chiropractor," *Social Forces*, 30 (1952), 339–48. Reprinted *in* E. G. Jaco, ed., *Patients, Physicians, and Illness*, New York: The Free Press of Glencoe, Inc., 1958.

WARDWELL, Walter I., "The Reduction of Strain in a Marginal Social Role," *American Journal of Sociology*, 61 (July, 1955), 16–25.

WARDWELL, Walter I., "Public Regulation of Chiropractic," *Journal of the National Medical Association*, 53 (March, 1961), 166–72.

WELLIN, Edward, "Water Boiling in a Peruvian Town," *in* B. D. Paul, ed., *Health, Culture, and Community*, New York: Russell Sage Foundation, 1955, 71–106.

WELLIN, Edward, "Pregnancy, Childbirth, and Midwifery in the Valley of Ica, Peru," *Health Information Digest for Hot Countries*, London: Tavistock Publications, Central Council for Health Education, 1956.

WESTBERG, Granger, "Religious Aspects of Medical Teaching," *Journal of Medical Education*, 32 (March, 1957), 204–9. Reprinted *in* E. G. Jaco, ed., *Patients, Physicians, and Illness*, New York: The Free Press of Glencoe, Inc, 1958.

WHITING, J. F., "Needs, Values, Perceptions and the Nurse-Patient Relationship," *Journal of Clinical Psychology*, 15 (April, 1959), 146–50.

WILLIAMS, J. J., "Patients and Prejudice: Lay Attitudes Toward Women Physicians," *American Journal of Sociology*, 51 (January, 1946), 283–87.

WILLIAMS, J. J., "The Woman Physician's Dilemma," *Journal of Social Issues*, 6 (1950), 38–44.

WILLIAMS, Thomas Rhys and Margaret M. Williams, "The Socialization of the Student Nurse," *Nursing Research*, 8 (Winter, 1959), 18–25.

WILLIE, Charles V., "The Social Class of Patients That Public Health Nurses Prefer to Serve," *American Journal of Public Health*, 50 (August, 1960), 1126–36.

WILSON, A. T. M., "Hospital Nursing Auxiliaries: Notes on a Background Survey and Job-Analysis," *Human Relations*, 3 (1950), 89–105.

WILSON, Bryan R., *Sects and Society: A Sociological Study of Elim Tabernacle, Christian Science, and Christadelphians*, Berkeley: University of California Press, 1961.

YOURGLICH, A., "Inconsistency in Career-Goals of a Group of Catholic Nursing Students," *American Catholic Sociological Review*, 14 (December, 1953), 244–49.

ZANDER, A. F. *et al.*, *Role Relations in the Mental Health Professions*, Ann Arbor: Institute for Social Research, University of Michigan, 1957.

IV. Sociology of Medical Care

ABERLE, David F., "Introducing Preventive Psychiatry into a Community," *Human Organization,* 9 (1950), 5–9.

ACKERKNECHT, Erwin H., "Problems of Primitive Medicine," *Bulletin of the History of Medicine,* 11 (1942), 503–21.

ACKERKNECHT, Erwin H., "Primitive Medicine and Culture Pattern," *Bulletin of the History of Medicine,* 12 (1942), 545–74.

ACKERKNECHT, Erwin H., "Psychopathology, Primitive Medicine and Primitive Culture," *Bulletin of the History of Medicine,* 14 (1943), 30–67.

ACKERKNECHT, Erwin H., "On The Collecting of Data Concerning Primitive Medicine," *American Anthropologist,* 47 (1945), 427–32.

ACKERKNECHT, Erwin H., "Natural Diseases and Rational Treatment in Primitive Medicine," *Bulletin of the History of Medicine,* 19 (May, 1946), 467–97.

ACKERKNECHT, Erwin H., "Primitive Surgery," *American Anthropologist,* 49 (January–March, 1947), 25–45.

ACKERKNECHT, Erwin H., "Medicine and Disease Among the Eskimo," *Ciba Symposia,* 10 (1948), 916–21.

ACKERKNECHT, Erwin H., "Medical Practices," *in* J. H. Steward, ed., *Handbook of South American Indians,* Washington: Smithsonian Institution, Bureau of American Ethnology, 5 (1949), 621–43.

ADAIR, John, "The Indian Health Worker in the Cornell-Navajo Project," *Human Organization,* 19 (1960), 59–63.

ADAIR, John and Kurt Deuschle, "Some Problems of Physicians on the Navajo Reservation," *Human Organization,* 16 (Winter, 1958), 19–23.

ADAIR, John, Kurt Deuschle, and Walsh McDermott, "Patterns of Health and Disease Among the Navahos," *The Annals of the American Academy of Political and Social Science,* 311 (May, 1957), 80–94.

ADAMS, Richard N., "A Nutritional Research Program in Guatemala," *in* B. D. Paul, ed., *Health, Culture, and Community,* New York: Russell Sage Foundation, 1955, 435–58.

ALLPORT, Gordon W., *Perception and Public Health,* Oakland, Calif.: Society of Public Health Educators, Health Education Monograph 2, 1958.

ANDERSON, Odin W. *et al.,* "Symposium on Community Self-Surveys in Health," *American Journal of Public Health,* 45 (1955), 273–84.

ANDERSON, Odin W. and Jacob J. Feldman, *Family Medical Costs and Voluntary Health Insurance: A Nationwide Survey,* New York: McGraw-Hill Book Company, Inc., 1956.

ANDERSON, Odin W., Patricia J. Collette, and Jacob J. Feldman, *Family Expenditure Patterns for Personal Health Services, 1953 and 1958: Nationwide Surveys,* New York: Health Information Foundation, Research Series 14, 1960.

ANDERSON, Odin W., Patricia J. Collette, and Jacob J. Feldman, *Health Insurance Benefits for Health Insurance Services, 1953 and 1958: Nationwide Surveys,* New York: Health Information Foundation, Research Series 15, 1960.

ANDERSON, Odin W. and Paul B. Sheatsley, *Comprehensive Medical Insurance—A Study of Costs, Use, and Attitudes Under Two Plans,* New York: Health Information Foundation, Research Series 9, 1959.

ANDERSON, Odin W. and the Staff of the National Opinion Research Center, *Voluntary Health Insurance in Two Cities: A Survey of Subscriber-Households,* Cambridge: Harvard University Press, 1957.

ANDERSON, T. R. and S. Warkov, "Organizational Size and Functional Complexity: A Study of Administration in Hospitals," *American Sociological Review*, 26 (February, 1961), 23–28.

APPLE, Dorrian, "How Laymen Define Illness," *Journal of Health and Human Behavior*, 1 (Fall, 1960), 219–25.

ARGYRIS, Chris, *Diagnosing Human Relations in Organizations: A Case Study of a Hospital*, New Haven, Conn.: Yale University Labor and Management Center, 1956.

ARGYRIS, Chris, *Personality and Organization: The Conflict Between System and the Individual*, New York: Harper & Row, Publishers, 1957.

ARMSTRONG, Barbara W., *The Health Insurance Doctor, His Role in Great Britain, Denmark and France*, Princeton, N.J.: Princeton University Press, 1939.

BAERREIS, David A., "A Note on a Winnebago Medical Technique," *Wisconsin Archeologist*, 34 (1953), 139–43.

BARKER, R. G. and H. F. Wright, *The Midwest and Its Children: The Psychological Ecology of an American Town*, New York: Harper & Row, Publishers, 1955.

BARNES, E., *People in Hospitals*, London: Macmillan & Co., Ltd., 1961.

BARRABEE, Paul, "The Community, the Mental Hospital, and the Aged Psychotic," *in* M. Greenblatt, D. J. Levinson, and R. H. Williams, eds., *The Patient and the Mental Hospital*, New York: The Free Press of Glencoe, Inc., 1957, 530–34.

BATEMAN, J. Fremont and H. Warren Dunham, "The State Mental Hospital as a Specialized Community," *American Journal of Psychiatry*, 105 (1948), 445–48.

BATES, Frederick L. and Rodney F. White, "Differential Perceptions of Authority in Hospitals," *Journal of Health and Human Behavior*, 2 (Winter, 1961), 262–67.

BAUMANN, B., "Diversities in Conceptions of Health and Physical Fitness," *Journal of Health and Human Behavior*, 2 (Spring, 1961), 39–46.

BEALS, Ralph L., *Cheran: A Sierra Tarascan Village*, Washington, D.C.: Smithsonian Institution, Publication 2 of the Institute of Social Anthropology, 1946.

BELCHER, J. C., "Medical Service Relationships in Harper County, Oklahoma," *Oklahoma Agricultural Extension Service Bulletin*, No. B-477, September, 1956.

BELCHER, John C., "Acceptance of the Salk Polio Vaccine," *Rural Sociology*, 23 (June, 1958), 158–70.

BELKNAP, I., *Human Problems of a State Mental Hospital*, New York: McGraw-Hill Book Company, Inc., 1956.

BENNIS, Warren G., Norman H. Berkowitz, M. Affinito and M. Malone, "Reference Groups and Loyalties in the Out-Patient Department," *Administrative Science Quarterly*, 2 (March, 1958), 481–500.

BERKOWITZ, Norman H. and Warren G. Bennis, "Interaction in Formal Service-Oriented Organizations," *Administrative Science Quarterly*, 6 (June, 1961), 25–50.

BERLE, B. B., *Eighty Puerto Rican Families in New York City: Health and Disease Studied in Context*, New York: Columbia University Press, 1958.

BERTRAND, Alvin L. and Clarance A. Storla, *Lay Attitudes and Opinion About Heart Disease*, Baton Rouge: Louisiana Agricultural Experiment Station, 1955.

BHASKARAN, K., "A Psychiatric Study of Schizophrenic Reaction Patterns in an Indian Mental Hospital," *International Journal of Social Psychiatry*, 5 (1959), 41–46.

BIBRING, Grete L., "Psychiatry and Medical Practice in a General Hospital," *New England Journal of Medicine*, 254 (February 23, 1956), 366–72.

BIELIAUSKAS, V. J. and J. D. Wolfe, "The Attitude of Industrial Employers Toward Hiring of Former State Mental Hospital Patients," *Journal of Clinical Psychology*, 16 (July, 1960), 256–58.

BISHOP, W. J., "Transport and the Doctor in Great Britain," *Bulletin of the History of Medicine*, 22 (July–August, 1948), 427–40.

BLACK, Bertram J., "The Workaday World: Some Problems in Return of Mental Patients to the Community," *in* M. Greenblatt, D. J. Levinson, and R. H. Williams, eds., *The Patient and the Mental Hospital,* New York: The Free Press of Glencoe, Inc., 1957, 577–84.

BOAG, T. J., "Psychiatric Hospital as Center of Hospital-Community Activities," *in* M. Greenblatt, D. J. Levinson, and Gerald L. Klerman, eds., *Mental Patients in Transition,* Springfield, Ill.: Charles C Thomas, Publisher, 1961, 59–71.

BOCKOVEN, J. Sandbourne, "Some Relationships Between Cultural Attitudes toward Individuality and Care of the Mentally Ill: An Historical Study," *in* M. Greenblatt, D. J. Levinson, and R. H. Williams, eds., *The Patient and the Mental Hospital,* New York: The Free Press of Glencoe, Inc. 1957, 517–26.

BOEK, Walter, "Social Science Applied to the Dynamics of Community Process," *in* E. G. Jaco, ed., *Patients, Physicians, and Illness,* New York: The Free Press of Glencoe, Inc., 1958, 143–47.

BRADLEY, Will T., "Medical Practices of the New England Aborigines," *Journal of the American Pharmaceutical Association,* 25 (1936), 138–47.

BRIGHT, Margaret L. and Donald G. Hay, "Health Resources and Their Use by Rural People," *Cornell University Rural Sociology Bulletin* 32, 1952.

BROOKS, George W., "Rural Community Influences and Supports in a Rehabilitation Program for State Hospital Patients," *in* M. Greenblatt, D. J. Levinson, and Gerald L. Klerman, eds., *Mental Patients in Transition,* Springfield, Ill.: Charles C Thomas, Publisher, 1961, 133–38.

BROOKS, Harlow, "The Medicine of the American Indian," *Journal of Laboratory and Clinical Medicine,* 19 (1933), 1–23.

BROTHERSTON, J. H. F., A. Cartwright, and F. M. Martin, "The Attitudes of General Practitioners Towards Alternative Systems of Remuneration," *British Medical Journal,* Supplement 2856 (October 17, 1959), 119–24.

BROWER, George J., "Conceptions and Evaluations of Functions of Medical and Health Care Agencies by Present and Future Homemakers, in Cortland County," *Rural Sociology,* 17 (March, 1952), 56–60.

BROWN, Esther Lucille, H. Warren Dunham, and Richard H. York, "The Application of the Sciences of Social Behavior in Ward Settings," *in* M. Greenblatt, D. J. Levinson, and R. H. Williams, eds., *The Patient and the Mental Hospital,* New York: The Free Press of Glencoe, Inc., 1957, 479–98.

BROWN, G. W., "Social Factors Influencing Length of Hospital Stay of Schizophrenic Patients," *British Medical Journal,* 2 (December 12, 1959), 1300–02.

BROWN, R. E., "Evaluating Hospital Administration," *Hospitals,* 35 (October, 1961), 42–44.

BROWN, W. Chapman, "Diseases Among the Aborigines of America and Their Knowledge of Treatment," *Canadian Journal of Medicine and Surgery,* 51 (1922), 155–58.

BROWNE, Edward G., *Arabian Medicine,* London: Cambridge University Press, 1921.

BUCHANAN, Charles Milton, "Some Medical Customs, Ideas, Beliefs, and Practices of the Snohomish Indians of Puget Sound," *St. Louis Courier of Medicine,* 21 (1899), 277–90, 355–70.

BUCHER, R. and L. Schatzman, "The Logic of the State Mental Hospital," *Social Problems,* 9 (Spring, 1962), 337–49.

BURGESS, Anne, "Traditional Systems of Child Care," *Health Education Journal,* 15 (May, 1957), 99–109.

BURGESS, Anne, "Nutrition Education in Public Health Programs—What Have We Learned," *American Journal of Public Health,* 51 (November, 1961), 1715–26.

BURGESS, Anne, "Nutrition and Food Habits," *International Journal of Health Education*, 4 (1961–62), 55–58.

BURLING, Temple E., Edith M. Lentz, and Robert N. Wilson, *The Give and Take in Hospitals: A Study in Human Organization*, New York: G. P. Putnam's Sons, 1956.

CANNON, W. G., "Voodoo Death," *American Anthropologist*, 44 (April–June, 1942), 169–81.

CARSTAIRS, G. Morris, "Medicine and Faith in Rural Rajasthan," *in* B. D. Paul, ed., *Health, Culture, and Community*, New York: Russell Sage Foundation, 1955, 107–34.

CARSTAIRS, G. Morris, "Some Problems of Psychiatry in Patients from Alien Cultures," *Lancet* (June 7, 1958), 1217–20.

CARSTAIRS, G. Morris, "The Social Limits of Eccentricity: An English Study," *in* M. K. Opler, ed., *Culture and Mental Health*, New York: The Macmillan Company, 1959, 373–90.

CARSTAIRS, G. Morris and Alastair Heron, "The Social Environment of Mental Hospital Patients: A Measure of Staff Attitude," *in* M. Greenblatt, D. J. Levinson, and R. H. Williams, eds., *The Patient and the Mental Hospital*, New York: The Free Press of Glencoe, Inc., 1957, 219–26.

CARTWRIGHT, A. and F. M. Martin, "Some Popular Beliefs Concerning the Causes of Cancer," *British Medical Journal*, 2 (September 6, 1958), 592–94.

CARTWRIGHT, A., F. M. Martin, and J. G. Thomson, "Efficacy of an Anti-Smoking Campaign," *Lancet* (February 6, 1960), 327–29.

CASSEL, John, "A Comprehensive Health Program Among South African Zulus," *in* B. D. Paul, ed., *Health, Culture, and Community*, New York: Russell Sage Foundation, 1955, 15–42.

CASSEL, John, "Social and Cultural Implications of Food and Food Habits," *American Journal of Public Health*, 47 (June, 1957) 732–40. Reprinted *in* E. G. Jaco, ed., *Patients, Physicians, and Illness*, New York: The Free Press of Glencoe, Inc., 1958.

CAUDILL, William, "Perspectives on Administration in Psychiatric Hospitals," *Administrative Science Quarterly*, 1 (September, 1956), 155–70.

CAUDILL, William, "Social Processes in a Collective Disturbance on a Psychiatric Ward," *in* M. Greenblatt, D. J. Levinson, and R. H. Williams, eds., *The Patient and the Mental Hospital*, New York: The Free Press of Glencoe, Inc., 1957, 438–71.

CAUDILL, William, *The Psychiatric Hospital as a Small Society*, Cambridge: Harvard University Press, 1958.

CAUDILL, William, "Observations on the Cultural Context of Japanese Psychiatry," *in* M. K. Opler, ed., *Culture and Mental Health*, New York: The Macmillan Company, 1959, 213–42.

CAUDILL, William, "Around the Clock Patient Care in Japanese Psychiatric Hospitals: The Role of the Tsukisoi," *American Sociological Review*, 26 (April, 1961), 204–14.

CAUDILL, William *et al.*, "Social Structure and Interaction Process on a Psychiatric Ward," *American Journal of Orthopsychiatry*, 22 (April, 1952), 314–34.

CAUDILL, William and Edward Stainbrook, "Some Covert Effects of Communication Difficulties in a Psychiatric Hospital," *Psychiatry*, 17 (1954), 27–40.

CLARK, Margaret, *Health in the Mexican-American Culture: A Community Study*, Berkeley: University of California Press, 1959.

CLARK, Margaret, "The Social Functions of Mexican-American Medical Beliefs," *California's Health*, 16 (1959), 153–56.

CLAUSEN, John A. and E. W. Linn, "Public Reaction to a Severe Polio Outbreak in Three Massachusetts Communities," *Social Problems*, 4 (July, 1956), 40–51.

CLAUSEN, John, Morton Seidenfeld, and Leila Deasy, "Parent Attitudes Toward Participation of Their Children in Polio Vaccine Trials," *American Journal of Public Health,* 44 (December, 1954), 1526–36. Reprinted *in* E. G. Jaco, ed., *Patients, Physicians, and Illness,* New York: The Free Press of Glencoe, Inc., 1958.

CLEMENTS, Forrest E., "Primitive Concepts of Disease," *University of California Publications in American Archeology and Ethnology,* 32 (1932), Berkeley: University of California Press, 185–252.

CLYNE, M. G., *Night Calls: A Study in General Practice,* London: Tavistock Publications, 1961.

COHEN, Robert A., "Some Relations Between Staff Tensions and the Psychotherapeutic Process," *in* M. Greenblatt, D. J. Levinson, and R. H. Williams, eds., *The Patient and the Mental Hospital,* New York: The Free Press of Glencoe, Inc., 1957, 301–8.

COLE, N. J. *et al.,* "Mental Illness: Survey Assessment of Community Rates, Attitudes and Adjustments," *A.M.A. Archives of Neurotic Psychiatry,* 77 (1957), 393–98.

COLEMAN, James S., Elihu Katz, and Herbert Menzel, "The Diffusion of an Innovation Among Physicians," *Sociometry,* 20 (1957), 253–70.

COLEMAN, James S., Herbert Menzel, and Elihu Katz, "Social Processes in Physicians' Adoption of a New Drug," *Journal of Chronic Diseases,* 9 (January, 1959), 1–19.

COMMITTEE FOR THE SPECIAL RESEARCH PROJECT IN THE HEALTH INSURANCE PLAN OF GREATER NEW YORK, *Health and Medical Care in New York City,* Cambridge: Harvard University Press, 1957.

COSER, Rose Laub, "A Home Away from Home," *Social Problems,* 4 (1956), 3–17. Reprinted *in* D. Apple, ed., *Sociological Studies of Health and Sickness,* New York: McGraw-Hill Book Company, Inc., 1960.

COSER, Rose Laub, "Authority and Decision-Making in a Hospital: A Comparative Analysis," *American Sociological Review,* 23 (February, 1958), 56–63.

COSER, Rose Laub, "Some Social Functions of Laughter: A Study of Humor in a Hospital Setting," *Human Relations,* 12 (1959), 171–82.

CRAWFORD, Fred R., Glen W. Rollins, and Robert L. Sutherland, "Variations Between Negroes and Whites in Concepts of Mental Illness and Its Treatment," *in* Vera Rubin, ed., "Culture, Society, and Health," *Annals of the New York Academy of Sciences,* 84 (December, 1960), 918–37.

CRAWFORD, Fred R., Glen W. Rollins, and Robert L. Sutherland, "Variations in the Evaluations of the Mentally Ill," *Journal of Health and Human Behavior,* 1 (Fall, 1960), 211–19.

CRAWFORD, Fred R., Glen W. Rollins, and Robert L. Sutherland, "Variations in the Evaluation of the Mentally Ill. Part II: The Viewpoint of the Rural Dweller," *Journal of Health and Human Behavior,* 2 (Winter, 1961), 267–75.

CROOG, S. H., "Patient Government: Some Aspects of Participation and Social Background on Two Psychiatric Wards," *Psychiatry,* 19 (1956), 203–7.

CULLEY, John, "The California Indians: Their Medical Practices and Their Drugs," *Journal of the American Pharmaceutical Association,* 25 (1936), 332–39.

CUMMING, Elaine, I. L. W. Clancey, and John Cumming, "Improving Patient Care Through Organizational Changes in the Mental Hospital," *Psychiatry,* 19 (1956), 249–61. Reprinted *in* D. Apple, ed., *Sociological Studies in Health and Sickness,* New York: McGraw-Hill Book Company, Inc., 1960.

CUMMING, Elaine and John Cumming, "The Locus of Power in a Large Mental Hospital," *Psychiatry,* 19 (November, 1956), 361–69.

CUMMING, Elaine and John Cumming, *Closed Ranks: An Experiment in Mental Health Education,* Cambridge: Harvard University Press, 1957.

CUMMING, Elaine and John Cumming, "Two Views of Public Attitudes Toward Mental Illness," *Mental Hygiene*, 43 (April, 1959), 211–21.

CUMMING, John and Elaine Cumming, "Mental Health Education in a Canadian Community," *in* B. D. Paul, ed., *Health, Culture, and Community*, New York: Russell Sage Foundation, 1955, 43–70.

CUMMING, John and Elaine Cumming, "Affective Symbolism, Social Norms, and Mental Illness," *Psychiatry*, 19 (February, 1956), 77–85.

CUMMING, John and Elaine Cumming, "Social Equilibrium and Social Change in the Large Mental Hospital," *in* M. Greenblatt, D. J. Levinson, and R. H. Williams, eds., *The Patient and the Mental Hospital*, New York: The Free Press of Glencoe, Inc., 1957, 50–72.

CUSSLER, Margaret and Mary L. de Give, *'Twixt the Cup and the Lip: A Study of American Food Habits*, New York: Twayne Publishers, 1952.

DAIN, N. and E. T. Carlson, "Social Class and Psychological Medicine in the U. S., 1789–1824," *Bulletin of the History of Medicine*, 33 (September–October, 1959), 454–65.

DALZELL-WARD, A. J., "Fluoridation and Public Opinion," *Health Education Journal*, 17 (November, 1959), 247–58.

DARBY, George E., "Indian Medicine in British Columbia," *Canadian Medical Association Journal*, 28 (1933), 433–38.

DARSKY, Benjamin J., Nathan Sinai, and Solomon J. Axelrod, *Comprehensive Medical Services Under Voluntary Health Insurance: A Study of Windsor Medical Services*, Cambridge: Harvard University Press, 1958.

DAVIS, Michael M., *Medical Care for Tomorrow*, New York: Harper & Row, Publishers, 1955.

DAVIS, Morris, "Community Attitudes Toward Fluoridation," *Public Opinion Quarterly*, 23 (1959), 474–82.

DEASY, Leila Calhoun, "Socio-economic Status and Participation in the Poliomyelitis Vaccine Trial," *American Sociological Review*, 21 (1956), 185–91. Reprinted *in* D. Apple, ed., *Sociological Studies of Health and Sickness*, New York: McGraw-Hill Book Company, Inc., 1960.

DENSEN, Paul M., Ellen W. Jones, Eva Balamuth and Sam Shapiro, "Prepaid Medical Care and Hospital Utilization in a Dual Choice Situation," *American Journal of Public Health*, 50 (November, 1960), 1710–26.

DENTLER, R. A. and B. Mackler, "The Socialization of Retarded Children in an Institution," *Journal of Health and Human Behavior*, 2 (Winter, 1961), 243–52.

DEUSCHLE, Kurt W., "Organizing Preventive Health Programs to Meet Health Needs," *Annals of the American Academy of Political and Social Science*, 337 (September, 1961), 20–28.

DEUSCHLE, Kurt W. and John Adair, "An Interdisciplinary Approach to Public Health on the Navajo Indian Reservation: Medical and Anthropological Aspects," *in* Vera Rubin, ed., "Culture, Society, and Health," *Annals of the New York Academy of Sciences*, 84 (December, 1960), 887–905.

DEVEREAUX, George, "The Social Structure of a Schizophrenia Ward and Its Therapeutic Fitness," *Journal of Clinical Psychopathology*, 6 (October, 1944), 231–65.

DEVEREAUX, George, "The Social Structure of the Hospital as a Factor in Total Therapy," *American Journal of Orthopsychiatry*, 19 (July, 1949), 492–500.

DI CICCO, Lena, and Dorrian Apple, "Health Needs and Opinions of Older Adults," *Public Health Reports*, 73 (1958), 479–87. Reprinted *in* D. Apple, ed., *Sociological Studies of Health and Sickness*, New York: McGraw-Hill Book Company, Inc., 1960.

DIGGORY, J. C., "Some Consequences of Proximity to a Disease Threat," *Sociometry*, 19 (1956), 47–53.

DINITZ, Simon *et al.*, "The Ward Behavior of Psychiatric Patients," *Social Problems*, 6 (1958), 107–15.

DODD, Stuart C., *A Controlled Experiment on Rural Hygiene in Syria*, London: Oxford University Press, 1934.

DOHAN, J. Lawrence, "Development of a Student Volunteer Program in a State Mental Hospital," *in* M. Greenblatt, D. J. Levinson, and R. H. Williams, eds., *The Patient and the Mental Hospital*, New York: The Free Press of Glencoe, Inc., 1957, 593–602.

DOHRENWEND, Bruce P., "The Stirling County Study: A Research Program on Relations Between Sociocultural Factors and Mental Illness," *American Psychologist*, 12 (1957), 78–85.

DOHRENWEND, Bruce P., "Some Aspects of the Appraisal of Abnormal Behavior by Leaders in an Urban Area," *American Psychologist*, 17 (1962), 190–98.

DOHRENWEND, Bruce P., Viola W. Bernard, and Lawrence C. Kolb, "The Orientations of Leaders in an Urban Area Toward Problems of Mental Illness," *The American Journal of Psychiatry*, 118 (February, 1962), 683–91.

DUNHAM, H. W. and S. K. Weinberg, *The Culture of the State Mental Hospital*, Detroit: Wayne State University Press, 1960.

EATON, Joseph and Robert Weil, *Culture and Mental Disorders*, New York: The Free Press of Glencoe, Inc., 1955.

EATON, Joseph, "Folk Obstetrics and Pediatrics Meet the M.D.: A Case Study of Social Anthropology and Medicine," *in* E. G. Jaco, ed., *Patients, Physicians, and Illness*, New York: The Free Press of Glencoe, Inc., 1958, 207–21.

ELLER, C. Howe, Gordon H. Hatcher, and Bradley Buell, "Health and Welfare Issues in Community Planning for the Problem of Indigent Disability," *American Journal of Public Health*, 48 (1958), 49.

ELLING, Ray H., Ruth Whittemore, and Morris Green, "Patient Participation in a Pediatric Program," *Journal of Health and Human Behavior*, 1 (Fall, 1960), 183–91.

ELLING, Ray H. and S. Halebsky, "Organizational Differentiation and Support: A Conceptual Framework," *Administrative Science Quarterly*, 6 (September, 1961), 185–209.

ELLSWORTH, R. B. and W. H. Clayton, "The Effects of Chemotherapy on Length of Stay and Rate of Return for Psychiatrically Hospitalized Patients," *Journal of Consulting Psychology*, 24 (1960), 50–53.

ENGELHARDT, David M. and Norbert Freedman, "An Approach to the Evaluation of Long-Term Pharmacological Therapy of Schizophrenic Outpatients," *in* M. Greenblatt, D. J. Levinson, and Gerald L. Klerman, eds., *Mental Patients in Transition*, Springfield, Ill.: Charles C Thomas, Publisher, 1961, 322–35.

ERASMUS, Charles J., "Changing Folk Beliefs and the Relativity of Empirical Knowledge," *Southwestern Journal of Anthropology*, 8 (Winter, 1952), 411–28.

ERASMUS, Charles J., "An Anthropologist Views Technical Assistance," *Scientific Monthly*, 78 (March, 1954), 147–58.

ETZIONI, Amitai, "New Directions in the Study of Organizations and Society," *Social Research*, 27 (Summer, 1960), 223–28.

ETZIONI, Amitai, "Interpersonal and Structural Factors in the Study of Mental Hospitals," *Psychiatry*, 23 (1960), 13–22.

ETZIONI, Amitai, *A Comparative Analysis of Complex Organizations: On Power, Involvement, and Their Correlates*, New York: The Free Press of Glencoe, Inc., 1961.

EVANG, Karl, *Health Service, Society, and Medicine: Present Day Health Services in Their Relation to Medical Science and Social Structures,* London: Oxford University Press, 1960.

EVANS-PRITCHARD, E. E., *Witchcraft, Oracles and Magic Among the Azande,* Oxford: Clarendon Press, 1937.

FALK, I. S., Margaret Klem, and Nathan Sinai, *The Incidence of Illness and the Receipt and Cost of Medical Care Among Representative Families,* Chicago: University of Chicago Press, 1933.

FEIN, Rashi, *Economics of Mental Illness,* New York: Basic Books, Inc., 1958.

FIELD Margaret J., *Religion and Medicine of the Ga People,* London: Oxford University Press, 1937.

FIELD, M. J., *Search for Security: An Ethnopsychiatric Study of Rural Ghana,* Evanston, Ill.: Northwestern University Press, 1960.

FIELD, Mark G., *Doctor and Patient in Soviet Russia,* Cambridge: Harvard University Press, 1957.

FIRTH, Raymond, "Health Planning and Community Organization," *Health Education Journal,* 15 (May, 1957), 118–25.

FOGELSON, Raymond D., "Change, Persistence, and Accommodation in Cherokee Medico-Magical Beliefs," *in* W. N. Fenton and J. Gulick, eds., *Symposium on Cherokee and Iroquois Culture,* Bureau of American Ethnology Bulletin 180, 1961, 213–25.

FOLKARD, S., "Comparative Study of Attitudes to the Rehabilitation of Psychiatric Patients," *British Journal of Preventive and Social Medicine,* 14 (1960), 23–27.

FORSYTH, Gordon and Robert F. L. Logan, *The Demand for Medical Care: A Study of the Case-Load in the Barrow and Furness Group of Hospitals,* London: Oxford University Press, 1960.

FOSTER, George M., "Relationships between Theoretical and Applied Anthropology: A Public Health Program Analysis," *Human Organization,* 11 (Fall, 1952), 5–16.

FOSTER, George M., "Relationships between Spanish and Spanish-American Folk Medicine," *Journal of American Folklore,* 66 (July–September, 1953), 201–17.

FOSTER, George M., "Working with People of Different Cultural Backgrounds," *California's Health,* 14 (January, 1956), 107–10. Reprinted *in Health Education Journal,* 15 (May, 1957), 63–71.

FOSTER, George M., *Problems in Intercultural Health Programs,* New York: Social Science Research Council, Pamphlet 12, 1958.

FOSTER, George M., *Traditional Cultures and the Impact of Technological Change,* New York: Harper & Row, Publishers, 1962.

FOSTER, G. M., C. Erasmus, I. Kelly, K. Oberg, and O. G. Simmons, *A Cross-Cultural Anthropological Analysis of a Technical Aid Program,* Washington, D.C.: Smithsonian Institution, 1951. Mimeo.

FOX, R. C., *Experiment Perilous: Physicians and Patients Facing the Unknown,* New York: The Free Press of Glencoe, Inc., 1959.

FOX, R. C., "Physicians on the Drug Industry Side of the Prescription Blank: Their Dual Commitment to Medical Science and Business," *Journal of Health and Human Behavior,* 2 (Spring, 1961), 3–16.

FOX, T. F., "The Personal Doctor and His Relation to the Hospital," *Lancet* (April, 1960), 743–60.

FRAKE, C. O., "The Diagnosis of Disease Among the Subanun of Mindanao," *American Anthropologist,* 63 (February, 1961), 113–32.

FREEMAN, Howard E., "Attitudes Toward Mental Illness Among Relatives of Former Patients," *American Sociological Review,* 26 (February, 1961), 59–66.

FREEMAN, Howard E. and Gene G. Kassebaum, "Relationship of Education and Knowledge to Opinions About Mental Illness," *Mental Hygiene*, 44 (1960), 43–47.

FREEMAN, Howard E. and Ozzie G. Simmons, "Feelings of Stigma among Relatives of Former Mental Patients," *Social Problems*, 8 (Spring, 1961), 312–21.

FREEMAN, Howard E. and Ozzie G. Simmons, "Treatment Experiences of Mental Patients and their Families," *American Journal of Public Health*, 51 (September, 1961), 1266–73.

FREIDSON, Eliot, "Specialties Without Roots: The Utilization of New Services," *Human Organization*, 18 (Fall, 1959), 112–16.

FREIDSON, Eliot, "Client Control and Medical Practice," *American Journal of Sociology*, 65 (1960), 374–82.

FREIDSON, Eliot, "The Organization of Medical Practice and Patient Behavior," *American Journal of Public Health*, 51 (January, 1961), 43–51.

FREIDSON, Eliot, *Patients' Views of Medical Practice—A Study of Subscribers to a Prepaid Medical Plan in The Bronx*, New York: Russell Sage Foundation, 1961.

FREIDSON, Eliot and Jacob J. Feldman, *The Public Looks at Hospitals*, New York: Health Information Foundation, Research Series 4, 1958.

FREIDSON, Eliot and Jacob J. Feldman, *Public Attitudes Toward Health Insurance*, New York: Health Information Foundation, Research Series 5, 1958.

FREIDSON, Eliot and Jacob J. Feldman, *The Public Looks at Dental Care*, New York: Health Information Foundation, Research Series 6, 1958.

FREYHAN, Fritz A. and Joan Merkel, "Clinical and Social Aspects of Compensatory Drug Treatment," *in* M. Greenblatt, D. J. Levinson, and Gerald L. Klerman, eds., *Mental Patients in Transition*, Springfield, Ill.: Charles C Thomas, Publisher, 1961, 302–12.

FRIEDL, Ernestine, "Hospital Care in Provincial Greece," *Human Organization*, 16 (Winter, 1958), 24–27.

FRY, J., "Why Patients Go to Hospitals: A Study of Usage," *British Medical Journal*, 2 (December 12, 1959), 1322–27.

GALIONI, E. F., Ralph R. Notman, Alfred H. Stanton, and Richard H. Williams, "The Nature and Purposes of Mental Hospital Wards," *in* M. Greenblatt, D. J. Levinson, and R. H. Williams, eds., *The Patient and the Mental Hospital*, New York: The Free Press of Glencoe, Inc., 1957, 327–56.

GALLAGHER, Eugene B., Daniel J. Levinson, and Iza Erlich, "Some Sociopsychological Characteristics of Patients and Their Relevance for Psychiatric Treatment," *in* M. Greenblatt, D. J. Levinson, and R. H. Williams, eds., *The Patient and the Mental Hospital*, New York: The Free Press of Glencoe, Inc., 1957, 357–79.

GALLOWAY, Robert E. and Harold F. Kaufman, "Use of Hospitals in Four Mississippi Counties," *Mississippi Agricultural Bulletin* 174, 1952.

GAMSON, William A., "Public Information in a Fluoridation Referendum," *Health Education Journal*, 19 (1961), 47–54.

GAMSON, William A., "Social Science Aspects of Fluoridation: A Summary of Research," *Health Education Journal*, 19 (1961), 159–69.

GAMSON, William A., "The Fluoridation Dialogue: Is It an Ideological Conflict?" *Public Opinion Quarterly* (Winter, 1961–62).

GAMSON, William A. and Peter H. Irons, "Community Characteristics and Fluoridation Outcome," *The Journal of Social Issues*, 17 (1961), 66–74.

GARDNER, George E., "The Establishment of Child Psychiatry Programs in a Children's Hospital," *American Journal of Orthopsychiatry*, 28 (July, 1958), 523–33.

GELFAND, M., *Medicine and Magic of the Mashona*, Cape Town, South Africa: Juta & Co., Ltd., 1956.

GILBERT, Doris C. and Daniel J. Levinson, "Ideology, Personality, and Institutional Policy in the Mental Hospital," *Journal of Abnormal and Social Psychology,* 53 (November, 1956), 253–71.

GILBERT, Doris C. and Daniel J. Levinson, "'Custodialism' and 'Humanism' in Mental Hospital Structure and in Staff Ideology," *in* M. Greenblatt, D. J. Levinson, and R. H. Williams, eds., *The Patient and the Mental Hospital,* New York: The Free Press of Glencoe, Inc., 1957, 20–35.

GILBERT, Doris C. and Daniel J. Levinson, "Role Performance, Ideology, and Personality in the Mental Hospital Aides," *in* M. Greenblatt, D. J. Levinson, and R. H. Williams, eds., *The Patient and the Mental Hospital,* New York: The Free Press of Glencoe, Inc., 1957, 197–208.

GILDEA, M. C. *et al.*, "Community Mental Health Research: Findings After Three Years," *American Journal of Psychiatry,* 114 (1958), 970–76.

GILLIN, John, *Moche: A Peruvian Coastal Community,* Washington, D.C.: Smithsonian Institution, Publication 3 of the Institute of Social Anthropology, 1947.

GILLIN, John, "Magical Fright," *Psychiatry,* 11 (August, 1948), 387–400.

GILLIN, John, *The Culture of Security in San Carlos: A Study of a Guatemalan Community of Indians and Ladinos,* New Orleans: Tulane University Middle American Research Institute, Publication 16, 1951.

GIOVANNONI, Jeanne M. and L. P. Ullmann, "Characteristics of Family Care Homes," *International Journal of Social Psychiatry,* 7 (1961), 299–306.

GLASER, W. A., "Doctors and Politics," *American Journal of Sociology,* 66 (November, 1960), 230–45.

GLASSER, M. A., "A Study of the Public's Acceptance of the Salk Vaccine Program," *American Journal of Public Health,* 48 (February, 1958), 141–46.

GOFFMAN, Erving, "On the Characteristics of Total Institutions," *in* Walter Reed Army Institute of Research, *Symposium on Preventive and Social Psychiatry,* Washington, D.C.: Government Printing Office, 1957, 43–84. Reprinted *in* E. Goffman, *Asylums,* Chicago: Aldine Publishing Co., 1962.

GOFFMAN, Erving, "The Moral Career of the Mental Patient," *Psychiatry,* 22 (May, 1959), 123–42. Reprinted *in* E. Goffman, *Asylums,* Chicago: Aldine Publishing Company, 1962.

GOFFMAN, Erving, *Asylums,* Chicago: Aldine Publishing Company, 1962.

GOLDSTEIN, B. and R. L. Eichhorn, "The Changing Protestant Ethic: Rural Patterns in Health, Work and Leisure," *American Sociological Review,* 26 (August, 1961), 557–65.

GOLDSTEIN, B., L. G. Northwood, and R. L. Goldstein, "Medicine in Industry: Problems of Administrators and Practitioners," *Journal of Health and Human Behavior,* 1 (Winter, 1960), 259–68.

GORDON, H. L. and G. Allen, "A Member-Employee Program as a Rehabilitation Technique," *American Journal of Physical Medicine,* 39 (1960), 114–19.

GORDON, H. L. and C. Groth, "Mental Patients Wanting to Stay in the Hospital: Attitudes," *A.M.A. Archives of General Psychiatry,* 4 (1961), 124–30.

GORDON, R. E. and K. K. Gordon, "Social Psychiatry of a Mobile Suburb," *International Journal of Social Psychiatry,* 6 (Summer, 1960), 89–100.

GOSS, Mary E. W., "Influence and Authority Among Physicians in an Out-Patient Clinic," *American Sociological Review,* 26 (February, 1961), 39–50.

GOULD, Harold A., "The Implications of Technological Change for Folk and Scientific Medicine," *American Anthropologist,* 59 (June, 1957), 507–16. Reprinted *in* D. Apple, ed., *Sociological Studies of Health and Sickness,* New York: McGraw-Hill Book Company, Inc., 1960.

GRAHAM, Saxon, "Socio-Economic Status, Illness, and the Use of Medical Services," *Milbank Memorial Fund Quarterly,* 35 (January, 1957), 58–66. Reprinted *in*

E. G. Jaco, ed., *Patients, Physicians, and Illness*, New York: The Free Press of Glencoe, Inc., 1958.

GREEN, Arnold L., "The Ideology of Anti-Fluoridation Leaders," *The Journal of Social Issues*, 17 (1961), 13–25.

GREENBLATT, Milton, "The Psychiatrist as Social System Clinician," *in* M. Greenblatt, D. J. Levinson, and R. H. Williams, eds., *The Patient and the Mental Hospital*, New York: The Free Press of Glencoe, Inc., 1957, 317–23.

GREENBLATT, Milton, David Landy, Robert W. Hyde, and J. Sanbourne Bockoven, "Rehabilitation of the Mentally Ill: Impact of a Project Upon Hospital Structure," *American Journal of Psychiatry*, 114 (May, 1958), 986–92.

GREENBLATT, Milton, Richard H. York, and Esther L. Brown, *From Custodial to Therapeutic Patient Care in Mental Hospitals*, New York: Russell Sage Foundation, 1955.

GREENBLUM, J., "The Control of Sick-Care Functions in the Hospitalization of a Child: Family Versus Hospital," *Journal of Health and Human Behavior*, 2 (Spring, 1961), 32–38.

GREENLEE, Robert F., "Medicine and Curing Practices of the Modern Florida Seminoles," *American Anthropologist*, 46 (July–September, 1944), 317–28.

GRIFFITH, G. Wynne, "The Introduction of Fluoridation in Anglesey," *Health Education Journal*, 14 (November, 1956), 222–30.

GRINSPOON, Lester, Phyllis H. Courtney, and Helen M. Bergen, "The Usefulness of a Structured Parents' Group in Rehabilitation," *in* M. Greenblatt, D. J. Levinson, and Gerald L. Klerman, eds., *Mental Patients in Transition*, Springfield, Ill.: Charles C Thomas, Publisher, 1961, 229–60.

GROSS, Martin and Walter P. Reeves, "Relapses After Withdrawal of Ataractic Drugs: An Interim Report," *in* M. Greenblatt, D. J. Levinson, and Gerald L. Klerman, eds., *Mental Patients in Transition*, Springfield, Ill.: Charles C Thomas, Publisher, 1961, 313–21.

GROTH, C., H. L. Gordon, and F. Dietrich, "The Problem of Unvisited Patients in a Mental Hospital," *Mental Hygiene*, 44 (1960), 210–17.

GRUENBERG, E., "Community Conditions and Psychoses of the Elderly," *American Journal of Psychiatry*, 100 (1954).

GRUSKY, O., "A Case for the Theory of Familial Role Differentiation in Small Groups," *Social Forces*, 35 (March, 1957), 209–17.

GURIN, G., J. Veroff, and S. Feld, *Americans View their Mental Health*, New York: Basic Books, Inc., 1960.

HAGAR, Stansbury, "Micmac Magic and Medicine," *Journal of American Folklore*, 9 (1896) 170–77.

HALL, Bernard H., "Vicissitudes of Psychiatric Ward Personnel," *in* M. Greenblatt, D. J. Levinson, and R. H. Williams, eds., *The Patient and the Mental Hospital*, New York: The Free Press of Glencoe, Inc., 1957, 231–36.

HALL, Edward T. and William F. Whyte, "Intercultural Communication: A Guide to Men of Action," *Human Organization*, 19 (1960), 5–12.

HALLETT, Leaman F., "Medicine and Pharmacy of the New England Indians," *Bulletin of the Massachusetts Archaeological Society*, 17 (1956), 46–49.

HALLOWELL, A. Irving, "Primitive Concepts of Disease," *American Anthropologist*, 37 (1935), 365–68.

HALLOWELL, A. Irving, "Sin, Sex, and Sickness in Saulteaux Belief," *British Journal of Medical Psychology*, 18 (1939), 191–97.

HALMOS, P., ed., *Sociology and Medicine: Studies Within the Framework of the British National Health Service*, Keele: University of Keele, 1962.

HAMBURG, David A., "Therapeutic Aspects of Communication and Administrative Policy in the Psychiatric Section of a General Hospital," *in* M. Greenblatt, D. J.

Levinson, and R. H. Williams, eds., *The Patient and the Mental Hospital*, New York: The Free Press of Glencoe, Inc., 1957, 91–107.

HAMILTON, D. M., "The Psychiatric Hospital as a Cultural Pattern," *in* B. Glueck, ed., *Current Therapies of Personality Disorder*, New York: Grune & Stratton, Inc., 1946.

HAMLIN, Robert H., "The Role of Voluntary Agencies in Meeting the Health Needs of Americans," *The Annals of the American Academy of Political and Social Science*, 337 (September, 1961), 93–102.

HAMLIN, Robert H., *Voluntary Health and Welfare Agencies in the United States*, New York: The Schoolmasters' Press, 1961.

HANKS, L. M., Jr., Jane R. Hanks, *et al.*, "Diphtheria Immunization in a Thai Community," *in* B. D. Paul, ed., *Health, Culture, and Community*, New York: Russell Sage Foundation, 1955, 155–88.

HANSON, Robert C., "Administrator Responsibility in Large and Small Hospitals in a Metropolitan Community," *Journal of Health and Human Behavior*, 2 (Fall, 1961), 199–204.

HANSON, Robert C., "The Systemic Linkage Hypothesis and Role Consensus Patterns in Hospital-Community Relations," *American Sociological Review*, 27 (June, 1962), 304–13.

HARLEY, George Way, *Native African Medicine: With Special Reference to Its Practice in the Mano Tribe of Liberia*, Cambridge: Harvard University Press, 1941.

HASSINGER, E. W. and R. L. McNamara, "The Pattern of Medical Services for Incorporated Places of 500-or-More Population in Missouri, 1950," *Rural Sociology*, 21 (June, 1956), 175–77.

HASSINGER, E. W. and R. L. McNamara, *Family Health Practices Among Open-Country People in a South Missouri County*, University of Missouri Agricultural Experiment Station, Research Bulletin 699, 1959.

HAWKES, R. W., "The Role of the Psychiatric Administrator," *Administrative Science Quarterly*, 6 (June, 1961), 89–106.

HAWKINS, N., "The Detailman and Preference Behavior," *Southwestern Social Science Quarterly*, 40 (December, 1959), 214–24.

HENRY, Jules, "The Formal Social Structure of a Psychiatric Hospital," *Psychiatry*, 17 (1954), 139–51. Reprinted *in* D. Apple, ed., *Sociological Studies of Health and Sickness*, New York: McGraw-Hill Book Company, Inc., 1960.

HENRY, Jules, "Types of Institutional Structure," *Psychiatry*, 20 (1957), 47–60.

HILTON-SIMPSON, M. W., *Arab Medicine and Surgery: A Study of the Healing Arts in Algeria*, London: Oxford University Press, 1922.

HIMES, Joseph S., "Social Distance to Three Types of Hospitals," *Journal of Health and Human Behavior*, 2 (Fall, 1961), 210–13.

HOFFER, Charles R. and Edgar A. Schuler, "Measurement of Health Needs and Health Care," *American Sociological Review*, 13 (December, 1948), 719–24.

HOFFER, Charles R., "Social Aspects of Health and Welfare in Rural Areas," *in* A. L. Bertrand, ed., *Rural Sociology*, New York: McGraw-Hill Book Company, Inc., 1958.

HOFFER, Charles R. *et al.*, *Health Needs and Health Care in Michigan*, East Lansing: Michigan State College, 1950.

HOFFMAN, Jay L., "Problems of Administration in a Large Mental Hospital," *in* M. Greenblatt, D. J. Levinson, and R. H. Williams, eds., *The Patient and the Mental Hospital*, New York: The Free Press of Glencoe, Inc., 1957, 46–49.

HOFFSOMMER, Harold, "The Health Culture Pattern of Rural People," *Public Health Nursing*, 44 (1952), 309–14.

HOLLAND, John B., Kenneth E. Tiedke, and Paul A. Miller, "A Theoretical Model for Health Action," *Rural Sociology*, 22 (June, 1957), 149–55.

HOLLIS, M. D., "Environmental Health Aspects of Future Metropolitan Area Complexes," *American Journal of Public Health*, 48 (1958), 484–88.

HOOD, Thomas R. and Virginia Pence, "Community Health Studies in Kansas," *American Journal of Public Health*, 50 (October, 1960), 1560–69.

HOPKINS, P., "Referrals in General Practice," *British Medical Journal*, 2 (October 13, 1956), 873–77.

HRDLICKA, Ales, "Disease, Medicine and Surgery Among the American Aborigines," *Journal of the American Medical Association*, 99 (1932), 1661–66.

HSU, Francis L. K., *Medicine and Magic in Western Yunnan*, New York: Institute of Pacific Relations, 1943.

HSU, Francis L. K., *Religion, Science, and Human Crises*, London: Routledge & Kegan Paul, Ltd., 1952.

HSU, Francis L. K., "A Cholera Epidemic in a Chinese Town," *in* B. D. Paul, ed., *Health, Culture, and Community*, New York: Russell Sage Foundation, 1955, 135–54.

HUGHES, C. C., M. Tremblay, R. N. Rapoport, and A. H. Leighton, *People of Cove and Woodlot*, New York: Basic Books, Inc., 1960.

HUNT, R. G., "Social Class and Mental Illness: Some Implications for Clinical Theory and Practice," *American Journal of Psychiatry*, 116 (1960), 1065–69.

HUNT, R. G., O. Gurrslin and J. L. Roach, "Social Status and Psychiatric Service in a Child Guidance Clinic," *American Sociological Review*, 23 (February, 1958), 81–83.

HUNTER, F., R. C. Schaffer, and C. G. Sheps, *Community Organization: Action and Inaction*, Chapel Hill: The University of North Carolina Press, 1956.

HUTCHISON, John A., "Small-town Fluoridation Fight," *Scientific Monthly*, 77 (1953), 240–43.

HYDE, D. R., P. Wolff, A. Gross, and E. L. Hoffman, "The American Medical Association: Power, Purpose, and Politics in Organized Medicine," *Yale Law Journal*, 63 (May, 1954), 938–1022.

HYDE, Robert W. and Richard H. Williams, "What is Therapy and Who Does It?" *in* M. Greenblatt, D. J. Levinson, and R. H. Williams, eds., *The Patient and the Mental Hospital*, New York: The Free Press of Glencoe, Inc., 1957, 173–96.

HYDRICK, J. L., *Intensive Rural Hygiene Work in the Netherlands East Indies*, New York: The Netherlands Information Bureau, 1942.

IANNI, F. A. J., R. M. Albrecht, and A. K. Polan, "Group Attitudes and Information Sources in a Polio Vaccine Program," *Public Health Reports*, 75 (1960), 665–71.

ISRAEL, R. H. and N. A. Johnson, "Discharge and Readmission Rates in 4,254 Consecutive First Admissions of Schizophrenia," *American Journal of Psychiatry*, 112 (1956), 903–9.

JABLOW, J., "Some Aspects of Technical Assistance in Liberia," *Transactions of the New York Academy of Science*, Series II, 17 (1954), 143–56.

JAMES, G., "Research by Local Health Departments; Problems, Methods, Results," *American Journal of Public Health*, 48 (March, 1958), 353–61.

JEFFREYS, Margot, "Social Class and Health Promotion: Some Obstacles in Britain," *Health Education Journal*, 15 (May, 1957), 109–18.

JEFFREYS, Margot, J. H. F. Brotherston, and A. Cartwright, "Consumption of Medicines on a Working-Class House Estate," *British Journal of Preventive and Social Medicine*, 14 (January, 1960), 64–76.

JELLIFFE, D. B., "Social Culture and Nutrition," *Pediatrics*, 20 (July, 1957), 128–38.

JENNESS, Diamond, "An Indian Method of Treating Hysteria," *Primitive Man*, 6 (1933), 13–20.

JENNEY, E. Ross and Ozzie G. Simmons, "Human Relations and Technical Assistance in Public Health," *Scientific Monthly*, 78 (June, 1954), 365–71.

JOHNSON, E. H., "Bureaucracy in the Rehabilitation Institution: Lower Level Staff as a Treatment Resource," *Social Forces*, 38 (May, 1960), 355–59.

JONES, Howard, "The Practice of Medicine Among Our Aborigines," *Annals of Medical History*, 2 (1930), 436–39.

JONES, Howard, "Aboriginal Medicine," *Medical Journal and Record*, 137 (1933), 34–35, 78–80.

JONES, Howard, "Indian Treatment for Paralysis," *Medical Record*, 155 (1942), 45–46.

JONES, M., "Social Rehabilitation with Emphasis on Work Therapy as a Form of Group Therapy," *British Journal of Medical Psychology*, 33 (1960), 67–71.

JONES, Maxwell *et al.*, *The Therapeutic Community*, New York: Basic Books, Inc., 1953.

JONES, Maxwell and Robert Rapoport, "The Absorption of New Doctors into a Therapeutic Community," *in* M. Greenblatt, D. J. Levinson, and R. H. Williams, eds., *The Patient and the Mental Hospital*, New York: The Free Press of Glencoe, Inc., 1957, 248–62.

JONES, N. W., "The Production of Change in a Pre-Natal Clinic: Some Influential Factors," *Human Organization*, 12 (Winter, 1954), 21–26.

JOURNAL OF SOCIAL ISSUES, "Socio-Cultural Approaches to Medical Care," 8 (October, 1952), entire issue.

JOURNAL OF SOCIAL ISSUES, "New Pathways from the Mental Hospital," 16 (1960), entire issue.

JOURNAL OF SOCIAL ISSUES, "Trigger for Community Conflict: The Case of Fluoridation," 17 (1961), entire issue.

KADUSHIN, C., "Individual Decisions to Undertake Psychotherapy," *Administrative Science Quarterly*, 3 (December, 1958), 379–411.

KAHN, J. P., "The Role of Ancillary Personnel in the Total Treatment of Psychiatric Patients," *Mental Hospital*, 10 (1959), 27.

KANTOR, David, "The Use of College Students as 'Case Aides' in a Social Service Department of a State Hospital: An Experiment in Undergraduate Social Work Education," *in* M. Greenblatt, D. J. Levinson and R. H. Williams, eds., *The Patient and the Mental Hospital*, New York: The Free Press of Glencoe, Inc., 1957, 603–8.

KAPLAN, Bert and Thomas F. A. Plaut, *Personality in a Communal Society: An Analysis of the Mental Health of the Hutterites*, Lawrence: University of Kansas Publications, 1956.

KARTUS, Irving and Herbert J. Schlesinger, "The Psychiatric Hospital Physician and His Patient," *in* M. Greenblatt, D. J. Levinson, and R. H. Williams, eds., *The Patient and the Mental Hospital*, New York: The Free Press of Glencoe, Inc., 1957, 286–99.

KATZ, A. H., *Parents of the Handicapped: Self-Organized Parents' and Relatives' Groups for Treatment of Ill and Handicapped Children*, Springfield, Ill.: Charles C Thomas, Publisher, 1961.

KEGELES, S. Stephen, "Some Unanswered Questions and Action Implications of Social Research in Fluoridation," *The Journal of Social Issues*, 17 (1961), 75–81.

KELMAN, Howard R., "An Experiment in the Rehabilitation of Nursing Home Patients," *Public Health Reports*, 77 (April, 1962), 356–66.

KELSEY, F. E., "The Pharmacology of Peyote," *South Dakota Journal of Medicine and Pharmacy*, 12 (1959), 213–33.

KEMP, P., *Healing Ritual: Studies in the Technique and Tradition of the Southern Slaves*, London: Faber & Faber, Ltd., 1935.

KENNARD, Edward A., "Psychiatry, Administrative Psychiatry, Administration: A Study of a Veterans Hospital," *in* M. Greenblatt, D. J. Levinson, and R. H. Williams, eds., *The Patient and the Mental Hospital*, New York: The Free Press of Glencoe, Inc., 1957, 36–45.

KENNARD, Edward A., "Major Patterns of the Mental Hospital—U. S. A.," *in* M. K. Opler, ed., *Culture and Mental Health*, New York: The Macmillan Company, 1959, 391–412.

KIMBALL, Solon T., "An Alabama Town Surveys Its Health Needs," *in* Benjamin D. Paul, ed., *Health, Culture, and Community*, New York: Russell Sage Foundation, 1955, 269–94.

KIMBALL, Solon T. and Marion Pearsall, *The Talladega Story*, University: University of Alabama Press, 1954.

KING, P. D., "The Changing Function of the Mental Hospital," *Mental Hospitals*, 10 (December, 1959), 16–17.

KING, William S., "Cross-Cultural Factors in Health Administration," *in* Bertram S. Kraus, ed., *Indian Health in Arizona*, Tucson: University of Arizona Bureau of Ethnic Research, Publication 2, 1954, 18–27.

KIRSCHT, John P. and Andie L. Knutson, "Science and Fluoridation: An Attitude Study," *The Journal of Social Issues*, 17 (1961), 37–44.

KISER, Clyde V., "The Indianapolis Fertility Study," *Public Opinion Quarterly*, 17 (Winter, 1953), 496–510.

KLERMAN, Gerald L., "Historical Baselines for the Evaluation of Maintenance Drug Therapy of Discharged Psychiatric Patients," *in* M. Greenblatt, D. J. Levinson, and Gerald K. Klerman, eds., *Mental Patients in Transition*, Springfield, Ill.: Charles C Thomas, Publisher, 1961, 287–301.

KLOPPER, W. G., J. S. Hillson, and A. A. Wylie, "Attitude Toward Mental Hospitals," *Journal of Clinical Psychology*, 12 (October, 1956), 361–65.

KNUTSON, Andie L., "Human Behavior Factors in Program Planning," *Public Health Reports*, 70 (1954), 1129–34.

KNUTSON, Andie L. and Bernard Shimberg, "Evaluation of a Health Education Program," *American Journal of Public Health*, 45 (January, 1955), 21–27.

KOOS, Earl L., *The Health of Regionville*, New York: Columbia University Press, 1954.

KOOS, Earl L., " 'Metropolis'—What City People Think of Their Medical Services," *American Journal of Public Health*, 45 (December, 1955), 1551–57. Reprinted *in* E. G. Jaco, ed., *Patients, Physicians, and Illness*, New York: The Free Press of Glencoe, Inc., 1958.

KOTINSKY, R. and H. Witmer, eds., *Community Programs for Mental Health*, Cambridge: Harvard University Press, 1955.

KRAMER, Bernard M., *Day Hospital*, New York: Grune & Stratton, Inc., 1962.

KRAMER, Morton, Hyman Goldstein, Robert H. Israel, and Nelson A. Johnson, *A Historical Study of the Disposition of First Admissions to a State Mental Hospital: Experience of the Warren State Hospital During the Period 1916–50*, Washington, D.C.: Government Printing Office, Public Health Monograph 32, 1955.

KRAMER, Morton, Philip H. Person, Jr., George Tarjan, Richard Morgan, and Stanley W. Wright, "A Method for Determination of Probabilities of Stay, Release, and Death, for Patients Admitted to a Hospital for the Mentally Deficient: The Experience of Pacific State Hospital During the Period 1948–1952," *American Journal of Mental Deficiency*, 62 (November, 1957), 481–95.

KRAMER, Morton *et al.*, "National Approach to the Evaluation of Community Mental Health Programs," *American Journal of Public Health*, 51 (July, 1961), 969–79.

KRAUS, P. Stefan, "Ward Assignments and Patient Movement in a Large Psychiatric Hospital," *in* M. Greenblatt, D. J. Levinson, and R. H. Williams, eds., *The Patient and the Mental Hospital*, New York: The Free Press of Glencoe, Inc., 1957, 472–78.

KRAUSS, Irving, "An Approach to Evaluating the Effectiveness of a Public Health Program," *Journal of Health and Human Behavior*, 3 (Summer, 1962), 141–46.

KRIESBERG, Louis and Beatrice R. Treiman, "The Public's Views on Dentistry as a Profession," *Journal of Dental Education*, 25 (September, 1961), 247–68.

KRIS, Else B., "Prevention of Rehospitalization Through Relapse Control in a Day Hospital," *in* M. Greenblatt, D. J. Levinson, and Gerald L. Klerman, eds., *Mental Patients in Transition*, Springfield, Ill.: Charles C Thomas, Publisher, 1961, 155–62.

KUTNER, Bernard *et al.*, *Five Hundred Over Sixty: A Community Survey on Aging*, New York: Russell Sage Foundation, 1956.

KUTNER, B. and G. Gordon, "Seeking Care for Cancer," *Journal of Health and Human Behavior*, 2 (Fall, 1961), 171–78.

LA BARRE, Weston, *The Peyote Cult*, New Haven, Conn.: Yale University Publications in Anthropology, 19, 1938.

LA BARRE, Weston, "Folk Medicine and Folk Science," *Journal of American Folklore*, 55 (1942), 197–203.

LA BARRE, Weston, "The Patient and His Families," *Casework Papers*, New York: Family Service Association of America, 1958, 61–71.

LA BARRE, Weston, "Twenty Years of Peyote Studies," *Current Anthropology*, 1 (1960), 45–60.

LANDY, David, "Exploration in Residential After-Care of Psychiatric Patients: A Men's Halfway House," *International Journal of Social Psychiatry*, 6 (Summer, 1960), 132–49.

LANDY, David, "Problems of the Person Seeking Help in Our Culture," *The Social Welfare Forum, 1960*, New York: Columbia University Press, 1960.

LANDY, David and Wilmot D. Griffith, "Employer Receptivity Toward Hiring Psychiatric Patients," *Mental Hygiene*, 42 (July, 1958), 383–90.

LANDY, David and Sara E. Singer, "The Social Organization and Culture of a Club for Former Mental Patients," *Human Relations*, 14 (1961), 31–41.

LANTIS, Margaret, "Folk Medicine and Hygiene: Lower Kuskokwim and Ninivak-Nelson Island Areas," *Anthropological Papers of the University of Alaska*, 8 (December, 1959), 1–75.

LEFTON, M., S. Dinitz, and B. Pasamanick, "Decision-Making in a Mental Hospital: Real, Perceived and Ideal," *American Sociological Review*, 24 (1959), 822–29.

LEFTON, M. *et al.*, "Mental Hospital Organization and Staff Evaluation," *A.M.A. Archives of General Psychiatry*, 2 (April, 1960), 462–67.

LEIGHTON, Alexander H., *My Name is Legion*, New York: Basic Books, Inc., 1959.

LEIGHTON, A. H. and Dorothea C. Leighton, "Elements of Psychotherapy in Navaho Religion," *Psychiatry*, 4 (November, 1951), 515–23.

LEIGHTON, A. H. and D. C. Leighton, *The Navaho Door*, Cambridge: Harvard University Press, 1944.

LEIGHTON, A. H. and D. C. Leighton, "Gregorio, the Hand-Trembler," *Papers of the Peabody Museum of American Archeology and Ethnology*, Harvard University, 40 (1949).

LEIGHTON, Alexander H. and A. Longaker, "The Psychiatric Clinic as a Community Innovation," *in* A. H. Leighton, J. A. Clausen, and R. N. Wilson, eds., *Explorations in Social Psychiatry*, New York: Basic Books, Inc., 1957, 365–85.

LEMKAU, Paul V. and Guido M. Crocetti, "An Urban Population's Opinion and Knowledge about Mental Illness," *American Journal of Psychiatry*, 118 (February, 1962), 692–700.

LENTZ, Edith M., "Morale in a Hospital Business Office," *Human Organization*, 9 (1950), 17–21. Reprinted *in* D. Apple, ed., *Sociological Studies of Health and Sickness*, New York: McGraw-Hill Book Company, Inc., 1960.

LENTZ, Edith M., "Hospital Administration—One of a Species," *Administrative Science Quarterly*, 1 (March, 1957), 444–63.

LERNER, Monroe, *Hospital Use and Charges by Diagnostic Category: A Report on the Indiana Study of a Blue Cross Population*, New York: Health Information Foundation, Research Series 13, 1960.

LERNER, Monroe, *Hospital Use by Diagnosis: A Comparison of Two Experiences*, New York: Health Information Foundation, Research Series 19, 1961.

LEVINE, Sol, Odin W. Anderson, and Gerald Gordon, *Non-Group Enrollments for Health Insurance: A Study of Administrative Approaches of Blue Cross Plans*, Cambridge: Harvard University Press, 1957.

LEVINE, Sol and Paul E. White, "Exchange as a Conceptual Framework for the Study of Interorganizational Relationships," *Administrative Science Quarterly*, 5 (March, 1961), 583–601.

LEWIS, Oscar, "Medicine and Politics in a Mexican Village," *in* B. D. Paul, ed., *Health, Culture, and Community*, New York: Russell Sage Foundation, 1955, 403–34.

LIDZ, Theodore, Georgiana Hotchkiss, and Milton Greenblatt, "Patient-Family-Hospital Interrelationships: Some General Conclusions," *in* M. Greenblatt, D. J. Levinson, and R. H. Williams, eds., *The Patient and the Mental Hospital*, New York: The Free Press of Glencoe, Inc., 1957, 535–44.

LIEBERSON, Stanley, "Ethnic Groups and the Practice of Medicine," *American Sociological Review*, 23 (October, 1958), 542–49.

LINN, E. L., "Drug Therapy, Milieu Change, and Release from a Mental Hospital," *American Medical Association Archives of Neurology and Psychiatry*, 81 (June, 1959), 685–704.

LINN, E. L., "Patients' Socioeconomic Characteristics and Release from a Mental Hospital," *American Journal of Sociology*, 65 (November, 1959), 280–86.

LITTLE, R. W., "The 'Sick' Soldier and the Medical Ward Officer," *Human Organization*, 15 (Spring, 1956), 22–24.

LITTMAN, R. A., J. Curry, and J. Pierce-Jones, "Where Parents Go For Help," *The Coordinator*, 6 (September, 1957), 3–9.

LOEB, Martin B., "Some Dominant Cultural Themes in a Psychiatric Hospital," *Social Problems*, 4 (July, 1956), 17–21.

LOEB, Martin B., "Role Definition in the Social World of a Psychiatric Hospital," *in* M. Greenblatt, D. J. Levinson, and R. H. Williams, eds., *The Patient and the Mental Hospital*, New York: The Free Press of Glencoe, Inc., 1957, 14–19.

LOFTIN, M. T. and R. E. Galloway, "The Use of Health Services by Rural People in Four Mississippi Counties," *Sociology and Rural Life*, Bulletin 5 of Mississippi State University, 1954.

LOOMIS, Charles P., "A Cooperative Health Association in Spanish-Speaking Villages," *American Sociological Review*, 10 (1945), 149–60.

LOUDON, J. B., "Social Structure and Health Concepts Among the Zulu," *Health Education Journal*, 15 (May, 1957), 90–99.

LOWE, C. R. and F. N. Garratt, "Sex Pattern of Admissions to Mental Hospitals in Relation to Social Circumstances," *British Journal of Preventive and Social Medicine*, 13 (1959), 88–102.

LOWIE, Robert H., "A Crow Indian Medicine," *American Anthropologist*, 35 (1933), 207ff.

LOWRY, S. G., C. M. Selz, and D. G. Hay, "Factors Associated with the Acceptance of Health Care Practices Among Rural Families," *Rural Sociology*, 23 (June, 1958), 198–202.

LURIE, Abraham and Louise Pinsky, "Collaboration Between Psychiatric Hospital and Community Agencies in the Rehabilitation of Mental Patients," *in* M. Greenblatt, D. J. Levinson, and Gerald L. Klerman, eds., *Mental Patients in Transition*, Springfield, Ill.: Charles C Thomas, Publisher, 1961, 163–74.

LYSTAD, M. H., "Day Hospital Care and Changing Family Attitudes Toward the Mentally Ill," *Journal of Nervous and Mental Disorders*, 127 (1958), 145–52.

MAAS, H. S. *et al.*, "Socio-cultural Factors in Psychiatric Clinic Services for Children: A Collaborative Study in the New York and San Francisco Metropolitan Areas," *Smith College Studies in Social Work*, 25 (February, 1955), 1–90.

MacEACHERN, M. T., *Hospital Organization and Management*, Chicago: Physician's Record Company, 1957.

MacGREGOR, Gordon, "Social Determinants of Health Practices," *American Journal of Public Health*, 51 (November, 1961), 1709–14.

MacLEISH, Kenneth, "Notes on Folk Medicine in the Hopi Village of Moenkopi," *Journal of American Folklore*, 56 (1943), 62–68.

MacMAHON, Brian, Thomas F. Pugh, and George B. Hutchison, "Principles in the Evaluation of Community Mental Health Programs," *American Journal of Public Health*, 51 (July, 1961), 963–68.

MacMILLAN, Duncan, "Community Treatment of Mental Illness," *Lancet*, (July 26, 1958), 201–4.

MADSEN, William, *Society and Health in the Lower Rio Grande Valley*, Austin, Tex.: The Hogg Foundation for Mental Health, 1961.

MAHAFFEY, T. E., "Proprietary Nursing Homes—A Report on Interviews with 35 Nursing Home Operators in Detroit, Michigan," New York: Health Information Foundation, Research Series 18, 1961.

MAIN, T. F., "The Hospital as a Therapeutic Institution," *Bulletin of the Menninger Clinic*, 10 (1946), 66–70.

MANGUS, A. R. and John R. Seeley, "Mental Health Needs in a Rural and Semi-Rural Area of Ohio," *in* A. M. Rose, ed., *Mental Health and Mental Disorders*, New York: W. W. Norton & Company, Inc., 1955, 203–14.

MANNING, Jane and Betty Ann Glasser, "The Home Visit in the Treatment of Psychiatric Patients Awaiting Hospitalization," *Journal of Health and Human Behavior*, 3 (Summer, 1962), 97–104.

MARDEN, P. W. and B. Farber, "High-Brow Versus Low-Grade Status Among Institutionalized Mentally Retarded Boys," *Social Problems*, 8 (Spring, 1961), 300–312.

MARRIOTT, McKim, "Western Medicine in a Village of Northern India," *in* B. D. Paul, ed., *Health, Culture, and Community*, New York: Russell Sage Foundation, 1955, 239–68.

MARTIN, J. P., *Social Aspects of Prescribing*, Melbourne, Australia: William Heinemann, Ltd., 1957.

MASON, A. S. *et al.*, "Discharges from a Mental Hospital in Relation to Social Class and Other Variables," *A.M.A. Archives of General Psychiatry*, 2 (1960), 1–6.

MAUSNER, B. and J. Mausner, "A Study of the Anti-Scientific Attitude," *Scientific American*, 192 (1955), 35–39.

MAY, Charles D., "Selling Drugs by 'Educating' Physicians," *Journal of Medical Education*, 36 (January, 1961), 1–23.

McCABE, Gracia S., "Cultural Influences on Patient Behavior," *American Journal of Nursing*, 60 (August, 1960), 1101–4.

McCARTHY, Raymond G., "Public Health Approach to the Control of Alcoholism," *American Journal of Public Health*, 40 (November, 1950), 1412.

McCARTHY, Raymond G., "Alcoholism: Attitudes and Attacks, 1775–1935," *The Annals of the American Academy of Political and Social Science*, 315 (January, 1958), 12–21.

McDERMOTT, Walsh *et al.*, "Introducing Modern Medicine in a Navajo Community," *Science*, 131 (January 22 and 29, 1960), 197–205 and 280–87.

McELRATH, Dennis C., "Perspective and Participation of Physicians in Prepaid Group Practice," *American Sociological Review*, 26 (August, 1961), 596–607.

McGINNIES, E., R. Lana, and C. Smith, "The Effects of Sound Films on Opinions About Mental Illness in Community Discussion Groups," *Journal of Applied Psychology*, 42 (1958), 40–46.

McNEIL, Donald R., *The Fight for Fluoridation*, New York: Oxford University Press, 1957.

MEAD, Margaret, ed., *Cultural Patterns and Technical Change*, New York: The New American Library of World Literature, 1955.

MEAD, Margaret, *Social and Cultural Backgrounds for Planning Public Health Programs in Africa*, Brazzaville: World Health Organization, 1957.

MECHANIC, David, "The Concept of Illness Behavior," *Journal of Chronic Diseases*, 15 (March, 1960), 189–94.

MELBIN, Murray, "Organization Practice and Individual Behavior: Absenteeism Among Psychiatric Aides," *American Sociological Review*, 26 (February, 1951), 14–23.

MENZEL, Herbert, "Innovation, Integration, and Marginality: A Survey of Physicians," *American Sociological Review*, 25 (October, 1960), 704–13.

MENZEL, Herbert, James Coleman, and Elihu Katz, "Dimensions of Being 'Modern' in Medical Practice," *Journal of Chronic Diseases*, 9 (January, 1959), 20–40.

MENZEL, Herbert and Elihu Katz, "Social Relations and Innovation in the Medical Profession: The Epidemiology of a New Drug," *The Public Opinion Quarterly*, 19 (Winter, 1955–56), 337–52. Reprinted *in* E. G. Jaco, ed., *Patients, Physicians, and Illness*, New York: The Free Press of Glencoe, Inc., 1958.

MENZIES, I. E. P., "A Case Study in the Functioning of Social Systems as a Defense Against Anxiety: A Report on a Study of the Nursing Service of A General Hospital," *Human Relations*, 14 (May, 1960), 95–121.

METRAUX, Alfred, "Religion and Shamanism," *in* J. H. Steward, ed., *Handbook of South American Indians*, Washington, D.C.: Smithsonian Institution, Bureau of American Ethnology, 5 (1949), 559–99.

MEYER, Henry J. and Edgar F. Borgatta, "Evaluating a Rehabilitation Program for Post-Hospital Mental Patients," *Public Health Reports*, 73 (July, 1958), 650–56.

MEYER, Henry J. and Edgar F. Borgatta, *An Experiment in Mental Patient Rehabilitation*, New York: Russell Sage Foundation, 1959.

MIDDLETON, J., "Prejudices and Opinions of Mental Hospital Employees Regarding Mental Illness," *American Journal of Psychiatry*, 110 (1953), 133–38.

MILLER, D. and J. Clancy, "An Approach to the Social Rehabilitation of Chronic Psychotic Patients," *Psychiatry*, 15 (1952), 435–43.

MILLER, D. H., "The Etiology of an Outbreak of Delinquency in a Group of Hospitalized Adolescents," *in* M. Greenblatt, D. J. Levinson, and R. H. Williams, eds., *The Patient and the Mental Hospital*, New York: The Free Press of Glencoe, Inc., 1957, 427–37.

MILLER, Paul A., *Community Health Action*, East Lansing: Michigan State College Press, 1953.

MINER, Horace, "Body Ritual Among the Nacirema," *American Anthropologist*, 58 (1956), 503–7.

MISCHEL, Frances, "Faith Healing and Medical Practice in the South Caribbean," *Southwestern Journal of Anthropology*, 15 (Winter, 1959), 407–17.

MISHLER, E. G. and A. Tropp, "Status and Interaction in a Psychiatric Hospital," *Human Relations*, 9 (1956), 187–205.

MITCHELL, Austin, "Fluoridation in Dunedin: A Study of Pressure Groups and Public Opinion," *Political Science* (New Zealand), 12 (1960), 71–93.

MOORE, J. W., "Patterns of Women's Participation in Voluntary Associations," *American Journal of Sociology*, 66 (May, 1961), 592–98.

MOSS, L. W. and S. C. Cappannari, "Folklore and Medicine in an Italian Village," *Journal of American Folklore*, 73 (1960), 95–102.

MULFORD, Harold and Donald E. Miller, "Public Definitions of the Alcoholic," *Quarterly Journal of Studies on Alcohol*, 22 (June, 1961), 312–20.

MURRAY, Edward J. and Melvin Cohen, "Mental Illness, Milieu Therapy, and Social Organization in Ward Groups," *The Journal of Abnormal and Social Psychology*, 58 (January, 1959). Reprinted *in* T. R. Sarbin, ed., *Studies in Behavior Pathology*, New York: Holt, Rinehart & Winston, Inc., 1961.

MURRAY, J. F., "An Experiment in Changing the Attitudes of Employers Toward Mental Illness," *Mental Hygiene*, 42 (July, 1958), 402–8.

MUSSEN, P. H. and R. G. Barker, "Attitudes toward Cripples," *Journal of Abnormal and Social Psychology*, 39 (1944), 351–55.

MYERS, Jerome K. and Leslie Schaffer, "Social Stratification and Psychiatric Practice: A Study of an Out-Patient Clinic," *American Sociological Review*, 19 (June, 1954), 307–10.

NAEGELE, Kaspar D., "A Mental Health Project in a Boston Suburb," *in* B. D. Paul, ed., *Health, Culture, and Community*, New York: Russell Sage Foundation, 1955, 295–324.

NEWELL, Kenneth W., "Medical Development Within a Maori Community," *Health Education Journal*, 15 (May, 1957), 83–90.

NUNNALLY, Jum C., "The Communication of Mental Health Information: A Comparison of the Opinion of Experts and the Public with Mass Media Presentations," *Behavioral Science*, 2 (1957), 222–30.

NUNNALLY, Jum C., *Popular Conceptions of Mental Health*, New York: Holt, Rinehart & Winston, Inc., 1961.

NUNNALLY, Jum C. and H. M. Bobren, "Variables Governing the Willingness to Receive Communications on Mental Health," *Journal of Personality*, 27 (1959), 38–46.

NUNNALLY, J. C. and J. M. Kittros, "Public Attitudes Toward Mental Health Professions," *American Psychologist*, 13 (1958), 589–94.

NURGE, Ethel, "Etiology of Illness in Guinhangdan," *American Anthropologist*, 60 (December, 1958), 1158–72.

OBERG, Kalervo and Jose Arthur Rios, "A Community Improvement Project in Brazil," *in* B. D. Paul, ed., *Health, Culture, and Community*, New York: Russell Sage Foundation, 1955, 349–76.

O'CONNOR, N. *et al.*, "Communication in a Mental Hospital Population, *International Journal of Social Psychiatry*, 3 (Winter, 1957), 183–87.

OGLE, William A. and James D. Taylor, "Experience of Psychiatrists Working with General Practitioners Caring for Discharged Mental Hospital Patients," *in* M. Greenblatt, D. J. Levinson, and Gerald L. Klerman, eds., *Mental Patients in Transition*, Springfield, Ill.: Charles C Thomas, Publisher, 1961, 175–86.

OLSHANSKY, Simon S., "Vocational Rehabilitation and the Ex-Mental Patient," *Journal of Rehabilitation*, 8 (November–December, 1960).

OLSHANSKY, Simon S., "Preventing Relapse of Ex-Mental Hospital Patients," *Journal of Rehabilitation*, 10 (January–February, 1962).

OXAAL, I., "Social Stratification and Personnel Turnover in the Hospital," *Engineering Experiment Station Bulletins*, Ohio State University, May, 1960.

PADILLA, Elena, *Up from Puerto Rico*, New York: Columbia University Press, 1958.

PARKER, Seymour, "Changes in the Administration of Psychotherapy During a Collective Upset," *Human Organization*, 16 (Winter, 1958), 32–37.

PARSONS, A., "Some Comparative Observations on Ward Social Structure: Southern Italy, England and the United States," *O'Ospedale Psichiatrico*, 2 (April–June, 1959), 3–23.

PARSONS, Talcott, "Social Structure and Dynamic Process: The Case of Modern Medical Practice," *in The Social System*, New York: The Free Press of Glencoe, Inc., 1951, 428–79.

PARSONS, Talcott, "The Mental Hospital as a Type of Organization," *in* M. Greenblatt, D. J. Levinson, and R. H. Williams, eds., *The Patient and the Mental Hospital*, New York: The Free Press of Glencoe, Inc., 1957, 108–29.

PARSONS, Talcott, "Definitions of Health and Illness in the Light of American Values and Social Structure," *in* E. G. Jaco, ed., *Patients, Physicians and Illness*, New York: The Free Press of Glencoe, Inc., 1958, 165–87.

PASAMANICK, Benjamin, Simon Dinitz, and Mark Lefton, "Psychiatric Orientation and Its Relation to Diagnosis and Treatment in a Mental Hospital," *American Journal of Psychiatry*, 116 (August, 1959), 127–32.

PATERSON, R. and J. Aitken-Swan, "Public Opinion on Cancer, Changes Following Five Years of Cancer Education," *Lancet*, (October 11, 1958), 791–93.

PATTEN, T. H. Jr., "Health and Behavior in Homes for Veterans: Some Old and New Patterns," *Journal of Health and Human Behavior*, 2 (Spring, 1961), 47–58.

PAUL, Benjamin D., "The Cultural Context of Health Education," *Symposium Proceedings*, University of Pittsburgh School of Social Work, 1953, 31–38.

PAUL, Benjamin D., "Respect for Cultural Differences," *Community Development Bulletin*, 4 (June, 1953), 42–47.

PAUL, Benjamin D., "The Role of Beliefs and Customs in Sanitation Programs," *American Journal of Public Health*, 48 (November, 1958), 1502–6.

PAUL, Benjamin D., "Synopsis of Report on Fluoridation," *Massachusetts Dental Society Journal*, 8 (January, 1959), 19–21.

PAUL, Benjamin D., "Fluoridation and the Social Scientist: A Review," *Journal of Social Issues*, 17 (1961), 1–12.

PEARSALL, Marion, "Healthways in a Mountain County," *Mountain Life and Work*, 36 (Winter, 1960), 7–13.

PEARSALL, M., "A Model for the Analysis of Cross-Cultural Action Programs," *Human Organization*, 19 (Winter, 1960-61), 212–15.

PERROW, C., "Organizational Prestige: Some Functions and Dysfunctions," *American Journal of Sociology*, 66 (January, 1961), 335–41.

PERROW, C., "The Analysis of Goals in Complex Organizations," *American Sociological Review*, 26 (September, 1961), 854–66.

PERRY, H. S., "The Evolution of a Potentially Deviant Subgroup," *Human Organization*, 18 (Summer, 1959), 85–87.

PERRY, Stewart E. and Gertrude N. Shea, "Social Controls and Psychiatric Theory in a Ward Setting," *Psychiatry*, 3 (August, 1957), 221–47.

PETERSON, Osler L. *et al.*, "An Analytical Study of North Carolina General Practice, 1953–1954," *Journal of Medical Education*, 31 (December, 1956).

PFAUTZ, Harold W. and Gita Wilder, "The Ecology of a Mental Hospital," *Journal of Health and Human Behavior*, 3 (Summer, 1962), 67–72.

PHILIPS, Jane, "The Hookworm Campaign in Ceylon," *in* H. M. Teaf, Jr., and P. G. Franck, eds., *Hands Across Frontiers: Case Studies in Technical Cooperation*, Ithaca, N.Y.: Cornell University Press, 1955, 265–306.

PLAUT, Thomas F. A., "Analysis of Voting Behavior on a Fluoridation Referendum," *Public Opinion Quarterly*, 23 (1959), 213–22.

POLANSKY, Norman A., Robert B. White, and Stuart C. Miller, "Determinants of the Role-Image of the Patient in a Psychiatric Hospital," *in* M. Greenblatt, D. J. Levinson, and R. H. Williams, eds., *The Patient and the Mental Hospital,* New York: The Free Press of Glencoe, Inc., 1957, 380–401.

POLGAR, Steven, "Evolution and the Thermodynamic Imperative," *Human Biology,* 33 (May, 1961), 99–109.

PRATT, Lois, "How Do Patients Learn About Disease?" *Social Problems,* 4 (July, 1956), 29–40.

PRATT, S. *et al.,* "Attitudes Toward the Mental Hospital and Selected Population Characteristics," *Journal of Clinical Psychology,* 16 (April, 1960), 214–18.

QUERIDO, A., "Forecast and Follow-Up. An Investigation into the Clinical, Social and Mental Factors Determining the Results of Hospital Treatment," *British Journal of Preventive and Social Medicine,* 13 (1959), 33–49.

RAMSEY, G. V. and M. Seipp, "Attitudes and Opinions Concerning Mental Illness," *Psychiatric Quarterly,* 22 (1948), 428–44.

RAPOPORT, R. N., "Oscillations and Sociotherapy," *Human Relations,* 9 (1956), 357–74.

RAPOPORT, R. N., *Community as Doctor: New Perspective on a Therapeutic Community,* London: Tavistock Publications, 1960.

RAPOPORT, Robert N. and Rhona Rapoport, "Community as the Doctor," *Human Organization,* 16 (Winter, 1958), 28–31.

RAULET, Harry M., "The Health Professional and the Fluoridation Issue: A Case of Role Conflict," *Journal of Social Issues,* 17 (1961), 45–54.

RAWNSLEY, K., J. B. Loudon, and H. L. Miles, "Attitudes of Relatives to Patients in Mental Hospitals," *British Journal of Preventive and Social Medicine,* 16 (January, 1962), 1–15.

READ, M., "Attitudes Toward Health and Disease Among Preliterate Peoples," *Health Education Journal,* 6 (1948), 166–72.

READER, George G. and Mary E. W. Goss, "Medical Sociology with Particular Reference to the Study of Hospitals," *Transactions of the Fourth World Congress of Sociology,* 2 (1959), 139–52.

REDFIELD, Robert, *The Folk Culture of Yucatan,* Chicago: University of Chicago Press, 1941.

REDFIELD, R. and M. P. Redfield, *Disease and Its Treatment in Dzitas, Yucatan,* Washington, D.C.: Carnegie Institute of Washington, Publication 523, 1940.

REDLICH, F. C., "What the Citizen Knows About Psychiatry," *Mental Hygiene,* 34 (1950), 64–79.

REEDER, Leo G. and George Donohue, *Employer Attitudes Toward Heart Disease,* Minneapolis: Minnesota Heart Association, 1954.

REES, T. P., "Some Observations on the Psychiatric Patient, the Mental Hospital and the Community," *in* M. Greenblatt, D. J. Levinson, and R. H. Williams, eds., *The Patient and the Mental Hospital,* New York: The Free Press of Glencoe, Inc., 1957, 527–29.

REICH, William T. and Odin W. Anderson, *Colorado's Medical Care Program for the Aged,* New York: Health Information Foundation, Perspectives A2, 1960.

RENNIE, Thomas A. C., Temple Burling, and Luther E. Woodward, *Vocational Rehabilitation of Psychiatric Patients,* New York: The Commonwealth Fund, 1950.

RICHARDS, Audrey I., *Hunger and Work in a Savage Community,* New York: The Free Press of Glencoe, Inc., 1948.

RIOUX, Marcel, "Some Medical Beliefs and Practices of the Contemporary Iroquois Longhouses of the Six Nations Reserve," *Journal of the Washington Academy of Sciences,* 41 (1951), 152–58.

RITZENTHALER, Robert E., "Chippewa Preoccupation with Health: Change in a Traditional Attitude Resulting from Modern Health Problems," *Bulletin of the Public Museum of the City of Milwaukee,* 19 (1953), 175–257.

RIVERS, W. H. R., *Medicine, Magic, and Religion,* New York: Harcourt, Brace & World, Inc., 1924.

ROBINSON, R., D. F. deMarche, and M. K. Wagle, *Community Resources in Mental Health,* New York: Basic Books, Inc., 1960.

ROEHER, G. Allan, "Significance of Public Attitudes in the Rehabilitation of the Disabled," *Rehabilitation Literature,* 22 (March, 1961), 66–72.

ROEMER, M. I., "Health Service Organization as a Task in Applied Social Science," *Canadian Journal of Public Health,* 45 (April, 1954), 133–45.

ROEMER, Milton I., "Social Science and Organized Health Services," *Human Organization,* 18 (1959), 75–77.

ROEMER, Milton I. and Max Shain, *Hospital Utilization under Insurance,* Chicago: American Hospital Association, 1959.

ROEMER, M. I., "General Hospitals in Europe," *in* J. K. Owen, ed., *Modern Concepts of Hospital Administration,* Philadelphia: W. B. Saunders Co., 1961.

ROEMER, Milton I. and Rodney F. White, "Community Attitudes Toward the Hospital," *Hospital Management,* Part I (January, 1960), Part II, (February, 1960).

ROGATZ, Peter and Guido M. Crocetti, "Home Care Programs: Their Impact on the Hospital's Role in Medical Care," *American Journal of Public Health,* 48 (September, 1958), 1125–33.

ROGERS, Edward S. and Arlene K. Daniels, "Attitudes toward Group Dental Care: A Survey of Consumers and Dentists," *Journal of the American College of Dentists,* 25 (1958), 174–237.

ROGERS, Spencer L., "Disease Concepts in North America," *American Anthropologist,* 46 (1944), 559–64.

ROHRER, Wayne C., "Demographic and Social Changes Affecting the Community Hospital," *Hospital Administration,* 7 (Summer, 1962), 32–51.

RONEY, James G., Jr., "The Place of Anthropology in a Technical Assistance Program," *Scientific Monthly,* 78 (1954), 159–62.

ROSE, Arnold M., "Attitudes of Youth Toward Mental Health Problems," *Sociology and Social Research,* 41 (1957), 343–48.

ROSE, Charles L., "Relatives' Attitudes and Mental Hospitalization," *Mental Hygiene,* 43 (April, 1959), 194–203.

ROSEN, George, "Evolving Trends in Health Education," *Canadian Journal of Public Health,* 52 (December, 1961), 499–506.

ROSENGREN, W. R., "Role Determinateness in Hospital Administrations," *Hospital Administration,* 5 (September, 1960), 46–57.

ROSENGREN, W. R., "Status Stress and Role Contradictions: Emergent Professionalization in Psychiatric Hospitals," *Mental Hygiene,* 45 (January, 1961), 28–39.

ROSENSTOCK, Irwin M., "What Research in Motivation Suggests for Public Health," *American Journal of Public Health,* 50 (1960), 295–302.

ROSENSTOCK, Irwin M., M. Derryberry, and B. K. Carriger, "Why People Fail to Seek Poliomyelitis Vaccination," *Public Health Reports,* 74 (February, 1959), 98–104.

ROSS, John A., "Social Class and Medical Care," *Journal of Health and Human Behavior,* 3 (Spring, 1962), 35–40.

ROTH, Julius A., "Ritual and Magic in the Control of Contagion," *American Sociological Review,* 22 (June, 1957), 310–14. Reprinted *in* E. G. Jaco, ed., *Patients, Physicians, and Illness,* New York: The Free Press of Glencoe, Inc., 1958. Reprinted *in* D. Apple, ed., *Sociological Studies in Health and Sickness,* New York: McGraw-Hill Book Company, Inc., 1960.

ROWLAND, H., "Interaction Processes in a State Mental Hospital," *Psychiatry,* 1 (1938), 323–27.

ROWLAND, H., "Friendship Patterns in a State Mental Hospital," *Psychiatry,* 2 (1939), 363–73.

RUBEL, Arthur J., "Concepts of Disease in Mexican-American Culture," *American Anthropologist,* 62 (October, 1960), 795–814.

SAMORA, J., L. Saunders, and R. F. Larson, "Medical Vocabulary Knowledge Among Hospital Patients," *Journal of Health and Human Behavior,* 2 (Summer, 1961), 83–92.

SAMPSON, Harold, Sheldon L. Messinger, and Robert D. Towne, "The Mental Hospital and Marital Family Ties," *Social Problems,* 9 (Fall, 1961), 141–55.

SANDERS, Irwin T., "The Stages of a Community Controversy: The Case of Fluoridation," *The Journal of Social Issues,* 17 (1961), 55–65.

SAUNDERS, J. V. D., "Characteristics of Hospitals and of Hospital Administrators Associated with Hospital-Community Relations in Mississippi," *Rural Sociology,* 25 (June, 1960), 229–32.

SAUNDERS, J. V. D. and J. H. Bruening, "Hospital-Community Relations in Mississippi," *Rural Sociology,* 24 (March, 1959), 48–51.

SAUNDERS, Lyle, *Cultural Difference and Medical Care,* New York: Russell Sage Foundation, 1954.

SAUNDERS, Lyle, "Healing Ways in the Spanish Southwest," *in* E. G. Jaco, ed., *Patients, Physicians and Illness,* New York: The Free Press of Glencoe, Inc., 1958, 189–206.

SAUNDERS, Lyle and Gordon W. Hewes, "Folk Medicine and Medical Practice," *Journal of Medical Education,* 28 (September, 1953), 43–46.

SAUNDERS, Lyle and Julian Samora, "A Medical Care Program in a Colorado County," *in* B. D. Paul, ed., *Health, Culture, and Community,* New York: Russell Sage Foundation, 1955, 377–400.

SCHAFFER, L. and J. K. Myers, "Psychotherapy and Social Stratification: An Empirical Study of Practice in a Psychiatric Out-patient Clinic," *Psychiatry,* 17 (February, 1954), 83–93.

SCHEFF, Thomas J., "Control Over Policy by Attendants in a Mental Hospital," *Journal of Health and Human Behavior,* 2 (Summer, 1961), 93–105.

SCHER, Jordan M., "Diffusion of Communication and Role Exchange in the Treatment of Schizophrenia," *in* M. Greenblatt, D. J. Levinson, and R. H. Williams, eds., *The Patient and the Mental Hospital,* New York: The Free Press of Glencoe, Inc., 1957, 309–16.

SCHER, Jordan M., "The Structured Ward: Research Method and Hypothesis in a Total Treatment Setting for Schizophrenia," *American Journal of Orthopsychiatry,* 28 (April, 1958), 291–99.

SCHNEIDER, David M., "Abortion and Depopulation on a Pacific Island," *in* B. D. Paul, ed., *Health, Culture, and Community,* New York: Russell Sage Foundation, 1955, 211–38.

SCHOOLER, C. and H. E. Spohn, "Social Interaction on a Ward of Chronic Schizophrenics," *International Journal of Social Psychiatry,* 6 (Summer, 1960), 115–19.

SCHULMAN, Sam, "Rural Healthways in New Mexico," *in* Vera Rubin, ed., "Culture, Society, and Health," *Annals of the New York Academy of Sciences,* 84 (December, 1960), 950–58.

SCHWARTZ, Charlotte G., "The Stigma of Mental Illness," *Journal of Rehabilitation,* 4 (July–August, 1956), 7–10.

SCHWARTZ, Charlotte G., "Problems for Psychiatric Nurses in Playing a New Role on a Mental Hospital Ward," *in* M. Greenblatt, D. J. Levinson, and R. H. Williams, eds., *The Patient and the Mental Hospital,* New York: The Free Press of Glencoe, Inc., 1957, 402–26.

SCHWARTZ, Charlotte G., Morris S. Schwartz, and Alfred H. Stanton, "A Study of Need-Fulfillment on a Mental Hospital Ward," *Psychiatry*, 14 (May, 1951), 223–42.

SCHWARTZ, Morris S., "Social Research in the Mental Hospital," *in* A. M. Rose, ed., *Mental Health and Mental Disorders*, New York: W. W. Norton & Company, Inc., 1955, 190–202.

SCHWARTZ, Morris S., "What is a Therapeutic Milieu?" *in* M. Greenblatt, D. J. Levinson, and R. H. Williams, eds., *The Patient and the Mental Hospital*, New York: The Free Press of Glencoe, Inc., 1957, 130–44.

SCHWARTZ, Morris S., "Functions of the Team in the State Mental Hospital," *American Journal of Orthopsychiatry*, 30 (January, 1960), 100–2.

SCHWARTZ, Morris S. and Gwen T. Will, "Low Morale and Mutual Withdrawal on a Mental Hospital Ward," *Psychiatry*, 16 (November, 1953), 337–53.

SEEMAN, M. and J. W. Evans, "Stratification and Hospital Care," *American Sociological Review*, Part I: 26 (February, 1961), 67–79, Part II: 26 (April, 1961), 193–203.

SEPPILLI, Tullio, "Social Conditions of Fertility in a Rural Community in Transition in Central Italy," *in* Vera Rubin, ed., "Culture, Society, and Health," *Annals of the New York Academy of Sciences*, 84 (December, 1960), 959–62.

SHANAS, Ethel, *Medical Care Among Those Aged 65 and Over—Reported Illness and Utilization of Health Services by the "Sick" and the "Well"*, New York: Health Information Foundation, Research Series 16, 1960.

SHANAS, E., "Meeting Medical Care Costs Among the Aging," New York: Health Information Foundation, Research Series 17, 1960.

SHAPIRO, S., L. Weiner, and P. M. Denson, "Comparison of Prematurity and Perinatal Mortality in General Population and in Population of Prepaid Group Practice," *American Journal of Public Health*, 48 (February, 1958), 170–87.

SHARAF, Myron R. and Daniel J. Levinson, "Patterns of Ideology and Role Definition Among Psychiatric Residents," *in* M. Greenblatt, D. J. Levinson, and R. H. Williams, eds., *The Patient and the Mental Hospital*, New York: The Free Press of Glencoe, Inc., 1957, 263–85.

SHEATSLEY, Paul B., "Public Attitudes Toward the Hospital," *Hospitals* (May 16, 1957).

SHEPHERD, I. L. and G. M. Guthrie, "Attitudes of Mothers of Schizophrenic Patients," *Journal of Clinical Psychology*, 15 (April, 1959), 212–15.

SHILOH, A., "Middle East Culture and Health," *Health Education Journal*, 16 (November, 1958), 232–44.

SHRYOCK, R. H., *National Tuberculosis Association, 1904–1954: A Study of the Voluntary Health Movement in the United States*, New York: National Tuberculosis Association, 1957.

SHUVAL, Judith, "Ethnic Stereotyping in Israeli Medical Bureaucracies," *Sociology and Medical Research*, 46 (July, 1962), 455–65.

SIEGEL, Nathaniel and Max Fink, "Motivation for Psychotherapy," *Comprehensive Psychiatry*, 3 (June, 1962), 170–73.

SILLS, D. L., *The Volunteers—Means and Ends in a National Organization*, New York: The Free Press of Glencoe, Inc., 1958.

SILLS, D. L. and R. E. Gill, "Young Adults' Use of the Salk Vaccine," *Social Problems*, 6 (Winter, 1958–59), 246–53.

SILVER, A., S. Wilner, and G. J. Sarwer-Foner, "Psychiatric Unit of a General Hospital," *in* M. Greenblatt, D. J. Levinson, and Gerald L. Klerman, eds., *Mental Patients in Transition*, Springfield, Ill.: Charles C Thomas, Publisher, 1961, 16–25.

SILVER, George A., "Social Medicine at the Montefiore Hospital—A Practical Approach to Community Health Problems," *American Journal of Public Health*, 48 (June, 1958), 724–31.

SIMMEL, Arnold, "A Signpost for Research on Fluoridation Conflicts: The Concept of Relative Deprivation," *The Journal of Social Issues,* 17 (1961), 26–36.

SIMMONS, Leo W., *The Role of the Aged in Primitive Society,* New Haven, Conn.: Yale University Press, 1945.

SIMMONS, Leo W., "Social Participation of the Aged in Different Cultures," *The Annals of the American Academy of Political and Social Science,* 279 (1952), 43–51.

SIMMONS, Ozzie G., "Popular and Modern Medicine in Mestizo Communities of Coastal Peru and Chile," *Journal of American Folklore,* 68 (January–March, 1955), 57–71. Reprinted *in* D. D. Apple, ed., *Sociological Studies of Health and Sickness,* New York: McGraw-Hill Book Company, Inc., 1960.

SIMMONS, Ozzie G., "Implications of Social Class for Public Health," *Human Organization,* 16 (Fall, 1957), 7–10. Reprinted *in* E. G. Jaco, ed., *Patients, Physicians, and Illness,* New York: The Free Press of Glencoe, Inc., 1958.

SIMOONS, F. J., *Eat Not This Flesh: Food Avoidances in the Old World,* Madison: Wisconsin University Press, 1961.

SLOTKIN, J. S., "Social Psychiatry of a Menomini Community," *Journal of Abnormal and Social Psychology,* 48 (1953), 10–16.

SMITH, Harvey L., "Two Lines of Authority: The Hospital's Dilemma," *The Modern Hospital* (March, 1955). Reprinted *in* E. G. Jaco, ed., *Patients, Physicians, and Illness,* New York: The Free Press of Glencoe, Inc., 1958.

SMITH, Harvey L., "Professional Strains and the Hospital Context," *in* M. Greenblatt, D. J. Levinson, and R. H. Williams, eds., *The Patient and the Mental Hospital,* New York: The Free Press of Glencoe, Inc., 1957, 9–13.

SOFER, Cyril, "Reactions to Administrative Change," *Human Relations,* 8 (1955), 291–316. Reprinted *in* D. Apple, ed., *Sociological Studies of Health and Sickness,* New York: McGraw-Hill Book Company, Inc., 1960.

SOLIEN, Nancie L. and Nevin S. Scrimshaw, "Public Health Significance of Child Feeding Practices Observed in a Guatemalan Village," *Journal of Tropical Pediatrics,* 3 (1957), 99–104.

SOLON, Jerry A., "The Public's Image and the Nursing Home's Vision," *Nursing Homes,* 11 (April, 1962), 8–10.

SOLON, Jerry A. *et al.*, "Delineating Patterns of Medical Care," *American Journal of Public Health,* 50 (August, 1960), 1105–31.

SOLON, Jerry A. *et al.*, "Patterns of Medical Care: A Hospital's Out-patients," *American Journal of Public Health,* 50 (December, 1960), 1905–13.

SOLON, Jerry A. *et al.*, "Patterns of Medical Care: Validity of Interview Information on Use of Hospital Clinics," *Journal of Health and Human Behavior,* 3 (Spring, 1962), 21–29.

SOMERS, Norman M. and Anne R. Somers, *Doctors, Patients, and Health Insurance: The Organization and Financing of Medical Care,* Washington, D.C.: The Brookings Institution, 1961.

SOMMER, R. and N. Osmond, "Symptoms of Institutional Care," *Social Problems,* 8 (Winter, 1960–61), 254–63.

SOWER, C., J. Holland, K. Tiedke, and W. Freeman, *Community Involvement,* New York: The Free Press of Glencoe, Inc., 1957.

SPENCER, D. M., *Disease, Religion and Society in the Fiji Islands,* Locust Valley, N.Y.: J. J. Augustin, Monographs of the American Ethnological Society, 2, 1941.

STAINBROOK, Edward, "Human Action in the Social System of the Psychiatric Hospital," *in* Ruth Knee, ed., *Better Social Services for Mentally Ill Patients,* New York: American Association of Psychiatric Social Workers, 1955.

STANTON, Alfred H. and Morris S. Schwartz, "The Management of a Type of Institutional Participation in Mental Illness," *Psychiatry,* 12 (February, 1949), 13–26.

STANTON, Alfred H. and Morris S. Schwartz, "Medical Opinion and the Social Context in the Mental Hospital," *Psychiatry*, 12 (August, 1949), 243–49.

STANTON, Alfred H. and Morris S. Schwartz, "Observations on Dissociation as Social Participation," *Psychiatry*, 12 (1949), 339–54. Reprinted *in* D. Apple, ed., *Sociological Studies of Health and Sickness*, New York: McGraw-Hill Book Company, Inc., 1960.

STANTON, Alfred H. and Morris S. Schwartz, *The Mental Hospital*, New York: Basic Books, Inc., 1954.

STEFANSSON, V., "Notes on the Theory and Treatment of Diseases Among the MacKenzie River Eskimo," *Journal of American Folklore*, 21 (1908), 43–45.

STEIN, H., "Socio-Cultural Factors in Psychiatric Clinics for Children," *Social Service Review*, 30 (March, 1956), 9–19.

STEIN, L. and S. A. Skloroff, "The Health of an Urban Community," *British Journal of Preventive and Social Medicine*, 6 (April, 1952), 118–51.

STEVENSON, George S., *Mental Health Planning for Social Action*, New York: McGraw-Hill Book Company, 1956.

STIERLIN, H., "Contrasting Attitudes Towards the Psychoses in Europe and the United States," *Psychiatry*, 21 (1958), 141–47.

STONE, Eric, "Medicine Among the Iroquois," *Annals of Medical History*, 6 (1934), 529–39.

STRAUS, Robert, "Medical Practice and the Alcoholic," *Annals of the American Society of Political and Social Science*, 315 (January, 1958). Reprinted *in* E. G. Jaco, ed., *Patients, Physicians, and Illness*, New York: The Free Press of Glencoe, Inc., 1958.

STYCOS, J. Mayone, "Birth Control Clinics in Crowded Puerto Rico," *in* B. D. Paul, ed., *Health, Culture, and Community*, New York: Russell Sage Foundation, 1955, 189–210.

SUSSMAN, Marvin B., "The Help Pattern in the Middle Class Family," *American Sociological Review*, 18 (February, 1953), 22–28.

SUSSMAN, Marvin B., "Psycho-Social Correlates of Obesity: Failure of 'Calorie Collectors,'" *Journal of the American Dietetic Association*, 32 (1956), 423–28.

SUSSMAN, Marvin B., "The Calorie Collectors: A Study of Spontaneous Group Formation, Collapse and Reconstruction," *Social Forces*, 34 (May, 1956), 351–56.

SWANTON, John R., "Religious Beliefs and Medical Practices of the Creek Indians," *42nd Annual Report of the Bureau of American Ethnology*, Washington, D.C.: Smithsonian Institution, 1928, 473–672.

TITCHENER, J. L. *et al.*, "Problems of Delay in Seeking Surgical Care," *Journal of the American Medical Association*, 160 (April 7, 1956), 1187–93.

TITMUSS, R. M., *Essays on "the Welfare State,"* London: George Allen & Unwin, Ltd., 1958.

TRUSSELL, Ray E. and Frank Van Dyke, "Utilization of Routinely Available Information on Health Insurance Studies," *American Journal of Public Health*, 50 (October, 1960), 1508–20.

TUDOR, Gwen E., "A Sociopsychiatric Nursing Approach to Intervention in a Problem of Mutual Withdrawal on a Mental Hospital Ward," *Psychiatry*, 15 (May, 1952), 193–217.

ULLMANN, L. P., *Home Care Placement of Neuropsychiatric Patients*, Washington, D.C.: VA Psychiatric Evaluation Project, 1961.

ULLMANN, L. P. and Virginia C. Berkman, "Types of Outcome in the Family Care Placement of Mental Patients," *Social Worker*, 4 (1959), 72–78.

ULLMANN, L. P. and Virginia C. Berkman, "The Efficacy of Placement of Neuropsychiatric Patients in Family Care," A.M.A. *Archives of General Psychiatry*, 1 (1959), 273–74.

VALIEN, P. and A. P. Fitzgerald, "Attitudes of the Negro Mother Toward Birth Control," *American Journal of Sociology*, 55 (November, 1949), 279–83.

VAN DER EERDEN, Sister M. Lucia, *Maternity Care in a Spanish-American Community of New Mexico*, Washington, D.C.: The Catholic University of America Press, Anthropological Series 13, 1948.

VAUGHAN, P., *Doctor's Commons: Short History of the B.M.A.*, London: William Heinemann, Ltd., 1959.

VON MERING, Otto, "The Social Self-Renewal of the Mental Patient and the Volunteer Movement," *in* M. Greenblatt, D. J. Levinson, and R. H. Williams, eds., *The Patient and the Mental Hospital*, New York: The Free Press of Glencoe, Inc., 1957, 585–92.

VON MERING, Otto and Stanley H. King, *Remotivating the Mental Patient*, New York: Russell Sage Foundation, 1957.

WAGLEY, Charles, *The Social and Religious Life of a Guatemalan Village*, Memoirs of the American Anthropological Association, 71 (1949).

WALLACE, Anthony F. C., "The Institutionalization of Cathartic and Control Strategies in Iroquois Religious Psychotherapy," *in* M. K. Opler, ed., *Culture and Mental Health*, New York: The Macmillan Company, 1959, 63–96.

WALLACE, Anthony F. C. and Harold A. Rashkis, "The Relation of Staff Consensus to Patient Disturbance on Mental Hospital Wards," *American Sociological Review*, 24 (December, 1959), 829–35.

WECHSLER, Henry, "The Ex-Patient Club: A General Survey and Case Study," *in* M. Greenblatt, D. J. Levinson, and Gerald L. Klerman, eds., *Mental Patients in Transition*, Springfield, Ill.: Charles C Thomas, Publisher, 1961, 104–13.

WEEKS, H. Ashley, Marjorie Davis, and Howard Freeman, "Apathy of Families Toward Medical Care," *in* E. G. Jaco, ed., *Patients, Physicians, and Illness*, New York: The Free Press of Glencoe, Inc., 1958, 159–64.

WEEKS, H. Ashley *et al.*, *Family Spending Patterns and Health Care*, Cambridge: Harvard University Press, 1961.

WEINBERG, S. Kirson, "Organization, Personnel, and Functions of State and Private Mental Hospitals: A Comparative Analysis," *in* E. G. Jaco, ed., *Patients, Physicians, and Illness*, New York: The Free Press of Glencoe, Inc., 1958, 478–90.

WEISKOTTEN, N. G. *et al.*, "Trends in Medical Practice—An Analysis of the Distribution and Characteristics of Medical College Graduates, 1915–1950," *Journal of Medical Education*, 35 (December, 1960), 1071–1121.

WELLIN, Edward, "Maternal and Infant Feeding Practices in a Peruvian Village," *Journal of the American Dietetic Association*, 31 (September, 1955), 889–94.

WELLIN, Edward, "Implications of Local Culture for Public Health," *Human Organization*, 16 (Winter, 1958), 16–18.

WELLIN, Edward *et al.*, "Community Aspects of Mental Subnormality—A Local Health Department Program for Retarded Children," *American Journal of Public Health*, 50 (January, 1960), 36–42.

WESSEN, Albert F., "Hospital Ideology and Communication Between Ward Personnel," *in* E. G. Jaco, ed., *Patients, Physicians, and Illness*, New York: The Free Press of Glencoe, Inc., 1958, 448–68.

WHATLEY, Charles D., "Social Attitudes Toward Discharged Mental Patients," *Social Problems*, 6 (1959), 313–20.

WHITMER, C. A. and C. G. Conover, "A Study of Critical Incidents in the Hospitalization of the Mentally Ill," *Social Work*, 4 (1959), 89–94.

WILL, Gwen Tudor, "Psychiatric Nursing Administration and Its Implication for Patient Care," *in* M. Greenblatt, D. J. Levinson, and R. H. Williams, eds., *The Patient and the Mental Hospital*, New York: The Free Press of Glencoe, Inc., 1957, 237–47.

WILLARD, William R. and Robert Straus, "Treatment of Alcoholism: Community Approaches to the Problems of Alcoholism," *New York State Journal of Medicine*, 58 (July, 1958), 2256–64.

WILLIAMS, Richard H., "Psychiatric Rehabilitation in the Hospital," *Public Health Reports*, 68 (November, 1953), 1043–51.

WILLIAMS, Richard H., "Psychiatric Rehabilitation in the Community," *Public Health Reports*, 68 (November, 1953), 1231–36.

WILLIAMS, T. F. *et al.*, "Patient Referral to a University Clinic: Patterns in a Rural State," *American Journal of Public Health*, 50 (October, 1960), 1493–1507.

WILLIE, Charles V. and Herbert Notkin, "Community Organization for Health: A Case Study," *in* E. G. Jaco, ed., *Patients, Physicians, and Illness*, New York: The Free Press of Glencoe, Inc., 1958, 148–58.

WILMER, Harry A., *Social Psychiatry in Action: A Therapeutic Community*, Springfield, Ill.: Charles C Thomas, Publisher, 1958.

WILSON, Robert N., "Teamwork in the Operating Room," *Human Organization*, 12 (Winter, 1954), 9–14. Reprinted *in* E. G. Jaco, ed., *Patients, Physicians, and Illness*, New York: The Free Press of Glencoe, Inc., 1958.

WILSON, Robert N., "The Physician's Changing Hospital Role," *Human Organization*, 18 (Winter, 1959–60), 177–83.

WING, J. K. and G. W. Brown, "Social Treatment of Chronic Schizophrenia: A Comparative Survey of Three Mental Hospitals," *Journal of Mental Science*, 107 (1961), 847–61.

WING, J. K., J. Denham, and A. R. Munro, "Duration of Stay in Hospital of Patients Suffering From Schizophrenia," *British Journal of Preventive and Social Medicine*, 13 (1959), 145–48.

WISDOM, Charles, *The Chorti Indians of Guatemala*, Chicago: University of Chicago Press, 1940.

WISDOM, Charles, "The Supernatural World and Curing," *in* Sol Tax, ed., *Heritage of Conquest*, New York: The Free Press of Glencoe, Inc., 1952.

WISHIK, S. M. *et al.*, "Attitudes and Reactions of the Public to Health Programs," *American Journal of Public Health*, 48 (February, 1958), 139–52.

WOLD, Patricia Neely, "A Long-Term Evaluation of Chlorpromazine in Six Chronic Schizophrenic Patients," *in* M. Greenblatt, D. J. Levinson, and Gerald L. Klerman, eds., *Mental Patients in Transition*, Springfield, Ill.: Charles C Thomas, Publisher, 1961, 336–52.

WOLFENSBERGER, Wolf P., "Attitudes of Alcoholics Toward Mental Hospitals," *Quarterly Journal of Studies on Alcohol*, 19 (September, 1958), 447–51.

WOODWARD, J., *Employment Relations in a Group of Hospitals. A Report of a Survey by the Department of Social Science of the University of Liverpool*, London: Institute of Hospital Administrators, 1950.

WOODWARD, Julian L., "Changing Ideas on Mental Illness and Its Treatment," *American Sociological Review*, 16 (August, 1951), 443–54. Reprinted *in* A. M. Rose, ed., *Mental Health and Mental Disorders*, New York: W. W. Norton & Company, Inc., 1955.

WORLD HEALTH ORGANIZATION, *Social Psychiatry and Community Attitudes*, Geneva: World Health Organization, Report of the Expert Committee on Mental Health, Technical Report Series 177, 1959.

YOUMANS, E. Grant, "Parental Reactions to Communications on the 1954 Polio Vaccine Tests," *Rural Sociology*, 23 (December, 1958), 377–84.

ZIMMER, Henry R., *Hindu Medicine*, Baltimore: Johns Hopkins Press, 1948.

V. Strategy, Method, and Status of Medical Sociology

ADAMS, Richard N., "Notes on the Application of Anthropology," *Human Organization*, 12 (Summer, 1953), 10–14.

ADAMS, Richard N., "On the Effective Use of Anthropology in Public Health Programs," *Human Organization*, 13 (1955), 5–15.

AMERICAN PUBLIC HEALTH ASSOCIATION, Committee on Research and Standards, "Research Needs in Mental Health," *American Journal of Public Health*, 46 (March, 1956), 349–52.

ANDERSON, Odin W., "The Roads to Social Research," *American Behavioral Scientist*, 5 (March, 1962), 8–11.

ANDERSON, Odin W. and Milvoy S. Seacat, *The Behavioral Scientists and Research in the Health Field: A Questionnaire Survey*, New York: Health Information Foundation, Research Series 1, 1957.

ANDERSON, Odin W. and Milvoy S. Seacat, "Behavioral Science Research in the Health Field: A Statement of Problems and Priorities," *Social Problems*, 3 (Winter, 1959), 268–71.

ANDERSON, Odin W. and Milvoy S. Seacat, *An Analysis of Personnel in Medical Sociology*, New York: Health Information Foundation, Research Series 21, 1962.

BANKS, E. P., "Methodological Problems in the Study of Psychiatric Wards," *Social Forces*, 34 (1956), 277–80.

BLOOM, Samuel W., "The Role of the Sociologist in Medical Education," *Journal of Medical Education*, 34 (July, 1959), 667–73.

BLOOM, Samuel W., "The Sociologist as Medical Educator," *American Sociological Review*, 25 (February, 1960), 95–102.

BLOOM, Samuel W., Albert F. Wessen, Robert Straus, George G. Reader, and Jerome K. Meyers, "The Sociologist as a Medical Educator: A Discussion," *American Sociological Review*, 25 (February, 1960), 95–101.

BRANCH, C. H. Hardin and Robert Anderson, "Clinical and Research Collaboration in Psychiatry and Anthropology," *The International Journal of Social Psychiatry*, 6 (Autumn, 1960), 247–51.

BRIGHTMAN, I. J., "Problems in Interdisciplinary Coordination and Communication," *Annals of the New York Academy of Science*, 74 (September, 1958), 35–39.

BRONFENBRENNER, Urie and Edward C. Devereaux, "Interdisciplinary Planning for Team Research on Constructive Community Behavior," *Human Relations*, 5 (May, 1952), 187–203.

BUCK, Rodger L., "Behavioral Scientists in Schools of Medicine," *Journal of Health and Human Behavior*, 2 (Spring, 1961), 59–64.

CAUDILL, William and Bertram Roberts, "Pitfalls in the Organization of Interdisciplinary Research," *Human Organization*, 10 (Winter, 1951), 12–15.

CONACHER, D. G., "Health Education and Anthropology," *Health Education Journal*, 15 (1957), 125–30.

CURTIS, Jack H., "Sociology and Medicine: Some Steps Toward Reapprochement," *American Catholic Sociological Review*, 21 (April, 1960), 9–17.

DERRYBERRY, Mayhew, "Psychological Work in Public Health," *Journal of Consulting Psychology*, 6 (March–April, 1942), 78–82.

DORN, Harold F., "Methods of Analysis for Follow-Up Studies," *Human Biology*, 22 (December, 1950), 238–48.

DORN, Harold F., "Some Problems Arising in Prospective and Retrospective Studies of the Etiology of Disease," *New England Journal of Medicine*, 261 (September, 1959), 571–79.

DOWNES, Jean, "Method of Statistical Analysis of Chronic Disease in a Longitudinal Study of Illness," *Milbank Memorial Fund Quarterly,* 29 (October, 1951) 404–22.

DUNHAM, H. Warren, "Current Status of Ecological Research in Mental Disorder," *Social Forces,* 25 (March, 1947), 321–26. Reprinted *in* A. M. Rose, ed., *Mental Health and Mental Disorders,* New York: W. W. Norton & Company, Inc., 1955.

EATON, Joseph W., "Social Processes of Professional Teamwork," *American Sociological Review,* 16 (October, 1951), 707–13.

EATON, Joseph W., "The Social Science Content of the Medical Curriculum," *American Sociological Review,* 21 (1956), 614–17.

FELDMAN, Jacob J., "Barriers to the Use of Health Survey Data in Demographic Analysis," *Milbank Memorial Fund Quarterly,* 36 (July, 1958), 203–19.

FELDMAN, Jacob J., "The Household Interview Survey as a Technique for the Collection of Morbidity Data," *Journal of Chronic Diseases,* 2 (May, 1960), 535–57.

FELIX, R. H. and J. A. Clausen, "The Role of Surveys in Advancing Knowledge in the Field of Mental Health," *Public Opinion Quarterly,* 17 (1953), 61–70.

FLECK, A. C., Jr. and Francis A. J. Ianni, "Epidemiology and Anthropology: Some Suggested Affinities in Theories and Method," *Human Organization,* 16 (1958), 38–40.

FOSTER, George M., "Use of Anthropological Methods and Data in Planning and Operation," *Public Health Reports,* 68 (1953), 841–57.

FOSTER, George M., "Public Health and Behavioral Science: The Problem of Teamwork," *American Journal of Public Health,* 51 (September, 1961), 1286–93.

FREADMAN, Maurice, "Health Education: How It Strikes an Anthropologist," *Health Education Journal,* 14 (March, 1956), 18–24.

FREEMAN, Howard E. and Ozzie G. Simmons, "The Use of the Survey in Mental Illness Research," *Mental Hygiene,* 34 (July, 1960), 400–410.

FRENCH, Katherine S., "Research Interviewers in a Medical Setting," *Human Organization,* 21 (Fall, 1962), 219–24.

GORDON, John E., "Problems of Team Endeavor in the Study of Chronic Disease," *Milbank Memorial Fund Quarterly,* 31 (1953), 223–33.

GOSS, Mary E. W. and George G. Reader, "Collaboration Between Sociologists and Physicians," *Social Problems,* 4 (July, 1956), 82–89.

GROUP FOR THE ADVANCEMENT OF PSYCHIATRY, *Some Observations on Controls in Psychiatric Research,* New York: Group for the Advancement of Psychiatry, Report 42, 1959.

HALL, Oswald, "Sociological Research in the Field of Medicine," *American Sociological Review,* 16 (October, 1951), 639–43.

HAYES, Donald P. and Joan J. Jackson, "Teaching Social Science in the Medical School," *Journal of Health and Human Behavior,* 1 (Spring, 1960), 34–41.

HILLEBOE, H. E., G. James, and J. T. Doyle, "Cardiovascular Health Center—Project Design for Public Health Research," *American Journal of Public Health,* 44 (July, 1954), 851–63.

JACO, E. Gartly, "Areas for Research in Medical Sociology," *Sociology and Social Research,* 42 (July–August, 1958), 441–44.

JACO, E. Gartly, "Problems and Prospects of the Social Sciences in Medical Education," *Journal of Health and Human Behavior,* 1 (Spring, 1960), 29–34.

KATZ, Martin M., "Problems in Evaluation of Effectiveness of Transitional Facilities," *in* M. Greenblatt, D. J. Levinson, and Gerald L. Klerman, eds., *Mental Patients in Transition,* Springfield, Ill.: Charles C Thomas, Publisher, 1961, 118–26.

KELMAN, Howard R. and Arthur Willner, "Problems in Measurement and Evaluation of Rehabilitation," *Archives of Physical Medicine and Rehabilitation,"* 43 (April, 1962), 172–81.

KISER, Clyde V., "Methodological Lessons of the Indianapolis Fertility Study," *Eugenics Quarterly*, 3 (September, 1956), 152–56.

KRAMER, Morton, "Problems of Research on the Population Dynamics and Therapeutic Effectiveness of Mental Hospitals," *in* M. Greenblatt, D. J. Levinson, and R. H. Williams, eds., *The Patient and the Mental Hospital*, New York: The Free Press of Glencoe, Inc., 1957, 145–69.

LANDY, David, "The Anthropologist and the Mental Hospital," *Human Organization*, 17 (Fall, 1958), 30–35.

LANDY, David, "Some Problems of Research in Psychiatric Rehabilitation," *Diseases of the Nervous System*, 102 (April, 1961), Monograph Supplement 1–5.

LANDY, David "An Anthropological Approach to Research in the Mental Hospital Community," *The Psychiatric Quarterly*, 35 (October, 1961), 741–57.

LARSON, Olaf F. and Donald G. Hay, "Hypotheses for Sociological Research in the Field of Rural Health," *Rural Sociology*, 16 (September, 1951), 225–37.

LEIGHTON, Alexander H., "The Stirling County Study: Some Notes on Concepts and Methods," *in* P. H. Hoch and J. Zubin, eds., *Comparative Epidemiology of the Mental Disorders*, New York: Grune & Stratton, Inc., 1961, 24–31.

LEMKAU, Paul V. and Benjamin Pasamanick, "Problems in Evaluation of Mental Health Programs," *American Journal of Orthopsychiatry*, 27 (January, 1957), 55–58.

LIPSCOMB, W. R., "Epidemiological Methods in the Study of Alcoholism," *American Journal of Public Health*, 49 (1959), 327–33.

LUSZKI, Margaret B., *Interdisciplinary Team Research: Methods and Problems*, New York: New York University Press, 1958.

MacMILLAN, Allister Miles, "A Survey Technique for Estimating the Prevalence of Psychoneurotic and Related Types of Disorders in Communities," *in* B. Pasamanick, ed., *Epidemiology of Mental Disorder*, Washington: American Association for the Advancement of Science, 1959, 203–28.

MALAMUD, W., "Research in Mental Health: Results Obtained and Plans for the Future," *Mental Hygiene*, 43 (1959), 222–29.

MANGUS, A. R., "Perspectives for Social Science Research in Mental Health," *Rural Sociology*, 21 (1956), 13–24.

McEWEN, W. J., "Position Conflict and Professional Orientation in a Research Organization," *Administrative Science Quarterly*, 1 (September, 1956), 208–24.

MECHANIC, David, "Illness and Social Disability: Some Problems in Analysis," *Pacific Sociological Review*, 2 (Spring, 1959), 37–41.

MORRISON, S. L., "Principles and Methods of Epidemiological Research and Their Application to Psychiatric Illness," *Journal of Mental Science*, 105 (1959), 999–1011.

NATIONAL INSTITUTE OF MENTAL HEALTH, *Highlights of Progress in Mental Health Research: 1960*, Washington, D.C.: Government Printing Office, Public Health Service Publication 824, 1960.

NATIONAL INSTITUTES OF HEALTH, "Methods in Public Health Research," *American Journal of Public Health*, 41 (August, 1951), Part 2.

POLLACK, Herbert and Dean E. Krueger, eds., "Epidemiology of Cardiovascular Diseases: Methodology," *American Journal of Public Health*, Supplement, 50 (October, 1960).

REDLICH, Frederick C. and Eugene B. Brody, "Emotional Problems of Interdisciplinary Research in Psychiatry," *Psychiatry*, 18 (August, 1955), 233–39.

REEDER, Leo G., "Mailed Questionnaires in Longitudinal Health Studies: The Problem of Maintaining and Maximizing Response," *Journal of Health and Human Behavior*, 1 (Summer, 1960), 123–29.

REID, D. D., *Epidemiological Methods in the Study of Mental Disorder*, Geneva: World Health Organization, W.H.O. Public Health Papers 2, 1960.

RICHARDS, Cara E., "Cooperation Between Anthropologist and Medical Personnel," *Human Organization*, 19 (1960), 64–67.

RONEY, James G., "Social Sciences in the Teaching of Public Health," *Journal of Health and Human Behavior*, 1 (Spring, 1960), 47–52.

ROSEN, George, "The Why and the How of Sociology in Medical Training," *Archives of Environmental Health*, 4 (April, 1962), 638–42.

ROSENSTOCK, Irwin M. and Godfrey M. Hochbaum, "Some Principles of Research Design in Public Health," *American Journal of Public Health*, 51 (February, 1961), 266–77.

ROTH, J. A., "Management Bias in Social Science Study of Medical Treatment," *Human Organization*, 21 (Spring, 1962), 47–50.

RUSSELL SAGE FOUNDATION, "An Appraisal of the Problems of Collaboration," *in Annual Report, 1958–1959*, New York: Russell Sage Foundation, 1959.

SAMORA, Julian, "The Social Scientist as Teacher and Researcher in the Medical School," *Journal of Health and Human Behavior*, 1 (Spring, 1960), 42–46.

SCOTT, William A., "Research Definitions of Mental Health and Mental Illness," *Psychological Bulletin*, 55 (January, 1958), 29–45. Reprinted *in* T. R. Sarbin, ed., *Studies in Behavior Pathology*, New York: Holt, Rinehart & Winston, Inc., 1961.

SHEPS, Cecil G. and Eugene H. Taylor, *Needed Research in Health and Medical Care*, Chapel Hill: The University of North Carolina Press, 1954.

SIMMONS, Leo W., "A Prospectus for Field Research in the Position and Treatment of the Aged in Primitive and Other Societies," *American Anthropologist*, 47 (July, 1945), 433–38.

SIMMONS, Leo W., "A Frame of Reference for Family Research in Problems of Medical Care," *in Research in Public Health*, New York: Milbank Memorial Fund, 1952, 162–83.

SIMMONS, Ozzie G. and James A. Davis, "Interdisciplinary Collaboration in Mental Illness Research," *American Journal of Sociology*, 63 (November, 1957), 297–303.

SMITH, M. Brewster, "Research Strategies toward a Conception of Positive Mental Health," *American Psychologist*, 14 (1959), 673–81.

STAINBROOK, Edward and Murray Wexler, "The Place of Behavioral Sciences in the Medical School," *Psychiatry*, (August, 1956), 263–69.

STRAUS, Robert, "The Nature and Status of Medical Sociology," *American Sociological Review*, 22 (April, 1957), 200–4.

STYCOS, J. Mayone, "Some Directions for Research on Fertility Control, *Milbank Memorial Fund Quarterly*, 36 (April, 1958), 126–48.

SUCHMAN, Edward A., Bernard S. Phillips, and Gordon F. Streib, "An Analysis of the Validity of Health Questionnaires," *Social Forces*, 36 (March, 1958), 223–32.

UNITED STATES NATIONAL ADVISORY MENTAL HEALTH COUNCIL, Community Services Committee, Subcommittee on Evaluation of Mental Health Activities, *Evaluation in Mental Health: A Review of the Problem of Evaluating Mental Health Activities*, Washington, D.C.: Government Printing Office, Public Health Service Publication 413, 1955.

WOOLSEY, T. D. and H. Nisselson, "Some Problems in the Statistical Measurement of Chronic Disease," *in Improving the Quality of Statistical Surveys*, Washington, D.C.: American Statistical Association, 1956.

INDEXES

NAME INDEX

The names included in the bibliography in Chapter 20 do not appear in this index.

C

D

N

O

P

T

U

V

W

SUBJECT INDEX

Q

R

S

T

U

V